PERGAMON INTERNATIONAL LIBRARY
of Science, Technology, Engineering and Social Studies

The 1000-volume original paperback library in aid of education,
industrial training and the enjoyment of leisure
Publisher: Robert Maxwell, M.C.

CONTROLLED BREEDING
IN FARM ANIMALS

THE PERGAMON TEXTBOOK
INSPECTION COPY SERVICE

An inspection copy of any book published in the Pergamon International Library
will gladly be sent to academic staff without obligation for their consideration for
course adoption or recommendation. Copies may be retained for a period of 60
days from receipt and returned if not suitable. When a particular title is adopted
or recommended for adoption for class use and the recommendations results in a
sale of 12 or more copies, the inspection copy may be retained with our
compliments. If after examination the lecturer decides that the book is not
suitable for adoption but would like to retain it for his personal library, then a
discount of 10% is allowed on the invoiced price. The Publishers will be pleased to
receive suggestions for revised editions and new titles to be published in this
important International Library.

Pergamon publications of related interest:

BUCKETT
  Introduction to Livestock Husbandry, 2nd Edition

CHRISTIE
  Lipid Metabolism in Ruminant Animals

LAWRIE
  Meat Science, 3rd Edition

LOWE
  Milking Machines

NELSON
  An Introduction to Feeding Farm Livestock, 2nd Edition

PARKER
  Health and Disease in Farm Animals, 3rd Edition

CONTROLLED BREEDING IN FARM ANIMALS

IAN GORDON, BSc, MA, PhD

Professor of Animal Husbandry & Head,
Department of Agriculture,
University College, Dublin,
Republic of Ireland

PERGAMON PRESS

OXFORD · NEW YORK · TORONTO · SYDNEY · PARIS · FRANKFURT

U.K.	Pergamon Press Ltd., Headington Hill Hall, Oxford OX3 0BW, England
U.S.A.	Pergamon Press Inc., Maxwell House, Fairview Park, Elmsford, New York 10523, U.S.A.
CANADA	Pergamon Press Canada Ltd., Suite 104, 150 Consumers Rd., Willowdale, Ontario M2J 1P9, Canada
AUSTRALIA	Pergamon Press (Aust.) Pty. Ltd., P.O. Box 544, Potts Point, N.S.W. 2011, Australia
FRANCE	Pergamon Press SARL, 24 rue des Ecoles, 75240 Paris, Cedex 05, France
FEDERAL REPUBLIC OF GERMANY	Pergamon Press GmbH, Hammerweg 6, D-6242 Kronberg-Taunus, Federal Republic of Germany

First edition 1983

Library of Congress Cataloging in Publication Data

Gordon, Ian R.
  Controlled breeding in farm animals.
  (Pergamon international library of science, technology, engineering, and social studies)
  Includes bibliographies and index.
  1. Livestock–Breeding. I. Title. II. Series.
SF105.G67 1982   636.08'2 82-594
ISBN 0-08-024410-6   Hard cover
ISBN 0-08-024409-2   Flexicover

Printed in Great Britain by A. Wheaton & Co. Ltd., Exeter

Preface

The aim of the present work is to provide a reasonably detailed view of the literature dealing with the different ways in which reproduction in cattle, sheep, pigs and horses can be controlled and manipulated. The hope is that the book may prove to be of some value and interest, not only to students of animal science and veterinary medicine but also to those who are concerned with the practical aspects of reproduction control, whether in an advisory capacity or in applying techniques on the farm itself. Although the book does not concern itself with reproductive disorders or infertility, certain of the material in the text may prove of interest to veterinary practitioners in the course of their work with farm animals. For those advanced undergraduates or graduates in animal science and veterinary medicine contemplating research in reproductive physiology the work may provide some insight into the nature and scope of current reproduction technology and of the numerous problems that await solution. It would be foolish to claim that any work such as that presented here can be other than incomplete, in view of the vastness of the literature, but an attempt has been made to ensure that most statements of substance are backed by an appropriate reference to the original work. It should be stressed that the text covers areas in which there is considerable research activity and for many readers the different chapters may serve as nothing more than a possible starting point for seeking out information on their particular interests. A major objective of the book is to draw attention to information which may be used directly to increase the efficiency of the livestock industry at the present time and to look at a few of the possibilities which may turn into practical realities in Animal Agriculture as we move towards the close of the 20th century.

The present text has been distilled from research and teaching interests spanning a period of 30 years in Britain, the United States and Ireland. As a graduate in Agriculture from Nottingham University keen to see science put into practice, the author was fortunate enough in 1951 to have the opportunity of working as a research student under the late Sir John Hammond at Cambridge University, becoming particularly interested in the development and practical application of controlled breeding techniques in sheep. At that time, one of the difficulties facing a researcher in animal reproduction at Cambridge was that of insufficient accommodation and space to keep farm animals. For that reason, the author spent much of the 1950's out of the laboratory working directly with farmers and their sheep and cattle in most of the counties of England and Wales.

Arriving in Ireland in 1963, the opportunity presented itself of initiating and developing applied animal physiology teaching and research programmes in the Agricultural Faculty of University College, Dublin. In this work, the author would wish to acknowledge his indebtedness to the late Professor James B. Ruane, an extremely able and dynamic figure in Irish Agriculture, who gave great support in developing this area of animal science. In Ireland, the approach has been one of working directly with farmers in developing controlled breeding procedures; in this, the author has always been ably supported by an enthusiastic group of graduate students working in reproductive physiology.

The material in the book is arranged in four parts and is based on that dealt within current teaching programmes. Part I deals with cattle, and in view of the considerable economic importance of this species in Ireland and elsewhere, particular attention is devoted to aspects such as oestrus synchronization, embryo transfer and twinning. In understanding the merits and limitations of techniques, it is necessary to include a certain amount of information on the normal situation in the animal so that space is devoted to considering the endocrinology of the oestrous cycle, of pregnancy and parturition. At the same time, the background information is minimal and for a fuller understanding of many topics it would be expected that the reader is already in possession of a reasonable amount of knowledge in reproductive physiology.

Part II is devoted to sheep, the other major farm ruminant; opportunity certainly does exist in sheep for achieving substantial improvements in lamb output, by increasing the lambing percentage, by adopting more frequent lambing systems or a combination of both. Part III is devoted to pigs and Part IV to horses. In all cases, the aim is to consider techniques which may be of interest in normal commercial practice rather than those which may be limited to the research-type situation. For those who may wish to refer to text-books and other sources of information

in reproductive physiology, a list of these is provided at the end of the book.

Although the hope is that the information dealt with in many sections of the book will be of interest to students and researchers in countries far removed from Ireland, it will be evident that the discussion in many parts does reflect the author's interest in the Irish animal production scene. Of all the countries in the European Economic Community, the Republic of Ireland is by far the most heavily dependent on its agriculture, so there is a very real incentive towards looking carefully at all ways in which animal production can be made more efficient.

Although the present work is mainly a matter of noting the various people who have published information on the controlled breeding of the farm animals, the data set out in the different tables come from one study or another in which the author has been involved in Ireland or Britain.

I am grateful to Dr. M. Boland and Dr. F. Crosby for comments and suggestions during the writing of this book. I should also like to thank Peggy O'Neill, Monica Cleary and Mrs. Patricia Magee for assistance in many stages of the work.

Contents

PART IV – CONTROL AND MANIPULATION OF REPRODUCTION IN HORSES

BOOKS AND JOURNALS DEALING WITH CONTROL AND MANIPULATION OF REPRODUCTION

INDEX

List of Illustrations

Introduction

The importance of reproduction as a factor influencing the efficiency of animal production on the farm requires no emphasis. Some improvement in the existing reproductive performance of cattle, sheep, pigs and horses should be possible as a result of expanding knowledge in reproductive physiology. In terms of improving animal quality, artificial insemination (AI) has already had a major impact in dairy cattle breeding in many countries around the world and it is possible that a similar opportunity exists for bringing about improvements in beef cattle once the techniques of oestrus and ovulation control are fully developed and exploited. Aside from the achievements of dairy cattle AI, it has to be said that as yet improvements in the efficiency of animal production arising from the direct manipulation of the female reproductive processes have been minimal. However, the increasing understanding of the physiological mechanisms controlling reproduction have led to procedures which may now be employed in many commercial situations. The present work seeks to bring together much of the information relating to techniques which may be used in attempts to improve reproductive efficiency; a further objective is in drawing attention to some possibilities for future developments in this area of animal production. The information which is given about techniques of possible commercial interest in the control and manipulation of reproduction must be viewed against the background of the increasingly sophisticated technology now evident in the livestock industry in the advanced countries of the world.

Many of the important advances in understanding reproduction in the farm animal species have come as a result of research in endocrinology. There has been, on the one hand, the development of assay procedures, especially the radioimmunoassays, which enable blood levels of the polypeptide and steroid hormones involved in reproductive function to be precisely measured. One practical outcome of developments in this area is the use of the milk progesterone assay which can be employed in cattle in detecting at 3 weeks after breeding those animals which fail to become pregnant. On the research side, however, the important consideration is in employing these exquisitely sensitive assay procedures to build up as complete a picture as possible of the hormonal events in the oestrous cycle, in pregnancy and in the *post-partum* period, in lactation and in other phases of a breeding animal's life. Clearly, when one is attempting to manipulate the oestrous cycle of a particular farm animal, it is essential to have the fullest knowledge of the way in which the cycle normally operates.

Among a number of exciting developments in hormone research in the past two decades has been the identification and subsequent synthesis of hypothalamic releasing and inhibiting hormones. The current availability of gonadotrophin releasing hormone (Gn-RH) and its several analogues is one practical outcome of that work. Although the commercial utilization of Gn-RH is limited at this time, the unravelling of the complex neuroendocrine relationships affecting reproductive function which this work represented was of importance in moving towards a fuller understanding of farm animal reproduction. On another front, during the 1970s, there was a great gain in knowledge about the synthesis, action and metabolism of prostaglandins in animals. Prostaglandins, which are now known to be widely distributed in mammalian tissue, are currently available in synthetic form together with some number of analogues; one of these,

$PGF_{2\alpha}$, can be very effectively employed to manipulate the oestrous cycle and ovarian function in certain of the mammalian species. In addition to its use in cattle oestrus synchronization, $PGF_{2\alpha}$ and its analogues are available commercially for the treatment of mares and for the induction of parturition in pigs.

Apart from the recent availability of new agents such as Gn-RH and $PGF_{2\alpha}$, and before that the introduction of some number of highly potent progestagens and glucocorticoids, another area of research has been that dealing with the development of appropriate hormone delivery systems. The work of Robinson and associates at Sydney University, in developing the intravaginal route for long-term progestagen administration, marked an important step forward in progress towards commercially viable oestrus control procedures for sheep, goats and cattle. In France, it is estimated that something approaching one million intravaginal sponge treatments are now applied annually in sheep and goat production. It might be mentioned in passing that certain of the agents which have been developed with a view to limiting or controlling human fertility have been used to good effect in the opposite direction, in promoting more efficient farm animal reproductive performance. Progestagens such as medroxyprogesterone acetate (MAP) or fluorogestone acetate (FGA) that are highly effective in the control of oestrus and ovulation in the ewe were developed by the pharmaceutical industry for use in human fertility control. The cost of developing progestagens and prostaglandins for use in reproduction control is so great that it would not be possible to use them in animal production but for the fact that they are available in the form of an overspill from the pharmaceutical research directed towards human fertility control. It should also be remembered that producing agents for use in farm animal reproduction faces other problems. The restrictions that currently apply to the introduction of new products in many countries, whether these are used to influence reproduction, growth or other processes, may often require considerable capital outlay on the part of pharmaceuticals in meeting the rigorous requirements of the drug regulatory agencies; this is one reason why it seems likely that there may be a decrease in the number of new agents coming forward for use in controlled breeding in the future.

In presenting information about many of the techniques currently used in reproduction control, it has to be remembered, despite the seeming profusion of literature that emerges daily from laboratories around the world, that application to animals on the farm may often have a considerable way to go. There will always be some controlled breeding techniques which can only be envisaged as applicable in a research station setting, but the main concern of the present work is with measures which can be expected to be taken up and used in commercial practice, not necessarily in the immediate future but certainly in the long-term. The induction of twinning in cattle, for instance, could well be one of the important developments in animal agriculture between now and the end of the century. Embryo transfer, which is particularly relevant to breeding improvement in cattle, is only in its infancy; future developments in this area of research may well prove to be of immense value to the farmer. Whether it becomes possible to proceed to the point of cloning in cattle as is currently done with amphibian eggs remains to be seen but it would not be sensible to dismiss the possibility.

The efficiency of reproduction in cattle, sheep, pigs and horses obviously depends on many factors; this book deals with procedures which may be employed as appropriate for the species in altering the age at which puberty occurs, controlling litter-size, the time of parturition and reducing the period of post-partum or seasonal anoestrus. The outcome of control measures, whether they take the form of oestrus synchronization or embryo transfer, must inevitably be influenced by genetic, environmental and nutritional influences, quite apart from the way in which it may also be influenced by the technique or agent that is being used. Conception rates in cattle bred by AI after oestrus synchronization or even pregnancy rates in recipient cattle after embryo transfer may be markedly influenced by the condition and nutrition of the animals. In all of this, it has to be kept in mind that the benefits derived from the measures imposed must, in any commercial situation, justify the expenditure involved. In the Irish context, in which agriculture is predominantly based on livestock and their products, there is clearly a real need for attention to be concentrated on ways and means of improving the efficiency of animal production and animal breeding procedures. Although the present work deals with the type of practical situation which applies in Ireland, the United Kingdom and other West European countries, the scope of many of the techniques dealt with is probably wide enough to encompass farming conditions in many other countries. In all of this, the successful application of procedures to control the reproductive processes in the farm animals will depend on how well current management systems can be adapted to utilize the technology which becomes available. It should always be remembered that no system, whether for controlled breeding or otherwise, has any value unless it can be put to use.

PART I

The Control and Manipulation of Reproduction in Cattle

CHAPTER 1

Introduction to Controlled Breeding in Cattle

1.1 INTRODUCTION

Reproduction is one of the most important considerations determining the profitability of cattle production, whether talking about dairy or beef animals. If the breeding cow does not show regular cyclic breeding activity, become pregnant at the appropriate time and deliver a live, healthy calf each year, then her other excellent qualities may be to no great avail. Although ample scope remains for increasing reproductive efficiency by adjustments in the traditional methods of breeding, feeding and management, there remains the possibility that useful improvements in the efficiency of cattle can result from appropriate application of controlled breeding techniques.

In the years ahead, the application of science to animal agriculture will become increasingly important in providing the animal products required by the peoples around the world; controlled breeding, in one form or other, can be expected to contribute substantially in improving efficiency in cattle production.

In the past two decades, livestock production systems in many countries have become increasingly intensified. The first species to be fed and managed at high density in larger-sized units was poultry but the same approach was rapidly established in the pig industry in many countries and similar trends are evident among cattle. Intensification may mean feeding and managing individual animals more intensively to achieve higher outputs; it can also refer to the production of cattle, sheep or pigs in large units without this necessarily implying a particular level of output per individual.

1.1.1 Growth of large units

The growth of large units may be a result of different political and economic factors operating in the various countries; in Eastern Europe, the development of State farms and co-operative farming systems has given rise to pigs and cattle being concentrated in large units in countries such as Soviet Russia, Yugoslavia, Roumania, Hungary and Czechoslovakia. In the case of cattle, units of 600 to 1000 are commonplace in

Fig. 1.1. Dairy cattle in the Irish Republic. The Republic of Ireland is the most heavily dependent on its agriculture of all the countries in the E.E.C. There is a cow population of around 2 million head in the country and this has been the position for the past several years. During the sixties and seventies, the Friesian has largely replaced the Shorthorn as the main dairy breed. About 75% of all cows in the country are now Friesian or Friesian crosses compared to 10% in 1960.

Czechoslovakia and Hungary (Watson, 1980). In Israel, the development of the Kibbutz system has led to an increase in the size of dairy herds, the average in one survey being 250 milking cows, largely made up of Holsteins imported from the U.S.A. (Quick and Mulholland, 1978).

In Western Europe and North America, the growing costs of production, especially labour, power and rent charges necessitates a continuous reappraisal of current housing, milking and general management practices in dealing with dairy cattle. Britt (1979) with the American scene in mind notes that automation of dairy herd management has increased the number of cows handled per man-hour and decreased the time available for dealing with the individual animal. It is also probable that growth in herd size brings about new considerations relating to the efficient reproduction of cattle, quite apart from those of animals receiving less individual attention. There would seem to be grounds for believing that reproductive problems, such as *post-partum* anoestrus, could be more troublesome in large herds and the question of pheromonal effects, somewhat along the lines of those operating in the Lee–Boot effect in mice (Lee and Boot, 1955) constitutes an area of investigation worthy of some attention.

1.2 AREAS OF CONTROLLED BREEDING UNDER DISCUSSION

Control and manipulation of reproduction in cattle covers several possibilities; these are summarized in Fig. 1.2 and are discussed at length in later parts of the present work.

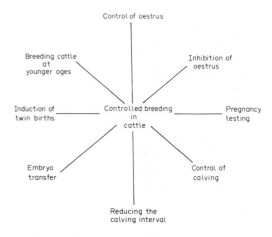

Fig. 1.2. Areas of controlled breeding in cattle.

Each of these possibilities has already been developed to the stage at which it can be applied to some extent in commercial practice; future developments and refinements in technique will certainly make all of them more valuable to the farmer. Cattle AI Stations as they presently exist in most countries around the world, will undoubtedly extend the service they offer farmers to include many of these controlled breeding procedures. In several instances, the new techniques available (e.g. fixed-time AI for use among maiden heifers) will be directly relevant to the insemination side of the business.

Embryo transfer, using non-surgical procedures much the same as those already employed in cattle AI, is an obvious development in cattle breeding services, once a suitable supply of frozen embryos becomes available. In this regard, it is as well to remember that embryo transfer technology, probably leading all the way up to successful nuclear transplant procedures at some date in the future, is still very much in its infancy. Those who occasionally decry the general applicability of embryo transfer to the cattle breeding scene might be wise to regard the present state of the art as only the first step towards more interesting developments. Only a few years ago, when the technique of cattle embryo transfer involved expensive and tedious surgical intervention, the possibility of using a cattle inseminating instrument (e.g. the *Cassou* inseminating gun) to carry out a transfer would have been dismissed as wishful thinking.

In cattle twinning by embryo transfer, which may well become a procedure of real commercial interest in future years under appropriate conditions of breed and management, the service required would again be one which could be dealt with most conveniently by Cattle AI Stations having well established links with farmers. In all of this, one extremely important consideration in developing controlled breeding procedures is their likely cost to the producer; to a considerable extent, cost will be determined by the scale of operations and the type of organization which brings them to the farm.

1.3 FACTORS INFLUENCING CATTLE FERTILITY

The reports of many authors have shown that fertility, measured in terms of the percentage of animals becoming pregnant to a single service, can vary markedly in cattle, according to a variety of factors. This pregnancy rate, or conception rate, is not to be confused with the non-return rates, as used by Cattle AI Stations to measure the efficiency of their service; pregnancy rate is defined here as the percentage of cattle becoming pregnant and subsequently calving and is quite different from the non-return rate, which may be 10–20% higher.

In the temperate regions, pregnancy rates in the cattle of Northern Europe are recognized as being among the highest in the world (Warwick, 1967). Most published figures relate to pregnancy rates in cattle bred by artificial insemination, and it would appear that the tendency is for rates to decrease rather than increase over the past 20 years or so. Laing (1970), summarizing data from several sources at that time, provides a figure of 64% pregnant to first service among dairy cattle bred by modern techniques of artificial in-

Fig. 1.3. Pregnancy rates in dairy and beef cattle in Ireland. Fertility levels of cattle in the Irish Republic are well in keeping with those in other countries. It is estimated that for every 100 cows presented for breeding each year, 9% of these are eventually culled for infertility and 12% of calves are lost before a month of age; about 79 calves per 100 cows are available for replacements and for beef production.

semination; in a more recent summary, the same author mentions a figure of 53% (Laing, 1979). In the United States, Foote (1952) surveyed the breeding efficiency of 2700 New York State dairy herds and reported a conception rate of 65.6%. About 25 years later, a similar field study of New York herds (Foote, 1979) provided a conception rate of 50%, the decline between the two periods being attributable to several factors, such as the use of frozen rather than fresh semen, larger-sized herds and increased level of milk production; in California, a similar type of survey among dairy cows revealed a figure of less than 50% (Pelissier, 1976).

Elsewhere in the United States, this time among beef cows, a pregnancy rate of 70% to first natural service was recorded (Turman et al., 1971) and 60% after artificial insemination (Laster et al., 1972). Figures for cattle bred by AI in Australia are provided by Donaldson (1976), who records 65.9% for 12 218 first inseminations; in New Zealand, conception rates in excess of 60% are reported by Macmillan (1979). In the Netherlands, a 65% conception rate is reported in dairy herds (de Kruif, 1975, 1976) and as noted by Spalding et al. (1975) in the U.S.A., the rate declined with increasing herd size. In the Irish Republic, where about half of the national cow herd is currently bred by AI, surveys have indicated pregnancy rates of 55–67% among spring-calving dairy calves (White and O'Farrell, 1972; Langley, 1978; Roche et al., 1978) and 60% in spring- and autumn-calving dairy cows (Crowley et al., 1967). In the U.K., David et al. (1971) gives a figure of 63% and Esslemont (1974, 1979a,b) reports first service pregnancy rates of 50 to 55% with the statistic varying between herds from 25 to 70%; a report by Pope and Swinburne (1980) states that a pregnancy rate of 55% is generally accepted as a mean value.

Table 1.1. Fertilization and pregnancy rates in beef heifer cattle

| | Heifers bred by A.I. | | |
| | Fresh semen | | Frozen semen |
	Checked for fertilization	Checked for pregnancy	Checked for pregnancy
Heifers	25	24	24
Yielded egg/embryo	20(80.0%)	18	15
Possessing viable egg or embryo	19(95.0%)	18(75.0%)	15(62.5%)

Work with beef heifers in the author's laboratory has confirmed that a very high fertilization rate can be achieved in such animals bred by artificial insemination. In Table 1.1 there are data for animals bred using either fresh or frozen semen with some indication that the pregnancy rate at 30 days after breeding was higher in the group bred with the frozen semen.

1.3.1 Identifying factors influencing fertility

Several authors have tried to identify the phases at which the reproductive process fails in cattle; in brief, the evidence shows that fertilization rates after natural or artificial insemination are normally of the order of 90% whereas pregnancy rates are closer to 50–60%. Looking at the situation in more detail, published estimates have been given showing 88–100% cattle eggs to be fertilized after fresh semen AI or natural service (Laing, 1949; Kidder et al., 1954; Bearden et al., 1956; Henricks et al., 1971; Ayalon, 1972) and 82–95% after frozen-thawed AI (Wishart and Young, 1974; Spitzer et al., 1978; Shelton et al., 1979; Diskin and Sreenan, 1980).

One of the more recent reports in this area has been that of Diskin and Sreenan (1980) who showed a fertilization rate of 90% and an embryo survival rate of 58% among 256 beef heifers bred by frozen-thawed semen from a bull of good fertility; these authors record that much of the embryonic mortality occurred between days 8 and 12 after breeding and the 58% embryo survival rate agreed with calving rates of 50–55% recorded after a single insemination in this category of animal. Elsewhere in Ireland, Roche et al. (1981) found evidence of a gradual loss of embryos between days 8 and 18.

1.3.2 Natural and artificial insemination

Authors have drawn attention to the fact that in the general population of cattle bred by artificial insemination, inaccurate oestrus detection probably accounts for some number of cows which are bred although not in oestrus or close to ovulation at the time (Hawk, 1979); clearly such animals do not have any chance of becoming pregnant. With natural mating, this type of breeding error should not occur, so that conception rates might be expected to be higher than with AI, given that bulls used in the two breeding methods are of comparable fertility; in California, one report shows a conception rate of 63% for cows mated naturally and 47% for those bred by AI (Pelissier, 1976). In Scotland (Appleyard and Cook, 1976), in Germany (Hoffman et al., 1976) and in Northern Ireland (McCaughey and Cooper, 1980) measurements of blood or milk progesterone levels at the time of AI have suggested that some proportion of cattle are bred when progesterone concentrations are too high for them to be genuinely in oestrus at that time; several reports from other countries have shown much the same evidence.

1.3.3 Nutrition and body condition

Authors have drawn attention to the fact that cow fertility can be influenced markedly by nutrition over the service period, as reflected by changes in the diet and fluctuations in body weight and condition (Haresign, 1979; Drew, 1981). Although dairy cows are rarely underfed deliberately by the farmer, it may not always be easy to supply them with a diet of sufficient energy content to support liveweight and high milk yield in early lactation. As noted in a review by Haresign (1979), loss in body weight in early lactation is often associated with a decline in reproductive efficiency, primarily stemming from a delay in the resumption of ovarian activity and a lowered conception rate; several reports show that cows which are losing weight around the time of mating are less likely to conceive than those that are gaining weight (King, 1968; Youdan, 1973; Youdan and King, 1977; Sonder-regger and Schurch, 1977). It is worth noting that the better the condition of the dairy cow at calving, the greater the degree of bodyweight loss that can be tolerated before the animal reaches a critical weight or condition, below which she becomes extremely sensitive to bodyweight and energy balance (Haresign, 1979).

Another point to keep in mind is that major changes in diet should be avoided during the service period in cattle. Drew (1981) notes that changes in diet, such as may occur in autumn when cows move from kale to silage or from silage to spring grass, are often accompanied by a temporary period of reduced fertility; the same author has drawn attention to the profound effect of nutrition among heifers bred after oestrus synchronization and to reduced conception rates in dairy cows when fixed-time AI was applied within 3 weeks of a major change in diet. In talking about liveweight changes in cattle, it appears that the important consideration is a long-term change; short-term variations in bodyweight may mean nothing more than changes in gutfill. There is no reason to believe that short-term increases in the energy intake of cattle before the time of breeding has any beneficial effect on the animal's ability to conceive (Haresign, 1979). The effect of specific dietary constituents on conception rate has not often been reported; several reports have identified a decrease in cattle fertility during the northern European winter (Ortavant et al., 1964; Bulman, 1977; de Kruif and Brand, 1978) and a relationship between plasma β-carotene levels and conception rate has been mentioned by some authors (Bulman and Lamming, 1978; Jackson et al., 1979).

1.3.4 Temperature and other effects

It is well enough accepted that the more severe the under-nutrition of the cow, the lower will be the level of fertility (i.e. effect of nutritional stress). There is also plenty of evidence showing that high ambient temperatures are likely to impose a number of adverse physiological effects on conception rate in cattle; each effect depends on the stage of reproduction at which the cow is exposed and the severity and duration of the stressful temperature. Much of the information recorded on cattle fertility relates to studies and surveys conducted in temperate climates but it is known that in other regions, for instance, the southern United States, fertility often decreases drastically during the summer period (Hawk, 1979). A critical period when cattle reproduction is especially sensitive to an increase in body temperature was shown by Stott and Wiersma (1976) to be around the time of breeding.

Talking in terms of the immediate environment of the animal, it should be noted that modern dairy cattle housing systems have been developed primarily for economic and labour benefits and may unwittingly influence the behaviour and performance of the cow adversely or favourably; Hafez and Bouisson (1975) make the point that there is a lack of information on social and individual behaviour in cattle that are housed, although the behaviour of cows at pasture has been reported on at length.

1.4 DAIRY CATTLE

In dealing more specifically with dairy animals, it is true that many farmers regard low fertility as being one of the most important herd problems; in the U.S.A., Foote et al. (1979) note that despite the virtual elimination of the specific infectious reproductive diseases prevalent when AI was introduced on a large scale in the 1940s, the dairyman's major problem today is low fertility in his cows. Gerritts et al. (1979), again dealing with the American scene, report that the average dairy cow may only live about 5 years, produce two calves and complete two lactations; reproductive failure is held to be a major reason for this very short productive life. In the U.S.A., as in many other countries, the trend is for the size of the dairy herd to increase; over a span of 25 years, the average size of dairy herds in the U.S.A. increased four-fold and similar if less dramatic increases have been noted in several other countries. Alongside the larger herd-size, there is the trend towards more cows per herdsman and less man-hours per cow (King, 1972; Hodgson, 1973; Seykora et al., 1980). Growth in the size of the average dairy herd has created a need to change conventional reproductive management practices to increase the efficiency of heat detection, artificial insemination, cow handling and record keeping (Britt, 1977; Britt et al., 1981).

It also becomes necessary to develop new management routines, such as housing cows in groups according to their reproductive status, to take advantage of the increased income derived from the maintenance of calving intervals at 12 months during the animal's productive life. Quite apart from the problems of oestrus detection, managing dairy cattle for low-cost milk production may result in some measure of increased stress affecting the animal's usual capacity to become pregnant. Greater herd size may bring more problems of herd health, the result to some extent of the management practices necessary with larger numbers. There may also be an adverse effect, arising from high milk production, on fertility in the early months of lactation (Pelissier, 1972; Spalding et al., 1975; Foote, 1978; Seykora et al., 1980); this could be a question of a direct effect (operating via the endocrine system) or an indirect one (inadequacies in energy intake). In view of the general trend in dairy cattle towards larger herd-size and higher production per cow, dairy farmers must devote attention increasingly to reproductive management in order to maintain acceptable conception rates and good fertility levels.

Wagner (1974) drew attention some years ago to the lack of adequate data on hormone levels in high and low milk-producing cattle which might assist in clarifying the degree of involvement of management and nutritional factors in the reproductive performance of animals; the same author emphasized the need to think much more about the dairy animal's contentment, by minimizing the incidence of stressful situations (whether social, environmental or man-induced). The use of the metabolic profile test in dairy cattle (Payne et al., 1973) when conventional procedures fail to provide a reason for herd subfertility has provided an additional diagnostic tool in recent years; at the same time, it has been noted that considerable caution is necessary in employing the test due to the complexities of interpretation (Adams et al., 1978).

Increasing knowledge in endocrinology should eventually result in the identification of the hormonal mechanisms by which different forms of stress affects reproduction and dairy herds may be monitored in such a way as to avoid the development of potentially stressful conditions which could adversely influence their breeding capabilities. As observed by Moberg (1976), the period from breeding to implantation a few weeks later is regarded as the phase most susceptible to the effects of stress. Although it may be thought that stress impairs normal reproductive processes either by way of glucocorticoids or progesterone produced by the adrenals or perhaps the steroids in combination, the adrenals have yet to be identified experimentally as a major contributor to the effects of stress on reproduction.

1.5 BEEF CATTLE

Although problems of supply and demand occasionally obscure the scene, there has always been a strong worldwide demand for beef, and in the years ahead it is a demand which can only be expected to grow. Improvements in living standards tend to generate demand for beef, whether for reason of social prestige or simply because people enjoy eating it. Consumers at large might be expected to benefit from greater efficiency in cattle production if this means an increased supply of beef at a lower price. Optimum reproductive performance in beef herds is a key factor in assuring that beef retains its strong position as a source of protein in the human diet.

In many parts of the world, the beef herds are mainly to be found in the range lands of countries such as North and South America and Australia or in the hillier regions of pastoral countries such as New Zealand. As in dairy cattle, reproductive performance in beef cows is closely related to profitability; good reproductive performance in beef terms means the production each year of a live calf capable of growing quickly to an appropriate weight at sale. Bellows *et al.* (1979), dealing with the American scene, note that in trying to improve the reproductive performance of beef cows, the low pregnancy rate and the high perinatal calf death-rate are barriers to be overcome; Gerritts *et al.* (1979) discussing the same problem, estimate that not more than 80–85% of beef cows calve in a year and calf losses from birth to weaning average 5–10%.

However, it has to be remembered that beef cattle usually exist under poorer nutritional conditions than dairy animals and much can be done towards improving reproductive performance by attention to the feeding of animals. In this regard, body condition can be a useful guide to nutritional status in beef cattle. If the cow is obtaining too little food to produce the milk required by the calf, she will make up as much of the deficit as possible by drawing on her body reserves and becoming thinner. Alternatively, if feed is in excess of her demands for milk production, the beef cow becomes fatter. Methods of methodically evaluating body condition using a scoring system have been reported by several authors in the U.K. (Lowman *et al.*, 1973; Kilkenny, 1978) and elsewhere; the evidence is that condition scoring can be a useful management aid.

1.6 ARTIFICIAL INSEMINATION

Undoubtedly, the most important development in cattle breeding in the years after World War II was the rapid growth of the Cattle AI services in countries around the world; AI brings to the farmer a choice of bulls which he would not normally be able to maintain or have access to. As a result of the sire-proving methods adopted with dairy bulls, substantial progress in improving the genetic quality of cattle in many countries has been possible. In the U.S.A., for example, it is

widely accepted that no other single technique has contributed so much to genetic improvement; the number of dairy cows bred by AI increased after World War II and eventually plateaued at a figure of about 7 million per year (King *et al.*, 1971). The proportion of dairy cows bred by AI annually has increased over the past 20 years, although the dairy cow population in the U.S.A. has decreased by more than 50% (Britt, 1979; Seykora *et al.*, 1980); in the same period, milk yield per cow has almost doubled, although it must be recognized that much improvement can be attributed to better management practices such as feeding, housing and general care of the animals.

Fig. 1.4. Artificial insemination of cattle in the Irish Republic. Artificial insemination as a method of breeding cattle was introduced into Ireland in the early 1940s and at present something in excess of 50% of the cows are put to AI each year. Dairy cattle |in Ireland| are regarded |as dual-purpose, the usual policy being to encourage dairy breeding from the best cows in the herd with beef crosses from the lower producers and from cows falling behind the industry's general spring-calving pattern. Traditionally, the crossing sires have been Herefords with Aberdeen Angus for the heifers, but there is a very real need to exploit the use of the Continental beef breeds.

The advantages of artificial insemination, which has enabled the bull's participation in the breeding of dairy cattle to be controlled, are well enough understood and accepted, although much remains in exploiting the full potential of the technique in cattle as a whole. Whatever the theoretical advantages of AI may be, the fact remains that it has made little headway as yet in beef herds. Some years ago, Phillips (1972) in the United States reported that 45% of dairy cows were bred by AI in 1969 as compared with only 2.5% of beef cattle; the relative figures for dairy and beef cows today would not be greatly different. In the U.S.A., as in many other countries, the majority of beef cattle rearing calves are mated by natural service because the practical difficulties of detecting oestrus and separating out individual cows for insemination appear to outweigh the benefits that can be obtained with performance tested, selected bulls. In has been mainly with beef cattle in mind that oestrus control techniques have been developed, although for various reasons they have yet to be applied to good effect in that category of animal. Artificial insemination should eventually permit the beef farmer to obtain a sire breed not available to him through natural service or perhaps a bull tested for ease of calving or growth performance. With the current forms of oestrus control in cattle, it should be remembered that the use of AI does not necessarily mean a great reduction in the number of bulls required in beef herds; natural service will be required to take care of returns to service 3 weeks after inseminations.

1.6.1 Evaluating bull fertility

The current method of evaluating the fertility of bulls standing at AI centres is by way of the non-return rate (NRR) which represents the proportion of cows that fail to return to oestrus during a certain specified period after the first insemination and are therefore considered to be pregnant. Several authors draw attention to the fact that the NRR overestimates the actual proportion of cows that are pregnant (Spalding et al., 1975; Pellissier, 1976) and it generally held that methods employed for evaluating semen quality by cattle AI stations may not be highly correlated with fertility levels (Bishop et al., 1954; Stewart et al., 1972, 1974; Linford et al., 1976). Most of those concerned in semen processing would agree that new and more sensitive approaches to fertility prediction would be welcome.

It is only to be expected that extensive information on fertility levels in cattle is to be found in records of the Cattle AI Stations in the different countries, although this is in the form of

Fig. 1.5. Collecting semen for use in artificial insemination on the University Farm. Semen being collected from a Charolais bull on the University farm for use in breeding beef heifer cattle that supply eggs for twinning work. There is need to use the Continental beef breeds such as the Charolais for producing beef calves on a much greater scale than is currently practised in the Republic. As well as the use of bulls that are known to have a record for easy calvings, there may be occasions when the induction of calving at a prearranged time of gestation may have application to help in the calving situation.

NR rates rather than actual calving statistics; the 30–60 day NRR is commonly used, this representing the percentage of cattle, inseminated for the first time, which have not been reported as returning to service 30 days after the end of the month in which they were inseminated. The records at Cattle AI Stations have shown that many factors can influence the conception rate in cows, including the fertility of the bulls themselves; significant and occasionally substantial differences between sires still remains a problem in AI (Macmillan, 1973; Macmillan and Watson, 1975).

1.6.2 Frozen semen

With the discovery of an effective method of freezing bull semen in media containing glycerol and the application of this technique to cattle AI (Polge and Rowson, 1952), frozen bull semen has been used increasingly in cattle breeding throughout the world. At this point in time, the major developed countries of the world have moved almost exclusively to a frozen semen service. In the U.S.A., during the 1970s, several substantial technical changes were made in the packaging and distribution of frozen semen used in the breeding of dairy and beef cattle (Senger, 1980). One major change, which also occurred in many other countries, was the general replacement of the glass 1 ml ampoule by the plastic straw (0.25 ml) as the packaging unit for frozen bull semen. As well as this, it should be noted that there has been a large increase in the sale of frozen semen directly to the dairy and beef farmer, with many herd-owners in the U.S.A. assuming total responsibility for semen purchase, handling AI of the cow and the keeping of fertility records. It has been estimated that in 1980, more than half (55%) of the cows bred by AI in the U.S.A. were inseminated by owners or herdsmen (Stevenson, 1981). In Britain, although not in the Irish Republic, Do-It-Yourself AI is growing.

It has only been in New Zealand that widespread use of fresh rather than frozen semen has continued in recent years. Fresh semen seemed appropriate for breeding New Zealand cattle because of the very marked seasonal pattern in semen demand and because most of the dairy cows are concentrated in specific areas of the country. New Zealand researchers and AI workers have exploited semen technology by achieving acceptable rates of conception with standard insemination doses down as low as two million total sperm dose (Macmillan, 1979), whereas it has been traditional in the U.K. and in North America to use 20 million live sperm per dose. New Zealand is, however, now moving more towards the use of frozen semen to enable semen to be stored from bulls out-of-season and to permit greater use of the outstanding sires during the cattle breeding season.

It can be claimed, with every justification, that the use of frozen semen has revolutionized the scope of dairy cattle breeding; where one bull was kept to breed 30–40 cows, it is now possible to think in terms of a single bull siring 100 000 offspring in a year, and his semen being used in several countries at the same time and for years after his death. The long-term preservation of bull sperm which is now possible at low temperatures enables the quarantining of semen which is required for international exchange, as well as the establishment of the most efficient cattle breeding programmes within any one country. Future progress in cattle AI would seem

to be a matter of ensuring a supply of the highest quality semen from the genetically outstanding bulls; there may well be a case for combining figures that measure the bull's genetic worth with those relating to his fertility by some formula which will permit the overall commercial value of his semen to be more accurately assessed.

1.7 TIMING OF ARTIFICIAL INSEMINATION

Hammond (1927), in his classic book on reproduction in the cow, recorded the average duration of oestrus as 18 h; as discussed later in this work, most reports that have appeared subsequently are in broad agreement with this, usually placing the figure between 12 and 24 h; it is generally accepted that ovulation occurs 10–12 h after the end of the heat period (Hansel, 1959). Early information for dairy cattle bred with fresh semen, which attempted to relate conception rate to the timing of AI, suggested that inseminations were effective over a period of many hours. Cattle inseminated not earlier than 6 h and not later than 24 h after the start of oestrus showed acceptable fertility with best results when inseminations were made during the middle and towards the end of the heat period (Trimberger and Davis, 1943; Trimberger, 1948; Salisbury and Van Demark, 1961); it was from such early data, generated under research conditions, that the *a.m.–p.m.* rule was developed (cattle detected in oestrus a.m. to be inseminated p.m.; cows noticed in heat p.m., inseminated the following morning). Subsequent field data collected under dairy farm conditions and involving large numbers of cattle generally substantiated this view (Barrett and Casida, 1946; Hall *et al.*, 1959; Macmillan and Watson, 1975) with minor differences among reports, partly due to variations in the time-interval between the onset of oestrus and its detection. Such differences can arise from the particular methods used in oestrus detection, from individual differences in the occurrence of ovulation after the end of oestrus and from a variety of breed and environmental factors.

In more recent times, several authors have dealt with the question of inseminating cattle at the one time (mid-morning, as a rule) in the day and it is clear that once-a-day AI can give acceptable conception results under suitable conditions of semen quality. Foote (1979) reported data for 44 707 cows bred with fresh semen, and showed that a single insemination in the morning period yielded near maximum conception rates, although the work made it clear that many variables could influence the optimum time to inseminate; with bulls of low fertility, inexperienced inseminators and low sperm doses, timing probably needs to be more critical than once-a-day. Studies among large numbers of beef cattle in the U.S.A. were reported by Robbins et al. (1978) who also showed that a satisfactory conception rate could be obtained after insemination once-a-day (in the morning) with frozen–thawed semen; under most conditions, improvements in conception rates that result from varying the time of day at which individual cows are inseminated would probably not justify the expense involved. In New Zealand, it has been observed that the greatest differences in conception rates between bulls and between semen processing methods (fresh or frozen) arise with the early to mid-oestrus inseminations (Macmillan, 1979); the same author makes the point that progress in cattle semen technology may have been hampered by advocating AI for the latter part of the heat period over the years.

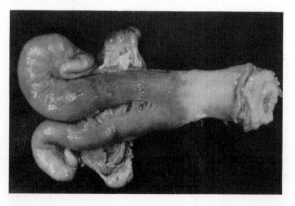

Fig. 1.6. Reproductive organs of the cow. The female reproductive organs are the ovaries, oviducts, uterus, vagina and external genitalia. The tract shown is about quarter-life size.

With below average fertility bulls, or when frozen rather than fresh semen is involved, it is probably more important to carry out the insemination at what is regarded to be the optimum time (late oestrus); presumably, it is a question of sperm survival within the reproductive tract when relatively small numbers of sperm are deposited in the uterus at time of insemination.

1.8 FACTORS INFLUENCING FERTILITY AND SEMEN QUALITY IN BULLS

It is important to consider bull fertility and methods of assessing semen quality, regardless of whether the male is for use in AI or natural mating. The great bulk of documentary evidence does, however, deal with animals that are in AI stations. Certainly, there is plenty of evidence to show that although the female component of cattle fertility is important, due attention must be given to the influence of the bull. Studies in California, as reported by Davidson and Farver (1980) for a large dairy herd, showed conception rates varying from 34 to 70% according to the bull used through AI to breed the cows; the financial cost to the dairy operation of using low fertility bulls can be quite substantial. Evidence about differences in bull fertility has been available for some time; Kidder et al. (1954) reported fertilization rates of 100% for bulls of high fertility and 70% for bulls of low fertility in one early study. Much the same line of evidence was in the report of Bearden et al. (1956); high fertility bulls were associated with a fertilization rate of 97% whereas low fertility bulls yielded a figure of 77%. In New Zealand, Macmillan and Watson (1975) showed how conception rates with AI could vary markedly with bull fertility when the timing of insemination differed during oestrus; although the authors record an overall difference in conception rate of 4.6% between high- and low-fertility bulls, these differences amounted to 16% for inseminations early in oestrus, 5.5% to AI in mid-oestrus and zero for inseminations at the end of heat. Such figures have led authors to suggest that early insemination may be useful in ranking AI bulls on fertility (Shannon, 1978; Foote, 1979).

Laboratory tests which predict bull fertility with reasonable accuracy are desirable, but the fact remains that the tests currently available leave much to be desired. In many Cattle AI centres, sperm motility is evaluated visually after placing a drop of semen on a glass slide heated to body temperature; although this is a method lacking precision and is too subjective, it has apparently served well in semen processing laboratories over the years. However, there is a very real need for greater accuracy in predicting bull fertility and several methods of obtaining an objective measure of sperm motility have been suggested in recent years. The development of equipment for measuring sperm motility such as the Quantimet (Katz and Dott, 1975), the fibre optic Doppler Anamometer (Foulkes, 1979) and the Sperm Motility Analyser (Bartoov et al., 1981) have been reported as suitably objective methods; the latter instrument (SMA), which can be operated by 'non-expert' technicians, enables the simultaneous determination of sperm concentration and motility in bull semen, which the Israeli workers suggest could be employed as a standard method of quality control applicable in semen processing laboratories around the world.

Laboratory testing of characteristics such as sperm motility is only part of the story in the evaluation of a bull's fertility; it is a matter of seeing how the sperm perform in effecting fertilization of the egg in the cow itself. There is evidence that individual bulls tend to show co\:.sistent levels of fertility, (Foulkes, 1979) and if it were possible to identify these bulls reliably, particularly if done early in their breeding careers, then much more effective use could be made of their semen. One line of work in the U.K. has shown that heterospermic insemination can provide a method of determining fertility levels without the need for conducting a large number of inseminations for each bull (Beatty et al., 1969, 1976; Stewart et al., 1974). Semen from several bulls is mixed and frozen and each cow inseminated receives an equal number of sperm from each bull; the more fertile bull will sire more calves under these conditions and the fertility of

the bulls can be ranked according to the number of progeny identified for each sire by blood typing.

1.9 PROBLEM OF OESTRUS DETECTION AND TECHNIQUES TO OVERCOME IT

It is probably true to say that the single most important problem which has faced the cattle AI industry since its inception is heat detection; detection is vital if there is to be successful application of AI in dairy herds, but the methods commonly used in detection have remained largely unchanged throughout the 70 years or so that the breeding technique has been employed. Kiddy (1979), looking at the American scene, notes that there seems to be an unwritten rule, which has evolved over the years, that oestrus should be checked twice daily, with even research workers accepting this. Whether that is true or not, the fact remains that the consequences of inefficient heat detection, in financial and other terms, have been well enough documented in the literature (Esslemont, 1974; Barr, 1975; Spalding et al., 1975; Pelissier, 1976; Booth, 1980); some argument still exists as to whether "silent-heats" in cattle genuinely occur or whether it is a question of certain periods being so short that they are all too easily missed. Certainly, there is evidence that an otherwise normal dairy cow may fail to have its oestrous symptoms detected as a result of factors such as inclement weather, domination by other cattle or lack of interest by other cows, especially if none of them are in the vicinity at or near, the time of oestrus (Ball and Jackson, 1979).

Among dairy cattle, AI has been used to the least extent among replacement heifers because they are the one group of females not usually under the close observation necessary for successful oestrus detection. Attention has been drawn earlier to the fact that AI has not been practised in beef cattle to any great extent because of problems in heat detection; this is one reason for the slower rate of breeding improvement in such animals as compared with dairy cattle. Although there is now a considerable volume of information published about techniques for oestrus detection, the fact remains that detection involves time and expense, no matter what approach is chosen.

1.9.1 Observations in detecting oestrus

It is essential that the farmer or herdsman should set aside enough time to observe his dairy cows for heat. It should be done on a regular basis covering every day; each observation period should occupy not less than 30 min duration, for some cows may only be mounted once in the space of 15–20 min. There is the need for three or more observation periods spread over the 24-h day; of particular importance is a period in the late evening, when many cows may first exhibit oestrous symptoms, because at this time, the animals are generally free to engage in mounting behaviour and are no longer distracted by being herded, milked or fed. Donaldson *et al.* (1968) were among the earliest to draw attention to the importance of frequent observations; 90% of possible heats were detected by one hour checks conducted three times daily at 07.00, 15.00 and 23.00 h. Esslemont (1979a) suggests that a realistic

Fig. 1.7. Observations and the detection of oetrus in cattle. Observation means looking at the herd for cattle that are in oestrus at very specific times. If observations are only made when cows are being driven to and from the milking parlour, there is likely to be a substantial proportion of missed heats. Even under good management a number of cows may not be detected as the period of standing heat is often of short duration. To achieve a high rate of heat detection, it is essential to examine the cows frequently during the day. Ideally, this should be done 4 to 5 times daily with probably the most critical observation period being last thing in the evening. The cowman must try and arrange to have frequent and regular periods set aside specifically for heat detection covering the whole day.

target would be 80% of cyclic cows being detected in a 3-week period. There are plenty of reports showing 50–60% detection rates and clearly these are not good enough. Hurnick *et al.* (1975) and Foote (1979) are among those providing evidence that the onset of oestrus occurs most frequently at night; there is also information showing more mounting activity at night than in the daytime, even when the animals are in darkness (Esslemont, 1974; Hurnick *et al.*, 1975).

Some of the techniques employed in oestrus detection are discussed below and several comprehensive reviews on the subject have been published in recent years (Foote, 1975; Sorensen, 1975). As well as the oestrus detection technique itself, there must be accurate identification of cows, accurate records and careful observations.

1.9.2 Tail-painting

The use of oil or water-based paints applied to the back of the cow's spine at the point most often rubbed by the brisket of the riding cow, was first promoted as an effective aid to oestrus detection in Australia and New Zealand and is rapidly gaining acceptance among farmers in many other countries. The tail-painting technique has been shown by New Zealand workers to identify accurately 99% of cyclic cows in experimental dairy herds (Smith and Macmillan, 1978) and proved to be better than the use of behavioural observations on their own. Macmillan and Curnow (1977) reported that the most successful paint they used in their New Zealand studies was a high gloss enamel; Williamson (1980), on the other hand, who apparently was the originator of tail-painting, preferred a water-soluble plastic paint applied with a roller. In the U.K., a proprietary tail-paint (Tel-Tail; I.C.I. Ltd) has been made available and the paint reported on by workers at Nottingham (Ball and Thompson, 1980). In this, an 8-in strip, about 2.5 in. wide was painted on the hair along the spine behind the pin bones, where it could be rubbed off by a mounting cow; a detection rate of 94% was shown to be possible.

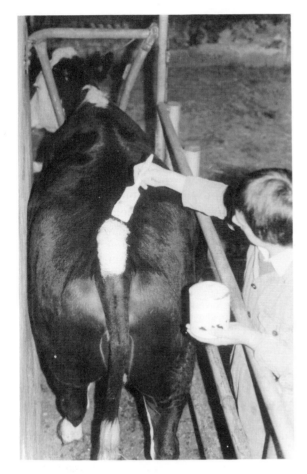

Fig. 1.8. Use of tail paint for helping to identify cows in heat. The technique of tail-painting was widely used in New Zealand before coming to Ireland. However, oil-based paints which worked satisfactorily in New Zealand appear to dry too slowly for conditions in this part of the world. The paint being applied here is a water-based product and dries in about 10 min. The system is not appropriate where free movement of the cows is prevented. Use of tail-painting can result in marked improvements in the percentage of cattle detected in heat. The idea is to apply the paste to the tail crest and not to the free part of the tail. The cattle must be able to interact with one another and should be inspected at least once daily. Trials in the United Kingdom have shown that 90% of ovulations can be identified. The use of paste on freshly calved cows can be useful in identifying non-cycling animals and if it is used after artificial insemination it can show those returning or not returning to oestrus.

1.9.3 Heat mount detectors

Several types of heat mount detectors are not available, all designed to record evidence that a cow has been mounted repeatedly with the herd being checked visually at least twice daily to see if the device has been activated. A related approach is simply to rub chalk on the rumps and tail heads of the cattle every day; the disappearance of the chalk mark is then taken as evidence that the cow has been mounted repeatedly (Britt et al., 1981).

1.9.4 Chinballs and marker animals

Bulls, steers and even hormone tested cows can be used as marker animals, fitted out with a chin-ball marking device; when the animal presses down with its chin on the back or the rump of a mounted cow, a spring in the device is depressed and marker fluid released. Marker bulls (also referred to as 'teasers') have been employed in the detection of oestrus, having first been rendered incapable of inseminating cows by vasectomy, deviation of the penis or fixing the penis within the sheath. All these techniques, which should not lessen the bull's libido but render him sterile have some disadvantages, including the cost of the operation and the possible risk of spreading venereal disease under certain conditions.

More recently, studies with steers and cows treated with testosterone (Signoret, 1975; Britt, 1976; Kiser et al., 1977) or testosterone in combination with oestradiol (Pool et al., 1978) have been conducted as a means of detecting heats in cattle. Response to testosterone has been variable; in the U.S.A., Kiser et al. (1977) recorded that 74% of cattle were detected by testosterone-treated cows, whereas in Ireland, only a 46% detection rate was reported by O'Farrell (1980). There is also the fact that the large doses of testosterone required can make treatment costly.

There is, however, evidence that ovarian steroids alone can induce substantial male behaviour in heifers (Fulkerson, 1978), in cattle freemartins (Greene et al., 1978) and in steers (Sawyer and Fulkerson, 1981). One of these reports has shown that a weekly injection of oestradiol benzoate provides an excellent treatment for the production of detector animals; the development of male behaviour usually takes 2–3 weeks and the response rate is recorded as being high and consistent in both steers and heifers (Sawyer and Fulkerson, 1981).

Fig. 1.9. Steers for aiding in heat detection in cattle. Detection of oestrus in cattle, whether dairy cows or beef animals, has become an increasing problem as herds become larger. Teaser bulls have been employed to help in the detection of oestrus — but it is also possible to employ steer, cows and heifers. Australian work shows that steers treated with 8 mg oestradiol benzoate/250 kg body weight once weekly were very effective in detecting heat. Development of male behaviour usually takes 2–3 weeks and the response rate is consistent and high.

Fig. 1.10. The use of the vaginal probe in cattle as a method of timing the use of AI. The vaginal–cervical mucus in cows undergoes many changes during the oestrous cycle of these various changes, the electrical conductivity has been one that has received quite a deal of attention. In the present instance, a ring-electrode type of vaginal probe is being inserted fully into the cow's vagina so that the electrodes are close to the cervical os. The lowest values are found at or close to oestrus. Workers at Cornell in the U.S.A. have shown the probe to be of value in establishing optimum time for breeding in cows. In pigs, such equipment is used as a means of timing breeding by AI or natural service.

1.9.5 Vaginal probes

There have been several reports providing evidence of a change in the electrical resistance of the fluids in the vagina at the time of oestrus (Aizinbudas and Dovil'tis, 1966; Schams and Butz, 1972; Krieger and Leidl, 1974; Foote, 1975; Gartland et al., 1976; Leidl and Stolla, 1976; Bohme and Bucholz, 1977; Feldman et al., 1978; Carter and Duffy, 1980; Edwards and Aizinbud, 1980) and it has been suggested that this could be the basis of an oestrus detection technique, using a probe which could measure these changes. Foote et al. (1979) reported favourably on a probe developed at Cornell University and suggested that the method may turn out to be particularly useful among cows housed indoors in tie-stalls or stanchions. One difficulty with the vaginal probe is the fact that electrical resistance can vary with the location in the animal; some have measured resistance in the vaginal vestibule (Edwards and Levin, 1974; Bohme and Bucholz, 1977) whereas others have reported that measurements at this site or in the posterior vagina are less reliable than those recorded in the anterior vagina (Owen, 1978; Carter and Duffy, 1980).

An eventual development of this approach to oestrus detection may be in implanting sensors in the animal; there have already been some studies indicating that a sensor can be implanted in the vaginal area to monitor remotely the changes in electrical resistance in the tissues in that region (Leidl and Stolla, 1976; Feldman et al., 1978).

1.9.6 Oestrus and progesterone levels

The availability of highly sensitive radio-immunoassay (RIA) procedures for measuring progesterone has provided an additional means of checking on oestrus, although this can only be after the event. In Germany, for example, the milk progesterone assay has been used to check whether the dairy cows presented for AI have been in oestrus (little or no progesterone) or at some other stage of the oestrous cycle. Until the progesterone assay method became available, it was not always easy to decide whether the absence of oestrus in certain cows after calving was due to poor heat detection or to ovarian malfunction; progesterone assay can now be the means of confirming the resumption of ovarian activity (Bulman and Lamming, 1978). It is also possible to show by this test that "silent-heats" (ovulation unaccompanied by oestrus) do exist and make up part of the problem.

1.9.7 Peroxidase concentration in cervical mucus

Work in the U.K. several years ago showed that peroxidase concentrations in the cervical mucus of heifer cattle declined to undetectable levels at time of oestrus (Linford, 1974). This approach was developed so that a finger-stall impregnated with an agent sensitive to peroxidase could be used as an aid to oestrus detection; the technique appeared to work well in heifers but was less successful in mature cows. Foulkes et al. (1981) attempted to get more reliable results in cows by taking mucus from the anterior vagina, but the problem of contamination of the sample of oestrous mucus with traces of peroxidase from the days preceding oestrus remained.

1.9.8 Temperature, activity, odours

Oestrus detection procedures which are being researched, some with a view to eventual commercial application, vary from techniques employing closed circuit TV cameras and time-lapse video recorders (Morris et al., 1976; Pollock and Hurnick, 1979) to measuring the temperature of milk in the clawpiece of the milking machine (Maatje and Rossing, 1976); it should be noted that the results of such studies on the temperature approach have not seemed particularly promising, although the use of temperature sensors implanted in the vaginal wall or elsewhere have also been described (Sambraus, 1980; Spahr et al., 1981). There have been those who have measured variations in the physical activity of cattle with pedometers and have shown significant increases in activity at time of oestrus (Kiddy, 1977); this American study reported 76% of heats being detected by visual observations whereas 96% were detected by pedometer readings. Further evidence provided by the same author showed that activity at oestrus increased to at least twice a cow's normal average in 92% of animals observed (Kiddy, 1979); activity monitoring is regarded as a potentially useful approach to heat detection, but the process needs to be refined to avoid the time taken up in reading and recording the pedometer data each day. Even the feasibility of using trained dogs to detect the odour of the oestrous cow is one area being explored in the U.S.A. (Kiddy, 1979).

There is an obvious need to explore novel methods for the detection of oestrus and in the age of the micro-chip and electronic technology it would seem likely enough that miniature sensing devices, implanted subdermally in the cow to detect changes in electrical resistance, temperature or activity at oestrus, could become a practical reality in the years ahead; coupled with new electronic methods for identifying cows, there would seem much scope for developments in this area, as noted by Britt (1979). It should also be mentioned that the effectiveness of oestrus detection can often be markedly improved when two criteria are used rather than just one; work in the U.S.A. showed that heats were identified with 95% accuracy when a positive reading from a heat detection device was combined with visual observations for oestrus, whereas only 68% of heats were detected by observations alone (Britt, 1978).

As noted above, in the years ahead, it is likely that electronic identification procedures may be utilized on a routine basis, especially in the larger herds (Holm, 1977); such systems will probably employ uniquely coded electronic implants in

Fig. 1.11. Identifying animals on the farm. In systems of controlled breeding and reproductive management, an essential requirement is for accurate identification of animals. Electronic identification of every dairy cow in Ireland by an implanted device is now considered to be technically possible, thanks to the microchip. However, before commercial development can really get under way, it will be necessary to agree on how to attach or implant the device, how to make it tamperproof and how it should be "interrogated" — as the jargon of the electronics industry puts it. Apart from the value of such devices in identifying animals, the introduction of a national cow identification scheme would enable progress to be made on many other fronts — such as milk recording of dairy cows.

each dairy cow, which can be read by directing a hand-held interrogator towards the individual animal.

1.10 REPRODUCTIVE MANAGEMENT PROGRAMMES

It is well accepted that there is a need for effective systems of management for high reproductive efficiency in cattle without it being a matter of concentrating attention only when there is a problem of herd fertility. There are many studies, most of them with dairy cattle, which have measured the reproductive performance achieved in milking herds (Britt, 1975; de Kruif, 1975; Esslemont and Ellis, 1975; Pelissier, 1976), so that it is known what can or cannot be achieved in terms of reproductive efficiency. Several reports have also shown that well supervised reproductive management programmes can improve reproductive efficiency in dairy herds (Britt and Ulberg, 1970; Esslemont and Eddy, 1977; Galton et al., 1977; de Kruif and Akabwa, 1978; Bloxham, 1980; Boyd and Munro, 1980; de Kruif, 1980). It has been suggested that such programmes would be most beneficial if utilized as part of a total reproductive management package offered by a consultant or service organization (Ulberg et al., 1974). In the U.S.A., Britt (1979) makes the point that recent advances in computer technology have now made it feasible to integrate new concepts in reproductive management into dairy herd operations, although such concepts will have to be evaluated by cost-benefit analysis. A reproductive management programme currently operated in the Netherlands and its computerized data processing has been described (de Kruif and Akabwal, 1978; de Kruif, 1980); this programme has resulted in an improvement in first service conception rate from 51 to 52% and some reduction in the calving interval (de Kruif, 1980).

1.11 FUTURE DEVELOPMENTS

The present discussion has sought to cover certain aspects of cattle reproduction as a backbround to information given on controlled breeding techniques. Obviously, it is as well to have some idea of problems encountered in the cow under normal conditions before attempting to set out some of the possibilities for modifying the animal's performance. It may be, that in addition to any specific merit in cattle production, application of controlled breeding techniques may occasionally serve to focus more critical attention on the normal fertility levels which obtain under different breeding, feeding and management conditions. This may suggest changes which, in themselves, prove useful in bringing about improvements in the general level of cattle fertility. The main objective in controlled breeding remains, however, in providing the farmer with techniques by which he can control, monitor or manipulate the reproductive processes, while permitting the heifer or cow to exhibit its normal level of fertility.

1.12 REFERENCES

Adams, R. S., Stout, W. L., Kradel, D. C., Guss, S. B. Jr., Moser, B. I. and Jung, G. A. (1978) Use and limitations of profiles in assessing health or nutritional status of dairy herds. J. Dairy. Sci. **61,** 1671–1679.

Aizinbudas, L. B. and Dovil'tis, P. P. (1966). Some results of tests with the electrometrical method of ascertaining the time to inseminate cows, Zhivotnovodstuo, **28**(5), 84–89.

Appleyard, W. T. and Cook, B. (1979) Detection of oestrus in dairy cattle. Vet. Rec. **99,** 253–256.

Ayalon, N. (1972) Fertility losses in normal cows and repeat breeders. Proc. 7th Int. Congr. on Anim. Reprod. and AI (Munich), **Vol. 1,** 741–744.

Ball, P. J. H. and Jackson, N. W. (1979) The fertility of the dairy cows inseminated on the basis of mild progesterone measurements. Br. Vet. J., **135,** 537–540.

Ball, P. J. H. and Thompson, A. D. (1980) The use of milk progesterone profiles for the evaluation of tail paste as an aid to oestrus detection. J. Anim. Sci. **51** (Suppl. 1), 257 (abs).

Barr, H. L. (1975) Influence of oestrus detection in dairy herds. J. Dairy Sci. **58,** 246–247.

Barrett, G. R. and Casida, L. E. (1946) Time of insemination and conception rate in artificial breeding. J. Dairy Sci. **29,** 556 (abs).

Bartoov, B., Kalay, D. and Mayevsky, A. (1981) Sperm motility analyzer (SMA) a practical tool of motility and cell concentration determinations in Artificial Insemination Centres. Theriogenology **15,** 173–182.

Bearden, H. J., Hansel, W. and Bratton, R. W. (1956) Fertilization of embryonic mortality rates of bulls with histories of either low or high fertility in artificial breeding. J. Dairy Sci. **39,** 312–318.

Beatty, R. A., Bennett, G. H., Hall, H. G., Hancock, J. L. and Steward, D. L. (1969) An experiment with heterospermic insemination in cattle. J. Reprod. Fert. **20,** 491–502.

Beatty, R. A., Stewart, D. L., Spooner, R. L. and Hancock, J. L. (1976) Evaluation by the heterospermic insemination technique of the differential effect on freezing at-196>C on fertility of individual bull semen. *J. Reprod. Fert.* **47,** 377–379.

Bellows, R. A., Short, R. E. and Staigmiller, R. B. (1979) Research areas in beef cattle reproduction. *Anim. Reprod. (BARC Symp. 3,* Harold Hawk, Ed). Allanheld. *Osmun. Montclair* pp 413–421.

Bishop, M. W. H., Campbell, R. C., Hancock, J. L. and Walton, A. (1954) Semen characteristics and fertility in the bull. *J. Agric. Sci. Camb.* **44,** 227.

Bloxham, P. A. (1980) A bovine herd fertility scheme. *Vet. Rec.* **107,** 558.

Bohme, K. and Buchholz, G. W. (1977) Determination of optimum insemination date in heifers and young cows by means of electrical resistance measurements (vaginal mucosa) after oestrus synchronization. *Arch. Exp. Vet. Med.* **31,** 671–680.

Booth, J. M. (1980) Milk progesterone pregnancy testing in cattle and other species. *Proc. 9th Int. Congr. Anim. Reprod. AI. (Madrid),* **2,** 119–224.

Boyd, H. and Munro, C. D. (1980). experiences and results of a herd-health programme, rectal palpation and progesterone assays in fertility control. *Proc. 9th Int. Congr. Anim. Reprod. AI (Madrid),* **2,** 373–380.

Britt, J. H. (1975). Early *Post-partum* breeding in dairy cows: a review. *J. Dairy Sci.* **58,** 266–271.

Britt, J. H. (1976). Testosterone induction of male-like sexual behaviour in cows for use in oestrus detection. *A.I. Digest* **24,** 14–15.

Britt, J. H. (1977) Strategies for managing reproduction and controlling health problems in groups of cows. J. Dairy Sci. **60,** 1345–1353.

Britt, J. H. (1978) Heat detection in dairy cattle. *Adv. Anim. Breeder,* **14**(9), 6–9.

Britt, J. H. (1979) New concepts in managing dairy cattle reproduction. In, *Anim. Reprod.* (BARC Symp. 3, Harold Hawk ed.). Allanheld, Osmun, Montclair 63–75.

Britt, J. H. and Ulberg, L. C. (1970) Changes in reproductive performance in dairy herds using the herd reproductive status system. *J. Dairy Sci.* **53,** 752–756.

Britt, J. H., Cox, N. M. and Stevenson, J. S. (1981) Advances in reproduction in dairy cattle. *J. Dairy Sci.* **64,** 1378–1402.

Bulman, C. D. (1977) Progesterone levels and fertility in lactating cows. Ph.D. thesis, Univ. Nottingham.

Bulman, D. C. and Lamming, G. E. (1978) Milk progesterone levels in relation to conception repeat breeding and factors influencing acyclicity in dairy cows. *J. Reprod. Fert.* **54,** 447–458.

Carter, P. D. and Duffy, J. H. (1980) Assessment of vaginal impedance measurements as an indicator of oestrus in cattle. *Aust. Vet. J.* **56,** 321–323.

Crowley, J. P., Harrington, D. and Lacey, M. (1967) A survey of reproductive efficiency in cattle. 1. The reproductive performance of Irish cattle artificially inseminated. *Ir. J. Agric. Res.* **6,** 237–240.

David, S. E., Bishop, M. W. H. and Cembrowicz, H. J. (1971) Reproductive expectancy and infertility in cattle. *Vet. Rec.* **89,** 181–185.

Davidson, J. N. and Farver, T. B. (1980) Conception rates of Holstein bulls for A.I. on a California dairy *J. Dairy Sci.* **63,** 621–626.

Diskin, M. G. and Sreenan, J. M. (1980) Fertilization and embryonic mortality rates in beef heifers after A.I. *J. Reprod. Fert.* **59,** 463–468.

Donaldson, L. E. (1976) A.I. of beef cattle. *Aust. Vet. J.* **52,** 565–569.

Donaldson, L. E., Little, D. A. and Hansel, W. (1968) The duration of oestrus and the time of ovulation in cattle of three breed types with and without synchronization of oestrus with a progestagen. *Aust. Vet. J.* **44,** 364–366.

Drew, B. (1981) Controlled breeding in dairy herd management. *Br. Friesian J. March, 1981,* 138–139.

Edwards, D. F. and Aizinbud, E. (1980) The timing of artificial insemination in cattle, sheep and pigs by measurement of vaginal conductivity. *Biblphy. Reprod.* **36,** 425.

Edwards, D. F. and Levin, R. J. (1974) An electrical method of detecting the optimum time to inseminate cattle, sheep and pigs. *Vet. Rec.* **95,** 416–420.

Esslemont, R. J. (1974) Economic and husbandry aspects of the manifestation of oestrus in cows—Pt. I. Economic aspects. *A.D.A.S. Q. Rev.* **12,** 175–184.

Esslemont, R. J. (1979a) Management with special reference to fertility. In, *Feeding Strategy for the High Yielding Dairy Cow* pp 258–294. (Broster, W. and Swan, H.). Crosby Lockwood, ?

Esslemont, R. J. (1979b) Improving conception rates. Br. Cattle Breed. Club Dig. **34,** 69–76.

Esslemont, R. J. and Eddy, R. G. (1977) The control of cattle fertility; the use of computerized records. *Br. Vet. J.* **133,** 346–355.

Esslemont, R. J. and Ellis, P. R. (1975) The Melbread dairy herd health recording scheme. A report on the economic, reproductive and husbandry changes in 22 herds over 3 seasons. *Vet. Epid., Econ. Res. Unit, Dept. Agric. Univ. Reading.*

Feldman, F., Aizinbud, E., Schindler, H. and Broda, H. (1978) The electrical conductivity inside the bovine vaginal wall. *Amin. Prod.* **26,** 61–65.

Foote, R. H. (1952) Survey of breeding efficiency on 2700 New York State dairy herds. Cornell Univ. Mimeo. (Quoted in Spalding *et al.,* 1975).

Foote, R. H. (1975) Estrus detection and estrus detection aids. *J. Dairy Sci.* **58,** 248–256.

Foote, R. H. (1978) Symposium on freezing of gametes and spermatozoa—Synopsis papers: Freezing bull spermatozoa: A review. *Cryobiology* **15,** 358–361.

Foote, R. H. (1979) Time of A.I. & Fertility in dairy cattle. *J. Dairy Sci.* **62,** 355–358.

Foote, R. H., Oltenacu, E. A. B., Mellinger, J., Scott, N. R. and Marshall, R. A. (1979) Pregnancy rate in dairy cows inseminated on the basic of electronic probe measurements. *J. Dairy Sci.* **62,** 69–73.

Foulkes, J. A. (1979) Maintenance of fertility in A.I. *Br. Cattle Breed. Club. Dig.* **34,** 69–76.

Foulkes, J. A., Hartley, P. E., Stewart, D. L. (1981) Bovine cervical mucus peroxidase concentrations at oestrus. *Res. Vet. Sci.* **30,** 14–17.

Fulkerson, W. J. (1978) Artificial induction of lactation: a comparative study in heifers. *Aust. J. Biol. Sci.* **31,** 65–71.

Galton, D. M., Barr, H. L. and Heider, L. E. (1977) Effects of a herd health program on reproductive performance of dairy cows. *J. Dairy Sci.* **60,** 1117–1124.

Gartland, P., Schiavo, J., Hall, C. E., Foote, C. E. and Scott, N. R. (1976) Detection of oestrus in dairy cows by electrical measurements of vaginal mucus by milk progesterone. *J. Dairy Sci.* **59,** 982–985.

Gerrits, R. J., Blosser, T. H., Purchase, H. G., Terrill, R. H. and

Warwick, E. J. (1979) Economics of improving reproductive efficiency in farm animals. *Anim. Reprod.* (BARC Symp. No. 3—Harold Hawk ed.). Allanheld. Osmun, Montclair., pp 413–421.

Greene, W. A., Mogil, L. and Foote, R. H. (1978) Behavioural characteristics of freemartins administered etradiol, esterone, testosterone and dihydrotestosterone. *Horm. Behav.* **10,** 71–84.

Hafez, E. S. E. and Bouisson, M. F. (1975) The behaviour of cattle. In, *The Behaviour of Domestic Animals* (ed. Hafez, 3rd Edit.) Baillière Tindall, London.

Hall, J. G., Branton, C. and Stone, E. J. (1959) Estrus, estrous cycles, ovulation time, time of service and fertility of dairy cattle in Louisiana. *J. Dairy Sci.* **42,** 1086.

Hammond J. (1927) The Physiology of Reproduction in the Cow. Cambridge Univ. Press, London.

Hansel, W. (1959) The oestrous cycle of the cow. In, *Reproduction in Domestic Animals* (Cole, H. H. and Cupps, P. T.) **Vol. 1,** p 223. Academic Press, London.

Haresign, W. (1979) Body condition, milk yield and reproduction in cattle. *Recent Advances in Anim. Nutrition, pp.* 107–122 Butterworths, London.

Hawk, H. W. (1979) Infertility in dairy cattle. *Anim. Reprod.* (BARC Symp. No. 3—Harold Hawk ed.) Allanheld, Osmun, Montclair, pp. 19–29.

Henricks, D. M., Dickey, J. F., Hill, J. R. (1971) Plasma estrogen and progesterone levels in cows prior to and during estrus. *Endocr.* **89,** 1350–1355.

Hodgson, R. E. (1973) Trends and needs in the dairy industry. *J. Dairy Sci.* **56**(5), 614–620.

Hoffman, B., Schams, D. and Karg, J. (1976) Cycle synchronization under hormonal control. Proc. EEC Seminar Egg Transfer in cattle. Camb. 209–218.

Holm, D. M. (1977) Effects of electronic identification, temperature monitoring and ELA on the meat industry. *Adv. Anim. Breed.* **25,** 6–9.

Hurnick, J. F., King, G. J. and Robertson, H. A. (1975) Estrous and related behaviour in post partum Holstein cows. *Appl. Anim. Ethol.* 2, 55–68.

Jackson, P. S., Johnson, C. T., Bulman, D. C. and Holdsworth, R. J. (1979) A study of cloprostenol induced oestrus and spontaneous oestrus by means of the milk progesterone assay. *Brit. Vet. J.* **135,** 578–590.

Katz, D. F. and Dott, H. M. (1975) Methods of measuring swimming speed of spermatozoa *J. Reprod. Fert.* **45,** 263–272.

Kidder, H. E., Black, W. G., Wiltbank, J. N., Ulberg, L. C. and Casida, L. E. (1954) Fertilization rate and embryonic death rate in cows bred to bulls of different levels of fertility. *J. Dairy Sci.* **37,** 691–697.

Kiddy, C. A. (1977) Variation in physical activity as an indication of estrus in dairy cows. *J. Dairy Sci.* **60,** 235–243.

Kiddy, C. A. (1977) Estrus detection in dairy cattle. *Anim. Reprod.* (BARC, Symp. 3. H. Hawk ed.), Allanheld, Osmun, Montclair, 77–89.

Kilkenny, J. B. (1978) Reproductive performance of beef cows. *Wld Rev. Anim. Prod.* **14,**(3), 65–74.

King, J. O. (1968) The relationship between the conception rate and changes in body weight, yield and SNF content of milk in dairy cows. *Vet. Rec.* **83,** 492–494.

King, J. O. (1972) Changes in dairy husbandry methods during the last 25 years. *Vet. Rec.* **91,** 401–406.

King, G. J., Dickinson, F. N., Rempendahl, A., Kienast, H. and Dixon, M. K. (1971) Artificial breeding report. *SEA, DK 1 Lett.*

Kiser, T. E., Britt, H. H. and Ritchie, H. D. (1977) Testosterone treatment of cows for use in detection of oestrus. *J. Anim. Sci.* **44,** 1030–1035.

Kreiger, H. and Leidl, W. (1974) Practical experience in the measurement of the electrical resistance of vaginal mucosa in cattle as an aid in determining the oestrus. *Tierarztl. Umsch.* **29**(1), 22–25.

Kruif, A. de (1975) An investigation of the parameters which determine the fertility of a cattle population and of some factors which influence these parameters. *Tijdschr. Diergenest.* **100,** 1089.

Kruif, A. de (1976) A fertility control programme in dairy herds in the Netherlands. *Tijdschr. Diergenest* **101,** 428.

Kruif, A. de (1980) Efficiency of a fertility control programme in dairy cows Proc. 9th Int. Congr. Anim. Reprod. A.I. (Madrid), **2,** 381–388.

Kruif, A. de and Akabwa, D. (1978) A herd fertility programme for dairy cattle and computerized data processing. *N.Z. Vet. J.* **26,** 202–208.

Kruif, A. de and Brand, A. (1978) Factors influencing the reproductive capacity of a dairy herd. *N. Z. Vet. J.* **26,** 178–189.

Laing, J. A. (1949) Infertility in cattle associated with death of ova at early stages after fertilization. *J. Comp. Pathol. Therap.* **59,** 97–108.

Laing, J. A. (1970) Normal fertility and the incidence of infertility. In, *Fertility and Infertility in the Domestic Anim* (2nd. Ed.), Bailliere Tindall, London.

Laing, J. A. (1979) Normal fertility and the incidence of infertility. In, *Fert. and Infert. in the Domestic Anim.* (Ed. J. A. Laing) (3rd Edit.), Bailliere Tindall, London. pp. 1–4.

Langley, O. H. (1978). Conception rate to A.I. and Natural Service. *Ir. Vet. J.* **33,** 4–8.

Laster, D. B.; Glimp, H. A.; Gregory, K. E. (1972) Age and weight at puberty and conception in different breeds and breed-crosses of beef heifers. *J. Anim. Sci.* **34,** 1031–1036.

Lee, vander S. and Boot, L. M. (1955) Spontaneous pseudopregnancy in mice. *Acta Physiol. Pharmac. Neèrl.* **4,** 442–444.

Leidl, W. and Stolla, R. (1976) Measurement of electrical resistance of the vaginal mucus as an aid for heat detection. *Theriog.* **6,** 237–249.

Linford, E. (1974) Cervical mucus: an agent or a barrier to conception. *J. Reprod. Fert.* **37,** 239–250.

Linford, E., Glover, F. A., Bishop, C. and Stewart, D. L. (1976) The relationship between semen evaluation methods and fertility in the bull. *J. Reprod. Fert.* **47,** 283–291.

Lowman, B. G., Scott, N. and Somerville, S. (1973) Condition scoring of cattle. *Bull. E. Scotl. Coll. Agric.* No. 6.

McCaughey, W. J. and Cooper, R. J. (1980) An assessment by progesterone assay of the accuracy of oestrus detection in dairy cows. *Vet. Rec.* **107,** 508–510.

Macmillan, K. L. (1973) Why do bulls differ in fertility?. *Proc. N.Z. Soc. Anim. Prod.* **33,** 49–61.

Macmillan, K. L. (1979) Factors influencing conception rates to artificial breeding in N.Z. dairy herds: a review. *Proc. N.Z. Soc. Anim. Prod.* **39,** 129–137.

Macmillan, K. L. and Curnow, R. J. (1977) Tail painting–a simple form of oestrus detection in N.Z. dairy herds. *N.Z. Jl. Exp. Agric.* **5,** 357–361.

Macmillan, K. L. and Watson, J. D. (1975) Fertility differences between groups of sires relative to the stage of oestrus at the time of insemination. *Anim. Prod.* **21,** 243–249.

Maatje, K. and Rossing, W. (1976) Detecting oestrus by

measuring milk temperatures of dairy cows during milking. *Livestock Prod. Sci.* **3**, 85–89.

Moberg, G. P. (1976) Effects of environment and management stress on reproduction in the dairy cow. *J. Dairy Sci.* **59**, 1618–1624.

Morris, C. A., Hurnik, J. J., King, G. J. and Robertson, H. A. (1976) A cost-benefit analysis for a monitoring system to detect oestrus in dairy cows. *Can. J. Anim. Sci.* **56**, 219–296.

O'Farrell, K. H. (1980) Fertility management in the dairy herd. *Ir. Vet. J.* **34**(12), 160–69.

Ortavant, R., Mauleon, P. and Thibault, C. (1964) Photoperiodic control of gonadal and hypophyseal activity in domestic animals. *Ann. N.Y. Acad. Sci.* **117**, 157, 193.

Owen, J. B. (1978) Automated AI in cattle. *Rpt. M.M.B. Breed & Prod. Div.* 1977–78, 106.

Payne, J. M., Rowland, G. J., Mansion, R. and Dew, S. M. (1973) A statistical appraisal of the results of metabolic profile tests on 75 dairy herds. *Br. Vet. J.* **129**, 370.

Pelissier, C. L. (1972) Herd breeding problems and their consequences. *J. Dairy Sci.* **55**, 385–391.

Pelissier, C. L. (1976) Dairy cattle breeding problems and their consequences. *Theriog.* **6**,(5), 575–583.

Phillips, R. W. (1972) Artificial insemination as a means of improving world animal production. *Reprod. Anim. Fecond. Artif. Bologna, Italy.* pp. 239–243. Edizioni Agricole.

Polge, C. and Rowson, L. E. A. (1952) Results with bull semen stored at –79°C. *Vet. Rec.* **64**, 851.

Pollock, W. E. and Hurnik, J. F. (1979) Effect of two confirment systems on estrous and diestrous behaviour in dairy cows. *Can. J. Anim. Sci.* **59**, 799–803.

Pool, S. H., Loyacano, A. F., Goodensaux, S. D. and Godke, R. A. (1978) Detecting oestrus in beef cattle with hormone treated steers and heifers. *Theriog.* **9**, 99–105.

Pope, G. S. and Swinburne, J. K. (1980) Reviews of the progress of dairy science: hormones in milk, their physiological significance and value as diagnostic aids. *J. Dairy Res.* **47**, 427–449.

Quick, A. J. and Mulholland, J. R. (1978) Rept. of study tour undertaken in Israel: high yielding herds. Reading, Min. of Agr. Fish. & Food, ADAS.

Robbins, R. K., Sullivan, J. J., Pace, M. M., Elliott, F. I., Bartlett, D. E. and Press, P. J. (1978) Timing the insemination of beef cattle. *Theriog.* **10**,(2/3), 247–255.

Roche, J. F., Boland, M. P., McGeady, T. A. and Ireland, J. J. (1981) Reproductive wastage following artificial insemination of heifers. *Vet. Rec.* **109**, 401–404.

Roche, J. F., Sherington, J., Mitchell, J. P. and Cunningham, J. F. (1978) Factors affecting calving rate to AI in cows. *Ir. J. Agric. Res.* **17**, 149–157.

Salisbury, G. W. and Van Demark, N. L. (1978) *Physiology of Reproduction and AI of Cattle.* (2nd Edit.) Freeman, San Francisco.

Sambraus, H. H. (1980) Telemetric measurement of the vaginal temperature of cows. *Dtsch. tierarztl. Wschr.* **87**, 292–294.

Sawyer, G. J. and Fulkerson, W. J. (1981) The effectiveness of steers and heifers treated with oestrogen or testosterone to detect oestrus in cattle. *Anim. Reprod. Sci.* **3**, 259–269.

Schams, D. and Butz, H. D. (1972) Relationship in time between estrual symptoms, variations in the electrical resistance of vaginal mucus, preovulatory secretion of the luteinization hormones and ovulation in bovines. *Zuchty* **9**,(7), 49–50.

Senger, P. L. (1980) Handling frozen bovine semen—Factors which influence viability and fertility. *Theriog.* **13**, 51–62.

Seykora, A. J., Sargent, F. D. and McDaniel, B. T. (1980)

Breeding practices on selected North Carolina Dairy farms. *J. Dairy Sci.* **63**, 2103–2110.

Shannon, P. (1978) Factors influencing the fertility of a cattle population. *J. Reprod. Fert.* **54**, 519–527.

Shelton, J. N., Heath, T. D., Old, K. G. and Turnbull, G. E. (1979) Non-surgical recovery of eggs from single-ovulating bovines. *Theriog.* **11**, 149–152.

Signoret, J. P. (1975) A new method for detecting estrus in cattle. *Ann. Zootech.* **24**, 125.

Smith, J. F. and Macmillan, K. L. (1978) The applied and economic aspects of oestrus synchronization in cattle. *N.Z. Vet. J.* **26**, 173–175.

Spahr, S. L., Puckett, H. B., Fernando, R. S., Olver, E. F. and McCoy, G. C. (1981) Subdermal electronic identification and temperature monitoring. *J. Dairy Sci.*, **64**,(Suppl. 1), 155 (Abs).

Spalding, R. W., Everett, R. W. and Foote, R. H. (1975) Fertility in New York A.I. Holstein herds in dairy herd improvement. *J. Dairy Sci.* **58**, 718–723.

Spitzer, J. C., Niswender, G. D., Seidel, G. E. Jr. and Wiltbank, J. N. (1978) Fertilization and blood levels of progesterone and LH in beef heifers on a restricted energy diet. *J. Anim. Sci.* **46**, 1071–1077.

Sonderegger, H. and Schurch, A. (1977) A study of the influence of the energy and protein supply of the fertility of dairy cows. *Livest. Prod. Sci.* **4**, 327–333.

Sorensen, A. M. (1975) Estrous detection in cattle. *S. West. Vet.* **28**, 127–134.

Stevenson, F. G. (1981) Choosing a herdsman—Inseminator school. *Adv. Anim. Breeder* **29**,(3), 8–10.

Stewart, D. L., O'Hagan, C. and Glover, F. A. (1972) The prediction of the fertility of bull semen from laboratory tests. Proc. 7th Int. Congr. Anim. Reprod. A.I. (Munich), **2**, 1280–1283.

Stewart, D. L., Spooner, R. L., Bennett, G. H., Beatty, R. A. and Hancock, J. L. (1974) A second experiment with hetereospermic insemination in cattle *J. Reprod. Fert.* **36**, 107–116.

Stott, G. H. and Wiersma, F. (1976) Short-term relief for improved fertility in dairy cattle during hot weather. *Int. J. Biometeor* **20**(4), 344–350.

Trimberger, G. W. (1948) Breeding efficiency in dairy cattle from AI at various intervals before and after ovulation. *Neb. Agric. Exp. Sta. Res. Bull.* 153.

Trimberger, G. W. and Davis, H. P. (1943) Conception rate in dairy cattle by A.I. at various stages of oestrus. *Neb. Agr. Exp. Sta. Res. Bull.* 129.

Turman, E. J., Laster, D. B., Renbarger, R. E. and Stephens, D. F. (1971) Multiple births in beef cows treated with equine gonadotrophin (PMS) and chorionic gonadotrophin (HGC). *J. Anim. Sci.* **32**, 962–967.

Ulberg, L. C., Brannen, L. and Craven, P. L. (1974) Programs for improving reproduction in dairy herds through management. *J. Anim. Sci.* **39**, (Suppl. 1), 31 (abs).

Wagner, W. C. (1974) Intensified dairy operations and their effect on preparturient diseases and postpartum reproduction. *J. Dairy Sci.* **57**, 354–360.

Warwick, E. J. (1967) Reproductive performance in world regions. In, *Factors Affecting Calf Crop.* Cunha, T. J., Warnick, A. C. and Koger, M.: Ed. Gainsville, Florida, U.S.A., Univ. of Flor. Press 4–10

Watson, W. A. (1980) Large livestock units and notifiable disease. *Br. Vet. J.* **136**, 1–17.

White, D. S. and O'Farrell, J. D. (1972) The AI service and conception rates. *Farm Bull.* 13.

Williamson, N. B. (1980) Tail painting as an aid to detection of oestrus in cattle. *Aust. Vet. J.* **56,** 98–100.

Wishart, D. F. and Young, I. M. (1974) Artificial insemination of progestin (SC 21009)-treated cattle at predetermined times.*Vet. Rec.* **95,** 503–08.

Youdan, P. G. (1973) Some effects of bodyweight changes during the *post-partum* period in dairy cows. Ph.D. Thesis, Univ. of Liverpool.

Youdan, P. G. and King, J. O. (1977) The effects of bodyweight changes during the *post partum* period in dairy cows. *Br. Vet. J.* **133,** 635–641.

CHAPTER 2

The Oestrous Cycle of the Cow

2.1 INTRODUCTION

With the advent of RIA procedures for measuring the steroid, polypeptide and other hormones involved in the reproductive processes of the farm mammals, a considerable volume of information has accumulated about events in the oestrous cycle and at other stages of the cow's reproductive life. Clearly, the hope is that such evidence will provide increasingly meaningful guidance to those who are concerned in the control and manipulation of the animal's reproductive processes.

2.2 OESTRUS AND OESTROUS CYCLE LENGTH

The cow is peculiar, among the farm animals, in having such a short heat period and this is unfortunate, in many ways, for the dairy and beef farmer. Hansel (1959), in an excellent review of data at that time, put the average duration of oestrus at about 18 h; reports since that time have probably put the average at a lower figure but it may be a matter of methods employed in checking cattle and the interval between tests (Asdell, 1964). Ovulation, which occurs spontaneously in the cow, occurs 10–12 h after the end of oestrus (Hansel, 1959).

The cow that is in oestrus will stand still when mounted from the rear by a bull, steer or companion cow. According to Harker (1980), sometimes a cow will mount another from the front and in this situation it is the riding cow which is in oestrus and not the one underneath. Cows that are in heat can be expected to display a variety of signs, including: discharge of clear mucus from the vulva; tail raising and switching; licking, sniffing and rubbing against other cattle; resting the chin on and mounting other cattle; swelling and reddening of the vulva; frequent bawling; general restlessness and attentiveness to the activities of other cattle and humans; ruffling of rump hair and mild abrasion of rump skin as a consequence of having been mounted and a temporary drop in milk yield. It has to be remembered that an observer has to be on the outlook for all or any of the above signs if he is to be successful in oestrus detection. It may be a matter of noting the animal's behaviour or symptoms in comparison with those shown on preceding days; the character of bovine cervical mucus changes around the time of oestrus, becoming the dilute, watery mucus which gives rise to the 'bulling-string' as often seen in heifers.

Reference has already been made elsewhere to the possibility of new methods being developed for the detection of oestrous symptoms in cattle. Already, there is work in sheep, as reported by Adam et al. (1981), who implanted electrodes in vulvar tissues, showing that the peak of electrical resistance within the vulvar and vaginal tissues coincided with oestrus; by using a subdermally implanted device, these workers found it was possible to obtain a suitably consistent result, presumably due to the fixed location of the

Fig. 2.1. Standing heat in the heifer and cow. A sure sign that a cow or heifer is in heat is when she stands to be ridden by another cow. During oestrus, there can be a large flow of mucus from the vulva which runs down the tail or flanks — the character of this mucus changing as heat proceeds — from a clear fluid to a thicker material of a yellowish or whitish colour. The cow differs from the sow in that there are no marked pro-oestrous changes of the external genitalia visible to the naked eye. During the heat period, the vulva can become slightly swollen and flushed but this may not be evident until a day or two after the heat is over. Very often there can be a flow of blood about 2–3 days after the commencement of oestrus–metoestrous bleeding.

implanted electrodes and their constant proximity to the surrounding tissues. On the basis of the sheep work, Adam et al. (1981) suggest that a system could be developed for the continuous recording of the oestrous cycle and for detecting cows in heat; technical problems will be simplified by the development of analogue telemetric systems, such as subdermal livestock electronic identification and temperature monitoring systems (Holm, 1977; Hoover, 1978; Spahr et al., 1981).

The length of the oestrous cycle is variable, but there is general agreement among those who have reviewed the literature that the modal length for heifers is 20 days and 21 days for cows (Asdell et al., 1949; Olds and Seath, 1951; Hansel, 1959). Despite the genuine difference between maiden and parous cattle in cycle length, there does not appear to be any increase in duration as the age of the parous cow becomes greater. Morris (1976) notes that although the traditional view is that about 85% of cycles are between 18 and 24 days in length with about 5% of cycles shorter and 10% longer, in fact he found, even in well-managed herds, that only 50% were in the

18–24 days category. It is true that the increased use of AI in the cattle industry has increased the general awareness of oestrous cycle lengths. It does appear that in dairy cows, the most frequent length of oestrous cycles of less than normal duration is found to be 8–10 days (Macmillan and Watson, 1971) and much the same has been reported by Odde et al. (1980) in beef cattle. It would also seem that variation in the duration of the pro-oestrus phase (interval between regression of the corpus luteum and the onset of oestrus) is greater in lactating cows than in dry heifers and this is one reason why a greater variability in cycle length occurs in that category (Macmillan, 1970).

Although it has occasionally been suggested that "silent heat" (ovulation without oestrus) in the cow is a myth (Esslemont, 1973) and it is doubtless true that certain instances of failure in oestrus detection accounts for some proportion of missed heats, there is a substantial body of evidence, now reinforced with data from progesterone assays, showing that the phenomenon genuinely does occur.

2.3 ENDOCRINOLOGY OF THE OESTROUS CYCLE

The various changes that occur in the blood plasma concentrations of steroids, such as progesterone and oestradiol and polypeptides such as LH and FSH have been detailed in the many reports published during the past decade. Prolactin is also known to be secreted at time of oestrus, presumably in response to the oestrogen level operating at that time; the question of its function in the bovine appears to remain unresolved.

2.4 PROGESTERONE AND REGRESSION OF THE CORPUS LUTEUM

The steroid hormone progesterone dominates the major part of the cow's oestrous cycle, detectable amounts being evident by 3–4 days after formation of the corpus luteum; daily production of progesterone rises markedly for several days until a plateau of secretion is reached by about day 8 of the cycle. The concentration of progesterone in peripheral blood is low (0.1–0.8 ng/ml) around the time of oestrus (Donaldson et al., 1970; Shemesh et al., 1971; Robertson, 1972; Wetteman and Hafs, 1973). The fact that it takes several days before a rise is evident in this concentration may suggest that during this transient phase the luteal tissue does not achieve functional significance. The concentration of progesterone rises to a mean value of about 5 ng/ml during the luteal phase of the cycle (Ayalon and Shemesh, 1974) and a mean peak value of about 6–7 ng/ml at the end of the luteal phase (Stabenfeldt et al., 1969; Donaldson et al., 1970; Henricks et al., 1971; Wetteman and Hafs, 1973). Hunter (1976) notes that it is only during the early part of the cycle that the developing corpus luteum of the cow is susceptible to breakdown following oxytocin treatment and it is during this same period that the corpus luteum is refractory to doses of prostaglandin.

The concentration of progesterone in peripheral blood during the luteal phase of the bovine cycle may influence ability of the animal to conceive at the next oestrus (Folman et al., 1973; Holness et al., 1977a, b). There is some evidence to show that progesterone concentration can be influenced by plane of nutrition (Hill et al., 1970) and season (Rosenberg et al., 1977); a mid-cycle decline in progesterone level has been reported by several authors (Donaldson et al., 1970; Sreenan and Gosling, 1976; Schams et al., 1977; Hale et al., 1981). Although there was one report (Ayalon and Shemesh, 1974) which recorded a pro-oestrus surge of short duration in the progesterone concentration about 16 h prior to oestrus, subsequent reports have not confirmed this (Chenault et al., 1975; Schams et al., 1977).

At the end of the oestrous cycle, reports agree that there is a precipitous decline in the blood concentration of progesterone 1–4 days prior to the onset of oestrus (Stabenfeldt et al., 1969; Henricks et al., 1971; Robertson, 1972; Blockey et al., 1973; Lamond, 1973; Dobson et al., 1973; Katongole et al., 1973; Christensen et al., 1974; Lemon et al., 1975). The onset of this decline in progesterone has been noted to commence between days 16 and 19 in animals; in some cows, blood levels of the steroid have declined from as high as 10 ng/ml to less than 1 ng/ml in one half day, whereas in others the regression was found to extend over at least 2 days (Lamond, 1973).

Whatever the exact mechanisms involved in regression of the corpus luteum towards the end of the cycle, progesterone concentration declines, within a period of about 2 days, to the negligible level which obtains through oestrus and until the fresh corpus luteum forms at the time of ovulation. Lamond (1974) suggested that the time interval between progesterone reaching its minimum concentration until the onset of oestrus may vary with a number of factors, including body condition, stress, season, and probably lactation and undernutrition; in an earlier report, there was evidence that Angus cattle showed a more abrupt cessation of progesterone secretion during the late cycle than did Herefords (Lamond et al., 1971). Clearly, data on the factors that may influence the rate of decline in progesterone in the normal cow may be relevant to interpreting the response of cattle to oestrus control measures, whether these take the form of progestagens, prostaglandins or other agents.

2.5 LUTEOLYSIS AND PROSTAGLANDINS

Rapid regression of the cow's corpus luteum is a key event in the bovine oestrous cycle. Decline in progesterone production at the end of the cycle was found to be so sudden and consistent that it suggested to researchers that it probably involved an active inhibition of steroid secretion. Much effort over the past 10–15 years has been devoted to elucidating the precise factors involved in luteolysis; evidence that prostaglandin $F_{2\alpha}$ is the uterine luteolysin has steadily evolved over the years, so that this now provides an acceptable explanation. Transfer of the uterine luteolysin from the cow's uterus to the ovary and the corpus luteum appears to be local rather than systemic, and elucidating the nature of this local transfer has been the subject of several reports (Hixon and Hansel, 1974; Baird, 1978).

There is evidence that prostaglandin (PG) is released in a pulsatile manner during a period of 2–3 days, in surges that last several hours and occur at similar time intervals, with regression of the corpus luteum occurring within 24–48 h after the first appreciable release of prostaglandin (Petersen et al., 1975; Kindahl et al., 1976). The hormonal mechanisms which trigger the onset of the pulsatile release of prostaglandin are not well understood. There is evidence to suggest that PG synthesis is probably triggered by oestrogens secreted by the ovary and, once initiated, the process is maintained by both oestrogens and progesterone (or perhaps progesterone alone); finally, only the progesterone level appears to be crucial in terminating prostaglandin release, which stops when progesterone concentration reaches basal values (Kindahl et al., 1979, 1980).

It appears that occasional time lapses in prostaglandin synthesis and release can occur in the cow, which can allow partial recovery of luteal function before the next PG release initiates luteolysis (Kindahl et al., 1977). This can lead to a longer than usual time for the occurrence of luteolysis, which can prolong the bovine oestrous cycle by 12–24 hours and is one of the causes of the variability in oestrous cycle length (Stabenfeldt et al., 1980a).

With the recent advent of widespread testing of milk and plasma for progesterone, some recent studies suggest that some cows may have persistent luteal phases, particularly during the first few months after parturition (King et al., 1976; Bulman and Lamming, 1977). What is not known is whether this persistence of luteal function in the cow is associated with a failure of the bovine uterus to return to a normal anatomic and physiological state after parturition. It seems possible, according to Stabenfeldt et al. (1980b), that the initiation of the persistent corpus luteum syndrome may occur in the cow because of inadequate $PGF_{2\alpha}$ synthesis.

2.6 OESTROGEN AND Gn-RH

Concentrations of oestrogens in the peripheral plasma during the oestrous cycle are in the picogram range, an average value of 3.6 pg/ml being reported by Wetteman et al. (1972) and a value of 2 pg/ml by Chenault et al. (1975 for the luteal phase of the cycle. The ovarian follicle is regarded as the major source of circulating oestrogens in cyclic cattle and oestradiol-17$_\beta$ is held to be the main oestrogenic steroid secreted by the follicular cells (England et al., 1973). Several reports deal with oestrogen levels in the period around oestrus (Shemesh et al., 1972; Blockey et al., 1973; England et al., 1973; Lamond, 1973; Christensen et al., 1974 Drinan and Cox, 1974; Chenault et al., 1975; Lemon et al., 1975). Three oestrogen peaks, the first during days 3–7, the second around days 7–10 and the third before ovulation have been reported during the cycle by several investigators (Shemesh et al., 1972; Glencross et al., 1973; Schams et al., 1977) and are presumed to be the result of FSH action on follicular growth.

The main build-up in oestrogen level occurs in the last day or so of the cycle and in the early hours of oestrus; peak oestrogen concentration coincides with the peak release of preovulatory LH. Chenault et al. (1975) found oestradiol levels rising abruptly to 7.4 pg/ml at the peak of LH release and then declining sharply by 50% in the space of a few hours and returning to basal levels by 41 h after the onset of oestrus.

According to Lamond (1973), the rate of increase in the production of follicular oestrogen in the late part of the cycle varies among individual cows, taking as little as 1 day in some and 4 days in others to reach the blood titre which results in the onset of oestrus. Clearly, such variations in response have implications in understanding the way in which cattle may respond to measures employed in the artificial control of oestrus in the species. The concentration of oestrogen declines markedly as the heat period proceeds and reaches the basal level by the time of ovulation (Hansel and Echternkamp, 1972; Shemesh et al., 1972; Chenault et al., 1975). It should be mentioned that a fairly precise time interval has been established, in several mammals, between a threshold level of oestrogen being attained in the animal and the subsequent release of LH; studies in spayed cattle injected with oestrogen show the interval to be of the order of 10–22 h (Cummins *et al.*, 1972; Hobson and Hansel, 1972; Short *et al.*, 1973).

2.6.1 Release of Gn-RH

As well as bringing the cow in oestrus, the blood titre of oestrogen which builds up after the decline of progesterone, affects other centres in the hypothalamus; when a certain level of oestrogen is reached, a releasing hormone is released and transmitted, via the hypophysial–portal blood system, to the anterior pituitary. A particularly potent agent, generally referred to as gonadotrophin-releasing hormone (Gn-RH), has been isolated and identified by workers; the agent has been synthesized and marketed by several commercial concerns over the past decade. The responsiveness of the pituitary to Gn-RH is known to be influenced by many factors, including the level of the ovarian steroid hormones.

2.7 THE GONADOTROPHINS, LH AND FSH

In the early hours of oestrus in the cow, there is a massive preovulatory rise in the concentration of luteinizing hormone (LH) in the blood. This follows a rising level of oestrogen which is responsible for initiating the surge release of LH, which reaches a peak during the early hours of oestrus in cattle (Cummins *et al.*, 1972; Wettemann and Hafs, 1973; Lamond, 1973; Christensen *et al.*, 1974; Mori *et al.*, 1974; Lemon *et al.*, 1975); there would appear to be a reasonably close association between the start of the preovulatory discharge of LH and the onset of oestrus (Cummins *et al.*, 1972; Blockey *et al.*, 1973; Lemon *et al.*, 1975). The basal level of LH during the luteal phase has been reported as 1.2–1.4 ng/ml^{-1} (Swanson and Hafs, 1971; Wettemann and Hafs, 1973) or 2–4 ng/ml^{-1} (Black and Hansel, 1972; Carr, 1972). The preovulatory peak of LH does not generally last for more than 6–8 h, at which time the concentration of LH has been reported as rising to 8.7 ng/ml^{-1} (Wettemann and Hafs, 1973), 19–35 ng/ml (Swanson and Hafs, 1971) or 50–65 ng/ml^{-1} (Black and Hansel, 1972; Tribble *et al.*, 1973). In an earlier study, Henricks *et al.* (1970) had observed peak levels of LH at

3–6 h after the onset of oestrus, with concentrations as high as 100 ng/ml^{-1} being recorded.

The preovulatory surge of LH initiates luteinization of granulosa and theca interna cells in the Graafian follicle destined for ovulation; among other events initiated by the gonadotrophin is the nuclear maturation of the oocyte and rupture of the follicle. Ovulation occurs in the cow about 1 day after the LH peak (Kiddy and Odell, 1969; Henricks *et al.*, 1970; Dobson *et al.*, 1973; Christensen *et al.*, 1974), which would be compatible with ovulation occurring about 30 h after the onset of heat, as shown in the data of Swanson and Hafs (1971) and Christensen *et al.* (1975). The interval between peak LH and follicle rupture also agrees with data on the occurrence of ovulation after administering an ovulating preparation (human chorionic gonadotrophin; hCG) to the cow in the early hours of oestrus (Scanlon, 1969) and with those for the time taken for the completion of nuclear maturation in the bovine oocyte *in vitro* (Sreenan, 1968, 1969).

One further point about the timing of follicle rupture in cattle might be mentioned; it has been shown that clitoral or cervical stimulation can bring forward the time of ovulation by several hours (Randel *et al.*, 1973). Presumably, this is an effect which can only operate during the early hours of oestrus when nervous stimuli appear capable of influencing the speed with which the LH peak is attained in the cow; once the LH peak passes, it would seem unlikely that the timing of ovulation would be open to such influences.

Evidence from several studies have shown that LH concentrations in the cow fluctuate in a pulsatile manner and that the pattern depends upon the period of the oestrous cycle. Rahe *et al.* (1980) have shown that in the early luteal period, pulses are of low amplitude (0.3–1.8 ng/ml^{-1}) and high frequency (20/30 pulses per day) whereas in the mid-luteal phase, pulses are of high amplitude (1.2–7 ng/ml^{-1}) and low frequency (6–8 pulses per day) without any inherent rhythmic pattern being evident; it is believed that LH levels are probably modulated by the ovarian steroids.

2.7.1 FSH concentrations

Knowledge of changes in the level of follicle-stimulating-hormone (FSH) during the oestrous cycle has been lacking until recent times (Akbar et al., 1974; Schams et al., 1977; Dobson, 1978; Jackson et al., 1979; Barnes et al., 1980). Before the advent of RIA procedures, the classic concept was that the FSH level increased after regression of the corpus luteum resulting in greater follicular development and an accompanying rise in the production of follicular oestrogen; along these lines, Hackett and Hafs (1969) had shown a rapid decline in pituitary FSH several days prior to oestrus in the cow and they suggested that peripheral amounts of the gonadotrophin probably rose at that time. In fact, much of the evidence derived from RIA work would not support this and tends to show several FSH peaks occurring during the cycle. It is assumed that final maturation and ovulation of follicles is blocked during the luteal phase because of the high progesterone concentration operating at that time.

Rajakoski (1960) noted two growth waves of follicles in the cow, one between days 1–12 and the second between day 12 and the time of ovulation; it was only in the second growth wave, and then after day 18, that Dufour et al. (1972) observed the largest follicle ovulating. Schams et al. (1977) found evidence of an FSH peak around

Fig. 2.2. Keeping the bovine free from stress to aid reproduction. The cow needs to be in complete harmony with its immediate environment to be able to reproduce and produce efficiently. There is plenty of scope for behavioural studies and the development of techniques (hormonal or otherwise) which can indicate to the farmer the reaction of the animal to its immediate environment. Whether it is a question of a cow kept isolated waiting for the inseminator to arrive or other situations which do not appeal to the animal's contentment of mind, there is a whole area in the stockman–animal interaction field that deserves attention.

day 18 of the cycle, which may be a stimulus for follicular growth, which always coincided with the decrease in progesterone level occurring at that time; the same authors reported that, apart from an FSH peak co-inciding with the preovulatory surge of LH, the pattern of release of the two gonadotrophins did not coincide closely elsewhere in the cycle. The existence of a second FSH peak, occurring some 28 h after that synchronous with the preovulatory LH, has been reported by several groups (Akbar et al., 1974; Dobson, 1978; Jackson et al., 1979); the role of this peak is not clear, but it is thought that it may have a function in ovulation or in selecting and conditioning these follicles destined to mature during the following cycle. It should be noted that, for practical purposes, exogenous FSH or substitutes such as pregnant mare serum (PMSG), administered around the time of regression of the corpus luteum or progesterone withdrawal, will result in the maturation of additional follicles.

2.8 STRESS AND THE OESTROUS CYCLE

The possibility exists that different forms of stress, whether arising from adverse feeding, management or environmental factors may influence the hormone levels that operate in the bovine oestrous cycle. It is believed that stress in the cow can result in elevated concentrations of progesterone of adrenal origin (Wagner et al., 1972) and it is known that many routine husbandry operations may bring about increases in plasma glucocorticoids in cattle. It is known that in humid, warm conditions, heat stress in cows (i.e. those of temperate zone origin) can substantially impair reproductive performance (Christison and Johnson, 1972; Ingraham et al., 1974; Miller and Alliston, 1974) although the precise mechanisms involved in this are not well understood. It is true that progesterone and LH levels among cattle subjected to nutritional stress have been investigated, but evidence is conflicting in showing a reduction in LH concentration in some instances (Gombe and Hansel, 1973), and an elevation in others (Dunn et al., 1974). It would seem important to bear in mind the possibility that controlled breeding techniques may not operate at full efficiency, if, in their application, they lead to additional stress in cattle.

2.9 REFERENCES

Adam, L., Aizinbud, E., Tadmor, A. and Schindler, H. (1981) Impedometric properties of the vulvar and vaginal tissues of ewes during the oestrous cycle. *J. Reprod. Fert.* **61**, 11–17.

Akbar, A. M., Reichert, L. E., Dunn, T. G., Kaltenbach, C. C. and Niswender, G. D. (1974) Serum levels of FSH during the bovine oestrous cycle. *J. Anim. Sci.* **39**, 360.

Asdell, S. A. (1964) *Patterns of Mammalian Reproduction.* (2nd Ed.) Cornell Univ. Press, New York.

Asdell, S. A., de Alba, J. and Roberts, S. G. (1949) Studies on the estrous cycle of dairy cattle. *Cornell Vet.* **39**, 389–402.

Ayalon, N. and Shemesh, M. (1974) Pro-oestrous surge in plasma progesterone in the cow. *J. Reprod. Fert.* **36**, 239–243.

Baird, D. T. (1978). Local utero-ovarian relationships. In: Control of Ovulation pp. 217–233 (Eds. D. B. Crighton, G. R. Foxcroft, N. B. Haynes & G. E. Lamming), Butterworths, London.

Barnes, M A., Kazmer, G. W., Bierley, S. T., Richardson, M. E. and Dickey, J. (1980) Follicle stimulating hormone and estradiol-17β in dairy cows treated with progesterone-releasing intravaginal devices. *J. Dairy Sci.* **63**, 161–165.

Black, D. L. and Hansel, W. (1972) Endocrine factors affecting reproduction in the bovine female. *Mass. Agr. Exp. Sta. Res. Bull.* 596.

Blockley, M A. de B., Chamley, W. A., Cummins, L., Perry, M. and Goding, J. R. (1973) Steroid plasma levels about oestrus in the beef cow. *J. Reprod. Fert.* **32**, 342–343.

Bulman, D. C. and Lamming, G. E. (1977) Cases of prolonged luteal activity in the non-pregnant dairy cow. *Vet. Rec.* **100**, 550–552.

Carr, W. R. (1972) Radioimmunoassay of luteinizing hormone in the blood of Zebu cattle. *J. Reprod. Fert.* **29**, 11–18.

Chenault, J. R., Thatcher, W. W., Kalra, P. S., Abrams, R. M. and Wilcox, C. J. (1975) Transistory changes in plasma progestins estradiol, and the luteinizing hormone approaching ovulation in the bovine. *J. Dairy Sci.* **58**(5), 709–717.

Christensen, D. S., Hopwood, M. L. and Wiltbank, J. N. (1974) Levels of hormones in the serum of cycling beef cows. *J. Anim. Sci.* **38**, 577–583.

Christenson, R. K., Echternkamp, S. E. and Laster, D. B. (1975) Oestrus LH ovulation and fertility in beef heifers. *J. Reprod. Fert.* **43**, 543–546.

Christison, G. L. and Johnson, H. D. (1972) Cortisol turnover in heat-stressed cows. *J. Anim Sci.* **35**, 1005–1010.

Cummins, L. J., Blockley, M. A. de B., Brown, J. M. and Goding, J. R. (1972) A study of luteinizing hormone secretion in the cow. *J. Reprod Fert.* **28**, 135–136

Dobson, H. (1978) radioimmunoassay of FSH in the plasma of *post partum* dairy cows. *J. Reprod. Fert.* **52**, 45–49.

Dobson, H., Hopkinson, C. R. N. and Ward, W. R. (1973) Progesterone, L7β-oestradiol and LH in relation to ovulation in cows. *Vet. Rec.* **93**, 76.

Donaldson, L. E., Bassett, J. M. and Thorburn, G. D. (1970) Peripheral plasma progesterone concentration of cows during puberty, oestrous cycles, pregnancy and lactation, and the effects of under-nutrition or exogenous oxytocin on progesterone concentrations. *J. Endocrin.* **48**, 599–614.

Drinan, J. P. and Cox, R. I. (1974) Oestrogens in bovine peripheral plasma. *J. Reprod Fert.* **36**, 489–490.

Dufour J., Whitmore, H. L., Ginther, O. J. and Casida, L. E. (1972) Identification of the ovulating follicle by its size and different days of the estrous cycle in heifers. *J. Anim. Sci* **34**, 85.

Dunn, T. G., Rone, J., Kaltenbach, C. C. Walt, van der, L. A., Riley, M. L. and Akbar, A. M. (1974), Hormone changes during underfeeding of beef cows. *J. Anim. Sci.* **39**, 206.

England, B. G., Karavolas, H. H., Hauser, E. R. and Casida, L. E. (1973) Ovarian follicular estrogens in Angus heifers. *J. Anim. Sci.* **37**, 1176–1179.

Esslemont, R. J. (1973) The economic and husbandry aspects of the manifestation and detection of heat in cows in large herds. Ph. D. Thesis, Univ. of Reading.

Folman, Y., Rosenberg, M., Herz, Z. and Davidson, M. (1973). The relationship between plasma progesterone concentration and conception in *post-partum* dairy cows maintained on two levels of nutrition. *J. Reprod. Fert.* **34**, 267–278

Glencross, R. G., Munro, I. B., Senior, B. E. and Pope, G. S. (1973) Concentrations of oestradiol-17β oestrone and progesterone in jugular venous plasma of cows during the oestrous cycle and in early pregnancy. *Acta Endocr.* **73**, 374.

Gombe, S. and Hansel, W. (1973) Plasma luteinizing hormone (LH) and progesterone levels in heifers on restricted energy intakes. *J. Anim. Sci.* **37**, 728–733.

Hackett, A. J. and Hafs, H. D. (1969) Pituitary and hypothalamic endocrine changes during the bovine estrous cycle. *J. Anim. Sci.* **28**, 531–536.

Hale, D. H., McCabe, C. T. and Holness, D. H. (1981) A method to evaluate various parameters of progesterone production in beef cows, using the levels of progesterone in peripheral blood samples on specific days of the oestrous cycle. *Anim. Reprod. Sci.* **3**, 279–288.

Hansel, W. (1959) The estrous cycle of the cow. In, *Reproduction in Domestic Animals* (Ed. Cole H. H. and Cupps, P. T.), Vol. 1, pp. 223. Academic Press, London

Hansel, W. and Echternkamp, S. E. (1972) Control of ovarian function in domestic animals. *Am. Zool.* **12**(2), 225–243.

Harker, D. B. (1980) oestrus detection aid. I.C.I. Ltd. Press Release.

Henricks, D. M., Dickey, J. F. and Niswender, G. D. (1970) Serum luteinizing hormone and plasma progesterone levels during the estrous cycle and early pregnancy in cows. *Biol. Reprod.* **2**, 346–351.

Henricks, D. M., Dickey, J. F. and Hill, J. R. (1971) Plasma estrogen and progesterone levels in cows prior to and during estrus. *Endocr.* **89**, 1350–1355.

Hill, J. R., Lamond, D. R., Henricks, D. M., Dickey, J. F. and Niswender, G. D. (1970) Effect of undernutrition on ovarian function and fertility in beef heifers. *Biol. Reprod.* **2**, 78.

Hixon, J. E. and Hansel, W. (1974). Evidence for preferential transfer of prostaglandin $F_{2\alpha}$ to the ovarian artery following intrauterine administration in cattle. *Biol. Reprod.* **11**, 543–552.

Hobson, G. W. and Hansel, W. (1972) Plasma LH levels after ovariectomy corpus luteum removal and estradiol administration in cattle. *Endocr.* **9**(1), 185–190.

Holm, D. M. (1977) Effects of electronic identification temperature monitoring and ELA on the meat industry. *Adv. Anim. Breed.* **25**, 6–9.

Holness, D. H., Ellison, J. A. and Wilkins, L. M. (1977a) Conception of beef cows in relation to the concentration of progesterone in peripheral blood. *Rhod. J. Agric. Res.* **15**, 3–9.

Holness, D. H., Ellison, J. A., Sprowson, G. W. and Carvalho, de A. (1977b) Aspects of fertility in Friesian dairy cows with particular reference to the concentration of progesterone in peripheral plasma. *Rhod. J. Agric. Res.* **15**, 109–117.

Hoover, N. W. (1978) Cow identification and recording systems. *J. Dairy Sci.* **61**, 1167–1180.

Hunter, R. H. F. (1976) Reproductive physiology in the bovine female: a review. In, *Beef Cattle Production in Developing Countries* (Ed. A. J. Smith) *Univ. Edinburgh, Conf.* pp. 79–104.

Ingraham, R. H., Gillette, D. D. and Wagner, W. D. (1974) Relationship of temperature and humidity to conception rate of Holstein cows in subtropical climate. *J. Dairy Sci.* **57**, 476–481.

Jackson, P. S., Johnson, Carl. T., Furr, B. U. and Beattie, H. F. (1979) Influence of stage of oestrous cycle on time of oestrus following cloprostenol treatment in the bovine. *Theriogenology* **12**, 153–167.

Katongole, C. B., Naftolin, F. and Younglai, E. V. (1973) Diurnal variations in ovarian steroids and luteinizing hormone in cows at oestrus. *Steroids Lipids Res.* **4**, 1–5.

Kiddy, C. A. and Odell, W. D. (1969) Radioimmunoassay of blood L H at estrus and ovulation in cattle. *J. Anim. Sci.* **29**, 192–193.

Kindahl, H., Edqvist, L. E., Bane, A. and Granstrom, E. (1976) Blood levels of progesterone and 15-keto 13,14-dihydro prostaglandin $F_{2\alpha}$ during the normal oestrous cycle and early pregnancy in heifers. *Acta Endoct. Copenh.* **82**, 134–149.

Kindahl, H., Granstrom, E., Edqvist, L. E., Gustafsson, B., Astrom, G. and Stabenfeldt, G. (1977) Progesterone and 15-leto-13, 14-dihydro prostaglanding $F_{2\alpha}$ levels in peripheral circulation after intrauterine iodine infusions in cows. *Acta Vet. Scand.* **18**, 274.

Kindahl, Hans, Lindell, Jan-Otto and Edqvist, L. E. (1979) On the control of prostaglandin release during the bovine estrous cycle. Effects of progesterone implants. *Prostaglandins* **18**, 813–820.

Kindahl, H., Lindell, J. O. and Edqvist, L. E. (1980) Luteolysis in domestic animals: Control of $PGF_{2\alpha}$ release. *Proc. 9th Intr. Congr. Anim. Reprod. AI (Madrid)* **2**, 17–26.

King, G. J., Nurnick, J. F. and Robertson, H. A. (1976) Ovarian function and estrus in dairy cows during early lactation. *J. Anim. Sci.* **42**. 692.

Lamond, D. R. (1973) The role of the bovine practitioner in synchronization and twinning in cattle. *Bovine Practit.* **8**, 2–8.

Lamond, D. R. (1974) Multiple births in cattle: An assessment. *Theriogenology* **1**, 181–212.

Lamond, D. R., Henricks, D. M., Hill, J. R., Jr. and Dickey, J. F. (1971) Breed differences in plasma progesterone concentration in the bovine during pro-estrus. *Biol. Reprod.* **5**, 258–261.

Lemon, M., Pelletier, J., Saumande, J. and Signoret, J. P. (1975) peripheral plasma concentrations of progesterone, Oestradiol-17β and luteinizing hormone around oestrus in the cow. *J. Reprod. Fert.* **43**, 137–140.

Macmillan, K. L. (1970) Return intervals to first insemination and conception rates to second insemination in New Zealand dairy cattle. *N.Z.J. Agric. Res.* **13**, 771–777.

Macmillan, K. L. and Watson, J. D. (1971) Short estrous cycles in N.Z. dairy cattle. *J. Dairy Sci.* **54**, 1526.

Miller, H. L. and Alliston, G. W. (1974) Bovine plasma progesterone levels at programmed circadian temperatures of 17 to 21°C. *Life Sci.* **11**, 705–710.

Mori, J., Masaki, J., Wakabayashi, K., Endo, T. and Hosoda, T. (1974) Serum luteinizing hormone levels in cattle under various reproductive states. *Theriogenology*, **1**, 131–136.

Morris, R .S. (1976) Diagnosis of infertility syndromes in large dairy herds. *Univ. Sydney Post-grad. Comm. Vet Sci. Proc.* **28**, 183–194.

Odde, K. G., Ward, H. S., Kiracofe, G. H., McKee, R. M. and Kittok, R. J. (1980) Short estrous cycles and associated serum progesterone levels in beef cows. *Theriogenology* **14**, 105–112.

Olds, D. and Seath, D. M. (1951) Repeatability of the estrous cycle length in dairy cattle. *J. Dairy Sci.* **34**, 626–632.

Peterson, A. J., Fairclough, R. J., Payne, E. and Smith, J. F. (1975) Hormonal changes around bovine luteolysis. *Prostaglandins* **10**, 675–684.

Rahe, C. H., Owens, R. E., Fleeger, J. L., Newton, H. J. and Harms, P. G. (1980) *Endocrinology* **107**, 497–503.

Rajakoski, E. (1960) Ovarian follicular system in sexually mature heifers with special reference to the seasonal cyclical and left right variations. *Acta Endocr.* **34**, Suppl. 1.

Randel, R. D., Short, R. E., Christensen, D. S., Bellows, R. A. (1973) Effects of various mating stimuli on the LH surge and ovulation time following synchronization of estrus in the bovine. *J. Anim. Sci.* **37**, 128–130.

Robertson, H. A. (1972) Sequential changes in plasma progesterone in the cow during the oestrous cycle., pregnancy, at parturition and *post-partum. Can. J. Anim. Sci.* **52**, 645–658.

Rosenberg, M., Hertz, Z., Davidson, M. and Folman, Y. (1977) Seasonal variations in post-partum plasma progesterone levels and conception in primiparous and multiparous dairy cows. *J. Reprod. Fert.* **51**, 363–367.

Scanlon, P. F. (1969) Studies in reproduction in the cow. *Ph. D. Thesis, N.U.I. Dublin*

Schams, D., Schallenberger, E., Hoffman, B. and Jurgh, H. (1977) The oestrous cycle of the cow: hormonal parameters and time relationships concerning oestrus, ovulation and electrical resistance of the vaginal mucus. *Acta Endocr.* **86**, 180–192.

Shemesh, M. Lindner, H. R. and Ayalon, N. (1971) Competitive protein binding assay of progesterone in bovine jugular venous plasma during the oestrous cycle. *J. Reprod. Fert.* **26**, 167–174.

Shemesh, M., Ayalon, N. and Lindner, H. R. (1972) Oestradiol levels in the peripheral blood of cows during the oestrous cycle. *J. Endocr.* **55**, 73–78.

Short, R. E., Howland, B. E., Randel, R. D., Christensen, D. S. and Bellows, R. A. (1973) Induced LH release in spayed cows. *J. Anim. Sci.* **36**, 551–557.

Spahr, S. L., Puckett, H. B., Fernando, R. S., Olver, E. F. and McCoy, G. C. (1981) Subdermal electronic identification and temperature monitoring. *J. Dairy Sci.* **64**, Suppl., 155(abs).

Sreenan, J. M. (1968) *In vivo* and *in vitro* culture of cattle eggs. *Proc. 6th Congr. Anim. Reprod. A.I. (Paris)* **1**, 577–580.

Sreenan, J. M. (1969). Studies related to ovum transfer in cattle. *Ph. D. Thesis, N.U.I., Dublin*.

Sreenan, J. M. and Gosling, J. P. (1976) Peripheral plasma progesterone levels in cycling and pregnant beef heifers. *Ir. Vet. J.* **29**, 105–108.

Stabenfeldt, G. H., Ewing, L. L. and McDonald, L. E. (1969) Peripheral plasma progesterone levels during the bovine oestrous cycle. *J. Reprod. Fert.* **19**(3), 433–442.

Stabenfeldt, G. H., Hughes, J. P., Neely, D. P., Kindahl, H., Edqvist, L. E. and Gustafsson, B. (1980a) Physiologic and pathophysiologic aspects of prostaglandin $F_{2\alpha}$ during the reproductive cycle. *J. Am. Vet. Med. Assoc.* **176,** 1187–1194.

Stabenfeldt, G. H., Neely, D. P., Hughes, J. P. and Kindahl, H. (1980b) Modification of uterine $PGF_{2\alpha}$ in domestic animals through pathologic or pharmacology processes. *Proc. 9th int. Congr. Anim. Reprod. AI (Madrid)* **2,** 27–34.

Swanson, L. V. and Hafs, J. S. (1971) LH and prolactin in blood serum from estrus to ovulation in Holstein heifers. *J. Anim. Sci.* **33,** 1038–1041.

Tribble, R. L., Sorensen, A. N., Woodward, T. L., Conor, J. S., Beverly, J. R. and Fleeger, J. L. (1973) Serum progestins and

luteinizing hormone level in non-suckled primiparous heifers. Nature, Lond. **246** 494–495.

Wagner, W. C., Stronbehn, R. E. and Harris, P. A. (1972) ACTH corticoids and luteal function in heifers. *J. Anim. Sci.* **35,** 789–793.

Wetteman, R. P., Hafs, H. D., Edgerton, L. A. and Swanson, L. V. (1972) Estradiol and progesterone in blood serum during the bovine estrous cycle. *J. Anim. Sci.* **34,** 1020–1024.

Wettemann, R. P., Hafs, H. D., Edgerton, L. A. and Swanson, L. V. hormones associated with fertile and non-fertile inseminations at synchronized and control estrus. *J. Anim. Sci.* **36,** 716–721.

CHAPTER 3

Artificial Control of Oestrus and Ovulation

3.1 INTRODUCTION

Although the possible advantages which would accrue from effective regulation of the oestrus cycle in cattle have been the subject of many reports for some time, it is only in the last few years that commercially acceptable forms of control have been developed and made available to farmers. As evident in the discussion that follows, there is much which remains to be done in making oestrus control fully acceptable on the farm; for any measure to be effective, it must obviously solve more problems than it creates. Different farmers will have different objectives that they wish to achieve; it may be a question of getting as many cows as possible bred by AI to a particular bull; it may be a matter of considering labour-saving as the main objective or it may be that some producers wish to have as many cows as possible becoming pregnant in a short period of time. It should also be kept in mind that careful, stress-free handling of cattle during an oestrus control programme, good feeding, well-

organized artificial insemination and accurate identification and herd records are known to be among the factors which lead to good results in oestrus synchronization programmes.

Oestrus control is designed to be an aid to the artificial insemination of cattle and it is among the beef cows that there is the greatest scope for the measure to be employed. If the current situation in the U.S.A. is examined, it would seem that only some 5% of the beef cattle are bred by AI, a figure which has remained unchanged for some years possibly because of increased labour requirements and a suspected lowered conception rate from AI compared to natural service (Bellows et al., 1979).

3.2 HISTORICAL BACKGROUND

There have been a great number of reports dealing with the hormonal control of oestrus in cattle, dating from the use of injections of progesterone by Casida's group at Wisconsin more than 30 years ago (Christian and Casida, 1948). Many of the early studies with progesterone were dealt with in reviews by Hansel et al. (1961) and Lamond (1964); these authors made it clear that oestrus and ovulation could be controlled with some accuracy, but conception rate at first service was usually unacceptably low. Emphasis and research interest during much of the 1960s centred almost exclusively around the orally active and highly potent progestagens, especially medroxyprogesterone acetate (MAP), chlormadinone acetate (CAP) and melengestrol acetate (MGA): treatment at the appropriate dose level for a period approximating to a cycle interval (18–21 days) was shown to be effective in controlling oestrus so that a majority of cattle showed a heat period within the space of about 3 days.

Apart from the fact that response to such oral treatments was more accurately described as the "grouping" of oestrus rather than "synchronization" (Robinson, 1975), first service conception rates remained unacceptably low. Extensive data from American studies conducted over a 5-year period with MGA, for instance, showed reasonable results in grouping heat periods, but a conception rate that was only 70% of the value recorded among controls (Zimbelman et al., 1970).

Treatment regimes incorporating progestagen in feed and its administration for the requisite period in physiologically effective doses have given rise to an acceptable oestrus control response in many studies, but it is obvious that under group feeding conditions it is just not possible to have precise control of the daily doses ingested. As well as that, the large capacity of the cow's digestive tract inevitably precludes the sharp and predictable cut-off in progestagen concentration which is probably necessary at the end of treatment. In the U.S.A., where the application of oral progestagen treatments was studied for several years among beef cattle, the problem was one of ensuring that cows consumed the correct quantities of the agent; it was not always easy training range-bred cattle to eat dry feed.

3.2.1 Subfertility at the controlled oestrus

As noted by Robinson (1969) some years ago, in attempting to control oestrus in the farm animals, the difficulties to be overcome are even greater than those confronting the endocrinologist working in human fertility control; in the cow, ewe, sow and mare, it is necessary to ensure that normal fertility operates simultaneously with oestrus control. Satisfactory methods have only become available in recent years with the advent of prostaglandins and after modifications to progestagen procedures. It should be mentioned here that there are two approaches to controlling oestrus in the cow; it is either possible to prolong the luteal phase of the cycle artificially using progesterone or progestagens or alternatively to shorten the cycle artificially by means of a luteolytic agent such as $PGF_{2\alpha}$. Acceptable fertility levels in synchronized cattle have been achieved either using PG or short-term progestagen treatment.

The physiological explanation of the improvement in conception rate observed among cattle synchronized by short- rather than long-term progestagen treatment is not altogether clear, but the evidence favours the view that events at the controlled oestrus are more normal the shorter the period that the animal spends on a completely artificial luteal phase (i.e. after the cow's cyclic corpus luteum regresses). This would be compatible with evidence in cattle (Wettemann and Hafs, 1973) and sheep (Willemse, 1969; Kruip and Brand, 1975) showing that conception rates were affected by the particular stage of the oestrous cycle at which long-term (18–21 day) progestagen treatment was initiated; animals starting on treatment in the early part of the cycle tended to conceive more readily than those commencing in the late stages of the cycle. Some evidence exists to show that short-term progestagen treatment may not result in the same degree of oestrogenic activity as is associated with a long-term progestagen regimen (Moseley et al., 1979; Smith et al., 1979); hyperoestrogenic effects could result in adverse changes in cervical mucus or in the normal rate of sperm and egg transport. Certainly, in sheep there is evidence showing that progesterone is a key hormone in regulating basal LH concentrations, so that the

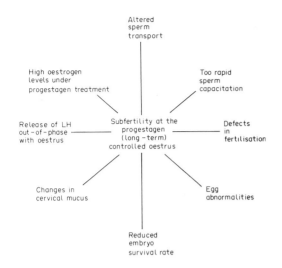

Fig. 3.1. Factors in the subfertility shown in cattle after cycle length progesterone treatment.

level of steroid that obtains during the synchronising treatment may be critical in relation to fertility (Hauger et al., 1977).

3.3 PROGESTERONE AND PROGESTAGENS

There are a variety of ways in which progesterone, or one of its potent analogues, can be administered; the methods include injection, oral, implant and by intravaginal device. Progesterone by injection may still be used in experimental programmes, the steroid being administered by daily or less frequent dosage (Moore, 1975). Progesterone has a short half-life in the cow which makes repeated or continuous administration procedures essential. In South Africa, Grosskopf (1974) did use a progesterone-by-injection regimen which appeared to result in an acceptable conception rate, but it did involve ten injections; clearly, for reason of the time and labour involved, such measures have no place in commercial applications.

Despite the limitations already mentioned with regard to oral treatments, there have been some conditions under which they have been used in a semi-commercial type application. Jochle (1975) has described work using CAP for oestrus control among zebu (Bos indicus) and European cattle in

Central America and Tanzania; under the particular nutritional and husbandry conditions in these tropical and sub-tropical areas, the main advantages of the oral applications seemed to be in overcoming the high incidence of anoestrus which otherwise prevailed among these cattle. Some methods of progestagen administration are set out in Fig. 3.2.

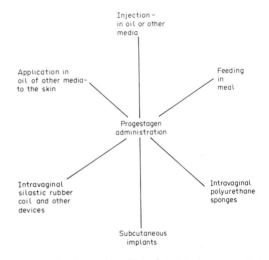

Fig. 3.2. Methods employed in administering progestagens for oestrus synchronization in cattle.

3.3.1 Intravaginal sponge pessaries

A method of continuous administration of progestagen obviously eliminates various of the management problems associated with oral applications. The technique of intravaginal administration, as first developed by Robinson (1964) and associates for sheep, is one approach which has also been explored in cattle. Early reports which dealt with the adaptation of the intravaginal technique for cattle, using CAP, MAP, fluorogestone acetate (FGA) and other progestagens showed evidence of considerable variation in the effectiveness of this approach in the control of oestrus; as well as the problem of retention of sponges, intravaginal treatments were not always effective in blocking oestrus in some animals (Carrick and Shelton, 1967; Shimizu et al., 1967; Mauleon et al., 1969; Rey, 1969; Hale and Symington, 1969; Hignett et al., 1970).

One country in which the sponge pessary was

persevered with was Ireland (Scanlon, 1969; Scanlon et al., 1972; Sreenan, 1969, 1974) and as a result of this, it is now clear that a high degree of synchronization and an acceptable fertility level follows the use of a short-term (9–10 day) intravaginal treatment in conjunction with progestagen/oestrogen injection at the time of initiating the application (Sreenan, 1975; Sreenan and Mulvihill, 1975; Mulvihill and Sreenan, 1977, 1978a, b). The Irish workers have achieved excellent rates of sponge retention (95%) in cows as well as heifers. The sponges have generally been impregnated with 3 g of the natural steroid or 200 mg of FGA. The sponges have been tested in cattle in the West of Ireland over a period of some years and it is anticipated that the FGA-based sponge will eventually become commercially available. It should be explained that the short-term sponge treatment is only possible in conjunction with the progestagen/oestrogen dose, the oestrogen being to enhance mature corpus luteum regression and the progestagen to shorten the life-span of any corpus luteum freshly formed at the time of initiating the intravaginal application. It was the work of Wiltbank and Gonzalez-Padilla (1975) in the U.S.A. that enabled the change to be made from cycle length

Fig. 3.3. The use of the intravaginal sponge in oestrus control in the Irish Republic. Sponges impregnated with the natural steroid–progesterone were employed on the University farm in the late 1960s to control oestrus in cattle. Workers in the State Research organization (An Foras Taluntais) have done a great deal of work in cows and heifers since that time, the sponges being impregnated with either progesterone or Cronolone®. It is possible to obtain excellent retention of sponges in short-term Cronolone® treatments and the device is extremely simple to prepare.

(18–21 day) progestagen treatment to short-term (9–12 day).

French, Israeli and New Zealand workers have also continued to explore the sponge pessary approach, usually with FGA-devices (Mauleon, 1974; Ayalon and Marcus, 1975; Smith, 1974); in one report, it was considered that the intravaginal approach was just as effective as the use of prostaglandins (Smith, 1974).

3.3.2 Progesterone releasing intravaginal device (PRID)

A further approach via the intravaginal route became possible with Abbott Laboratories' PRID, a metal spiral coated with progesterone-impregnated silicone rubber which was shown by Mauer et al. (1975) and Roche (1975) to be capable of releasing physiologically effective quantities of progesterone for 2–3 weeks. Much work in Ireland has been devoted to developing the PRID into an effective short-term treatment (Roche, 1979). The currently recommended procedure with the PRID, which is commercially available in Ireland and some other countries, is to insert it with a gelatine capsule containing oestrogen (10 mg oestradiol benzoate) attached and leave it in situ for 12 days; Webel (1976), in the U.S.A., had shown that 10 mg oestradiol benzoate in the gelatine capsule was as effective as 5 mg by injection, a finding that was supported in studies in Ireland (Mawhinney and Roche, 1977; Roche, 1978) although not in New Zealand (Smith and Tervit, 1980). It is held that additional progesterone or progestagen is not necessary at the commencement of PRID treatment, as a consequence of the initial high rate of progesterone release from the device itself (Mawhinney and Roche, 1978).

In an effort to avoid the need for employing oestrogen at all, the duration of PRID treatment was extended from 12 to 14 days but it was found that fertility was significantly decreased (Roche, 1979); it may be that 12 days is the limit to the duration of the PRID treatment and possibly the sponge as well, because the devices may not be capable of maintaining an appropriate level of progesterone/progestagen in the blood beyond this point (Mauer et al., 1975; Roche and Gosling, 1977; Sreenan et al., 1977; Roche and Ireland,

1981). Experience with the PRID over several years revealed that one problem with the 12-day treatment was that 8–12% of dairy cows came into oestrus 1–4 days after the expected time and very few of these animals would stand a chance of conceiving if a fixed-time AI schedule had been followed. Studies aimed at resolving this problem showed that poor control of luteal function rather than variation in follicular gowth was the cause; a close correlation was found between the level of progesterone in milk 24 h after PRID removal and the subsequent onset of oestrus (Roche, 1979). In trying to ensure that the cyclic corpus luteum is always regressed at the end of the PRID treatment, there may be a case for establishing the optimum oestrogen/progestagen combination to employ. Roche (1979) notes that oxytocin is luteolytic between days 2 and 6 of the cow's cycle (Armstrong and Hansel, 1959) and that use of this agent might be worth examining.

Fig. 3.4. The application of the PRID method of oestrus control in cattle. Much of the research and development work on the progesterone coil (PRID) was carried out in Ireland by Professor Jim Roche and this method of oestrus control has been commercially available for the past few years. There is the possibility that the PRID can be useful to dairy farmers who want to calve their herds over a shorter period in the early months of the year — those engaged in creamery milk production. The use of top AI bulls can be maximized on the earliest calvers in the herd to get well-bred strong replacement heifers. Providing management and handling facilities are good, there are good reasons for making use of the coil.

3.3.3 Other intravaginal devices

What is reported to be a simple and inexpensive intravaginal device, made of silastic rubber tubing containing progesterone and oestradiol, has been described by Rajamahendran et al. (1981); the device apparently releases sufficient progesterone to control oestrus in heifers. Although the retention rate in cows had not been tested, the authors suggest that their device was easier to insert and remove than the PRID and caused less irritation to the vaginal wall.

3.3.4 Implants

The ability of silicone rubber implants to release steroids continuously over a period of weeks was demonstrated some time ago (Dziuk and Cook, 1966). For cattle oestrus control, this finding subsequently led to studies in which silicone implants, carrying 4 g progesterone, were applied subcutaneously (in the dewlap) for a normal cycle interval; treatment, although effective in grouping heats was not associated with acceptable fertility (Roche, 1974a); reducing the duration of treatment from 20 to 10 days by administering a dose of oestrogen resulted in a normal conception rate but a less satisfactory grouping of oestrus.

The employment of a much smaller type of implant, which can be inserted in the ear rather

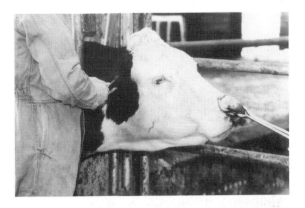

Fig. 3.5. Ear implants as a method of oestrus control in cattle. Ear-implants are commonly used in cattle carrying agents that promote growth. Much work has been devoted to the use of ear implants impregnated with the potent progestagen Norgestamet® in the U.S.A., U.K., France and Ireland as well as other countries. In the Republic of Ireland, much useful research and development work on the Norgestamet® implant has been carried our by Dr. Joe Sreenan and colleagues in An Foras Taluntais — using a short (9-day) treatment period. The same implant has been employed in ewes, but is not regarded in Ireland as a serious alternative to the intravaginal sponge.

than elsewhere in the body became possible with the advent of an extremely potent progestagen (SC-21009; Norgestamet, G. D. Searle); work in the U.K., France and the United States showed that ear-implants containing 6 mg Norgestamet were effective in controlling oestrus in cyclic cattle (Wishart and Young, 1974; Mauleon, 1974; Wiltbank and Gonzalez-Padilla, 1975). The use of an injection of a combination of 3 mg SC 21009 and 5 mg oestradiol valerate at time of implantation was necessary to take account of cattle which were either in the early or late stages of their oestrous cycle. Removal of the implant after a 9-day period has been followed by a satisfactory oestrous response and normal fertility (Wishart, 1976; Wishart et al., 1977; Drew, 1978; Spitzer et al., 1978). With this Norgestamet implant treatment, as well as when using intravaginal sponges, the PRID or other intravaginal devices, the majority of heifer cattle can be expected to exhibit oestrus 24–48 h after removal of the implant. In an early study reported by Wishart (1976), the oestrous response was 83% in 350 heifers observed closely for heat symptoms every 4 h. It should be noted, in talking about the percentage of animals in oestrus after a synchronizing treatment, that this is often substantially lower in cattle than is found in sheep, when an oestrous response in excess of 95% is by no means uncommon (Gordon, 1975); this probably reflects differences between cattle and sheep in the average duration of heat (18 h vs 36 h) and in the corresponding ease of heat detection.

3.4 PROSTAGLANDINS AND ANALOGUES

During the past decade, a considerable amount of research has been conducted into the biological properties of prostaglandins. These substances were first detected in the seminal fluid of rams and were thought to be secreted by the prostate gland, hence the term, prostaglandin. A great deal has been written about the distribution and biological effects of the various prostaglandins, but it is $PGF_{2\alpha}$ which is of greatest interest in reproduction control (Lauderdale, 1972, 1974; Walpole, 1975). Prostaglandins are

synthesized in cell membranes as required and are not stored; the very short half-life of prostaglandins and lack of storage suggests that the body has the capacity to synthesize and use PGs in different organs, such as the uterus, as the need arises. The availability of $PGF_{2\alpha}$ and several highly potent analogues in the 1970s has been followed by many reports describing applications in cattle for oestrus control. The advantages of the analogues are held to be two-fold; they are generally much more potent than the natural agent and they differ in their side-effects. The analogue cloprostenol (I.C.I. Ltd., Estrumate) is more potent than $PGF_{2\alpha}$ and differs in its effect upon smooth muscle to some extent. Nevertheless, the natural $PGF_{2\alpha}$ agent as well as the analogues have wide margins of tolerance and safety, both for the animal and those handling the substances.

Studies in the early seventies showed that $PGF_{2\alpha}$, administered in two daily doses (0.5–1.0 mg) by intrauterine injection into the horn ipsilateral to the ovary containing the active corpus luteum, would induce regression of that body; this was held to be followed by a sequence of events essentially similar to that occurring at a natural oestrus, the signs of heat usually appearing after an interval of 48–96 h (Hansel and Schechter, 1972; Liehr et al., 1972; Rowson et al., 1972; Hearnshaw et al., 1974; Nancarrow et al., 1974; Smith, 1974). At the same time, intrauterine administration, although only calling for small doses of PG, does demand skill and experience, may not always be easy with heifers and may carry some risk of uterine infection.

3.4.1 Prostaglandin by intramuscular injection

For such reasons, later workers employed single intramuscular injections using much higher doses (20–30 mg) or an appropriate dose of one of the potent analogues (Lauderdale, 1972; Hill et al., 1973; Lauderdale et al., 1973; Louis et al., 1973; Tervit et al., 1973; Stellflug et al., 1973; Cooper, 1974; Cooper and Furr, 1974; Roche, 1974a; Dobson et al., 1975; Nancarrow and Radford, 1975; Leaver et al., 1975); the general consensus was that single dose treatment resulted in the rapid morphological regression of corpora lutea susceptible to the prostaglandin. It appeared that hormonal events after PG treatment were well in keeping with those at natural oestrus (Dobson et al., 1975). It was evident that the agent could not effectively control the cycle if administered prior to day-5 or after about day-18, i.e. for a period of about one-third of the cycle. For that reason, anything up to 40% of cyclic cattle may fail to be synchronized after just the one injection of PG; by employing a two-dose routine, with an interval of 10–13 days between PG injections, all animals may be expected to possess susceptible corpora lutea at the time of the second administration. For cyclic heifers, the above remarks have stood the test of time, but in milking cattle, response may not be always as predictable and consistent.

It would seem that maturation of the bovine corpus luteum is associated with increased sensitivity to prostaglandin treatment and that this may be a question of a rapid increase in the concentration and total content of specific $PGF_{2\alpha}$ receptors in the corpus luteum early in the oestrous cycle (Bartol et al., 1977). Studies reported by Beal et al. (1980), who were able to induce CL regression by twice-daily doses of PG on days 3 and 4 of the cycle, suggested that the ability of a given treatment to inhibit luteal function in cattle may depend on an interaction between the age of the corpus and the frequency of prostaglandin administration.

There is general agreement that the fertility in cyclic heifer cattle after PG treatment is not impaired and that fixed-time inseminations can result in perfectly acceptable conception rates. However, the same may not be so true in lactating cows and it is apparent that the precision of the oestrous response and the occurrence of ovulation may not always permit satisfactory results when AI is performed without reference to oestrus.

3.4.2 Interval, PG to oestrus onset

One problem, which was not always apparent in the early days of PG applications in cattle, is the fact that in lactating dairy and beef cattle, the interval between PG and the post-treatment oestrus may be less well synchronized than in heifers. It is this lack of precision, which may result in cows showing oestrus several days after

the expected time, which creates a problem if fixed-time AI is employed as the method of breeding; in large-scale farm trials in Ireland, for example, some 10–18% of PG-treated dairy cows were observed to be in oestrus more than 4 days after the second PG injection (Roche and Prendiville, 1979). It has been suggested by some that the problem in dairy cows may be associated with abnormal cycles in the post-partum period (Schams et al., 1978; Waters and Ball, 1978) but this may not be the full explanation. Evidence reported from several sources would suggest that it may be a question of variability in the duration of the pro-oestrus period, i.e. the time-interval between induced regression of the corpus luteum and the onset of oestrus (Eddy, 1977; Macmillan, 1978; Macmillan et al., 1980). If it is accepted that the time-course of luteolysis after PG treatment is uniform (Cooper and Rowson, 1975), the indications are that variations arise primarily because of differences in the growth and development of the mature Graafian follicles capable of ovulating.

There appears to be a lack of quantitative data on the rate of follicular growth, whether this is after surgical (Brock and Rowson, 1952) or PG induced (Cooper and Rowson, 1975) destruction of the cyclic CL. Scaramuzzi et al. (1980) have suggested that it may be a problem associated with the size of the largest follicle present at the time of PG treatment and the time required for that follicle to complete its development to the preovulatory stage. In the case of cyclic heifers and in support of the preceding suggestion, it has been observed that oestrus and ovulation after the second of two PG injections, 11 days apart, occurred sooner and over a narrower time-range for a group of cattle than was found in the same animals responding to the first PG dose (Cooper, 1974; Dobson et al., 1975; Leaver et al., 1975; Jackson et al., 1979); this may be because most heifers were at day-8 when the presence of a single large Graafian follicle could be expected to be in one or other ovary.

If account is also taken of evidence showing that the corpus luteum of some lactating cows may not become susceptible to PG until the fifth, sixth or even the seventh day of the cycle, the lack of a precise oestrous response in lactating dairy or suckler cattle would seem more understandable; evidence presented by Macmillan (1978) suggested that 40% of New Zealand dairy cows did not respond to PG at day-6 of the oestrous cycle. Elsewhere, it has been observed by way of progesterone assays that 18% of dairy cows showed evidence of low progesterone levels in the early days of the cycle after natural oestrus which may suggest that CL were not fully functional at that time; this may be a factor affecting the susceptibility of the corpus to exogenous PG.

Although it is now realized that lactating cattle may pose problems, in that the onset of oestrus after PG treatment is less precise than that with heifers, it is also worth noting that there is evidence of a higher pregnancy rate among prostaglandin-treated cows detected in heat and inseminated when compared with untreated herd-mates (Day, 1977; Macmillan et al., 1977, 1980); although the precise factors involved in this effect are not known, it is thought that it may arise because of AI being performed at an optimum time, relative to the occurrence of ovulation.

3.4.3 Prostaglandins require cyclic cattle

An essential factor in using prostaglandins in cattle is to be sure that only cyclic animals are treated. According to Roche (1979), dealing with the Irish dairy cattle scene, it has been found that more than 20% of cows, calved at least 6 weeks, show evidence of inactive ovaries, based on progesterone assay data. Such findings have been supported in the earlier report of Macmillan et al. (1977) who found that 16% of New Zealand dairy cows were anoestrous 42 or more days after calving, and by the later data in dairy herds in Scotland reported by Boyd and Munro (1980). There is also the question of whether the cattle are showing regular or irregular cycles. According to Cooper (1981) there are cows which are incapable of producing a normal ovarian response after PG, and the suggestion is that this may be the result of nutritional stress; failure to cycle normally has been examined by serial milk progesterone testing and has been noted to be around 5% of the sampled population, although it could be as high as 30% under some conditions.

Fig. 3.6. Use of prostaglandins in oestrus control in lactating dairy cattle. The ability to control the cow's oestrous cycle by applying prostaglandins as luteolytic agents, has opened up many new possibilities for effective oestrus control in cattle. Many different systems for employing prostaglandins have been developed in one country or another around the world. In the U.K. and Ireland, prostaglandins have been commercially available since late 1975. By far the greatest use of the agent in the U.K. has been with dairy heifers.

As noted earlier, abnormal corpus luteum function in lactating cattle may influence whether PG is effective in inducing regression of the corpus or not.

It should also be noted that a longer interval elapses between the time of PG treatment and the onset of oestrus than between progestagen withdrawal and oestrus; cattle receiving PG tend to be about a day slower in showing oestrous symptoms because of the delay before regression of the corpus luteum brings the progesterone level down to the basal value, a situation which obtains very soon after withdrawing sponges, the PRID or implants.

3.5 PROBLEMS IN USE OF TECHNIQUES IN MILKING COWS AND SUCKLER COWS

There is a problem in using prostaglandins in lactating dairy cows as part of a fixed-time AI programme. Although some reports have shown normal fertility (Christie and Medcalf, 1976; Esslemont et al., 1977), others have not (de Kruif et al., 1976; Macmillan and Curnow, 1976; Macmillan et al., 1977; Kalis and Dielman, 1978; Macmillan, 1978; Phatak et al., 1979; Roche and Prendiville, 1979). It therefore is a matter of inseminating on the basis of oestrus detection. In New Zealand, for example, one system devised for dairy herds involves the selection of cyclic cows, treatment with a single PG dose and a single insemination on detection of oestrus; the system uses "tail-painting" as an aid in detecting animals in heat (Smith and Macmillan, 1978). In Australia, Miller (1979) reported that many veterinarians were using a single dose PG treatment in a 10-day programme; in this, it is a matter of observing and breeding cows in oestrus during the first 5 days, administering PG on day-5 and inseminating after heat detection. The same author states that Australian veterinarians did start by using two-dose PG treatment with two fixed-time inseminations but did not find them to be economically acceptable. Donaldson (1980) is another author who suggested that this 10-day AI programme was the method of choice and reported data to substantiate this view; as he describes the situation, the savings in labour covered the cost of the PG treatment.

3.5.1 Beef suckler cows

A considerable amount of work, in France, the U.S.A. and elsewhere, has been devoted to the question of oestrus control in beef cattle. After all, it is in this category that much opportunity exists for bringing about breeding improvements through the use of AI. However, it may be more a matter of overcoming the problem of *postpartum* anoestrus rather than seeking to control the oestrous cycle. Clearly, there is little point in using prostaglandin if no corpus luteum exists upon which it can act. Progestagen treatment alone cannot be relied upon to initiate cyclical breeding activity among anoestrous beef cattle, although it should be noted that there is evidence showing that progestagen treatment may initiate cyclical activity under conditions when treatment with PG alone will not. A profound period of sexual inactivity may occur in beef cattle after parturition and when the cows are nursing; treatment for oestrus control in such animals becomes one of inducing rather than inhibiting ovarian activity. In the case of beef cattle, much more than in dairy animals, because the profitability of the production system is likely to be low, it is normal practice for beef suckler cattle

to be maintained on a system which maximizes the use of grass and forage crops. Thus, the nutritional environment may not be as closely controlled as in dairy animals.

3.6 TREATMENT COMBINATIONS

In the development of oestrus control methods by the various pharmaceutical companies who produce prostaglandins and progestagens, there has inevitably been a tendency for investigations to be concerned with the use of the one synchronizing agent; in actual practice, and from the farmer's point of view, there may sometimes be a case for looking at particular combinations of agents; progestagen in combination with prostaglandin would be one obvious example.

3.6.1 Ovulating hormone after synchronizing treatment

Use has been made of hormone preparations such as Gn-RH, given 30–40 h after the removal of Norgestamet implants or PRID's, in an effort to bring about the release of LH, with ovulation occurring a day or so later; a similar response may follow in prostaglandin-treated cattle if the Gn-RH is given 60 h after the dose of PG. The objective of the Gn-TH treatment is to permit a single AI to be conducted about 12–18 h after the agent is given. According to Kaltenbach (1980), more information is required to determine whether Gn-RH administration provides sufficient benefit, in comparison with normal fixed-time AI procedures, to justify the cost of using the agent.

The availability of the synthetic Gn-RH has meant that it is possible to induce the cow to release its own LH in more physiological amounts and this should be an advantage over methods in which a gonadotrophin such as HCG is employed as the ovulating agent; the possibility that the use of HCG might result in antibody formation is another objection occasionally voiced by authors. Outside the U.S.A., attempts have been made to induce synchronous ovulation after the use of the PRID (Roche, 1975, 1976), the intravaginal sponge (Sreenan, 1977) and PG treatment (Coulson et al., 1980). Elsewhere in the U.S.A., Zaid et al. (1976) have reported on the agent's use after Norgestamet implant treatment and Burfening et al. (1978) used Gn-RH after PG. Results of these studies would be in line with the view of Kaltenbach (1980) who feels that a cost-effective case for the use of Gn-RH has yet to be made.

3.6.2 Oestrogen and synchronizing treatment

It is known that an injection of an oestrogen in spayed heifers will induce an LH peak of a similar magnitude to that observed in intact heifers before ovulation (Hobson and Hansel, 1972; Short et al., 1973). In the days of using oral progestagen treatments, the administration of 2 mg oestradiol doses by Wiltbank et al. (1971) 24 h after progestagen withdrawal did improve the precision of the synchronization response but apparently at the expense of some depression in conception rate. Hansel and Schechter (1972) reported that a dose of 400 μg oestradiol benzoate given 20 h after the last feeding of MAP hastened the onset of oestrus without adversely affecting conception rate. Roche (1974) used a similar dose of 400 μg oestradial benzoate, giving it to beef heifers 16 h after progesterone implant removal and did find a reduction in conception rate; it may be that the dose level and timing of oestrogen injection after progestagen treatment is critical. Certainly, in sheep, there is a great amount of evidence showing that oestrogen, even in minute (μg) doses, can have a very adverse effect on conception rate when administered around the time of oestrus (Robinson, 1969).

3.6.3 Progestagen and prostaglandin

As previously mentioned, there may be reasons why treatment regimens involving progestagen in combination with prostaglandin may have advantages that the agents, employed singly, may not possess. One way of dealing with the early luteal phase, during which period the cow's corpus luteum is not susceptible to the action of $PGF_{2\alpha}$, is to put all animals under progestagen treatment for at least 5 days before following up with a luteolytic dose of prosta-glandin; several investigators have reported on

this possibility using either the Norgestamet implant or the PRID for a 7-day period and administering a luteolytic dose of $PGF_{2\alpha}$ 24 h before or at the time of progestagen withdrawal (Wishart, 1974; Thimonier et al., 1975; Hansel and Beal, 1979; Heersche et al., 1979). The use of such combinations appears to have given good results in the heifers in which they were employed; the combination avoids the need for oestrogen or oestrogen/progestagen doses at the start of short-term progestagen treatments.

3.6.4 Gonadotrophins and synchronizing treatments

Work in Ireland with intravaginal sponges and a low dose of PMSG (500–800 i.u.) at withdrawal in beef suckler cattle has been followed by an up to 15% increase in the calving rate to first service (Mulvihill and Sreenan, 1977; Sreenan, 1977); similar results were reported by French workers using Norgestamet ear implants or PRIDs (Chupin et al., 1975; Mauleon et al., 1978). However, Saumande (1978) has reported that after PMSG injection in cattle that have a functional corpus luteum, progesterone levels may actually increase (luteotrophic effect of

Fig. 3.7. Oestrus control in suckler cattle. Beef production by way of suckler cows is the least profitable sector of Irish farming. Profitability in this area could be markedly improved by increasing stocking rates, better winter feeding and greater use of the Continental beef breeds. The average herd size for suckler cattle is no more than six. The fact that herds are so small means that farmers are less likely to keep a bull and more likely to use AI Station. Oestrus control can be extremely useful in getting cows bred to the AI service, even though the suckler animal may need oestrus to be induced rather than simply controlled in the normal sense.

PMSG?). When a low dose of PMSG was given at the end of progestagen treatment to cyclic cattle, it reduced conception rate to fixed-time AI (Chupin et al., 1978) apparently because some cows had the functional life of their corpora lutea prolonged.

A treatment which involves the use of progestagen, PMSG and prostaglandin in combination can deal with that difficulty, if the PG is given 2 days before progestagen withdrawal (Chupin et al., 1978; Chupin and Pelot, 1978). In a report dealing with Friesian cattle, the PMSG (500 i.u.) was also administered 2 days prior to implant removal and simultaneously with the PG (Chupin and Saumande, 1979). The danger of using PMSG is that there is no way of avoiding some number of multiple births. Among beef herds, and even in some dairy herds, the additional calves born to cows that do respond to PMSG by shedding more than one egg may not always be regarded as being a disadvantage, always assuming that twin-pregnancy diagnosis is subsequently carried out and advice on calving and feeding management given.

3.7 BREEDING BY FIXED-TIME AI

The important event deciding whether a cow becomes pregnant or not after natural or artificial insemination is ovulation rather than the symptoms of oestrus. Research and development work in cattle oestrus control has really been with a view to providing the farmer with a procedure which enables his cow to be inseminated at a predetermined time. By this means, so the theory goes, the farmer is saved the time and labour involved in oestrus detection. The fact remains, however, that despite recent advances in the development of short-term progestagen treatments and in the use of prostaglandin, there is still some way to go in meeting the needs of a farmer who expects an optimally high calving rate after a single, fixed-time insemination. However, as the preceding discussion has shown, the successful use of controlled breeding techniques in which fixed-time AI is employed does require accurate control of luteal regression, follicular develop-

ment and the accurate timing of ovulation. Progestagens or prostaglandin can provide control over luteal function, but particularly in lactating cows, variability in follicular development and the time of ovulation remain as difficulties to be overcome.

With heifer cattle, in which there is general agreement that insemination at a predetermined time is feasible, it is a matter of deciding when the inseminations should be carried out and whether one AI or two is necessary. Most reports accept that it is necessary to employ two inseminations, although there are those who suggest that a single insemination can provide acceptable rates. As noted earlier, a longer interval elapses between prostaglandin administration and the onset of oestrus than between progestagen withdrawal and oestrus; for that reason, the usual timings for AI have been 72 h, and again at 96 h after prostaglandin and 48–56 h and again at 60–74 h after short-term progestagen (sponge, PRID and Norgestamet implant). Those who have reported a lower conception rate in heifers treated with PG after a single insemination at 72 h as compared with AI at 72 h and 96 h are Cooper (1976) in the U.K., Roche (1977) in Ireland and Hansel and Fortune (1978) in the U.S.A. In studies involving nearly 4000 cattle reported by Cooper and Furr (1976) the evidence supported the view that a reduction in conception rate occurred with a single insemination after PG; others make the point that any recommendation for single AI systems should only be on the basis of statistically significant numbers of pregnancies recorded in field trials at a number of sites. There is also the view, as expressed by Cooper (1978), on the basis of much experience in the application of PG, that an advantage can always be demonstrated in favour of two inseminations rather than one, whatever the techniques or timings of AI; he concludes that any technique which calls for critical timing is likely to fail in commercial practice because of the practical difficulties in ensuring that cows are bred at the correct time.

The initial recommendations for using PG in commercial practice involved two doses of the agent, given 10–13 days apart with the heifers then bred twice, at 72 and 96 h; this is termed the double/double (2/2) system. Modifications of this 2/2 routine have been reported; in New Zealand, one variant involves pre-treatment selection of cyclic beef and dairy heifers, a single PG dose and double-fixed time AI (Smith and Macmillan, 1978); in this single-double (1/2) system, a teaser fitted with a chin-ball is employed for 3 weeks prior to the start of breeding. The low value of cattle in countries such as New Zealand, compared to animals in Europe and North America and the similarity in the cost of PG, probably means that the cheaper single-PG, single-insemination regimens, with the initial exclusion of unsuitable animals through pre-treatment identification, are likely to be features that appeal under these conditions. It is of some relevance to note that in the sheep AI world, satisfactory progress has been made in moving from a double insemination technique to that involving just one (Gordon and Crosby, 1980) without an adverse effect on the conception rate. In fact, in terms of reducing handling stress, there may be something in favour of concentrating on one rather than two inseminations. Workers using the PRID have reported that the calving rate after one or two fixed-time inseminations at 56 h or at 56 and 74 h after removal of the device was similar to that in untreated control cows (O'Farrell, 1977; Roche et al., 1977; Drew et al., 1978). In talking about fixed-time AI, when any large group of cattle is involved, it is as well to remember matters such as inseminator fatigue and the need for good handling facilities; Drew (1981) mentions that no more than 30 cows should be inseminated by the one individual in a group to avoid the fatigue factor.

the service period (Leaver, 1977; Wishart et al., 1977; Mulvihill and Sreenan, 1978). Studies in heifer cattle reported by Drew (1978) attempted to quantify the effect of feeding over the service period; results showed that, compared with the usual farm ration, supplementation of the diet to provide an additional 20 M/J metabolizable energy/day improved calving rates after oestrus control (progestagen and prostaglandin methods) from 50 to 69%. The same worker and her associates (Drew et al., 1979), this time dealing with beef suckler cattle, concluded that traditional suckler cow rations in the U.K. are often inadequate for acceptable fertility but that the provision of a diet to sustain a predicted level of milk production of 9.0 kg is likely to result in an acceptable conception rate. A further report (Drew and Gould, 1980) showed that conception rate results with well-fed dairy cows treated with PG at more than 42 days post-partum were quite satisfactory after breeding by fixed-time AI at 72 and 96 h; this would be in line with the view that "nutritional stress" could be one cause of problems in dairy cows subjected to oestrus control (Cooper, 1981).

The present commercial application of synchronization techniques will no doubt serve to focus attention more sharply on the effect of nutritional and other forms of stress on first service conception rates in cattle; this may help in accelerating the adoption of feeding and management measures which will permit optimum pregnancy rates to be achieved in the general run of cattle as well as in those subjected to oestrus control.

3.8 NUTRITION AND OESTRUS CONTROL

Quite apart from the merits of the methods employed to achieve oestrus synchronization in cattle, it has to be clearly recognized that the conception rates achieved may be markedly affected by the animals' nutritional status and general body condition. As noted elsewhere, studies on the effect of body condition and nutrition on conception rate at first service have provided ample evidence that fertility can be influenced by the level of feeding provided over

3.9 ADJUSTMENTS IN AI ROUTINES

Rather than relying entirely on hormonal agents in the oestrus control procedure, it may be worth considering the modification of factors such as sperm dose and semen quality so that fertilization may be effected more readily after a fixed-time AI schedule. Some work was reported by Roche (1979), who increased the dose of frozen–thawed sperm inseminated from 30 to 60 x 10[6] after PRID treatment, but this did not improve conception rate. The fact that bulls can vary in their fertility quite markedly may mean that with some, single fixed-time AI is possible, whereas with others it is not.

3.9.1 Gn-RH as semen additive

There is some preliminary evidence reported by Convey et al. (1980) that a Gn-RH analogue incorporated into semen at a dose level of 50 μg was effective in inducing the release of LH; these findings confirmed and extended the earlier work of Dermody et al. (1976) who reported LH release after intrauterine treatment of cows with large doses (1–10 mg) of Gn-RH in semen. The studies of Convey et al. (1980) suggested that sperm motility and acrosomal attachment was not adversely affected by the addition of Gn-RH to the semen; as these authors note, it may be of interest examining the possibility that Gn-RH analogue given via the uterus at the normal time of AI or in fixed-time controlled breeding programmes can improve fertility.

3.10 TECHNIQUES FOR INHIBITING OESTRUS

The occurrence of heat periods in post-pubertal heifer cattle being reared for beef can increase the farmer's management problems, at any event under certain conditions: with the type of large-scale feed-lot conditions operating in North America, normal oestrous activity in beef heifers is associated with mounting, reduced feed intake and lower weight gains. The fact that bulls yield more lean meat per carcass than castrates (Taylor, 1974) means that some producers have taken up bull beef production, a practice which may bring new management problems if cyclic beef heifers are in the vicinity of the intact males.

The undesirable consequences of oestrus in feed-lot beef heifers under American conditions can be minimized by spaying (Dinusson et al., 1950) but this is no longer a commercially feasible procedure. For several reasons, a practical method of inhibiting heat symptoms in beef heifers, which would simultaneously increase the efficiency of conversion of feed into lean meat, could appeal to cattle producers. Although there have been some claims that the use of a plastic

intravaginal device could improve growth performance and suppress oestrus in feed-lot heifers the outcome of experiments with grazing and feed-lot heifers, as reported in the scientific literature, have not apparently shown evidence of any improvement in daily weight gain and feed conversion efficiency and no suppression of heat symptoms (Utley et al., 1978; Horton et al., 1979).

3.10.1 Use of progestagens

Work in the mid-sixties with melengestrol acetate (MGA) administered orally was the first to show that a progestagen can have a growth-promoting action over and above its oestrus inhibiting capacity. In a comprehensive evaluation of MGA in beef heifers, Zimbleman et al. (1970) showed that cattle treated with the agent had a mean improvement of 11% in daily rate of gain and 7.6% in feed conversion over control animals; these authors suggest that the progestagen probably exerts its growth-promoting action indirectly in heifers by permitting substantial oestrogen production to occur in the ovaries of the heat-suppressed animal; in this regard, progestagen in heifers may achieve its growth effect in much the same way as the steer treated with oestrogen. The fact that the growth-promoting action of MGA is not shown until the heifers reach puberty (Randel et al., 1973) may explain some differences in female cattle in the way they respond to the treatment.

In more recent times, there has been evidence from Canadian workers that MGA in combination with monensin resulted in Hereford heifers (293 kg) gaining weight 17% faster and utilizing feed 8% more efficiently than controls (Horton et al., 1980).

In countries such as Ireland where beef heifers may often be at pasture rather than in pens receiving dry food, the implantation method is clearly the method of choice. Roche and Crowley (1973a,b) conducted several studies, using silastic implants impregnated with MGA; heifers were held out of oestrus for about 4 months with a single implant, and a useful growth-promoting effect (8–10% in daily gain) was evident during this period of treatment. The commercial availability of progestagens and other agents for use in beef heifers will vary from one country to another, according to whether approval for use by regulatory agencies has been granted.

3.11 UPTAKE OF OESTRUS CONTROL MEASURES

Although oestrus control measures for cattle have been commercially available for the past few years in a number of countries, the general run of reports in the popular farming press do not suggest that they are being availed of on any great scale, with the possible exception of their use in the fixed-time breeding of maiden heifer dairy cattle. In Ireland, where the natural prostaglandin, the Cloprostenol analogue and the PRID have been commercially available for a few years, uptake has been slower than expected (Roche, 1979). The control measures themselves, quite apart from their cost and the labour involved in their application, have other points that must be considered. The administration of PG can be carried out readily enough and without stress to the animal but it does require professional supervision and if inadvertently given to pregnant cattle can prove to be a highly effective abortifacient at the dose levels employed in oestrus control.

There is, of course, the fact that PG can only be effective among cattle that possess a functional corpus luteum. The insertion of Norgestamet implants, in those countries where they do become available commercially, generally involves a two-man operation; both FGA-sponges and PRID's, on the other hand, can be inserted by a single operator without difficulty. Strict asepsis must be observed in the implantation procedure and there may be minor reservations on the approach in view of accumulating scar-tissue consequent on treatments being repeated during the animal's breeding life. One possible advantage in the short-term progestagen treatment is in initiating ovulation in some proportion of previously acyclic animals; the oestrogen/progestagen doses administered are likely to influence the hypothalamus–pituitary axis more directly than prostaglandins. The fact that synthetic progestagens now have a long history in human fertility control may make their accept-ance by regulatory agencies a less expensive and complex task than in the case of some other agents.

3.12 REFERENCES

Armstrong, D. T. and Hansel, W. (1959) Alteration of the bovine estrous cycle with oxytocin. *J. Dairy Sci.* **42**, 533–542.

Ayalon, N. and Marcus, S. (1975) Estrus synchronization and conception rate in dairy cattle treated with progestin-impregnated vaginal sponges. *Theriogenology*, **3**, 95.

Bartol, F. F., Kimball, F. A., Thatcher, W. W., Bazer, W., Chenault, J. R., Wilcox, C. J. and Kittock, R. J. (1977) Follicle, luteal and uterine parameters during the bovine estrous cycle. *J. Anim. Sci.* **45**, Suppl. 1, 34.

Beal, W. E., Milvae, R. A. and Hansel, W. (1980) Oestrous cycle length and plasma progesterone concentrations following administration of prostaglandin $F_{2\alpha}$ early in the bovine oestrous cycle. *J. Reprod. Fert.* **59**, 393–396.

Bellows, R. A., Short, R. E. and Staigmiller, R. B. (1979) Research areas in beef cattle reproduction. *Anim. Reprod.* (BARC. Symp. 3 pp. 3–18, Harold Hawk, ed.) Allanheld. Osmun. Montclair.

Boyd, H. and Munro, C. D. (1980). Experiences and results of a herd-health programme, rectal palpation and progesterone assays in fertility control. *Proc. 9th Int. Congr. Anim. Reprod. AI (Madrid)*, **2**, 373–380.

Brock, H. and Rowson, L. E. (1952). The production of viable bovine ova. *J. Agric. Sci. Camb.* **42**, 479.

Burfening, P. J., Anderson, D. C., Kinkie, R. A., Williams, J. and Friedrich, R. L. (1978) Synchronization of estrus with $PGF_{2\alpha}$ in beef cattle. *J. Anim. Sci.* **47**, 999–1003.

Carrick, M. J. and Shelton, H. N. (1967) The synchronization of oestrus in cattle with progestagen-impregnated intra-vaginal sponges. *J. Reprod. Fert.* **14**, 21–32.

Christian, R. E. and Casida, L. E. (1948) The effects of progesterone in altering the estrous cycle of the cow. *J. Anim. Sci.* **7**, 540 (abs).

Christie, E. H. L and Medcalf, J. D. (1976) Observations on the use of cloprostenol in a large dairy herd in Cheshire. *Vet. Rec.* **99**, 272–273.

Chupin, D. and Pelot, J. (1978) Fertility of dairy cows treated with progestagen implants, prostaglandin analogue and PMSG. *Theriogenology* **10**, 307–312.

Chupin, D. and Saumande, J. (1979) New attempts to decrease the variability of ovarian response to PMSG in cattle. *Ann. Biol. Anim. Biochem. Biophys* **19**, 1489–1498.

Chupin, D., Pelot, J. and Thimonier, J. (1975) The control of reproduction in the nursing cow with a progestagen short-term treatment. *Ann. Biol Anim. Bioch. Biophys.* **15**, 263–272.

Chupin, D., Pelot, J. and Mauleon, P. (1978) Improvement of the oestrous control in adult dairy cows. In, *Control of Reproduction in the Cow*, pp. 546–561 Galway, J. Sreenan., ed. C.E.C. Luxembourg.

Convey, R. M., Beck, T.W. and Neitzel, R. (1980) Release of LH following intrauterine administration gonadotropin-releasing hormone. *Can. J. Anim. Sci.* **60**, 1023–1026.

Cooper, M. J. (1974) Control of oestrous cycles on heifers with a synthetic prostaglandin analogue. *Vet. Rec.* **95**, 200–203.

Cooper, M. J. (1976) The use of prostaglandins in the breeding management of cattle. Proc. 27th ann. meet. European Assoc. Anim. Proc., Zurich, Aug. 23–26.

Cooper, M. J. (1978) Ovulation control in the cow. *Control of Ovulation*, pp. 413–420. (Ed. Crighton, D. H., Foxcroft, N. B., Haynes, G. R. and Lamming, G. E.), Butterworths, London.

Cooper, M. J. (1981) Prostaglandins in veterinary practice. *In Practice* 3(1), 30–34.

Cooper, M. J. and Furr, B. J. A. (1974) The role of prostaglandins in animal breeding. *Vet. Rec.* **94,** 161.

Cooper, M. J. and Furr, B. J. A. (1976) The use of prostaglandins in the control of the bovine oestrous cycle. Proc. EEC Seminar Egg Transfer in Cattle, Cambridge, 249–260.

Cooper, M. J. and Rowson, L. E. A. (1975) Control of the estrous cycle in Friesian heifers with ICI 80996. *Ann. Biol Anim. Bioch. Biophys.* **15,** 427–436.

Coulson, A., Noakes, D. E., Hamer, J. and Cockrill, T. (1980) Effect of gonadotrophin releasing hormone in cattle synchronised with dinoprost. *Vet. Rec.* **107,** 108–09.

Day, A. M. (1977) Cloprostenol as an aid in dairy herd management: 1. Mating Management. *N.Z. Vet. J.* **25,** 300–305.

Dermody, W. E., Reel, J. R., Beck, C. C. and Coopock, R. W. (1976) Serum LH concentrations in dairy heifers after intravenous and intrauterine administration of LH-RH. *Vet. Med. Small Anim. Clin.* **71,** 419–422.

Dinusson, W. E., Andrews, F. N. and Beeson, W. M. (1950) The effects of stilbestrol, testosterone, thyroid alteration and spaying on growth and fattening beef heifers. *J. Anim. Sci.* **9,** 321.

Dobson, H., Cooper, M. J. and Furr, B. J. A. (1975) Synchronization of oestrus with ICI 79,939, an analogue of $PGF_{2\alpha}$ and associated changes in plasma progesterone, oestradiol-17β and LH in heifers. *J. Reprod. Fert.* **42,** 141–144.

Donaldson, L. A. (1980) The development and marketing of estrus synchronization in cattle in Australia using prostaglandins. *Theriogenology* **14,** 391–401.

Drew, S. B. (1978) Management factors in oestrous cycle control. *Control of Reproduction in the Cow.* pp. 445–485 (Galway, J. Sreenan ed.) C. E. C., Luxembourg.

Drew, B. (1981) Controlled breeding in dairy herd management. *Brit. Friesian J.* 138–139.

Drew, S. B. and Gould, C. M. (1980) Fertility of cloprostenol treated dairy cows. *Vet. Rec.* **107,** 88–89.

Drew, S. B., Gould, C. M. and Bulman, D. C. (1978) The effect of treatment with progesterone releasing intravaginal device on the fertility of spring calving Friesian dairy cows. *Vet. Rec.* **103,** 259–262.

Drew, S. B., Wishart, D. F. and Young, I. M. (1979) Fertility of norgestomet treated suckler cows. *Vet. Rec.* **104,** 523–525.

Dziuk, P. H. and Cook B. (1966) Passage of steroids through silicone rubber. *Endocrin.* **78,** 208–211.

Eddy, R. G. (1977) Cloprostenol as a treatment for no visible oestrus and cystic ovarian disease in dairy cows. *Vet. Rec.* **100,** 62–65.

Esslemont, R. J., Eddy, R. G. and Ellis, P. R. (1977) Planned breeding in autumn calving dairy herds. *Vet. Rec.* **100,** 426–427.

Gordon, I. (1975) Hormonal control of reproduction in sheep. *Proc Br. Soc. Anim. Prod.* **4,** 79–93.

Gordon, I. and Crosby, T. F. (1980) AI in sheep promises well. *Ir. Fmrs J.* 32(25) 12–13.

Grosskopf, J. F. W. (1974) Synchronization of ovulation in beef herds; improved conception rate after an interrupted course of progesterone administration. *S. Afr. J. Anim. Sci.* **4,** 61–65.

Hale, D. H. and Symington, R. B. (1969) Control of sexual activity in ranch cows by intramuscular and intravaginal administration of progestagens. *J. Reprod. Fert.* **19,** 193–199.

Hansel, W. and Beal, W. E. (1979) ovulation control in cattle. In, *Anim. Reprod.* BARC Symp. 3, pp. 91–110. Harold Hawk, ed. Allanheld. Osum. Montclair.

Hansel, W. and Fortune, J. (1978) The applications of ovulation control. In, *Control of Ovulation* pp. 237–263. (Crighton et al., eds.) Butterworth, London.

Hansel, W., Maluen, P. V. and Black, D. W. (1961) Estrous cycle regulation in the bovine. *J. Anim. Sci.* **20,** 621.

Hansel, W. and Schechter, R. E. (1972) Biotechnical procedures for control of the oestrous cycles of domestic animals. *Proc. 7th Int. Congr. Anim. Reprod A.I., (Munich)* **1,** 75–96.

Hauger, R. L., Karsch, F. J. and Foster, D. L. (1977) A new concept for control of the estrous cycle of the ewe based on the temporal relationships between luteinizing hormone, estradiol and progesterone in peripheral serum. *Endocrin.* **101,** 807.

Hearnshaw, H. Restall, B. J., Nancarrow, C. D. and Mattner, P. E. (1974) Synchronization of oestrus in cattle, sheep and goats using a prostaglandin analogue. *Proc. Aust. Soc. Anim. Prod.* **10,** 242–245.

Heersche, G., Jr., Kiracofe, G. H., Benedetti, R. S. de, Wen, S. and McKee, R. M. (1979) Synchronization of estrus in beef heifers with a norgestamet implant and prostaglandin $F_{2\alpha}$. *Theriogen.* **11,** 197–208.

Hignett, P. G., Boyd, H. and Wishart, R. D. (1970) Synchronization of oestrus in Ayrshire heifers by the use of progestinated intravaginal pessaires. *Vet. Rec.* **86,** 528–31.

Hill, H. R. Jr., Dickey, J. F. and Henricks, D. M. (1973) Estrus and ovulation in $PGF_{2\alpha}$/PMS treated heifers. *J. Anim. Sci.* **37,** 315 (abs.).

Hobson, W. C. and Hansel, W. (1972) Plasma LH after ovariectomy, corpus luteum removal and estradiol administration in cattle. *Endocrin.* **91,** 185–190.

Horton, G. M. J., Stricklin, W. R., Mans, J. G. and Mapletoft, R. J. (1979) Intravaginal devices for feedlot heifers. *J. Anim. Sci.* **49,** 915–918.

Horton, G. M. J., Manns, J. G. and Nicholson, H. H. (1980) Effect of melengestrol acetate and monensin on performance and estrus activity of feedlot heifers. *J. Anim. Sci.* **51** (Suppl.) 13 (abs.).

Jackson, Peter S., Johnson, Carl T., Furr, B. J. and Beattie, J. F. (1979) Influence of stage of oestrous cycle on time of oestrus following Cloprostenol treatment in the bovine. *Theriogen.* **12,** 153–167.

Jochle, W. (1975) The use of progestogens in cattle under tropical or sub-tropical conditions. *Ann. Biol. Anim. Bioch. Biophys.* **15,** 481–492.

Kalis, C. H. J. and Dieleman, S. J. (1978) Oestrous cycle control by means of prostaglandins and the progesterone levels in milk in dairy cattle. In, *Control of Reproduction in the Cow.* pp. 596–604 (Galway, J. Sreenan, ed.) C.E.C., Luxembourg.

Kaltenbach, C. C. (1980) Control of oestrus in cattle. In, *Current Therapy in Theriogenology.* pp. 169–174 (D. A. Morrow, ed.).

Kruip, T. A. M. and Brand, A. (1975) Follicular growth during the normal cycle and after treatment with progestagens in the ewe. *Ann. Biol. Anim. Biochem. Biophys.* **15,** 191–204.

Kruif, A. de, Zikken, A., Kommerij, R. and Bois de. D. H. W. (1976) Results obtained after synchronization of oestrus by prostaglandins in dairy cows. *Tijdschr. Diergenesk* **101,** 1257–1261.

Lamond, D. R. (1964) Synchronization of ovarian cycles in sheep and cattle. *Anim. Breed. Abs.* **32,** 269–285.

Lauderdale, J. W. (1972) Effects of PGF$_{2\alpha}$ on pregnancy and oestrous cycles of cattle. *J. Anim. Sci.* **35,** 246 (abs.).

Lauderdale, J. W. (1975) The use of prostaglandins in cattle. *Annls. Biol. Anim. Bioch. Biophys.* **15,** 419–425.

Lauderdale, J. W., Chenault, J. R., Sequin, B. E. and Thatcher, W. W. (1973) Fertility of cattle after PGF$_{2\alpha}$ treatment. *J. Anim. Sci.* **37,** 319.

Leaver, J. D. (1977) Rearing dairy cattle: 7. Effect of level of nutrition and body condition on the fertility of heifers. *Anim. Prod.* **25,** 219–224.

Leaver, J. D., Glenroos, R. G. and Pope, G. S. (1975) Fertility of Friesian heifers after luteolysis with a prostaglandin analogue (ICI 80996). *Vet. Rec.* **96,** 383–384.

Liehr, R. A., Marion, G. B. and Olson, H. H. (1972) Effects of prostaglandins on cattle estrous cycles. *J. Anim. Sci.* **35,** 247 (abs.).

Louis, T. M., Hafs, H. D. and Sequin, B. E. (1973) Progesterone, LH, estrus and ovulation after prostaglandin F$_{2\alpha}$ in heifers. *Proc. Soc. Exp. Biol. Med.* **143,** 152–55.

Macmillan, K. L. (1978) Oestrus synchronization with a prostaglandin analogue III. Special aspects of synchronization. *N.Z. Vet. J.* **26,** 104–108.

Macmillan, K. L. and Curnow, R. J. (1976) The application of oestrus synchronization in N.Z. dairy herds. *Proc. N.Z. Soc. Anim. Prod.* **36,** 50–57.

Macmillan, K. L., Curnow, R. J. and Morris, G. R. (1977) Oestrus synchronization with a prostaglandin analogue: 1. Systems in lactating dairy cattle. *N.Z. Vet J.* **25,** 366–372.

Macmillan, K. L., Day, A. M. and Smith, J. F. (1980) onset of oestrus and fertility in lactating dairy cows injected with an analogue of prostaglandin F$_{2\alpha}$ cloprostenol. *Anim. Reprod. Sci.* **31,** 171–180.

Mauer, R. E., Webel, S. K. and Brown, M. D. (1975) Ovulation control in cattle with progesterone intravaginal device (PRID) and gonadotrophin releasing hormone (Gn RH). *Ann. Biol. Anim. Bioch. Biophys.* **15,** 291–296.

Mauleon, P. (1974) new trends in the control of reproduction in the bovine. *Livest. Prod. Sci.* **1,** 117–131.

Mauleon, P., Rey, J. and Mariana, J. C. (1969) Control of the oestrous cycle of the cow with vaginal sponges impregnated with fluoro-gettone acetate and possibility of producing limited superovulation. *Proc. 6th Int. Congr. Anim. Reprod. AI (Paris)* 1479–1482.

Mauleon, P., Chupin, D., Pelot, J. and Aguer, D. (1978) Modifying factors of fertility after different oestrous control treatments in beef cattle. In, *Control of Reprod. in the Cow.* pp. 531–545 (Galway, J. Sreenan., ed.) C.E.C., Luxembourg.

Mawhinney, S. and Roche, J. F. (1978) Factors involved in oestrous cycle control in the bovine. *Control of Reproduction in the Cow.* pp. 511–530. (Galway, J. Sreenan., ed.) C.E.C., Luxembourg.

Miller, S. J. (1979) *Proc. Aust. Vet. Assoc., Queensland Div.*

Moore, N. W. (1975) The control of time of oestrus and ovulation and the induction of superovulation in cattle. *Aust. J. Agric. Res.* **26,** 295–304.

Moseley, W. M., Forrest, D. W., Kaltenbach, C. C. and Dunn, T. G. (1979) Effect of Norfestamet on peripheral levels of progesterone and estradiol-17$_l$ in beef cows. *Theriogen.* **11,** 331–343.

Mulvihill, P. and Sreenan, H. M. (1978a) Field-scale evaluation of short-term progestagen synchronization treatments in beef cow herds. *Ir. J. Agric. Res.* **17,** 241–248.

Mulvehill, P. and Sreenan, J. M. (1978b). Oestrous cycle control and fertility in beef cattle following short-term progestagen treatments. *Control of Reproduction in the Cow.* pp. 486–510 (Galway, J. Sreenan., ed.) C.E.C., Luxembourg.

Nancarrow, C. D. and Radford, J. M. (1975) Use of oestradiol benzoate to improve synchronization of oestrus in cattle. *J. Reprod. Fert.* **43,** 404.

Nancarrow, C. D., Hearnshaw, H., Mattner, P. E., Connell, P. J. and Restall, B. J. (1974) Hormonal changes in cattle following the administration of prostaglandin F$_{2\alpha}$. *J. Reprod. Fert.* **36,** 484–485.

O'Farrell, K. J. (1977) A comparison of natural service and A.I. in seasonally calving dairy herds. *Ir. J. Agric. Res.* **16,** 251–257.

O'Farrell, K. J. (1980) Fertility management in the dairy herd. *Ir. Vet. J.* **34,** 160–169.

Phatak, A. P., Williams, J B., Young, C. W. and Sequin, B. E. (1979) Estrumate (ICI 80996) as a management tool in dairy cattle production. *J. Dairy Sci.* **62,** (Suppl. 1), 172 (abs.).

Rajamahendran, R., Laque, P. C. and Baker, R. D. (1981) Serum hormone levels and occurrence of oestrus following use of an intravaginal device containing progesterone and estradiol-17$_\beta$ in heifers. *Anim. Reprod. Sci.* **3,** 271–277.

Randel, R. D., Short, R. E., Christensen, D. S. and Bellows, R. A. (1973) Effects of various mating stimuli on the LH surge and ovulation time following synchronization of estrus in the bovine. *J. Anim. Sci.* **37,** 128–130.

Rey, J. (1969) Synchronization, oestrous response and fertility of heifers after a shortened period of inhibition of sexual activity by means of fluorogestone acetate. *Proc. 6th Congr. Anim. Reprod. A.I. (Paris)* **2,** 1515–1518.

Robinson, T. J. (1964) Synchronization of oestrus in sheep by intravaginal subcutaneous application of progestin in pregnated sponges. *Proc. Aust. Soc. Anim. Prod.* **5,** 47–52.

Robinson, T. J. (1969) The synchronization of the oestrous cycle and fertility. *Proc. 6th Int. Congr. Anim. Reprod. A.I. (Paris)* **2,** 1347–1383.

Robinson, T. J. (1975) The colloquium in perspective. *Ann. Biol. Anim. Bioch. Biophys.* **15,** 481–492.

Roche, J. F. (1974a) Effect of short-time progesterone treatment on oestrus response and fertility in heifers. *J. Reprod. Fert.* **40,** 433–440.

Roche, J. F. (1974b) Synchronization of oestrus and fertility following artificial insemination in heifers given prostaglandin F$_{2\alpha}$ *J. Reprod. Fert.* **37,** 135–138.

Roche, J. F. (1975) Synchronization of oestrus in cows using intravaginal silastic coils containing progesterone. *Ann. Biol Anim. Biol. Biophys.* **15,** 301–302.

Roche, J. F. (1976) Synchronization of oestrus in heifers and cows using a twelve-day treatment with progesterone coils with or without Gn RH. Proc. EEC Seminar Egg Transfer in Cattle (Camb) pp. 231–244.

Roche, J. F. (1977) Synchronization of oestrus with prostaglandins. *Vet. Sci. Comm.* **1,** 121.

Roche, J. F. (1978) Control of oestrus in cattle using progesterone coils. *Anim. Reprod. Sci.* **1,** 145–154.

Roche, J. F. (1979) Control of oestrus in cattle. *Wld. Rev. Anim. Prod.* **15,** 49–56.

Roche, J. F. and Crowley, J. P. (1973a) Suppressing heat periods could make beef heifer production more efficient. *Farm Food Res.* **4**(2), 44–54.

Roche, J. F. and Crowley, J. P. (1973b) the long-term suppression of heat in cattle with implants of melengestrol acetate. *Anim. Prod* **16**, 245–250.

Roche, J. F. and Gosling, J. P. (1977) Control of estrus and progesterone levels in heifers given intravaginal progesterone coils and injections of progesterone and estrogen. *J. Anim. Sci.* **44**, 1026–1029.

Roche, J. F. and Ireland, J. J. (1981) Effect of exogenous progesterone on time of occurrence of the LH surge in heifers. *J. Anim. Sci.* **52**, 580–586.

Roche, J. F. and Prendiville, D. J. (1979) Control of estrus in dairy cows with a synthetic analogue of prostaglandin $F_{2\alpha}$. *Theriogen.* **11**, 153–162.

Roche, J. F., Prendiville, D. J. and Davis, W. D. (1977) Calving rate following fixed time insemination after a 12-day progesterone treatment in dairy cows, beef cows and heifers. *Vet. Rec.* 417–419.

Rowson, L. E. A., Tervit, R. and Brand, A. (1972) The use of prostaglandins for synchronization of oestrus in cattle. *J. Reprod. Fert.* **29**, 145 (abs.).

Saumande, J. (1978) Relationship between ovarian stimulation by PMSG and steroid secretion. In, *Control of Reprod. in the Cow*, pp. 169–94 (Galway, J. Sreenan., ed.) E.E.C., Luxembourg.

Scanlon, P. F. (1969) Studies in reproduction in the cow. *Ph. D. Thesis, N.U.I. Dublin.*

Scanlon, P. F., Sreenan, J. and Gordon, I. (1972) Synchronization of oestrus in heifers by intravaginal application of progesterone. *Vet. Rec.* **90**, 440–441.

Scaramuzzi, R. J., Turnbull, K. E. and Nancarrow, C. D. (1980) Growth of Graafian follicles in cows following luteolysis induced by the prostaglandin $F_{2\alpha}$ analogue, Cloprostenol. *Aust. J. Biol. Sci.* **33**, 63–69.

Schams, D., Gombe, S., Schallenberger, E., Reinhardt, V. and Claus, R. (1978) Relationships between short-term variations of LH, FSH prolactin and testosterone in peripheral plasma of prepubertal bulls. *J. Reprod. Fert.* **54**, 145–148.

Shimizu, H., Toyoda, Y. Takeuchi, S., Kawai, T. and Adachi, S. (1967) Synchronization of oestrus and subsequent fertility of beef cattle following the intravaginal administration of gestagen. *J. Reprod Fert.* **13**, 555–558.

Short, R. E., Howland, B. E., Randel, R. D., Christensen, D. S. and Bellows, R. A. (1973) Induced LH release in spayed cows. *J. Anim. Sci.* **37**, 551–557.

Smith, J. F. (1974) Oestrous synchronization in cattle. *J. Reprod. Fert.* **36**, 482.

Smith, J. F. and Macmillan, K. L. (1978) An applied and economic aspect of oestrus synchronization in cattle. *N.Z. Vet. J.* **26**, 173–175.

Smith, J. F. and Tervit, H. R. (1980) The successful development of a PRID regime for oestrus synchronization in N.Z. beef cattle. *Proc. N.Z. Soc. Anim. Prod.* **40**, 272–279.

Smith, J. F., Fairclough, R. J. and Petersen, A. J. (1979) Plasma levels of progesterone, Provera oestradiol-17$_\beta$ and 13,14-dihydro-15-keto-prostaglandin F in cows treated with provera-impregnated intravaginal sponges. *J. Reprod. Fert.* **55**, 359-364.

Spitzer, J. G., Burrell, W. C., LeFever, D. G., Whitman, R. W. and Wiltbank, J. N. (1978) Synchronization of estrus in beef cattle. *Theriogen.* **10**, 181–200.

Sreenan, J. M. (1969) Studies related to ovum transfer in cattle. *Ph. D. Thesis, N.U.I. Dublin.*

Sreenan, J. M. (1974) Retention of intravaginal sponge pessaries by cattle. *Vet. Rec.* **94**, 45.

Sreenan, J. M. (1975) Effect of long and short-term intravaginal progestagen treatments on synchronization of oestrus and fertility in heifers. *J. Reprod. Fert.* **45**, 479–485.

Sreenan, J. M. (1977) Ovulation rate and calving rate following the use of PMSG or Gn-RH in post-partum beef cows. *Ir. Grass. Anim. Prod. Assoc. J.* **12**, 127 (abs.).

Sreenan, J. M. and Mulvihill, P. (1975) Synchronization of oestrus in cattle. 2. The effect of short-term (10-day) progestagen-oestrogen administration on oestrous response and fertility in cattle. *J. Reprod. Fert.* **45**, 367.

Sreenan, J. M., Mulvihill, P. and Gosling, J. P. (1977) The effect of progesterone and oestrogen treatment in heifers on oestroys cycle control and plasma progesterone levels. *Vet. Rec.* **101**, 13–14.

Stellflug, J. M., Louis, T. M., Sequin, B. E. and Hafs, H. D. (1973) Luteolysis after 30 or 60 mg. $PGF_{2\alpha}$ in heifers. *J. Anim. Sci.* **37**, 330.

Taylor, J. C. (1974) Bull-beef; Britain and New Zealand compared. *Span.* **17**(1), 8–11.

Tervit, H. R., Rowson, L. E. A. and Brand, A. (1973) Synchronization of oestrus in cattle using a prostaglandin$_{2\alpha}$ analogue (ICI 79939). *J. Reprod. Fert.* **34**, 179–181.

Thimonier, J., Chupin, D. and Pelot, J. (1975) Synchronization of oestrus in heifers and cyclic cows with progestagens and prostaglandin analogues alone or in combination. *Ann. Biol. Anim. Biochim. Biophys.* **15**, 437–449.

Utley, P. R., Neville, W. E., Jr. and McCormick, W. C. (1978) Monesin fortified corn supplements in combination with testosterone-estradiol implants and vaginal devices for finishing heifers on pasture. *J. Anim. Sci.* **47**, 239–245.

Walpole, A. L. (1975) Characteristics of prostaglandins. *Annls. Biol. Anim. Bioch. Biophys.* **15**, 419–425.

Waters, R. J. and Ball, R. (1978) Commercial ovulation control and fixed-time artificial insemination in cattle. *Vet. Rec.* **103**, 585–587.

Webel, S. K. (1976) Control of the estrous cycle in cattle with a progesterone releasing intravaginal device. *Proc. 8th Int. Congr. Anim. Reprod. A.I. (Krakow)* **3**, 521–523.

Wettemann, R. P. and Hafs, H. D. (1973) L H, prolactin, estradiol and progesterone in bovine blood serum during early pregnancy. *J. Anim. Sci.* **36**, 51–56.

Willemse, A. H. (1969) Relation between the day of the oestrual cycle at the time of the intravaginal application of a MAP impregnated sponge and synchronization rate and conception rate in Texel sheep. *Proc. 6th Int. Congr. Anim. Reprod. A.I. (Paris)* **2**, 1539–1541.

Wiltbank, J. N. and Gonzalez-Padilla, E. (1975). Synchronization and induction of estrus in heifers with a progestagen and estrogen. *Annls. Biol. Anim. Bioch. Biophys.* **15**, 255–262.

Wiltbank, J. N., Sturges, J. C., Wideman, D., Le Fever, D. G. and Faulkner, L. C. (1971) Control of estrus and ovulation using subcutaneous implants and estrogens in beef cattle. *J. Anim. Sci.* **33**, 600–606.

Wishart, D. F. (1974) Synchronization of oestrus in cattle using a potent progestin (SC 21009) and $PGF_{2\alpha}$. *Theriogen.* **1**, 87–91.

Wishart, D. F. (1976) Controlled breeding of progestin treated cattle. Egg Transfer in Cattle, Camb., EEC. Seminar, December, 1975, 129–136.

Wishart, D. F. and Young, I. M. (1974) Artificial insemination of progestin (SC 21009) — treated cattle at predetermined times. *Vet. Rec.* **95**, 503–508.

Wishart, D. F., Young, I. M. and Drew, S. B. (1977) A comparison between the pregnancy rates of heifers inseminated once or twice after progestin treatment. *Vet. Rec.* **101,** 230–231.

Zaid, A. A., Humphreys, W. D., Kaltenbach, C. C. and Dunn, T. G. (1976) Fertility of beef females following controlled estrous cycles and ovulation. *J. Anim. Sci.* **43,** 311–312.

Zimbelman, R. G., Lauderdale, J. W., Sokolówski, J. H. and Schald, T. G. (1970) Safety and pharmacologic evaluations of melengestrol acetate in cattle and other animals; a review. *J. Am. Vet. Med. Assoc.* **157,** 1528–1536.

ORDER FORM

To: **LANDSMAN'S BOOKSHOP LTD., Buckenhill,**

Bromyard, Herefordshire

Telephone: Bromyard (0885) 83420

Please send to: **Name** _____

Address _____

_____

Date _____   _____

The books listed below are wanted : new only, secondhand only, or secondhand if available otherwise new.

I enclose £ _____ / Please send an account.

Adjustments will be invoiced, refunded or credited as requested.

(Please delete the above as necessary).

	Postage	
	Total £	

NOTE: For those wishing to send cash with order, postage can be roughly assessed as 10p for every £1.00 worth of books — e.g. send 30p for a £3.00 book.

Postage will be charged at current P.O. rates. U.K. orders over £40 will be sent post free.

We regret that because of current economic conditions all prices quoted in the catalogue are subject to alteration without prior notice. Books will be sent at the prices ruling at the date of despatch.

THE SPECIALIST BOOKSHOP FOR FARMERS AND GARDENERS

ORDER FORM

To: **LANDSMAN'S BOOKSHOP LTD., Buckenhill,**

Bromyard, Herefordshire

Telephone: Bromyard (0885) 83420

Please send to: **Name** _____

Address _____

_____

Date _____ _____

The books listed below are wanted : new only, secondhand only, or secondhand if available otherwise new.

I enclose £ _____ / Please send an account.

Adjustments will be invoiced, refunded or credited as requested.

(Please delete the above as necessary).

	Postage	
	Total £	

NOTE: For those wishing to send cash with order, postage can be roughly assessed as 10p for every £1.00 worth of books — e.g. send 30p for a £3.00 book.

Postage will be charged at current P.O. rates. U.K. orders over £40 will be sent post free.

We regret that because of current economic conditions all prices quoted in the catalogue are subject to alteration without prior notice. Books will be sent at the prices ruling at the date of despatch.

ORDER FORM

The Landsman's Bookshop, started in 1946, offers you a unique service. Our job is to make available, by post and from our mobile show unit, every current publication dealing with farming, gardening, and allied subjects.

We would like to bring to your attention the following services:

✱ A 40p catalogue, produced annually, listing our full stock of books currently available worldwide.

✱ A supplement to the catalogue issued every two months with reviews of new books to keep the catalogue up-to-date. An annual subscription of £1.00 includes a new catalogue each year.

✱ The opportunity to part exchange or sell, secondhand books on the following terms:

	Part Exchange	Cash
Current editions bought from us	80% (of purchase price)	60% (of purchase price)
Current editions not bought from us	70% „ „ „	50% „ „ „

Quotations will be given for books other than current editions and we reserve the right to refuse copies of books where we are overstocked.

✱ Secondhand books although not listed, are available on most subjects covered by our catalogue.

✱ The replacement of books lost or damaged in transit. Fortunately this is quite rare.

✱ Book tokens are issued and accepted.

CHAPTER 4

Pregnancy Testing in Cattle

4.1 INTRODUCTION

The practical importance to the farmer of ensuring that his breeding animals become pregnant needs little emphasis, whether talking in terms of cattle or the other farm animal species. The growing costs of labour and feed in milk production and the fact that selection has produced dairy cattle capable of much higher yields than hitherto has increased the importance of maximum fertility and a calving interval (CI) close to 1 year has become the target of most efficient producers. Extra costs from delays in rebreeding arise from loss in milk production before the next lactation starts and from the price of feedstuffs during the period of low milk production. Failure to achieve a 12-month calving interval represents substantial economic loss of milk and progeny per cow or herd per year. The problem that the cattle producer has to face is that although a proportion of cows appear to become pregnant after breeding, the true percentage is not obvious to him as early as he would wish; Zemjanis (1970) estimated that there are 15–25% of cattle which may not show oestrus soon after breeding and yet not be pregnant. The availability of a simple on-the-farm early pregnancy test would have a considerable impact on the cattle scene, especially a test that can alert the farmer to the fact that the animal is not pregnant before the time arrives for attempting to re-breed her (at 3 weeks after first mating).

4.2 ENDOCRINOLOGY OF EARLY PREGNANCY

An essential feature of the establishment of pregnancy in the farm animal species, as well as in other mammals, is the prolongation of luteal function beyond the approximately 2-week duration that occurs in the non-pregnant animal, by way of mechanism which appears to involve suppression of the release of luteolytic quantities of prostaglandin $F_{2\alpha}$ into the blood vascular system. Bazer and Thatcher (1977) suggest that the basic mechanism for establishing the corpus luteum of pregnancy in the cow is probably one of re-directing PG secretion away from the blood vascular system (endocrine) to the uterine lumen (exocrine) rather than simply being a suppression of PG release. Thatcher et al. (1979) showed that this occurred in the cow about 15 days after ovulation, a time just prior to marked luteolytic release of PG in the non-pregnant animal. The fact that the bovine embryo undergoes extensive development just prior to the time when corpus luteum regression normally occurs, places a demand on the cow's reproductive tract to supply substantial amounts of nutrients; certainly the timing of expansion coincides with the observed changes in the secretory direction of PG.

Several reports have dealt with progesterone concentrations in cattle that have become pregnant, compared with their non-pregnant companions, in the weeks soon after breeding, and have shown the steroid to be at a higher level in pregnant animals (Henricks et al., 1970, 1971; Erb et al., 1976; Lukaszewska and Hansel, 1980; Thompson et al., 1980); the general conclusion drawn is that pregnancy may have a stimulating effect on progesterone levels. In cattle, unlike other farm animal species such as sheep, the corpus luteum is apparently the only major source of progesterone throughout the entire period of gestation (Stabenfeldt et al., 1970; Wagner et al., 1974). In the pregnant cow, progesterone values in peripheral plasma increase with the development of the corpus luteum up to concentrations of the order 5–10 ng/ml on days 15–20 after conception; these concentrations remain fairly constant thereafter until shortly before delivery (Pope et al., 1969; Stabenfeldt et al., 1970; Schams et al., 1972). Although not unique to the cow, but unlike other ruminants such as the ewe (Challis, 1971), there is a gradual increase in oestrogen production towards the end of pregnancy (Robinson et al., 1970; Robertson, 1974). While the dominating oestrogen in urine appears to be oestradiol–17β, the major oestrogen found in peripheral plasma is oestrone (Randel and Erb, 1971; Edqvist et al., 1973; Smith et al., 1973). In the cow, progesterone and oestrogen are so far the only two steroid hormones known which show a consistently elevated level either throughout the whole period of pregnancy (progesterone) or at least throughout a substantial part of it (oestrogen). The increased rate of progesterone secretion in the pregnant cow has been observed to occur from about day-10 after breeding (Lukaszewska and Hansel, 1980) and there is an increase in the blood flow through the gravid horn of the reproductive tract around day-15 (Ford et al., 1979).

4.3 RECTAL PALPATION

Rectal palpation has been used for pregnancy diagnosis in cows for many years and has remained one of the most simple and valuable methods. It is possible to apply the method from about 35 days after breeding, which should enable a careful watch to be kept for oestrous symptoms on those found to be non-pregnant around the 6 weeks (2 x 21 days) period. There is still some argument as to whether skilful rectal palpation contributes to embryonic mortality in some instances; those who have reported on the method recently conclude that only about 5% of conceptuses palpated fail to reach term (Mutiga et al., 1977; Vaillancourt et al., 1979) and that these foetal losses occur in the 35- to 70-day period. Apart from the cost factor, those with the necessary professional skill and experience may not always be available.

Fig. 4.1. Rectal palpation as a means of pregnancy diagnosis in cattle. As diagnosis of pregnancy per rectum in the cow depends, at least in the early weeks, on the position, size and consistency of the uterus, it is necessary to keep in mind the age of the cow when making an examination, as differences do exist between heifers which have not produced a calf and older cows. The first indication of pregnancy is the unequal size of the two horns of the uterus; the larger side will be softer to the touch than the firmer, smaller, non-pregnant horn of the uterus.

4.4 USE OF ULTRASONICS

Although ultrasonic techniques have become commonplace in the pig industry for the diagnosis of pregnancy and are used to a lesser extent in sheep, little information has appeared in the literature about the use of this approach in the cow. Two ultrasonic instruments, one a foetal principle and the other an amplitude-depth (A-principle and the other on amplitude-depth (A-mode sound) instrument enabling the operator to distinguish differences in tissue densities, were tested against rectal palpation by Bartlett and Sorensen (1980); the results suggested that the Doppler instrument was not accurate enough for practical use, but the other A-mode device (Scanoprobe) was found to have a greater than 90% accuracy after 55 days and appeared to be of value in detecting pregnancy at that time. Ultrasonics have also been employed for research purposes in monitoring foetal and maternal blood circulations (Mitchell, 1975).

4.5 PROGESTERONE ASSAY METHODS

The advent of the extremely sensitive RIA techniques in the past decade means that methods are now available by which the hormones of pregnancy can be detected, not only in blood plasma and tissue fluids, but also in milk. In dealing with early pregnancy diagnosis in the milking cow, this has opened up an extremely valuable new approach which has been rapidly put into commercial practice in several countries (U.K., U.S.A., Germany, France, Ireland and others).

An early pregnancy test based on the cyclical nature of progesterone production during the bovine oestrous cycle was suggested for cattle more than a decade ago (Shemesh et al., 1968); this was a test measuring the concentration of progesterone in peripheral blood plasma. It subsequently became evident that progesterone levels in cow's milk follow the same pattern as in plasma and that the new RIA procedures could be readily employed to measure progesterone in milk (Laing and Heap, 1971; Darling et al., 1972; Heap et al., 1973; Hoffman and Hamburger, 1973); it appeared that application of the progesterone assay technique in commercial practice was feasible, since there was no difficulty in obtaining and preserving the milk samples. In applying the method, one limitation is the fact that mid-luteal concentrations of the hormone

are similar to those in the pregnant cow. It therefore became important to determine the days most appropriate for sampling.

Shemesh et al. (1968) observed a marked difference between blood levels of progesterone in pregnant and non-pregnant cattle at 19 days after breeding. Most investigators are now agreed that 21–24 days after breeding is the most suitable time to carry out the test (Heap et al., 1973; Hoffman et al., 1976a,b; Pennington et al., 1976). In the commercial testing service provided by the Milk Marketing Board (MMB) in the U.K., a single sample of whole milk is collected on the 24th day after breeding rather than on the 21st day to give the farmer the chance to exclude from testing those cows which show heat before that date; results from the test are back with the producer by day-31, well in advance of the time when the next oestrus would be expected. The sample is collected at the evening milking and progesterone levels above 7.5 ng/ml are taken as indicative of pregnancy, 5.5 ng/ml and below are taken to indicate non-pregnancy (Booth, 1980); samples showing values between 5.5 and 7.5 ng/ml are followed by a free repeat test at 42 days.

Non-pregnancy in cattle can be routinely detected with almost 100% accuracy (Booth and Holdsworth, 1976; Heap et al., 1976; Pennington et al., 1976; Hoffman et al., 1976b; Shemesh et al., 1978; Foote, 1979; Holdsworth et al., 1979; Foote et al., 1980; O'Farrell, 1980). The high degree of accuracy associated with this diagnosis is regarded as the most valuable feature of the test; the herdsman can confidently take appropriate action towards cattle that have clearly not conceived and at a much earlier stage than was possible when only rectal pregnancy diagnosis at 35 days and beyond was possible.

The accuracy of the progesterone test is much lower when predicting pregnancy; a common finding among the pregnancy testing laboratories has been that about one animal in five classified as pregnant on day-24, fails to support a viable pregnancy (Heap, 1978; Foote et al., 1980). One of the reasons for this would appear to be the occurrence of early embryonic mortality.

Looking at the current pregnancy-testing scene in the U.K., where more than 100,000 milk samples are tested annually (5% or so of dairy farmers), a highly significant correlation (+0.99) has been reported between herd size and use of the test (Booth, 1980). In contrast to the situation among dairy herds, applications of the progesterone test for pregnancy diagnosis in beef suckler herds has received little attention, although there have been one or two reports (MacFarlane et al., 1977; Rahim et al., 1980).

4.5.1. Sampling procedures

It has been noted by Foote (1979) that milk represents a composite sample over a period of several hours and for that reason it may provide more uniform material than a plasma sample. At the same time, considerable differences have emerged in the milk sampling methods adopted by various workers; it may be a question of using whole milk or different fractions of milk as the starting point. About 80% of progesterone in whole milk is associated with the fat fraction (Heap et al., 1975 and this means that the type of milk sample (foremilk, strippings, fat-free milk) can have a considerable effect on the progesterone concentration that is measured.

Milk sampling procedures must be reasonably simple and accurate for a successful commercial milk progesterone service for pregnancy detection in dairy cattle. The first commercial service, launched in the U.K. in 1975, determined progesterone concentration in a whole milk sample collected at the afternoon milking; there is evidence that progesterone levels are significantly higher in the evening samples than in the morning ones (Darling et al., 1974; Thibier et al., 1976; Batra et al., 1980) although the reason for this is not clear. For routine testing, when it is simply a matter of distinguishing high progesterone levels from basal levels, it was felt in the U.K. to be an unnecessary expenditure of effort to separate the different fractions of milk before assay; according to Holdsworth et al. (1979), this decision has been fully justified in practice.

4.5.2 Fore-milk and Stripping samples

Pregnancy diagnosis based on milk progesterone has been carried out on stripping samples in Germany (Hoffman et al., 1976a, 1978) and on foremilk samples in France (Thibier et al.,

1976). Higher concentrations of progesterone can be expected in milk from strippings than from foremilk due to the close relationship between milk progesterone and milk fat (Pope et al., 1976). The results of a study on the effectiveness of three sampling procedures (fore-milk, composite or strippings) suggested that use of strippings was the preferred method due to the ease of sampling and to a reduced chance of making a faulty diagnosis (Shelford et al., 1979). In another study, Gowan and Etches (1979) pointed to the possible advantage of using a solid-phase RIA procedure in view of the fact that foremilk, whole milk and strippings could all be well accommodated in such an assay.

4.5.3 Milk fat and de-fatted milk

There are those who maintain that when it is desirable to study small change in progesterone levels, it is best to measure these in milk fat or defatted milk. In Germany, Hoffman et al. (1977) inproved the success rate of their pregnancy-testing service by estimating progesterone directly in milk fat; Claus and Rattenbergen (1979) described what is claimed to be a simpler and improved method based on milk fat. Elsewhere, Batra et al. (1980) found progesterone in milk fat to be 9–10 times higher than in whole milk, which they attributed to the greater solubility of the steroid in the lipid phase.

Several groups have concluded that fat-free milk is less prone to error than other fractions (Pope et al., 1976; McCaughey and Gordon, 1979; Oltner and Edqvist, 1981); with defatted milk, the fat content or the original milk sample is no longer important, thereby making a standard sampling procedure on the farm unnecessary.

4.5.4 Other considerations

Pregnancy-testing by measuring progesterone in milk, rather than in blood plasma or serum, can be applied without difficulty in dairy cattle but it is obviously a different story with beef suckler cows and maiden heifers. Rahim et al. (1980) note that variations in milk fat content associated with time of suckling in beef cows may be a limitation to the use of the milk test in suckler herds.

In some studies, workers have shown that accurate assessments of pregnancy status can be done on a herd basis, employing tests conducted on milk samples taken from cows at intervals of 8-days (Laing et al., 1980).

4.6 Progesterone and oestrus detection

In certain countries, West Germany would be an example, the milk progesterone testing services, as made available to farmers, veterinarians and Cattle AI Stations, aim at covering a wider field than just pregnancy diagnosis. In the event, early testing by rectal palpation is the traditional method employed and the milk assay has been employed in various fertility studies and oestrus detection (Hoffman et al., 1976b, 1978, Karg et al., 1980). One factor which may contribute towards a sub-optimal conception rate in cows bred by AI is the fact that the insemination was not carried out at a time coinciding with ovulatory oestrus; the incidence of this in some reports rose as high as 15–26% in certain herds (Gunzler et al., 1976; Karg et al., 1976; Braun, 1978) although Norwegian workers have noted a much lower value of 4% in their corresponding studies (Oltner and Edqvist, 1981). Although these reports are based on the assumption that the measurement of progesterone is an excellent way of identifying cattle inseminated during the active corpus luteum phase and which cannot possibly conceive, Holdsworth et al. (1980) suggest that some caution is required in interpreting milk progesterone levels in individual cows at the time of AI, in view of the evidence which has been accumulated in the U.K. on animals being successfully inseminated even though they had shown elevated levels of progesterone; these authors suggest that the udder may act as a reservoir of progesterone or that there may be some cross-reacting substance in the milk at the time of oestrus.

4.7 PROGESTERONE AND SUBFERTILITY

Undoubtedly, milk progesterone assays have potential use in the study of various forms of cattle subfertility, which can otherwise make life difficult for the dairy farmer. By way of collecting regular milk samples from each cow after parturition, a progesterone profile can be built up which will reveal any abnormalities in the normal pattern (Bulman and Lamming, 1976; Dobson and Fitzpatrick, 1976; Lamming and Bulman, 1976; Lamming, 1980); Bulman (1976) suggests that, coupled with computer analysis to warn the dairy farmer of problem cows, progesterone measurement could be a valuable aid. Although it can usually be assumed that progesterone in milk (or blood) during the post-partum period indicates that the cow has ovulated and is therefore cyclic (Thibier et al., 1976; Boyd and Munro, 1980), there have been instances of cows showing a transient, relatively minor, elevation in the progesterone concentration prior to the time of the first ovulation after calving (Donaldson et al., 1970; Tribble et al., 1973; Lamming and Bulman, 1976). As well as that, completely atypical post-partum progesterone profiles have been recorded by Watson and Munro (1981); it was not possible to define the source of progesterone, but it did not appear to be ovarian. Such instances could occasionally lead to difficulties in the employment of milk progesterone as a means of monitoring the reproductive status of cows. Nevertheless, it is clear that ovarian dysfunction can be diagnosed more accurately if the progesterone test can be employed alongside clinical examinations (Kalis and Wiel, 1980).

4.8 OESTROGEN AND POSITIVE PREGNANCY DIAGNOSIS

Progesterone in the cow's blood and milk is derived from the corpus luteum and not from the products of conception; for this reason, luteal secretion in the absence of a viable conceptus can lead, on occasions, to a false diagnosis of pregnancy. The corpus luteum can continue secreting for some time beyond the day at which embryo death occurs. The detection of substances produced by the conceptus would have a particular value for the early positive detection of pregnancy, especially if they could be found in milk. There is now evidence, in work conducted in France and the U.K., that oestrone sulphate concentrations in blood and milk may provide a useful laboratory test for the confirmation of pregnancy when used in conjunction with an early progesterone test. In the U.K., Heap and Hamon (1979) reported on the occurrence of oestrone sulphate in the milk of dairy cows; values rose from about 30 pg/mL$_1$ to 151 pg/mL$_1$ in whey between days 41 and 60 of gestation to reach maximum concentrations of about 1000 pg/mL$_1$ at 220–240 days. In later work (Hamon et al., 1981), results suggested that it was not until after day-100 of gestation that the test could be used to diagnose pregnancy positively. French studies (Terqui, 1979) measured total oestrogen concentrations throughout gestation in Friesian and Charolais cattle and showed that levels rose between 90 and 120 days, with a further increase occurring at about 250 days; much variation was found among animals, oestrogen levels differing at 220 days from 1 to 7.5 ng/mL$_1$, but there was a good correlation with the birthweights of calves. In the U.K., the MMB has now extended its commercial pregnancy testing service to include oestrone testing.

4.9 DETECTING TWIN PREGNANCIES

For a number of reasons, it would be highly desirable that farmers should be aware, by the seventh month of pregnancy, of cows carrying twins in any commercial exploitation of natural or induced twinning in cattle. Early diagnosis of twins (at 6–8 weeks) is possible by way of rectal palpation but even when expertly done may not be without hazard to the conceptus (Gordon et al., 1962). An attempt to palpate per rectum at a later stage is not without its difficulties because of the need to reach far beyond the pelvic brim.

Although the presence of cattle twins has been established with varying degrees of accuracy using foetal electro-cardiography by Japanese (Kanagawa et al., 1965), American (Lindahl et al., 1968) and French workers (Bosc and Chupin, 1975) such equipment is for research rather than for use in the farmyard. One potentially useful approach to twin detection was first reported on by Terqui et al. (1975) in France; these workers found differences in oestrogen concentrations,

from about day 220 of gestation, in single and twin-bearing cows (based on oestrone). Collaborative studies between Sreenan and McDonagh (1979) and the French workers produced similar evidence for Irish beef cows carrying singles and twins. In the U.S.A., on the other hand, Anderson et al. (1980) reported that their testing for concentrations of unconjugated oestrone in blood failed to reveal differences between single and twin-bearing Hereford cattle which were consistent enough or of sufficient magnitude to be of real value; oestrone levels did not rise until the 246–250th days of gestation and the observed concentrations of 129±8.8 and 150±8.7 pg/ml for single and twin pregnancies, respectively, were not significantly different. Elsewhere, Adelakoun et al. (1978) and Matton et al. (1979) in Canada reported studies in which they measured oestradiol-17β levels and found evidence of differences in cows with singles and twins.

It should be mentioned that twinning is not the only factor that can be expected to affect blood levels of oestrogen in the pregnant cow. It has

Fig. 4.2. Blood samples can establish whether a cow carries a single or twins. A cow pregnancy testing service has been operated by the Milk Marketing Board in the U.K. on a commercial scale since 1975. At present, well over half a million cows have been tested for pregnancy by measuring the levels of progesterone in milk. A further development has been to provide a service for checking out the level of oestrone sulphate as an indication of pregnancy — and this can be done from about 100 days of pregnancy onwards. Oestrogen levels in twin-bearing cows are generally higher than for cattle carrying singles. As part of a cattle twinning service operated from the University farm in Co. Dublin a blood sample is taken at the end of the seventh month of gestation and assayed for oestrogens.

already been mentioned above that the oestrogen level can be influenced by the weight of the calf foetus. Osinga and Hazeleger (1979) have reported evidence that the foetal genotype can affect the urinary excretion of oestrogens by the dam. In view of the fact that the foetal genotype can influence the incidence of dystocia-related stillbirths in heifers, the possible association between the amount of oestrogen produced by the placenta in late pregnancy and the incidence of stillbirths is an important practical consideration. According to Osinga and Hazeleger (1979), high urinary oestrogen levels in late pregnancy are usually associated with easy births, even in instances of high birth weights; the suggestion is that the oestrogen exerts a local preparative effect on the birth canal. If it were possible to predict those animals which might experience dystocia on the basis of their endocrine profile, this could certainly be a useful piece of information for the farmer.

4.9.1 Bovine placental lactogen and twins

There is now clear evidence from work in goats to show that the level of placental lactogen (PL) in that species is determined by litter-size; milk yield in the subsequent lactation can be markedly higher in goats producing twins and triplets than those producing single offspring (Hayden et al., 1979). The occurrence of placental lactogen in cattle (bPL) was reported some time ago by workers at Reading (Forsyth, 1973) and RIA studies indicate that the bPL concentration is markedly higher in twin-bearing cattle than in those with singles (Bolander et al., 1976); the possibility may, therefore, exist that bPL levels could serve as the basis of a test to diagnose twins. In view of the fact that both oestrogen and bPL are present in milk and presumably can be assayed in milk probably means that the test could be readily applied in dairy cattle.

4.10 FUTURE PREGNANCY TESTING DEVELOPMENTS

The relative ease of milk sampling, combined with the information which can be obtained from progesterone levels, ensures the future of progesterone assay technology. The milk test, as currently carried out in the commercial laboratories, employs radioisotopes and requires several days to return test results to the farmer because of the need to conduct the assay in a central laboratory having the necessary and expensive isotope counting equipment. The progesterone test would be much more useful to the dairy farmer if it could be modified so that it might be used on the farm by the herdsman (without the need for specialized equipment) and be fast enough to provide a result within a matter of hours rather than days.

The employment of non-isotopic labelling techniques would allow the possibility of such a simplified test for use on the farm. Enzyme-based immunoassays for plasma and milk progesterone have been described by several groups (Joyce et al., 1977; Estergreen, 1978; Arnstadt and Cleere, 1981). Enzyme-immunoassays employ an enzyme as a label, in place of a radioisotope, and require less expensive equipment in the processing laboratory; this could probably permit many small laboratories to provide a progesterone testing service.

As a possible means of providing an immediate answer to the herdsman taking a sample of milk, Estergreen (1978) describes a test employing enzyme-labelled progesterone which competes with progesterone in the milk sample for binding sites on an antiprogesterone antibody bonded to test paper; the antibody complex is then reacted with an enzyme substrate to cause colour development. Thus, according to this possibility, colour changes would immediately reveal the progesterone level of the milk; by conducting the test around day-19 or 20 it would often be possible to re-breed non-pregnant animals at the 3-week stage.

4.10.1 Detecting early pregnancy factors

At the present time, there is no test in cattle that detects pregnancy during the first two weeks after breeding; those means which are now generally available only permit the measurement of progesterone levels after day-18, checking for returns to oestrus at days 18 to 24 and diagnosis by rectal palpation after 5–6 weeks. However, there have been reports which suggest that the blood of the pregnant cow contains pregnancy-specific substances which could be the basis of an early test to distinguish the animal from one that failed to conceive (Laster, 1977; Noble et al., 1980). There is also the fact that Australian researchers have developed a test which can detect pregnancy in mice, sheep and humans as early as 6–24 h after a fertile mating (Morton et al., 1976, 1977, 1979). The appearance in the cow's blood of an early pregnancy factor (EPF) has been demonstrated by a procedure known as the rosette inhibition test (RIT). In this test, maternal lymphocytes are mixed with red blood cells from another species. The lymphocytes spontaneously form rosettes, a flower-like arrangement in which a lymphocyte has several red blood cells attached to it; lymphocytes from pregnant animals form fewer rosettes than those from non-pregnant animals. If lymphocytes from a non-pregnant animal are incubated in the blood serum of a pregnant female, the rosetting ability of these lymphocytes is decreased indicating that an immunosuppressive factor is present in the serum of the pregnant animal. The detection of EPF by the rosette inhibition test is at present a slow tedious procedure with the output of one technician being of the order of six tests per day (Shaw and Morton, 1980); for the future, however, it is envisaged by those working with cattle (Gimenez, 1981) that developments will occur to provide a rapid and cheap test which could be of great value to cattle farmers.

4.11 REFERENCES

Adelakoun, V., Matton, P. and Dufour, J. J. (1978) Steroid hormone levels in beef cows during pregnancy terminating in normal calving or abortion and with single or multiple ovulation *J. Anim. Sci.* **58**, 345–354.

Anderson, G. B., BonDurant, R. H., Cupps, P. T. and Stabenfeldt, G. H. (1980) Serum levels in beef cows and heifers during twin pregnancy. *J. Anim. Sci.* **51** (Suppl. 1), 254–255.

Arnstadt, K. I. and Cleere, W. F. (1981) Enzyme-immunoassay for determination of progesterone in milk from cows. *J. Reprod. Fert.* **62**, 173–180.

Bartlett, D. C. and Sorensen, A. M., Jr. (1980) Pregnancy detection in the bovine by ultrasonics. *J. Anim. Sci* **51** (Suppl. 1), 18 (Abs).

Batra, S. K., Pahwa, G. S., Suri, A. K. and Pandey, R. S. (1980) Diurnal variation of progesterone levels in milk and fat of crossbred cows during the oestrous cycle and early pregnancy. *Anim. Prod.* **31**, 127–131.

Bazer, F. W. and Thatcher, W. W. (1977) Theory of maternal recognition of pregnancy in swine based on estrogen controlled endocrine versus exocrine secretion of prostaglandin $F_{2\alpha}$ by the uterine endometrium. *Prostaglandins* **14**,(2), 397–401.

Bolander, F. F. Jr., Ulberg, L. C. and Fellows, R. E. (1976) Circulating placental lactogen levels in dairy and beef cattle. *Endocrin.* **99** 1273–1278.

Booth, J. M. (1980) Milk progesterone pregnancy testing in cattle and other species. *Proc. 9th Int. Congr. Anim. Reprod. A.I. (Madrid)*, **2**, 109–117.

Booth, J. M. and Holdsworth, R. J. (1976) The establishment and operation of a central laboratory for pregnancy testing in cows. *Br. Vet. J.* **132**, 518–528.

Bosc, M. J. and Chupin, D. (1975) Studies in the application of electrocardiography in the diagnosis of multiples in cattle. *Ann. Zootech.* **24**, 117–123.

Boyd, H. and Munro, C. D. (1980) Experiences and results of a herd-health programme rectal palpation and progesterone assays in fertility control. *Proc. 9th Int. Congr. Anim. Reprod. AI (Madrid)*, **2**, 373–380.

Braun, V. (1978) Progesterone concentration in the blood plasma of the cow in pregnancy. *Schweiz. Arch. Tierheilk.* **120**, 253–261.

Bulman, C. (1976) Progesterone in milk; A potential aid to dairy management. *Span.* **19**(3), 102–105.

Bulman, D. C. and Lamming, G. E. (1976) Diagnosis of subfertility in lactating cows by measuring milk progesterone levels. *Proc. 8th Int. Congr. Anim. Reprod. AI (Krakow)*, **4**(4) 564–567.

Challis, J. R. G. (1971) Sharp increase in free circulating oestrogens immediately before parturition in sheep. *Nature, Lond.* **229**, 208–209.

Clause, R. and Rattenbergen, E. (1979) Improved method for progesterone determination in milk fat. *Br. Vet. J.* **135**, 464–469.

Darling, J. A. B., Kelly, R. W., Laing, A. H. and Harkness, R. A. (1972) The isolation and identification of progesterone obtained from cow's milk during pregnancy. *J. Endocr.* **54**, 347–348.

Darling, J. A. B., Laing, A. H. and Harkness, R. A. (1974) A survey of the steroids in cow's milk. *J. Endocr.* **62**, 291–297.

Dobson, H. and Fitzpatrick, R. J. (1976) Clinical application of the progesterone-in-milk test. *Br. Vet. J.* **132**, 538–542.

Donaldson, L. E., Bassett, J. M. and Thorburn, G. D. (1970) Peripheral plasma progesterone concentration of cows during puberty, oestrous cycles, pregnancy and lactation, and the effects of undernutrition or exogenous oxytocin on progesterone concentration. *J. Endocrin.* **48**, 599–614.

Edqvist, L. E., Ekman, L. and Gustafsson, B. (1973) Peripheral plasma levels of oestrogens and progesterone during late bovine pregnancy. *Acta. Endocr. (Copenh.)* **72**, 81–88.

Erb., R. E., Malven, P. V., Monk, E. L. and Milet, T. A. (1976) Hormone induced lactation in the cow. IV. Relationships between lactational performance and hormone concentrations in blood plasma. *J. Dairy Sci.* **59**, 1420–1428.

Estergreen, V. L. (1978) A simplified test for milk progesterone and pregnancy testing. *Adv. Anim. Breed.* Sept. 10–13.

Foote, R. H. (1979) Hormones in milk that may reflect reproductive changes. *Anim. Reprod.* (BARC. Symp. No. 3

pp. 111–130 Harold Hawk, Ed.) Allanheld. Osmun. Montclair.

Foote, R. H., Smith, R. D., Oltenacu, E. A. B., Braun, R. K. and Reimers, T. J. (1980) Milk progesterone assays as part of a reproductive management program for dairy cattle. *Proc. 9th Int. Congr. Anim. Reprod. A.I. (Madrid)*, **2**, 135–141.

Ford, S. P., Chenault, J. R. and Enchternkamp, S. E. (1979) Uterine blood flow of cows during the oestrous cycle and early pregnancy: effect of the conceptis on the uterine blood supply. *J. Reprod. Fert.* **56**, 53–62.

Forsyth, I. A. (1973) Secretion of a prolactin-like hormone by the placenta in ruminants. In, *Le Crops jaune p. 239 (Denamur and Netler, Ed.) Masson, Paris.*

Gimenez, T. (1981) Very early pregnancy diagnosis in the cow. *Adv. Anim. Breed.* **29**(3), 6.

Gordon, I., Williams, G. and Edwards, J. (1962) The use of serum gonadotrophin (PMS) in the induction of twin pregnancy in the cow. *J. Agric. Sci. Camb.* **59**, 143–198.

Gowan, E. W. and Etches, R. J. (1979) A solid-phase radioimmunoassay for progesterone and its application to pregnancy in the cow. *Theriogen.* **12**, 327–343.

Gunzler, O., Korndorfer, L., Hamburger, R. and Hoffman, B. (1976) The importance of the milk progesterone test for fertility control and diagnosis of infertility in the bovine. *Proc. 8th Int. Congr. Anim. Prod. AI (Kracow)*, **4**, 582–585.

Hamon, M., Fleet, I. R., Holdsworth, R. J. and Heap, R. B. (1981) The time of detection of oestrone sulphate in milk and diagnosis of pregnancy in cows. *Brit. Vet. J.* **137**, 71–77.

Hayden, T. J., Thomas, C. R. and Forsyth, I. A. (1979) Effect of number of young born (litter-size) on milk yield of goats; role for placental lactogen. *J. Dairy Sci.* **62**, 53–57.

Heap, R. B. (1978) Studies on pregnancy. *Br. Cattle Breed. Club Dig.* **33**, 48–49.

Heap, R. B. and Hamon, M. (1979) Oestrone sulphate in milk as an indicator of a viable conceptus in cows. *Br. Vet. J.* **135**, 355–363.

Heap, R. B., Gwyn, M., Laing, J. A. and Walters, D. E. (1973) Pregnancy diagnosis in cows; changes in milk progesterone concentration during the oestrous cycle and pregnancy measured by a rapid radio immunoassay. *J. Agric. Sci. Camb.* **81**, 151–157.

Heap, R. B., Henville, A. and Linzell, J. L. (1975) Metabolic clearance rate, production rate and mammary uptake and metabolism of progesterone in cows. *J. Endoc.* **66**, 239–247.

Heap, R. B., Holdsworth, R. J., Gadsby, J. E., Laing, J. A. and Walters, D. E. (1976) Pregnancy diagnosis in the cow from milk progesterone concentration. *Br. Vet. J.* **132**, 445–464.

Henricks, D. M., Dickey, J. F. and Niswender, G. D. (1970) Serum luteinizing hormone and plasma progesterone levels during the estrous cycle and early pregnancy in cows. *Biol. Reprod.* **2**, 346–351.

Henricks, D. M., Dickey, J. F. and Hill, J. R. (1971) Plasma estrogen and progesterone levels in cows prior to and during estrus. *Endocr.* **89**, 1350–1355.

Hoffman, B. and Hamburger, R. (1973) Progesterone in milk; determination by means of radioimmunoassay, relationships with corpus luteum function and milk fat concentration. *Zuchthyg.* **8**(4), 154–162.

Hoffman, B., Hamburger, R., Gunzler, O., Karndurfer and Lohoff, H. (1976a) Determination of progesterone in milk applied for pregnancy diagnosis in the cow. *Theriogen.* **2**, 21.

Hoffman, B., Gunzler, O., Hamburger, R. and Schmidt, W. (1976b) Milk progesterone as a parameter for fertility control in cattle: methodological approaches and present state of application in Germany. *Br. Vet. J.* **132**, 489–496.

Hoffman, Von. B., Hamburger, R. and Hollwich, W. (1977) Determination of progesterone directly in milk-fat as an improved method for fertility control in cattle. *Zuchthyg.* **12**, 1–7.

Hoffman, B., Tattenberger, E. and Gunzler, O. (1978) Fertility control in cattle by determining progesterone in milk and milk-fat. In, *Control of Reprod. in the Cow*, pp. 562–575 Galway, C. E. C., Luxembourg.

Holdsworth, R. J., Chaplin, V. M. and Booth, J. M. (1979) Radioimmunoassay of progesterone in milk; development of techniques for large-scale use as a test of pregnancy. *Br. Vet. J.* **135**, 470–477.

Holdsworth, R. J., Booth, J. M., Sharman, G. A. M. and Rattray, E. A. S. (1980) Measurement of progesterone levels in whole and fore-milk from dairy cows. *Br. Vet. J.* **136**, 546–554.

Joyce, B. G., Read, G. F. and Fahmy, D. R. (1977) A specific enzyme-immunoassay for progesterone in plasma. *Steroids* **29**, 761–770.

Kalis, D. G. J. and Wiel, van de, D. F. M. (1980) Relationship of clinical examination to milk progesterone profiles. *Proc. 9th Int. Congr. Anim. Reprod. A.I. (Madrid)*, **2**, 119–124.

Kanagawa, H., Too, K., Kawata, K. and Ono, H. (1965) Fetal electro-cardiogram in dairy cattle. II. Diagnosis for twin pregnancy. *Jap. J. Vet. Res.*, **13**, 111-123.

Karg, V. H., Hartl, M., Hoffman, B. and Schmidt, W. (1976) Oestrus synchronization in cattle using a prostaglandin analogue and applying hormone analytical and clinical control procedures. *Zuchthyg.* **11**, 7–18.

Karg, H., Claus, R., Gunzler, O., Rattenberger, E., Hahn, R., and Hocke, P. (1980) Milk progesterone pregnancy testing in cattle and other species. *Proc. 9th Int. Congr. Anim. Reprod. A.I. (Madrid)*, **2**, 119–124.

Lamming, G. E. (1980) Milk progesterone for assessing response to treatment of sub-fertile cattle. *Proc. 9th Int. Congr. Anim. Reprod. A.I. (Madrid)*, **2**, 142–152.

Lamming, G. E. and Bulman, D. C. (1976) The use of milk progesterone radioimmunoassay in the diagnosis of treatment of sub-fertility in dairy cows. *Br. Vet. J.* **132**, 507–517.

Laing, J. A. and Heap, R. B. (1971) The concentration of progesterone in the milk of cows during the reproductive cycle. *Br. Vet. J.* **127**(8), 19–22.

Laing, J. A., Gibbs, H. A. and Eastman, S. A. K. (1980) A herd test for pregnancy in cattle based on progesterone levels in milk. *Br. Vet. J.* **136**, 413–415.

Laster, D. B. (1977) A pregnancy-specific protein in the bovine uterus. *Biol. Reprod.* **16**, 682–690.

Lindahl, J. L., Reynolds, P. J. and Allman, K. E. (1968) Fetal electro-cardiograms in dairy cattle. *J. Anim. Sci.* **27**, 1412–1417.

Lukaszewska, Janina and Hansel, W. (1980) Corpus luteum maintenance during early pregnancy in the cow. *J. Reprod. Fert.* **59**, 485–493.

McCaughey, W. J. and Gordon, F. J. (1979) Milk progesterone assay: A comparison on inter-quarter and sampling time variation. *Br. Vet. J.* **135**, 512–518.

MacFarlane, J. S., Booth, J. M., Deas, D. W. and Lowman, B. G. (1977) Pregnancy test and evaluation of embryonic and fetal mortality based on progesterone concentrations in foremilk. *Vet. Rec.* **100**, 565–566.

Matton, P., Adelakoun, V. and Dufour, J. J. (1979) Concentrations of progesterone, oestrogens and cortisol in the blood plasma of cows at parturition and their relationship to retained placentas. *Can. J. Anim. Sci.* **59**, 481–490.

Mitchell, D. (1975) Detection of foetal circulation in the mare and cow by Doppler ultrasound. *Vet. Rec.* **93**, 365–368.

Morton, H., Hegh, V. and Clunie, G. J. A. (1976) Studies of the rosette inhibition test in pregnant mice; evidence of immunosuppression?. *Proc. R. Soc. B.* **193**, 413–419.

Morton, H., Rolfe, B. Clunie, G. J. A., Anderson, M. J. and Morrison, J. (1977) An early pregnancy test factor detected in human serum by the rosette inhibition test. *Lancet* **i** 394–397.

Morton, H., Nancarrow, C. D., Scaramuzzi, E. J., Evison, B. M. and Clunie, G. J. A. (1979) Detection of early pregnancy in sheep by the rosette inhibition test. *J. Reprod. Fert.* **56**, 75–80.

Mutiga, E. R., Ogaa, J. S. and Agumba, G. J. O. (1977) Early manual pregnancy diagnosis in dairy cattle in Kenya. *E. Afr. Agric. For. J.* **42**(4), 431–434.

Noble, R. C., Kesler, D. J. and Bahr, J. (1980) An immunological test for pregnancy in the cow. *J. Anim. Sci.* **51** (Suppl. 1). 310 (abs.).

O'Farrell, K. J. (1980) Fertility management in the dairy herd. *Ir. Vet. J.* **34**(12), 160–169.

Oltner, R. and Edquist, L. E. (1981) Progesterone in defatted milk; Its relation to insemination and pregnancy in normal cows as compared with cows on problem farms and individual problem animals. *Br. Vet. J.* **137**, 78–87.

Osinga, A. and Hazeleger, W. (1979) The influence of the Sire on the oestrogen production of the bovine foetus-placental unit. In, *Calving Problems and Early viability of the Calf*, pp. 282–292 E.E.C. Seminar, Luxembourg.

Pennington, J. A., Spahr, S. L. and Lodge, J. R. (1976) Pregnancy diagnosis in dairy cattle by progesterone concentration in milk. *J. Dairy Sci.* **59**, 1528.

Pope, G. S., Gupta, S. K. and Munro, I. B. (1969) Progesterone levels in the systemic plasma of pregnant, cycling and ovariectomized cows. *J. Reprod. Fert.* **20**, 369–381.

Pope, G. S., Majzlik, I., Ball, P. J. H. and Leaver, J. D. (1976) Use progesterone concentrations in plasma and milk in the diagnosis of pregnancy in domestic cattle. *Br. Vet. J.* **132**, 497–506.

Rahim, Abdel, S. F. A., Lowman, B. G. and Deas, D. W. (1980) Clinical application of milk progesterone in the diagnosis of sub-fertility in suckled cows. *Vet. Rec.* **106**, 28–30.

Randel, R. D. and Erb, R. E. (1971) Reproductive steroids in the bovine VI. Changes and interrelationships from 0 to 260 days of pregnancy. *J. Anim. Sci.* **33**, 115.

Robertson, H. A. (1974) Changes in the concentrations of unconjugated oestrone oestradiol-17 and oestradiol-17$_\alpha$ in the maternal plasma of the pregnant cow in relation to to the initiation of parturition and lactation. *J. Reprod. Fert.* **36**, 1–7.

Robinson, R., Baker, R. D., Anastassiadis, P. A. and Common, R. H. (1970) Estrone concentrations in the peripheral blood of pregnant cows. *J. Dairy Sci.* **53**, 1592–1595.

Schams, D., Hoffmann, B. Fischer, S., Marz, E. and Karg, H. (1972) Simultaneous determination of LH and progesterone in peripheral bovine blood during pregnancy, normal

and corticoid-induced parturition and the *post-partum* period. *J. Reprod. Fert.* **29**, 37–48

Shaw, F. D. and Morton, H. (1980) The immunological approach to pregnancy diagnosis. A review. *Vet. Rec.* **106**, 268–269.

Shelford, J. A., Grisenthwaite, T., Barrington, S, Peterson, R. G. and Fisher, L. J. (1979) Milk sampling methods for a progesterone assay for early pregnancy diagnosis. *Can. J. Anim. Sci.* **59**, 77–82.

Shemesh, M., Ayalon, N. and Lindner, H. R. (1968) Early effects of conceptus on plasma progesterone level in the cow. *J. Reprod. Fert.* **15**, 161–164.

Shemesh, M., Ayalon, N., Shalev, E., Herya, A., Schindler, H. and Milguir, F. (1978) Milk progesterone measurement in dairy cows: concentration with estrus and pregnancy determination. *Theriogen.* **9**(4), 343–352.

Smith, V. G., Edgerton, L. A., Hafs, H. D. and Convey, E. M. (1973) Bovine serum, oestrogens, progestins and gluco-corticoids during late pregnancy. *J. Anim. Sci.* **36**, 391.

Sreenan, J. M. and McDonagh, T. (1979) Embryo transfer in cattle is now a practical proposition. *Farm and Food Res.* **10**(2), 53–55.

Stabenfeldt, G. H., Osburn, B. I. and Ewing, L. L. (1970) Peripheral plasma progesterone levels in the cow during pregnancy and parturition. *Am. J. Physiol.* **218**, 571–575.

Terqui, M. (1979) Personal communication.

Terqui, M., Celouis, C., Thimonier, J. and Ortavant, R. (1975) Oestrogens during pregnancy in Charolais cattle. *C.R. Hebd. Seanc. Acad. Sci. Paris* **280**, 2789–2792.

Thatcher, W. W., Wilcox, C. J., Bazer, F. W., Collier, R. J., Eley, R. M., Stover, D. G. and Bartol, F. F. (1979) Bovine conceptus effects prepartum and potential carryover effects *post-partum* In, *Anim. Reprod. BARC Symp. No. 3.* pp. 259–275, Allanheld, Osmon, Montclair.

Thibier, M., Fourbet, J. F. and Parez, M. (1976) Relationship between milk progesterone concentration and milk yield, fat and total nitrogen. *Br. Vet. J.* **132**, 477–486.

Thompson, F. N., Clekis, T., Kiser, T. E., Chen, H. J. and Smith, C. K. (1980) serum progesterone concentrations in pregnant and non-pregnant heifers and after gonadotrophin releasing hormone in luteal phase heifers. *Theriogen.* **13**, 407–417.

Tribble, R. L., Sorenson, A. M., Woodward, T. L., Connor, J. S., Beverley, J. R. and Fleeger, J. L. (1973) Serum progestins and LH levels in non-suckled primiparous heifers. *Nature* **246**, 494–495.

Vaillancourt, D., Bierschwal, C. J., Ogwu, D., Elmore, R. G., Martin, C. E., Sharp, A. J. and Youngquist, R. S. (1979). Correlation between pregnancy diagnosis by membrane slip and embryonic mortality. *J. Am. Vet. Med. Assoc.* **175**, 466–468.

Wagner, W. C., Thompson, F. M., Evans, L. E. and Molokwu, E. C. I. (1974) Hormonal mechanism controlling parturition. *J. Anim. Sci.* **39**, (Suppl. 1), 39–54.

Watson, E. D. and Munro, G. D. (1981) A typical milk progesterone profiles in two post-partum dairy cows. *Br. Vet. J.* **137**, 188–191.

Zemjanis, R. (1970) *Diagnostic and Therapeutic Techniques in Animal Reproduction.* Williams & Wilkins, Baltimore.

CHAPTER 5

Control of Calving

5.1 INTRODUCTION

Calving is a major event in the life of the breeding cow and any attempt to control or manipulate the process artificially should only be undertaken after careful consideration of the possible consequences, both short- and long-term. From the farmer's point of view, the greatest interest in techniques for the induction of calving has been in using them as an additional management tool in preventing what would otherwise be late calvings; this enables the cow's breeding pattern to be brought back in line with that of the main herd for the subsequent breeding and calving season (Welch et al., 1973). In this instance, synchronizing the grazing season and the onset of milk production is the main practical consideration. The other way in which controlled calving could have merit in the farmer's eyes is in helping to ensure the viability of the calf, either because of the particular value of the newborn pedigree animal, or as a means of minimizing the general level of perinatal mortality. Indeed, in most countries outside New Zealand, the induced calving technique is seen as a means of avoiding dystocia by shortening the duration of pregnancy and reducing the size and weight of the calf (Christiansen and Hansen, 1974; Gravert and Kordts, 1979; Plenderleigh, 1979). One problem in attempting to apply the induction treatment in this area is in deciding the correct pregnancy stage, for accurate conception dates may not always be known and gestation periods can be variable.

5.2 FACTORS AFFECTING DURATION OF PREGNANCY

The normal duration of gestation in the cow is 9 months; the existence of statistically significant differences between breeds of cattle in the length of gestation is well documented in the literature (Lush, 1945; Brakel et al., 1952; Anderson and Plum, 1965; Preston and Willis, 1974). Attempts have also been made to group gestation periods into those that may be considered normal and those regarded as abnormal. MacMillan and Curnow (1976) designated cows showing gestation periods of less than 251 days as possible abortions, 251 to 271 days as possible premature births, 272 to 293 as normal gestation periods and 294 to 314 as possible prolonged gestations. These authors note that among the factors which may appear at first sight to affect the average gestation period is method of breeding (AI or natural service); the average gestation period in dairy cows bred to Friesian or Jersey bulls was 281.2 ± 4.5 for animals bred by AI and 282.0 ± 4.6 for naturally bred cattle (Macmillan and Curnow, 1976). This presumably arises because inseminated cows lose a day as a result of being bred at the end of heat or later by AI, rather than around the start of heat if the bull is running with them.

Although many reports on gestation length refer to cows bred to bulls of the same breed, it is well recognized that a bull can confer a characteristic gestation length on the cattle to which he is mated; studies in the U.K. show that Friesian and Ayrshire cows in-calf to a Hereford or Beef Shorthorn bull can be expected to show an average gestation period of 283 days, whereas this will be 3–4 days shorter if they are bred to their own Friesian/Ayrshire bulls and 3–6 days longer if they are pregnant to males of the Charolais or Simmental breed (Laird and Hunter, 1977). There is probably a case, in efforts to reduce problems of dystocia, to follow the suggestion of Laird and Hunter (1977); this is for Cattle AI Stations to survey and publish information on the mean gestation intervals associated with their bulls, thereby allowing farmers to modify, where necessary, the *pre-partum* feeding of their cattle. There is ample evidence that the bull can be a significant influence on both gestation length and the birthweight of the calf (Everett and Magee, 1965; Gianola and Tyler, 1974); even within the one breed a 12-day range in the gestation lengths between Holstein sires has been shown (Fisher and Williams, 1978).

There have been those who have considered the possibility of reducing the gestation period through selective breeding; De Fries *et al.* (1959), dealing with data representing the five major dairy cattle breeds in the U.S.A. at that time, calculated that mean gestation length could be decreased by 10 days in three generations if 5% of males and 50% of the female calves resulting from the shorter generations were retained as breeding stock.

The most striking differences in the gestation period of cattle are found when European (*Bos taurus*) and Zebu (*Bos indicus*) species are compared. In the zebu Afrikaner breed, gestation length can be more than 296 days (Skinner and Joubert, 1963) which is 3–25 days longer than the periods usually held to be normal in European breeds such as the Friesian or Jersey (MacMillan and Curnow, 1976). As well as breed of sire and dam, factors such as sex of the foetus

can also play a minor role in influencing gestation, the bull calf being carried a day or so longer than the heifer.

5.3 CALF MORTALITY

Calf mortality is a worldwide problem and methods of minimizing it, particularly where the calf is normally reared for beef or breeding, justify a great deal of thought and attention. Looking at the situation in Ireland, mortality has been estimated at 13%, this figure covering 1.5–2% abortions, 3–5% perinatal deaths and 6–8% deaths between birth and the age of 3 months (Anon., 1977). In an Irish study reported by Greene (1978), it was shown that about 5% of calves were stillborn, most cases of these deaths being the result of anoxia; in fact, the large incidence of anoxic calves born outside normal working hours in the study suggested that insufficient supervision and attention at calving time was probably a major factor involved in the problem. There was support for this view, when improvements in management introduced by Greene (1978) reduced perinatal deaths to little

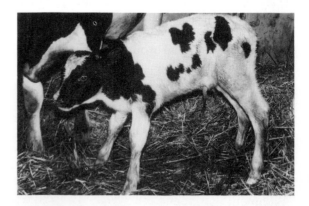

Fig. 5.1. Calf mortality as it occurs in Irish herds. In Ireland, it is estimated that about 12% of calves die each year, with more than half of these dying at time of birth. Studies in Ireland have shown that many instances of stillbirths are due to anoxia occurring immediately before, during or immediately after calving. It is also true that most stillbirths have followed a difficult or inadequate supervized calving, particularly if the dam is a heifer delivering a foetus which is too large for the birth canal. Certainly, there is plenty of evidence to show that adequate supervision at calving can have a marked impact on reducing calf mortality.

more than 1%. There are those who have tried to reduce calf mortality at calving by predicting instances in which special care is required. Attempts to predict the ease of calving by determining various maternal and foetal body measurements have been made by Rice and Wiltbank (1972) in the U.S.A. and Hindson (1978) and Clarke-Williams et al. (1979) in the U.K. It is well accepted that perinatal calf mortality is much more of a problem in first-calving heifers than in the parous cow.

5.4 ENDOCRINOLOGY OF LATE PREGNANCY AND PARTURITION

Despite the many reports published in recent years about the endocrine control of parturition in the cow, the precise mechanisms involved are still not fully understood; a firm experimental basis does exist, however, for the concept that maturation of the foetal pituitary–adrenal system is responsible for the initiation of parturition in the sheep.

During late pregnancy in the cow RIA studies reported by Edqvist et al. (1978) showed that peripheral blood concentrations of progesterone gradually and continuously decrease during the last 60 days whereas oestrogen levels increase significantly over the same time interval; it was found that $PGF_{2\alpha}$ levels increased 24–48 h before calving and remained elevated after the event before eventually returning to basal levels 10–20 days after delivery. Prolactin level is much increased the day before calving. The corpus luteum usually stops secreting progesterone about 30–40 h before parturition; this cessation of function may be due to a luteolytic mechanism which is activated by a synergistic action of foetal glucocorticoids and oestrogens at the site of attachment of foetal and maternal tissues (Fairclough et al., 1975; Hoffman and Schams, 1975; Hoffman et al., 1976, 1977; First, 1979); it may be, as suggested by Hoffman et al. (1979), that placental oestrogen synthesis and luteal progesterone production are two independent systems in the cow, and that an increased conversion of progesterone into oestrogens does not operate as it does in the ewe (Anderson et al.,

1975). There is a 10-fold or greater increase in the level of foetal glucocorticoids in the cow in the final week or so of gestation (Fairclough et al., 1975; First, 1979), which is similar to what occurs in the ewe (Liggins, 1973).

5.5 CORTICO-STEROID TREATMENT

A considerable volume of literature is now available on the response of cattle to corticosteroids since the initial reports (Adams, 1969; Adams and Wagner, 1970; Jochle, 1971) and the use of the technique to induce premature calvings is now an established feature of New Zealand dairy farming, with several hundred thousand cows treated annually (Welch et al., 1979); in New Zealand, the number of induced calvings in dairy cattle increased from a figure of 2000 in 1970 to 120 000 in 1972 and 400 000 by 1978.

The evidence shows that parturition can be induced reliably in the cow by a single glucocorticoid treatment of the animal after about day 255 and less reliably as early as day 235; the potent synthetic glucocorticoids employed include dexamethasone, betamethasone and flumethasone. It is believed that the synthetic glucocorticoid crosses the maternal component of the placenta, leading to a decline in progesterone production in the foetal component of the placenta and an acceleration in the synthesis of oestrogen. The effectiveness of the treatment is dependent on the permeability of the ruminant placenta to the glucocorticoid. In sheep, it appears that the placenta remains relatively impermeable to the agent until about 1 week before full-term; in the cow, on the other hand, the glucocorticoid can be active over a period of about a month before the due calving date. The fact remains, however, that the precise way in which the glucocorticoid causes luteolysis and parturition remains unknown. It is also true to say that the mechanism responsible for the control of corpus luteum function in the pregnant cow is poorly understood; the corpus luteum may be maintained by a maternal gonadotrophin or a placental gonadotrophin.

5.5.1 Short and long-acting glucocorticoids

Two main glucocorticoid formulations are available for use in induction, each preparation having its own particular advantages and disadvantages. The synthetic steroid can be administered in a quick-acting form as a free alcohol or soluble ester; it can also be given in a much slower-acting form prepared by esterification of the side-chain alcohol or other means (MacDiarmid, 1979). In response to the quick-acting form, parturition is initiated about 2 days later; with the slow-acting formulation, calving may not occur until 2 weeks after administration. Retention of the foetal membranes has been a consistent feature in cattle receiving the quick-acting preparation, but the calf is generally viable. Early New Zealand work was usually on the basis of a single injection of a long-acting formulation and one major problem that emerged was a perinatal calf mortality rate of 10–40% (Welch et al., 1973).

Subsequent studies by Welch et al. (1977), using the same long-acting agent as well as other treatments, showed a much lower rate of calf mortality (9–16%) which the authors ascribed mainly to a greater awareness on the part of dairy farmers at calving-time and to a lesser degree of prematurity among the calves (about 2 weeks rather than 3 weeks). These same studies also showed that the use of a short-acting formulation as a second injection resulted in an improvement in the pattern of induced calving as compared to the standard, single depot treatment.

5.5.2 Glucocorticoid and prostaglandin

Further studies in New Zealand by Welch et al. (1979) examined the relative merits of two dexamethasone depot preparations and the effects of either a short-acting corticosteroid or a prostaglandin analogue (Cloprostenol) given as a second injection 7–12 days later; the effectiveness of this second injection was found to depend on the stage of gestation. For cows several weeks away from calving, the depot injection was followed, 12 days later, by administering the short-acting glucocorticoid preparation; for cows close to calving, the timing of the two injections was varied according to the effect required. Employing a 7-day interval, cows would

calve within 2–3 days of the second injection; if the injection was left until 12 days, many cows had already calved by that time and only the remainder required treatment.

5.5.3 New Zealand efforts

The use of the long-acting formulation, with or without treatments, has generally been associated with New Zealand efforts to induce calvings as part of dairy herd management in that country. However, it would seem that despite the extensive use of the technique and the reassuring results which have been published in relation to reproduction and milk production by Welch and colleagues (Welch, 1977; Welch and Kaltenbach, 1977; Welch et al., 1977, 1979), the technique remains associated in the minds of some farmers with a list of disadvantages including high calf mortality, additional problems in rearing bobby calves, high cow mortality or illness, plus infertility and reduced milk production. In actual fact, the severity of these problems is thought to be much exaggerated and the induction technique may be especially useful in reducing the proportion of cows remaining non-pregnant at the end of the New Zealand cattle breeding season by extending that season by several weeks and inducing calving in all late-bred cows (Welch, 1977).

5.5.4 Short-acting glucocorticoids and retained membranes

Attempts to reduce the incidence of retained foetal membrane after a single dose of the short-acting formulation have taken the form both of using exogenous progesterone (Jochle et al., 1972) and oestradiol-17β (La Voie and Moody, 1973; Garverick et al., 1974; Schmitt et al., 1975; Grunert et al., 1975; Beardsley et al., 1976); progesterone treatment appears to have no merit, but oestrogen did apparently result in some ameliorative effect. Although research reports do show that the concentration of circulating oestrogen does increase in cows that are induced to calve early after glucocorticoid treatment (Chew et al., 1978), it is not clear whether levels are the same as in untreated cows at time of calving. It may be that synchronization of placental maturation and parturition requires a longer period of elevated oestrogen levels before calving than occurs in some animals that are induced.

There is general agreement among reports that the incidence of problems, such as retained foetal membranes, tends to decrease as the interval between glucocorticoid treatment and the due calving date becomes shorter. It is also clear, however, that cattle differ from sheep and goats in their response to the corticosteroids; in both these latter species, the foetal membranes are discharged in the normal way at parturition. It remains for further research to show the full extent of the hormonal interactions involved in corticosteroid induced parturition in the cow, so that increasingly effective control of this event can be achieved without adverse side-effects.

5.6 PROSTAGLANDINS AND INDUCED CALVINGS

In the cow, progesterone is produced by the corpus luteum during pregnancy and removal of the body before day 200 of gestation or after day 260 will usually result in abortion (Estergreen et al., 1967; Hoffman et al., 1977). However, during the seventh or eighth month of gestation, enucleation of the corpus luteum may not be followed immediately by abortion and it seems possible that an extra-ovarian source of progesterone exists at that time. As already mentioned, prostaglandin $F_{2\alpha}$ levels have been studied around the time of parturition and it is known that PG secretion occurs around the time that progesterone concentration falls (Edqvist et al., 1975; Fairclough et al., 1975).

There are some number of reports in which natural $PGF_{2\alpha}$ or one of its analogues have been used for the induction of calving. Zerobin et al. (1973) administered $PGF_{2\alpha}$ intravenously or by intrauterine injection (5–50 mg) and recorded calvings 2–3 days later; Kordts and Jochle (1975) made a similar finding, using 20 mg $PGF_{2\alpha}$ administered intravenously. In the U.K. and elsewhere, studies have shown that PG analogues can induce calving satisfactorily when given reasonably close to the expected calving date (Spears et al., 1974; Bosc et al., 1975; Henricks et

al., 1977a; Johnson and Jackson, 1980). In New Zealand, Day (1979) has provided evidence that acceptable results can be obtained in cows within 2 weeks of term using the normal luteolytic dose of Cloprostenol (500 μg); the same author indicated that for dealing with less advanced pregnancies, the regimen should include a priming dose of depot corticosteroid prior to the Cloprostenol. It is not clear from New Zealand reports whether the natural $PGF_{2\alpha}$ agent is to be regarded as effective as Cloprostenol (Day, 1979; Langford, 1979); there does appear to be a question of side-effects with the $PGF_{2\alpha}$ agent which do not occur with the analogue.

5.7 TECHNIQUES FOR TERMINATING PREGNANCY

There are several practical situations in which it may be desirable to terminate an established pregnancy in the cow. Pregnancy in beef heifers entering feedlots in North America is one such example; this can result in economic loss by interfering with the growth of the heifer, whose carcass is also down-graded at slaughter. It may occasionally be a matter of misalliance in the breeding of a valuable cow.

It is generally accepted that the bovine corpus luteum maintains pregnancy until about day-200 (McDonald et al., 1953). When it comes to using prostaglandins to induce regression of the corpus luteum and thus precipitate abortion, it is now recognised that the efficacy of the agent decreases as the stage of pregnancy approaches 150 days; up to that time, PG-induced terminations are rapid and uncomplicated and the foetal membranes are delivered along with the foetus (Lamond et al., 1973; Millar, 1974; Jackson and Cooper, 1976; Day, 1977; Copeland et al., 1978). Beyond the 150 day stage, the efficacy of PG in terminating pregnancy can decrease rapidly (Sequin, 1980); Day (1977) describes experiences in the 151–251 day period with Cloprostenol, with only 2/51 cows and 12/26 heifers responding to the agent. There are reports, however, of combined PG and glucocorticoid (e.g. 500 μg Cloprostenol and 25 mg dexamethasone) being successful as a termination treatment at all stages of pregnancy (Johnston et al., 1981). It may be a matter, as reported for cattle in the 200–250 day period by Murray et al. (1981), of using glucocorticoid with PG analogue given 11 days later.

Returning to the earlier months of an unwanted pregnancy, cows that are induced with PG before 80 days of gestation generally will show standing oestrus after expulsion of the foetus and if mated can become pregnant at that time; cattle that are pregnant for more than 100 days will usually retain the foetal membranes and show no heat period (Lindell et al., 1981). Elsewhere, it is reported that a greater percentage of PG-treated cattle abort and have fewer complications if treated in the first 100 days of pregnancy rather than between 100 and 160 days of gestation and later (Sequin et al., 1978).

5.8 TEMPORARY DELAY OF CALVING

A circadian rhythm of parturition, with a higher incidence of births during the night has been shown for humans, horses, pigs and mice; reports for sheep are rather confusing and for cattle, authors as long ago as Richter (1933) and as recent as Edwards (1979) have shown that the distribution of parturition times is not biased in favour of night calvings. There are, however, reports from North America and Scotland that an alteration in the feeding pattern of beef cows can result in a much higher percentage of cows calving during the hours of daylight. A late evening feed can apparently result in cows delaying the start of calving until the following day; in simple terms, the beef cows give priority to feeding rather than to calving (Lowman et al., 1981).

5.8.1. Use of tocolytic agents

Organs in farm mammals which have sympathetic innervation contain α and β-receptors; in most animal species, the smooth muscle of the respiratory tract and the uterus contain few α receptors but many β receptors. Two distinct types of β-receptors have been identified, the β_1 and β_2 receptors. Stimulation of receptors will

result in broncho-dilation, relaxation of the uterus, vasodilation and glycolysis.

Based on the availability of compounds which react selectively with α- and β-receptors, therapeutic effects can be achieved by either stimulating or inhibiting functions mediated by these receptors. The value of such compounds is decided by their side-effects and their duration of action; it appears that many β-mimetic compounds have a marked stimulatory effect on cardiac β_2 receptors, a characteristic which severely restricts their use.

In recent times, a β_2-mimetic agent (NAB365; Planipart) has become available for use in farm species. The pharmacological profile of this compound has been reported and it appears that the agent is highly selective for β_2-receptors; several reports have already appeared for its use in cattle (Arbeiter and Thurnher, 1977; Ballarini et al., 1978; Arbeiter and Holler, 1980; Greene, 1981). According to present reports, the agent can be employed successfully as a tocolytic agent either to interrupt parturition or to delay it. There

Fig. 5.2. Ways and means of achieving a temporary delay in calving. Stillbirths can account for many calf losses, especially during night-time calvings. As a means of reducing this potential loss a new agent Planipart® has been tested by workers in several countries in recent years — including Ireland. The agent has proved to be most effective in preventing night-time calvings. Planipart® can delay calvings by up to 10 h, acting by inhibiting uterine contractions. The later in labour the agent is used, the less the delaying effect. It would seem to have a good future as a means of delaying calving for several hours. The agent has also been successfully employed in pigs and sheep. As well as this type of intervention, Scottish workers have shown that it is possible to modify the time of calving in beef cattle by time of feeding during the day.

appears to be some suggestion that deliveries after interruption or postponement proceed faster and easier than usual; possible advantages may stem from interrupting parturition if labour has commenced before the birth canal is fully prepared or by holding calvings that would otherwise occur at night over until the next day. The availability of the agent does provide a further possibility for controlling the parturition process.

In considering methods of altering the time taken for parturition, it might be mentioned that there is some evidence that cows of certain beef breeds, such as the Charolais, take longer to calve than do the dairy breeds; an interval of 4–5 hours for the second stage of labour is not uncommon in the Charolais (Hartigan, 1979).

5.9 REFERENCES

Adams, W. M. (1969) The elective induction of labour and parturition in cattle. *J. Am. Vet. Med. Assoc.* **154**, 261.

Adams, W. N. and Wagner, W. G. (1970) The role of corticoids in parturition. *Biol. Reprod.* **3**, 223.

Anderson, H. and Plum, M. (1965) Gestation length and birth weight in cattle and buffaloes: a review. *J. Dairy Sci.* **48**, 1224–1235.

Anderson, A. B. M., Flint, A. P. F. and Turnbull, A. C. (1975). Mechanisms of action of glucocorticoids in induction of ovine parturition: effect on placental steroid metabolism. *J. Endocr.*, **66**, 61–70.

Anon (1977) Cattle fertility-management for efficient reproduction. *Ir. Vet. Assoc./Agric. Sci. Assoc. Liaison Comm.*

Arbeiter, K. and Holler, W. (1980) Control of births; about the influence on partus, puerperium, and rate of conception following injection of Flumethason/Dexamethason (corticoids) and planipart (B-adrenergic agent) in cattle. *Dtsch. tierarztl. Eschr.* **87**, 249–251.

Arbeiter, K. and Thurnher, M. (1971) About the effect of the sympathomimetic compound planipart (NAB 365) on parturition in cattle. *Tierarztl, Umschau* **32**, 423.

Ballarini, G., Molino, L. and Munafo, A. (1978) Treatment of cattle with tocolytre agent "clenbuterolo". *Clin. Vet.* **1**, 11–16.

Beardsley, G. L., Muller, L. D., Owens, M. J., Ludens, F. C. and Tucker, W. L. (1974) Initiation of parturition in dairy cows with dexamethasone. II. Response to dexamethasone in combination with estradiol benzoate. *J. Dairy Sci.* **59**, 241–247.

Bosc, M. J., Fevre, J. and Vaslet de Fontaubert, Y. (1975) A comparison of induction in parturition with dexamethasone or with an analogue of prostaglandin $F2_{\alpha}$ (A-PGF) in cattle. *Theriogen.* **3**(5), 187–191.

Brakel, W. J., Rife, D. C. and Salisbury, S. M. (1952) Factors associated with the duration of gestation in dairy cattle. *J. Dairy Sci.* **35**, 179–194.

Chew, B. P., Erb, R. E., Randel, R. D. and Touquette, F. M. Jr. (1978) Effects of corticoid induced parturition on lactation and on prepartum profiles of serum progesterone and the estrogens among cows retaining and not retaining fetal membranes. *Theriogen.* **10**(1), 13–35.

Christiansen, I. J. and Hansen, L. H. (1974). Dexamethasone-induced parturition in cattle. *Br. Vet. J.* **130**, 221–229.

Clarke-Williams, J. F., O'Gorman, M. G. and Roger, P. A. (1979) Some observations on the prediction of calving difficulty. *Vet. Rec.* **105**, 533–534.

Copeland, D. D., Schultz, R. H. and Kemtrup, M. E. (1978) Induction of abortion in feedlot heifers with cloprostenol (A synthetic analogue of prostaglandin $F_{2\alpha}$). A dose response study. *Can. Vet. J.* **19**, 29–32.

Day, A. M. (1977) Cloprostenal for termination of pregnancy in cattle. A. Induction of parturition. *N.Z. Vet. J.*, **25**, 136–136.

Day, A. M. (1979) Induced termination of the calving season in a large dairy herd. *N.Z. Vet. J.* **27**, 22–29.

De Fries, J. C., Touchberry, R. W. and Hays, R. L. (1959) Heritability of the length of the gestation period in dairy cattle. *J. Dairy Sci.* **42**, 598.

Edqvist, S., Einarsson, S., Gustafsson, B., Linde, C. and Lindell, J. O. (1975) The *in vitro* and *in vivo* effects of prostaglandins EL and $F_{2\alpha}$ of oxytocin on the tubular genital tract of ewes. *Int. J. Fert.* **20**, 234–238.

Edqvist, L. E., Kindahl, H. and Stabenfeldt, G. (1978) Release of prostaglandin $F_{2\alpha}$ during the bovine peripartal period. *Prostaglandins*, **16**,(1), 111–119.

Edwards, S. A. (1979) The timing of parturition in dairy cattle. *J. Agric. Sci. Camb.* **93**, 359–363.

Estergreen, V. L., Frost, O. I., Gomes, W. R., Erb, R. E. and Bullard, J. F. (1967) Effect of ovariectomy on pregnancy maintenance and parturition in dairy cows. *J. Dairy Sci.* **50**, 1293–1295.

Everett, R. W. and Magee, W. T. (1965) Maternal ability and genetic ability of birth weight and gestation length. *J. Dairy Sci.* **48**, 957.

Fairclough, R. J., Hunter, J. R., Welch, R. A. S. and Payne, E. (1975) Plasma corticosteroid concentrations in the bovine foetus near term. *J. Endocr.* **65**, 139–140.

First, N. L. (1979) Mechanisms controlling parturition in farm animals. *Anim. Reprod. BARC. Symp. No. 3*, pp. 215–257, Ed. H. Hawk, Allanheld, Osmun, Montclair.

Fisher, L. J. and Williams, C. J. (1978) Effect of environmental factors and foetal and maternal genotype on gestation length and birth weight of holstein calves. *J. Dairy Sci.* **61**, 1462–1467.

Garverick, J. A., Day, B. N., Mathner, E. C., Gomez, L. and Thompson, G. B. (1974) Use of estrogen with dexamethasone for inducing parturition in beef cattle. *J. Anim. Sci.* **38**, 584–590.

Gianola, D. and Tyler, W. J. (1974) Influences on birthweight and gestation period of Holstein-Friesian cattle. *J. Dairy Sci.* **57**, 235.

Gravert, H. O. and Kordts, E. (1979) Some results with induced parturition in cows and heifers. Calving Problems & Early Viability of the Calf, E.E.C. Seminar, Friesing. pp. 338–350.

Greene, H. J. (1978) Causes of dairy calf mortality. *Ir. J. Agric. Res.* **17**, 295–301.

Greene, H. J. (1981) Clinical study of clenbuterol for postponing parturition in cows. *Vet. Rec.* **109**, 283–285.

Grunert, T., Schultz, L. Cl. and Ahlers, D. (1975) Retained placenta problems with induced labour in cattle. *Proc. 20th Wld. Vet. Congr.* **1**, 273–278.

Hartigan, P. J. (1979) Some data on the length of gestation and on dystokia in primiparous cows in a grade A. Charolais herd. *Ir. Vet. J.* **33**, 7–11.

Henricks, D. M., Rawlings, N. C. and Ellicott, A. R. (1977a) Plasma hormone levels in beef heifers during prostaglandin-induced parturition. *Theriogen.* 7(1), 17–27.

Henricks, D. M., Rawlings, N. C., Ellicott, A. R., Dickey, J. F. and Hill, J. R. (1977b) Use of prostaglandin $F_{2\alpha}$ to induce parturition in beef heifers. *J. Anim. Sci.* **44**, 438–441.

Hindson, J. C. (1978) Quantification of obstetric traction. *Vet. Rec.* **103**, 327–332.

Hoffmann, B. and Schams, D. (1975) Control of parturition and lactation in cattle. Endocrinological aspects. Proc. E.E.C. Symp. on Early Calving of heifers & its impact on Beef Production, June, 1975, pp. 58–75.

Hoffmann, B., Wagner, W. C. and Gimenez, T. (1976) Free and conjugated steroids in maternal and fetal plasma in the cow near term. *Biol. Reprod.* **15**, 126–133.

Hoffmann, B., Wagner, W. C., Rattengerger, E. and Schmidt, J. (1977) Endocrine relationships during late gestation and parturition in the cow. In, *Ciba Foundation Symp. 47. The Foetus and Birth*, pp. 107–125, Elsevier, Oxford.

Hoffman, B., Schmidt, J. and Schallenberger, E. (1979) Hormonal mechanisms involved in control of parturition in the cow. In, Calving Problems and Early Viability of the Calf, E.E.C. Seminar, Friesing, 63–281.

Jackson, P. S. and Cooper, M. J. (1976) The use of cloprostenol (ICI 80996) in the treatment of infertility in cattle. Proc. Int. Congr. Diseases of Cattle (Paris).

Jochle, W. (1971) Corticosteroid induced parturition in domestic animals; mechanism of action and economic importance. *Folio Vet. Latina, Italy.* **1**, 229–259.

Jochle, W., Esparaza, H., Gimerez, T. and Hidalgo, M. A. (1972) Inhibition of corticoid-induced parturition by progesterone in cattle: Effect on delivery and calf viability. *J. Reprod. Fert.* **28**, 407–412.

Johnson, C. T. and Jackson, P. S. (1980) Induction of parturition in the bovine with cloprostenol. *Vet. Rec.* **106**, 366.

Johnston, W. H., Barth, A. D., Adams, W. M., Manns, J. M., Rawlings, N. W. and Mapletoft, R. J. (1981) Induction of abortion in feedlot heifers using a combination of $PGF_{2\alpha}$ and dexamethasone. *Theriogen.* **15**, 129(abs.).

Kordts, E. and Jochle, W. (1975) Induced parturition in dairy cattle: a comparison of a corticoid (Flumethasone) and a prostaglandin ($PGF_{2\alpha}$) in different age groups. *Theriogen.* **3**, 171–177.

Laird, R. and Hunter, E. A. (1977) The length of gestation period of Ayrshire cows when mated with bulls of other breeds. *Anim. Prod.* **24**, 63–67.

Lamond, D. R., Tomlinson, R. V., Drost, M., Henricks, D. M. and Jochle, W. (1973) Studies of prostaglandin $F_{2\alpha}$ in the cow. *Theriogen.* **4**, 269.

Langford, S. H. (1979) Induction of parturition in cows. *N.Z. Vet. J.* **27**, 107–08.

La Voie, V. A. and Moody, E. L. (1973) Estrogen pre-treatment of corticoid induced parturition in cattle. *J. Anim. Sci.* **37**, 770–775.

Liggins, G. C. (1973) The physiological mechanisms controlling the initiation of ovine parturition. *Rec. Prog. Hormone Res.* **29**, 110–149.

Lindell, J. O., Kindahl, H. and Edqvist, L. E. (1981) Prostaglandin induced early abortions in the obovine. Clinical outcome and endogenous release of prostaglandin $F_{2\alpha}$ and progesterone. *Anim. Reprod. Sci.* **3**, 289–299.

Lowman, B. G., Hankey, M. S., Scott, N. A. and Deas, D. W. (1981) Influence of time of feeding on time of parturition. *Vet. Rec.* **109**, 557–559.

Lush, J. L. (1945) *Animal Breeding Plans.* (3rd Ed.) Iowa State College Press Ames.

MacDiarmid, S. C. (1979) Betamethasone alcohol suspension for the induction of parturition in dairy cows. A comparison with dexamethasone trimethyl acetate. *N.Z. Vet. J.* **27**, 86–89.

McDonald, L. E., McNutt, S. H. and Nichol, R. E. (1953) On the essentiality of the bovine corpus luteum of pregnancy. *Am. J. Vet. Res.* **14**, 539–541.

MacMillan, K. L. and Curnow, R. J. (1976) Aspects of reproduction in New Zealand Dairy Herds. I. Gestation Length. *N.Z. Vet. J.* **24**(2) 243–252.

Millar, P. G. (1974) Methods of early termination of pregnancy in the cow. *Vet. Rec.* **94**, 626.

Murray, R. D., Smith, J. H. and Harker, D. B. (1981) Use of cloprostenol with dexamethasone in the termination of advanced pregnancy in heifers. *Vet. Rec.* **108**, 378–380.

Plenderleigh, R. W. J. (1979) Induction of parturition in the bovine. Calving Problems and Early Viability of the Calf, E.E.C. Seminar, Friesing, pp. 338–340.

Preston, T. R. and Willis, M. B. (1974) *Intensive Beef production* (2nd. Ed.), Pergamon Press, Oxford.

Rice, L. E. and Wiltbank, J. N. (1972) Factors affecting dystocia in beef heifers. *J. Am. Vet. Med. Assoc.* **161**, 1348–1358.

Richter, J. (1933) Die gubertshilfich-gynakalogische Tierklink der Universital Leipzig in den Jahren 1927–1931. *Berliner Tier. Wochenschrift,* **49**, 517–521.

Schmitt, D., Garverick, H. A., Mather, E. C., Sikes, J. D., Day, B. N. and Erb, R. E. (1975). Induction of parturition in dairy cattle with dexamethasone and estradiol benzoate. *J. Anim. Sci.* **40**, 261–268.

Sequin, B. E. (1980) Role of prostaglandins in bovine reproduction. *J. Anim. Vet. Med. Assoc.* **176**(10), 1178–1181.

Sequin, B. E., Rufsal, R. R. and Goerke, T. P. (1978) Field trial experiences with prostaglandins in Minnesota and Wisconsin beef cattle. *Minn. Vet.* **18**, 9–14.

Skinner, J. D. and Joubert, D. M. (1963) A further note on the duration of pregnancy and birthweight in beef cattle in the sub-tropics. *Proc. S. Afr. Soc. Anim. Prod.* **2**, 104.

Spears, L. L., Vercouitz, A. B., Reynolds, W. L., Kreider, J. L. and Godke, R. A. (1974) Induction of parturition in beef cattle with estradiol and $PGF_{2\alpha}$ *J. Anim. Sci.* **39**, 227(Abs).

Welch, R. A. S., Newling, P. and Anderson, D. (1973) Induction in parturition in cattle with corticosteroids: an analysis of field trials. *N.Z. Vet. J.* **21**, 103–108.

Welch, R. A. S. (1977) The use of corticosteroids to induce parturition. *N.Z. Vet. J.* **25**, 224.

Welch, A. S. and Kaltenbach, C. C. (1977) Induced calving with corticosteroids: A comparison between induced cows and their calves and control calves. *Proc. N.Z. Soc. Anim. Prod.* **37**, 52–57.

Welch, R. A. S., Crawford, J. E. and Duganzich, D. M. (1977) Induced parturition with corticosteroids: A comparison of four treatments. *N.Z. Vet. J.* **25**, 111–114.

Welch, R. A. S., Day, A. M., Duganzich, D. M. and Featherstone, P. (1979) Induced calving: A comparison of treatment regimes. *N.Z. Vet. J.* **27**, 176–180.

Zerobin, K., Jochle, W. and Steingruber, Ch. (1973) Termination of pregnancy with prostaglandins E_{25} (PGE_2) and $F_{2\alpha}$ ($PGF2\alpha$) in cattle. *Prostaglandins,* **4**(6), 891–901.

CHAPTER 6

Reducing the Calving Interval

6.1 INTRODUCTION

The fertility of the cow in the months that follow calving depends on the satisfactory involution of the uterus and the re-establishment of cyclical breeding activity. The interval between successive calvings, the calving interval (CI), is one of the important factors determining the profitablility of the dairy herd; the ideal, for most dairying situations, is held to be a 1-year interval. For those using AI this can only be achieved if the conception rate and efficiency of oestrus detection is high and the interval between calving and first-service is less than about 90 days (Esslemont, 1974; Pelissier, 1976). It is also true to say that success in the synchronization of oestrus in cattle can be markedly influenced by the early re-establishment of reproductive activity after parturition.

The components of the CI are gestation (taken at about 282 days) and the variable non-gravid period. In practice, the management decision on the period that elapses between calving and rebreeding will be influenced by the various interested parties, including the AI service. It has been noted that despite some trend towards earlier breeding, 60 days is still widely quoted as the earliest that dairy cows should be mated after calving. For optimum reproductive perform-

ance, the beef cow must also raise a live calf during each year of her productive life and have a calving interval of 12 months.

Whether cows can be re-bred and become pregnant in time to calve once each calendar year, will depend on their showing oestrous symptoms as well as their ability to conceive when bred. Whatever the reasons, the fact remains that under many environmental husbandry conditions, including autumn calving conditions in Ireland (Crowley, 1971), the calving interval in dairy cows is often nearer 13 months than 12. For New Zealand dairying conditions, in which most cows are engaged in creamery milk production, a concentrated seasonal calving pattern needs to be maintained and dairy cattle have to be submitted for breeding during a 4-week breeding period (Fielden and Macmillan, 1973; Macmillan *et al.*, 1975; Fielden *et al.*, 1976). This can only apply to cattle that have resumed cyclical breeding activity, which may present some New Zealand farmers with a substantial problem, especially among 2-year old cows that may not be in good condition at calving and in the more stressful conditions of the large herd.

In dairy herds, it should be mentioned, there may be more to profitability than ensuring a 12-month calving interval. Efforts to determine the best CI for profitability may well show longer than average intervals to be optimum for high yielding cows and the normal year-long interval for the general run of animals in the herd or it may be a question of factors such as the cost of concentrate feeding and the price of milk operating at that time (James and Esslemont, 1979). There have been those who suggest that average milk production per day of life might be maximized with calving intervals of 13 or even 14 months (Spalding, 1976; Shaffer, 1977); as noted by Kiddy (1979) there are several factors to be considered before a final conclusion can be drawn about optimal calving intervals for a herd.

6.2 ENDOCRINOLOGY OF THE *POST-PARTUM* COW

As a result of RIA studies, a much more accurate picture of the endocrine changes which occur when cows return to full ovarian cyclicity after parturition is now emerging. This should enable better interpretation of factors that affect the interval from calving to first ovulation and oestrus between and within different breeds and according to whether cows are suckling or milked. The growing body of evidence will also aid the development of hormone treatments for cattle in which there is a delay in the resumption of ovarian activity.

Wagner and Oxenreider (1971) reviewed the literature at that time on patterns of follicular growth, oestrus, ovulation and fertility after calving and the endocrine changes associated with these events. It is clear that in most lactating cows there is a suppression of follicular development immediately after calving but that changes occur rapidly 7–10 days after parturition (Wagner and Hansel, 1969; Morrow *et al.*, 1966, 1969). The process of uterine involution in the normal dairy animal should be complete within 21–30 days of parturition, and the first ovulation should occur within 45 days (Johanns *et al.*, 1967; Marion and Gier, 1968; Wagner and Oxenreider, 1971). Early estimates suggested that 80% of first ovulations among *post-partum* cattle may not be accompanied by oestrus, the incidence being greater among beef cattle than in dairy animals (Morrow *et al.*, 1966; Wagner and Hansel, 1969).

Involution of the uterus and resumption of ovarian activity after calving is faster among multiparous than in primiparous cattle and involution may be facilitated by suckling (Tennant *et al.*, 1967).

Both first ovulation and first oestrus tend to occur earlier in dairy than in beef suckler cows (Morrow *et al.*, 1969; Casida, 1971). In general, the interval from calving to first ovulation would be taken as about 3 weeks in dairy cows although this interval can be affected by factors such as the frequency of milking (Carruthers *et al.*, 1977) milking ability and output (Marion and Gier, 1968; Whitmore *et al.*, 1974), rate of uterine involution (Marion and Gier, 1968; Morrow, 1969) and the onset of episodic LH secretion (Stevenson and Britt, 1979).

6.2.1 LH considerations

A gradual increase in the level of tonic LH from calving to around day-10 *post-partum* has been observed (Echternkamp and Hansel, 1973; Kesler *et al.*, 1977; Goodale *et al.*, 1978); this rise may be related to removal of an inhibitory effect of the previous pregnancy on pituitary LH content in view of evidence showing an increase in pituitary LH content from parturition until 20–30 days *post-partum* (Wagner and Hansel, 1969). The early increase in tonic LH is regarded as an important feature in the sequence of events leading up to first ovulation and the resumption of normal ovarian cyclical activity. On the basis of their own data and those of other workers, Stevenson and Britt (1979, 1980) have put forward a possible sequence of events leading up to the initiation of cyclic ovarian activity in dairy cattle milked twice-daily.

The suggested sequence involves follicle development in the ovary promoted by FSH, which results in an increase in oestrogen secretion, the elevated oestrogen concentration leading to increased tonic LH by way of a positive feed back effect; the increased LH level plus sustained FSH promotes the final maturation of a Graafian follicle, which produces oestradiol in quantities sufficient to initiate the pre-ovulatory surge of LH, which brings about first ovulation.

6.2.2 Evidence from progesterone assays

Because milk progesterone levels are closely correlated with those in the blood, milk assays are now being used extensively in surveys of ovarian function in dairy herds (Bulman and Lamming, 1978; Foote et al., 1979; Gunzler et al., 1979; Van de Wiel et al., 1979; Peters et al., 1980). In most *post-partum* animals, it would appear that the first complete ovarian cycle is preceded by a short period in which blood levels of progesterone are elevated (Pope et al., 1969; Donaldson et al., 1970; Robertson, 1972; Tribble et al., 1973; Lamming and Bulman, 1976; Webb et al., 1980); the origin of this transient increase in progesterone level is not known but it has been suggested that developing follicles are the most likely source (Webb et al., 1980). There are reports dealing with LH and progesterone levels showing that in many of the *post-partum* cows investigated, the first ovarian cycle was shortened by 6–7 days and progesterone values remained low (Schams et al., 1978); this shortened cycle may be a consequence of deficiencies in the corpus luteum arising from inadequacies in the level of preovulatory LH. Information from plasma progesterone levels reported by Pope and Swinburne (1980) supports the view that corpora lutea of shorter than normal life-span are common after the first *post-partum* ovulation, but that there can be considerable irregularity in both the apparent life span of the corpus luteum and the levels of progesterone associated with them; the authors conclude that there can be much individual variability in the time taken for normal ovarian function and normal CI life-span to become established.

6.3 BEEF SUCKLER CATTLE

It has been noted that first ovulation occurs later after parturition in beef cattle than in dairy cows; it is well-established that the frequency and intensity of suckling can affect the duration of the *post-partum* anoestrus (Short et al., 1972; England et al., 1973; Randel and Welker, 1976; Wettemann et al., 1976; Wyatt et al., 1977) although the precise mechanisms by which suckling produces this effect are not known.

Studies reported by Carruthers et al. (1980) have shown a greater frequency of episodic LH releases in non-suckled cows compared with those nursing calves; this could be taken as indicating more frequent releases of Gn-RH, with the pituitaries of non-suckled animals receiving more Gn-RH priming than the suckler cows, resulting in greater pools of LH being available for release in the cattle without calves. There is also evidence in the report of Forest et al. (1980) that the suckling stimulus depresses LH levels in beef cows and that an increase in suckling intensity will depress LH concentrations still further. Along the same lines, first *post-partum* heats were observed by Gimenez et al. (1980) on days 67 and 88 in cows nursing single and twin calves, respectively; the same workers did not find any evidence that the inhibitory action of suckling on the resumption of ovarian activity after calving was mediated by prolactin.

Fig. 6.1. Resumption of cyclical breeding activity in suckler cattle. In the suckler herd, one of the limiting factors to increased production is the fertility level. The rebreeding of cows after calving can often be very slow and this can result in a protracted calving season. MLC figures from Britain have shown that more than 60% of suckler herds recorded there have calving seasons longer than 6 months. Estimates for beef herds in the west of Ireland show the same picture. The main advantage of oestrus control in the beef suckler herd is in terms of introducing AI on a larger scale.

6.3.1 Nutrition as a key factor

Authors such as Topps (1977) and Wiltbank (1978) have concluded that body condition of the beef cow and whether the animal is gaining or losing weight are major determinants of the interval between calving and first oestrus; each author has proposed a system of condition scoring or the checking of weights at 28-day intervals to plan the most appropriate nutritional regimen during late pregnancy and early lactation so that cows are in moderate condition at calving and weight losses during early lactation are limited. As noted already for dairy cattle, there is also plenty of evidence showing that an energy deficit affects primiparous beef cows to a greater extent than multiparous animals (Wiltbank, 1970).

It is mainly a question of a long period of ovarian inactivity in the beef cow, especially under poor feed conditions. Under range conditions, *post-partum* anoestrus, particularly in cattle that calve late in the season, may mean an interval to first oestrus of 80 days or more (Casida, 1971), which makes it impossible to maintain a yearly calving interval. If it is kept in mind that the conception rate at the first *post-partum* oestrus may be lower than that at later heats, as noted for dairy cattle by Thatcher and Wilcox (1973), then it may be that reproductive efficiency could be improved in beef animals nursing calves if oestrous cycles could be initiated sooner after calving.

6.4 HORMONAL INDUCTION OF BREEDING

Attempts to reduce the calving interval have involved both management and hormonal treatments. Management practices, apart from those aimed at providing an adequate nutritional plane for the animals, include early or temporary weaning of calves or otherwise restricting the suckling of beef cows (Smith and Vincent, 1972; Laster et al., 1973; Bellows et al., 1974; La Voie and Moody, 1976; Randel and Welker, 1976; Short et al., 1976; Baud and Cummins, 1977; Holness et al., 1978). Hormonal attempts have generally centred around the use of progestagens or Gn-RH as the means of stimulating the early resumption of ovarian activity.

6.4.1 Fertility prophylaxis on a herd basis

Several papers by workers in East Germany have dealt with what they term *fertility prophylaxis*, which is put forward as a new management concept in dairy cattle production. One report dealt with daily oral doses of 10 mg CAP for a 20-day period (days 15 to 35 after calving) in clinically healthy dairy cows (Kordts et al., 1974); over a 4-year period, the data provided evidence of an earlier than usual resumption of cyclical activity, a consequent decrease in the calving interval (by 10.5 days on average) and a reduction in the level of infertility in the cattle herds so treated. The authors claimed that the advantages of the CAP treatment were more pronounced in cows older than 5 years and in those producing less than 25 kg of milk daily in the first 2 months of lactation. Although it is reported that no residue of CAP or of a biologically active metabolite has been detected in the milk of cattle receiving the treatment, there would be difficulties in satisfying the requirements of regulatory agencies in many countries; that apart, the data would still seem of interest in supporting the view that exogenous progestagen may be useful as an organizer of hypothalamic–pituitary–ovarian events leading to ovulation and normal cyclical activity. Even if regulations within a country permitted CAP treatment along the lines indicated, the costs involved in conducting such *fertility prophylaxis* on a herd basis would certainly require careful cost–benefit evaluation.

6.4.2 Use of progestagens

Of the various agents employed in attempts to stimulate resumption of ovarian activity, MGA has been the subject of several reports. Britt et al. (1974b) did report that the administration of this progestagen for a 14-day period, starting on day-21 after calving, was effective in reducing the interval between parturition and conception. The workers at that time were unable to define the physiological mechanisms involved in this response although they did note that there was no benefit in using oestrogen with the MGA (Britt et al., 1974b); it did not seem related to changes in uterine involution but rather to the ability of the MGA-treated cattle to exhibit more pronounced symptoms of oestrus than untreated animals. This could fit in with evidence, already noted, that cattle showing cyclical breeding activity (which includes luteal activity) early rather than late conceive more readily in the *post-partum* period.

Other workers reporting some evidence in favour of the MGA treatment include Huertas Vega et al. (1972) and Brannen et al. (1977).

6.4.3 Short-term progestagen treatment

As noted earlier, in studies directed primarily towards oestrus synchronization in beef cattle, a problem commonly experienced is that of anoestrus in some proportion of animals. Short-term progestagen treatments have been employed in such animals and it is clear, under some conditions, that these treatments can result in the occurrence of oestrus and ovulation in cattle that otherwise would not be reproductively active (Chupin et al., 1975; Roche, 1976 a & b; Zaied et al., 1976; Roche, 1977; Tervit et al., 1977; Bulman et al., 1978). Although it is true that a regimen involving short-term progestagen, gonadotrophin (PMSG) and prostaglandin can be one means of stimulating the occurrence of oestrus and ovulation under most conditions and regardless of whether or not the animal in question is cyclical or anoestrus, apart from cost and problems with a regimen involving several agents, multiple ovulations resulting from the gonadotrophin component of this complex, is one objection to this approach.

Fig. 6.2. Post-partum anoestrus in dairy cattle. The failure of dairy cows to become pregnant early enough after calving can be very costly. Various factors can influence the *Post-partum* interval and the body condition of the cow can be an important consideration in deciding whether she becomes pregnant after service. Milking cows invariably lose weight during the period of rising milk production at the start of lactation and regain it as milk production declines. There is evidence to show that the faster the dairy cow puts on weight after milk production peak, the better her chance of an early conception.

On the other hand, there is evidence in several reports that short-term progestagen treatment on its own may prove of some use; Drew (1981) found evidence of ovarian activity being initiated in 70% of non-cyclical cows by PRID treatment at the particular time she applied the treatment in herds with a seasonal calving pattern. Work in Ireland suggested that the use of the PRID to control oestrus in cows nursing calves gave better results than when such control was attempted by Cloprostenol (Roche, 1976b); the thought was that PRID treatment, by virtue perhaps of the oestradiol and progesterone components, might have a beneficial effect in restoring normal ovarian function in *post-partum* dairy cows. Work elsewhere in which the PRID and Cloprostenol techniques were compared produced evidence that the PRID was superior.

6.4.4 More on management routines

New Zealand workers have been among those who have reported in some detail on the problem of anoestrus in their dairy cattle in the early months after parturition (Fielden and Macmillan, 1973); in the absence of economical, effective and practicable controlled breeding techniques for such cattle, herd management routines which could help in stimulating resumption of ovarian activity have been suggested (Macmillan et al., 1975); routines include dividing large herds into smaller groups to reduce social stress and competition for feed. On the beef cattle front in the same country, Tervit et al. (1977) conclude that the best way the farmer can keep the CI at a year is by ensuring that the animals are in good condition at calving and making some weight gain before and after parturition.

6.4.5 Progesterone and oestradiol

An approach to initiating ovarian activity in which prolactin concentration was suppressed by drug treatment has been evaluated and reported on by Williams and Ray (1980); although prolactin suppression had no apparent effect, it was noted that a single dose of progesterone (30 mg) on day-15 *post-partum* with oestradiol-17β given after 48 h resulted in ovulation and cyclical activity in a majority of adequately-fed beef cattle. Less success with this simple regimen was recorded by Williams et al. (1980) and the workers suggested that there may have been an inadequate release of preovulatory LH as a consequence of nutritional stress.

6.4.6 Use of Gn-RH

As a means of initiating cyclical ovarian activity in the early weeks after calving, several groups have examined the use of Gn-RH; hypothalamic Gn-RH and its synthetic analogues cause the release of LH from the anterior pituitary of the cow (Mauer and Rippel, 1972; Convey, 1973; Zolman et al., 1973; Kaltenbach et al., 1974; Kesler et al., 1977, 1978; Fernandes et al., 1978). In the post-partum cow, the injection of Gn-RH has resulted in a preovulatory surge of LH leading to ovulation, when administered as early as 14 to 20 days after parturition (Schams et al., 1973; Britt et al., 1974a); cattle in these studies continued showing normal oestrous cycles subsequently. It is now recognized, however, that the responsiveness of the bovine pituitary to Gn-RH and the subsequent levels of LH released are influenced by the post-partum interval and by the level of endogenous oestrogens and progesterone; oestrogens apparently enhance the Gn-RH induced release of LH whereas progesterone may block such a release. Kesler et al. (1977) proposed that follicular maturity and growth are important to the Gn-RH induced LH response and to establishing ovarian cycles at 12–14 days post-partum; Zaied et al. (1980) and Garverick et al. (1980) supported these conclusions in their studies in post-partum dairy cattle. The fact that a single dose of Gn-RH on day-14 post-partum or two injections given 10–14 days apart have led to contradictory results in initiating breeding activity is presumably explicable on the basis of the levels of ovarian steroids operating at time of treatment. As well as that, the mode of administration of Gn-RH may be a consideration; Britt et al. (1974a) showed that subcutaneous administration of Gn-RH in a gelatine capsule induced ovulation in all animals treated, whereas others (Kesler et al., 1978; Zaied et al., 1979) only achieved a 50% response with Gn-RH at the same dose level in saline, indicating that carrier and mode of administration may be important.

6.4.7 Gn-RH and anterior pituitary response

Responses to Gn-RH among beef suckler cattle have been more variable than in dairy cows (Webb et al., 1977; Lishman et al., 1979; Fonseca et al., 1980) and this may be a question of the inhibitory influences of suckling and the generally poorer level of nutrition on ovarian follicular growth. A decline in LH concentration as a result of suckling has been mentioned earlier, and this appears to stem from a decrease in the ability of the bovine anterior pituitary to respond to Gn-RH during the early post-partum period. Foster (1978) has noted, however, that a "priming" dose of Gn-RH can increase the LH response to a second injection in dairy cattle; Padmanabhan et al. (1978) also report that they could demonstrate this "priming" effect in vitro and it would appear that the amount of LH released from the bovine pituitary is increased by previous exposure of pituitary cells to Gn-RH.

Work at Nottingham with double-suckling post-partum cows has led to the conclusion that pulsatile LH release may be achieved by repeated low doses of Gn-RH and that this may be followed by ovulation and ovarian cycles (Webb et al., 1977); it remains to be seen whether a constant infusion of Gn-RH in the form of a subcutaneous implant, could be developed as a feasible practical treatment for anoestrus in the beef cow.

6.4.8 Gn-RH and Zebu cattle

In contrast to the findings of those dealing with European dairy breeds in the early weeks after calving, the studies of Holness and Hale (1980) in Afrikander cows showed that treatment with Gn-RH did not reduce the duration of the post-partum period nor did it improve subsequent reproductive performance. In view of evidence that the response to Gn-RH, as measured by LH levels, has been shown to become greater with increasing time after calving (Webb et al., 1977; Fernandes et al., 1978), a better response may be achieved at a later point among the Zebu cattle.

6.4.9 Gn-RH and cystic follicles

Some reports for high yielding dairy cattle estimate that 15% or so of such animals may develop ovarian cysts prior to the first post-partum ovulations (Morrow et al., 1966; Britt et *al.*, 1977). These cystic follicles are most frequently found 15–45 days *post-partum*, in the older cows of the herd, in the autumn and winter seasons and among the higher producing animals (Shanks *et al.*, 1979); ovarian cysts apparently arise in the early stages of one form of follicular atresia, when a follicle, rather than decreasing in size, suddenly doubles in size from about 1 cm to 2 cm diameter and sometimes enlarges further over a period of days or even weeks (Marion and Gier, 1968). One view of cystic follicles is that they may represent a safety mechanism in the high-yielding dairy cow to avoid the additional stresses of conception and pregnancy. Fortunately, it would appear that treatment with Gn-RH can be the means of returning cows to oestrus after cystic follicles earlier than with spontaneous recovery (Bierschwal *et al.*, 1975; Kittok *et al.*, 1973; Sequin *et al.*, 1976).

Endocrine studies by Kesler *et al.* (1979) indicate that the problem is not a result of low oestrogen level but rather one in which the hypothalamus and pituitary appear to be less responsive in the matter of bringing about the release of LH because of the influence of follicular oestrogen. In such circumstances, exogenous Gn-RH can stimulate LH release (Cantley *et al.*, 1975; Garverick *et al.*, 1976; Sequin *et al.*, 1976; Kesler *et al.*, 1979), although some 20% of cows may not resume ovarian cycles. For those that do not respond, it has been suggested that the cystic structures are not responsive to Gn-RH-induced LH release due to the degeneration of the theca interna and granulosa cell layers. In the cattle that do respond, the Gn-RH-induced LH release apparently results in the luteinization of ovarian cysts, oestradiol concentration rapidly declines, and normal progesterone concentrations operate by 5–9 days after treatment (Kesler *et al.*, 1979); prior to the subsequent oestrus, which should occur about 18–23 days after Gn-RH treatment, progesterone concentrations decline as in the normal cycle.

6.5 PROGESTAGEN AND CALF REMOVAL

With reference to beef suckler cattle, it has been shown, in a number of American studies, that the induction of oestrus in a high percentage of anoestrous cows nursing calves can be achieved using short-term progestagen treatment combined with 48-h calf removal at the time of implant removal; this procedure is known as the "Shang" treatment, as suggested by a Texas rancher. Work reported by Wiltbank and Mares (1977) involved Norgestamet implants as the short-term progestagen treatment, with calves being separated from their dams for 48 h, or from the time of implant removal; there was a 73% increase among cows exhibiting oestrus shortly after treatment and a 41% increase in pregnancies in the first 3 weeks after implant removal and calf separation. It is important that the beef cows are in reasonable body condition and that they should be receiving adequate amounts of feed at the time of treatment (Wiltbank and Spitzer, 1978). Favourable results with the Shang treatment have also been reported by Smith *et al.* (1977); Kiser *et al.* (1980) used a calf separation period of 24 h but found it to be less successful than 48-h. It is generally felt that the temporary removal of the calf can facilitate the re-establishment of *post-partum* reproductive activity by eliminating the otherwise suppressive effect on pituitary gonadotrophin release caused by suckling.

6.6 CONCEPTION RATES IN *POST-PARTUM* COWS

An increasing first service conception rate and a declining number of services per conception as the interval between calving and breeding increases has been reported by many investigators in the U.S.A. and elsewhere (Van Demark and Salisbury, 1950; Trimberger, 1954; Louca and Legates, 1868; Morrow *et al.*, 1969; Bozworth *et al.*, 1972; Whitmore *et al.*, 1974; Williamson *et al.*, 1980). These workers recorded conception rates varying from 5 to 35% in matings occurring within 2 weeks of calvings; the conception rate steadily improved as the *post-partum* interval increased, but there was relatively little change after about 80 days. In an analysis of data from 69 000 inseminations in dairy cattle, the New Zealand Dairy Board showed that of cows mated within 30 days of calving, 31.3% conceived to first service; 42% conceived within 40 days; 49% within 50 days and 54% within 60 days. A conception rate of 62% in matings within the 60–90 day period *post-partum* was increased only fractionally in cows bred beyond that time.

For those who may attempt to maintain a CI of 1 year on the basis of breeding cows as early as they show oestrus after calving, there would not appear to be any reason why this cannot be done, although the low conception rate and associated costs of rebreeding are factors that have to be kept in mind. The earlier ovarian activity is re-established after calving the better, in terms of conception rates in breedings carried out at the 2-month *post-partum* stage; Thatcher and Wilcox (1973) conducted a study covering a 10-year period and showed that cows which had failed to exhibit oestrus in the first 30 days after calving required more services than those that did.

6.7 REFERENCES

Baud, S. R. and Cummins, L. J. (1977) The effect of partial weaning on the rebreeding performance of primiparous Hereford heifers. *Theriogen.* **8,** 189.

Bellows, R. A., Short, R. E., Urick, J. J. and Pahnish, O. F. (1974) Effects of early weaning on post-partum reproduction of the dam and growth of calves born as multiples or singles. *J. Anim. Sci.* **39,** 589–600.

Bierschwal, C. J., Garverick, H. A., Martin, C. E., Youngquist, R. S., Cantley, T. C. and Brown, M. D. (1975) Clinical response of dairy cows with ovarian cysts to GnRH. *J. Anim. Sci.* **41,** 1660.

Bozworth, R. W., Ward, G., Call, E. P and Bonewitz, E. R. (1972) Analysis of factors affecting calving intervals of dairy cows. *J. Dairy Sci.* **55,** 334.

Brannen, L. R., Ulberg, L. C. and Zimbelman, R. G. (1977) Managing reproduction in dairy cattle. III. Changes in culling patterns with increased reproduction. *J. Dairy Sci.* **60,** 1125–1132.

Britt, J. H., Kittok, R. J. and Harrison, D. S. (1974a). Ovulation, estrus and endocrine response after GnRH in early post-partum cows. *J. Anim. Sci.* **39,** 915–919.

Britt, J. H., Morrow, D. A., Kittok, R. J. and Sequin, B. E. (1974b) Uterine involution, ovarian activity, and fertility after melengestrol acetate and estradiol in early post-partum cows. *J. Dairy Sci.* **57,** 89–92.

Britt, J. H., Harrison, D. S. and Morrow, D. A. (1977) Frequency of ovarian follicular cysts, reasons for culling, and fertility in Holstein-Friesian cows, given gonadotrophin-releasing hormone at two weeks after parturition. *Am. J. Vet. Res.* **38**(6), 749–751.

Bulman, D. C., McKibbin, P. E., Appleyard, W. T. and Lamming, G. E. (1978) Effect of a progesterone-releasing intravaginal device on the milk progesterone levels, vaginal flora, milk yield and fertility of cyclic and non-cyclic dairy cows. *J. Reprod. Fert.* **53,** 289–296.

Bulman, D. C. and Lamming, G. E. (1978) Milk progesterone levels in relation to conception, repeat breeding and factors influencing acyclicity in dairy cows. *J. Reprod. Fert.* **54,** 447–458.

Cantley, T. C., Garverick, H. A., Bierschwal, C. J., Martin, C. E. and Youngquist, R. S. (1975) Hormonal response of dairy cows with ovarian cysts to GnRH. *J. Anim. Sci.* **41,** 1666.

Carruthers, T. D., Kosugiyama, M. and Hafs, H. D. (1977) Effects of suckling on interval to first post-partum ovulation and on serum LH and prolactin in Holsteins. *J. Anim. Sci.* **45** (Suppl. 1), 142.

Carruthers, T. D., Convey, E. M., Kesner, J. S., Hafs, H. D. and Chang, K. W. (1980) The hypothalamo-pituitary gonadotrophic axis of suckled and nonsuckled dairy cows post-partum. *J. Anim. Sci.* **51,** 949–957.

Casida, L. E. (1971) The post-partum interval and its relation to fertility in the cow, sow and ewe. *J. Anim. Sci.* **32** (Suppl. 1), 66–72.

Chupin, D., Pelot, J. and Thimonier, J. (1975) The control of reproduction in the nursing cow with a progestagen short term treatment. *Ann. Biol. Anim. Bioch. Biophys.* **15**(2), 263–272.

Convey, E. M. (1973) Neuroendocrine relationships in farm animals: a review. *J. Anim. Sci.* **37,** 745–757.

Crowley, J. P. (1971) Increasing the supply of calves for beef production. *Beef in the 70s.* An Foras Taluntais, Dublin.

Donaldson, L. E., Bassett, J. M. and Thorburn, G. D. (1970) Peripheral plasma progesterone concentrations of cows during puberty, oestrous cycles, pregnancy and lactation, and the effects of under nutrition or exogenous oxytocin on progesterone concentrations. *J. Endocrin.* **48,** 599–614.

Drew, B. (1981) Controlled breeding in dairy herd management. *Br. Friesian J.* March 1981, 138–139.

Echternkamp, S. E. and Hansel, W. (1973) Concurrent changes in bovine plasma hormone levels prior to and during the first post-partum estrous cycle. *J. Anim. Sci.* **37,** 1362–1370.

England, B. G., Hauser, E. R. and Casida, L. E. (1973) Some effects of unilateral ovariectomy in the post-partum beef cow. *J. Anim. Sci.* **36,** 45–50.

Esslemont, R. J. (1974) Economic and husbandry aspects of the manifestation of oestrus in cows. I. Economic aspects. *A.D.A.S. Q. Rev.* No. 12.

Fernandes, L. C., Thatcher, W. W., Wilcox, D. J. and Call, E. P. (1978) LH release in response to Gn-RH during the post-partum period of dairy cows. *J. Anim. Sci.* **46,** 443–448.

Fielden, E. D. and Macmillan, K. L. (1973) Some aspects of anoestrus in New Zealand dairy cattle. *Proc. N.Z. Soc. Anim. Prod.* **33,** 87–93.

Fielden, E. D., Macmillan, K. L. and Moller, K. (1976) The pre-service anoestrous syndrome in New Zealand dairy cattle. *Bovine Pract.* **11,** 10–14.

Foote, R. H., Oltenzcu, E. A. B., Kummerfeld, H. L., Smith, R. D., Riek, P. M. and Braun, R. K. (1979) Milk progesterone as a diagnostic aid. *Br. Vet. J.* **135,** 550–558.

Fonseca, F. A., Britt, J. H., Kosugiyama, M., Ritchie, H. D. and Dillard, E. U. (1980) Ovulation, ovarian function and reproductive performance after treatments with Gn-RH in post-partum suckled cows. *Theriogen.* **13,** 171–181.

Forest, P. K., Rhodes, R. C. and Randel, R. D. (1980) Effect of bleeding stress and variable suckling intensity upon serum luteinizing hormone in Brangus heifers. *Theriogen.* **13,** 321–332.

Foster, J. P. (1978) Plasma LH concentrations after single or double injections of synthetic LH-RH in dairy cows. *J. Reprod. Fert.* **54,** 119–121.

Garverick, H. A., Kesler, D. J., Cantley, T. C., Elmore, R. G., Youngquist, R. S. and Bierschwal, C. J. (1976) Hormone response of dairy cows with ovarian cysts after treatment with HCG or GnRH. *Theriogen.* **6,** 413.

Garverick, H. A., Elmore, R. G., Vailancourt, D. H. and Sharp, A. J. (1980) Ovarian response to gonadotrophin-releasing hormone in post partum dairy cows. *Am. J. Vet. Res.* **41,** 1582–1585.

Gimenez, T., Henricks, D. M., Ellicott, A. R., Chang, C. H., Rone, J. D. and Grimes, L. W. (1980) Prolactin and luteinizing hormone (LH) release throughout the post-partum period in the suckled first-calf beef cow. *Theriogen.* **14,** 135–149.

Goodale, W. S., Garverick, H. A., Kesler, D. J., Bierschwal, C. J., Elmore, R. G. and Youngquist, R. S. (1978) Transitory changes of hormones in plasma or post partum dairy cows. *J. Dairy Sci.* **61,** 740–746.

Gunzler, O., Rattenberger, E., Gorlach, A., Hahn, R., Hocke, P., Claus, R. and Karg, H. (1979) Milk progesterone determination as applied to the confirmation of oestrus, the detection of cycling and as an aid to veterinarian and biotechnical measures in cows. *Br. Vet. J.* **135,** 541–549.

Holness, D. H. and Hale, D. H. (1980) The response of lactating Agricander cows to treatment with a progesterone-releasing intravaginal device or injection of synthetic GnRH. *Anim. Reprod. Sci.* **3,** 181–188.

Holness, D. H., Hopley, J. D. and Hale, D. H. (1978) The effects of plane of nutrition, live weight, temporary weaning and breed on the occurrence of oestrus in beef cows during the post-partum period. *Anim. Prod.* **26,** 47–54.

Huertas Vegas, E., Britt, H. H. and Ulberg, L. C. (1972) System for managing reproduction in dairy cattle. *J. Dairy Sci.* **55,** 401 (Abs.).

James, A. D. and Esslemont, R. J. (1979) The economics of calving intervals. *Anim. Prod.* **29,** 157–162.

Johanns, C. J., Clark, T. L. and Herrick, J. B. (1967) Factors affecting calving interval. *J. Vet. Med. Assoc.* **151,** 1692–1704.

Kaltenbach, C. C., Dunn, T. G., Kiser, T. E., Corah, L. R., Akbar, A. M. and Niswender, G. D. (1974) Release of FSH and LH in beef heifers by synthetic gonadotrophin releasing hormone. *J. Anim. Sci.* **23,** 995–1001.

Kesler, D. J., Garverick, H. A., Youngquist, R. S., Elmore, R. G. and Bierschwal, C. J. (1977) Effect of days post-partum and endogenous reproductive hormones on Gn-RH induced LH release in dairy cows. *J. Anim. Sci.* **46,** 797–803.

Kesler, D. H., Garverick, H. A., Youngquist, R. S., Elmore, R. G. and Bierschwal, C. J. (1978) Ovarian and endocrine response and reproductive performance following GnRH treatment in early postpartum dairy cows. *Theriogen.* **9**(4), 363–369.

Kesler, D. H., Garverick, H. A., Bierschwal, C. J., Elmore, R. G. and Youngquist, R. S. (1979) Reproductive hormones associated with normal and abnormal changes in ovarian follicles in post-partum dairy cows. *J. Dairy Sci.* **62,** 1290–1296.

Kiddy, C. A. (1979) Estrus detection in dairy cattle. *Anim. Reprod. BARC, Symp. 3,* H. Hawk, Ed. pp. 77–89. Allanheld, Osmun, Montclair.

Kiser, T. E., Dunlop, S. E., Benyshek, L. L. and Mares, S. E. (1980) The effect of calf removal on estrous response and pregnancy rate of beef cows after synchromate B. treatment. *Theriogen.* **13,** 381–389.

Kittok, R. H., Britt, J. H. and Convey, E. M. (1973) Endocrine response after GnRH in luteal phase cows and cows with ovarian follicular cysts. *J. Anim. Sci.* **37,** 985.

Kordts, E., Hochle, W. and Kaltschitsch, K. (1974) Prophylactic effect of a progestin (chlormadinone acetate CAP) on fertility of dairy cows after post-partum use. *Theriogen.* **1**(5), 169–176.

Lamming, G. E. and Bulman, D. C. (1976) The use of milk progesterone radioimmunoassay in the diagnosis and treatment of subfertility in dairy cows. *Br. Vet. J.* **132,** 507–517.

Laster, D. B., Glimp, H. A. and Gregory, K. E. (1973) Effects of early weanings on post-partum reproduction of cows. *J. Anim. Sci.* **36,** 734–740.

Louca, A. and Legates, J. E. (1968) Production losses in dairy cattle due to days open. *J. Dairy Sci.* **51,** 573.

La Voie, V. A. and Moody, E. L. (1976) Suckling effects on steroids in post-partum cows. *J. Anim. Sci.* **43,** 292–293.

Lishman, A. W., Allison, M. J., Fogwell, R. L., Butcher, R. L and Inskeep, E. K. (1979) Follicular development and function of induced corpora lutea in underfed post-partum anoestrous beef cows. *J. Anim. Sci.* **48,** 867.

Macmillan, K. L., Fielden, E. D. and Watson, J. D. (1975) The anoestrous syndrome in New Zealand dairy cattle. 2. Some factors influencing submission rates in Taranaki herds. *N.Z. Vet. J.* **23,** 4–8.

Marion, G. G. and Gier, H. T. (1968) Factors affecting bovine ovarian activity after parturition. *J. Anim. Sci.* **27,** 1621–1626.

Mauer, R. E. and Rippel, R. H. (1972) Response of cattle to synthetic gonadotrophin releasing hormone. *J. Anim. Sci.* **35,** 249.

Morrow, D. A. (1969) Post partum ovarian activity and involution of the uterus and cervix in dairy cattle. *Vet. Scope* **14,** 2.

Morrow, D. A., Roberts, S. J., McEntee, K. and Gray, H. G. (1966) Post-partum ovarian activity and uterine involution in dairy cattle. *J. Am. Vet. Med. Assoc.* **149,** 1596–1609.

Morrow, D. A., Tyrrell, J. F. and Trimberger, G. W. (1969) Effect of liberal concentrate feeding on post-partum reproduction in dairy cattle. *J. Am. Vet. Med. Assoc.* **155,** 1946.

Padmanabhan, V., Kesner, J. S. and Convey, E. M. (1978) Effects of estradiol on basal LH-RH induced release of LH from bovine pituitary cells in culture. *Biol. Reprod.* **18,** 608.

Pelissier, C. L. (1976) Dairy cattle breeding problems and their consequences. *Theriogen.* **6**(5), 575–583.

Peters, A. R., Riley, G. M., Rahim, S. E. A. and Bowman, B. G. (1980) Milk progesterone profiles and the double injection of cloprostenol in post-partum beef cows. *Vet. Rec.* **107,** 174–177.

Pope, G. S. and Swinburne, J. K. (1980) Reviews of the progress of dairy science; hormones in milk; their physiological significance and value as diagnostic aids. *J. Dairy Res.* **47,** 427–449.

Pope, G. S., Gupta, S. K. and Munro, I. B. (1969) Progesterone levels in the systemic plasma of pregnant cycling and ovariectomized cows. *J. Reprod. Fert.* **20,** 369.

Randel, R. D. and Welker, A. (1976) Once daily suckling effect on cow-calf performance. *J. Anim. Sci.* **43,** 301.

Robertson, H. A. (1972) Sequential changes in plasma progesterone in the cow during the estrous cycle, pregnancy, at parturition and post-partum. *Can. J. Anim. Sci.* **51,** 250–251.

Roche, J. F. (1976a) Synchronization of oestrus in cattle. *Wld. Rev. Anim. Prod.* **12**(2), 79–88.

Roche, J. F. (1976b) Comparison of pregnancy rate in heifers and suckler cows after progesterone or prostaglandin treatments. *Vet. Rec.* **99,** 184–186.

Schams, D., Hofer, F. Hoffmann, B., Ender, M. L. and Karg, H. (1973) Effects of synthetic LH-RH treatment or bovine ovarian function during oestrus cycle and post-partum period. *Acta endocr. Copenh.* **73** (Suppl. 177) 296.

Schams, D., Schallenberger, E., Menzer, C., Stangl, J. Zottmeir, k., Hoffmann, B. and King, H. (1978) Profiles of LH, FSH and progesterone in post-partum dairy cows and their relationships to the commencement of cyclic functions. *Theriogen.* **10,** 453.

Sequin, B. E., Convey, E. M. and Oxender, W. D. (1976) Effect of Gn-RH and HCG on cows with ovarian follicular cysts. *Am. J. Vet. Res.* **37,** 153.

Shaffer, H. E. (1977) Early post-partum breeding. *Prod. 72nd Ann. Meet. Am. Dairy Sci. Assoc.*

Shanks, R. D., Freeman, A. E. and Berger, P. J. (1979) Relationship of reproductive factors with interval and rate of conception. *J. Dairy Sci.* **62,** 74–84.

Short, R. E., Bellows, R. A., Moody, E. L. and Howland, B. E. (1972) Effects of suckling and mastectomy on bovine post-partum reproduction. *J. Anim. Sci.* **34,** 70–74.

Short, R. E., Staigmiller, B. B., Baber, J. K., Carr, J. B. and Bellows, R. A. (1976) Effects of mammary deneruation in post-partum reproduction. *J. Anim. Sci.* **43,** 304.

Smith, L. E. Jr. and Vincent, C. K. (1972) Effects of early weaning and exogenous hormone treatment on bovine post-partum reproduction. *J. Anim. Sci.* **35,** 1228–1232.

Smith, M. F., Burrell, W. C., Shipp, L. D., Sprott, L. D., Songster, W. N. and Wiltbanks, J. N. (1979). Hormone treatments and use of calf removal in post-partum beef cows. *J. Anim. Sci.* **48,** 1285–1294.

Smith, M. F., Walters, D. L., Harms, P. G. and Wiltbank, J. N. (1977) LH levels after steroids and/or 48 hr. calf removal in anoestrous cows. *J. Anim. Sci.* **45,** (Suppl. 1), 209.

Spalding, R. W. (1976) Improving dairy cattle reproductive efficiency. *Proc. 71st Ann. Meet. Am. Dairy Sci. Assoc.*

Stevenson, J. S. and Britt, J. H. (1979) Relationships among LH estradiol, progesterone, glucocorticoids, milk yield, body weight and post-partum activity in Holstein cows. *J. Anim. Sci.* **48,** 570.

Stevenson, J. S. and Britt, J. H. (1980) Models for prediction of days to first ovulation based on changes in endocrine and nonendocrine traits during the first two weeks post-partum in Holstein cows. *J. Anim. Sci.* **50,** 103–112.

Tennant, B., Kendrick, J. W. and Peddicord, R. G. (1967) Uterine involution and ovarian function in the post-partum cow. A retrospective analysis of 2,338 genital organ examinations. *Cornell Vet.* **57,** 543–557.

Tervit, H. R., Smith, J. F. and Kaltenbach, C. C. (1977) Post-partum anoestrus in beef cattle: A review. *Proc. N.Z. Soc. Anim. Prod.* **37,** 109–119.

Thatcher, W. W. and Wilcox, C. J. (1973) Post-partum estrus as indicator of reproductive status in the dairy cow. *J. Dairy Sci.* **56**(5), 608–610.

Topps, J. H. (1977) The relationship between reproduction and under-nutrition in beef cattle. *Wld. Rev. Anim. Prod.* **13,** 43–49.

Tribble, R. L., Sorensen, A. M., Woodward T. L., Connor, J. S., Beverly, J. R. and Fleeger, J. L. (1973) Serum progestins and luteinizing hormone levels in non-suckled primiparous heifers. *Nature.* **246,** 494–495.

Trimberger, G. W. (1954) Conception rates in dairy cattle from services at various intervals after parturition. *J. Dairy Sci.* **37,** 1042.

Van Demark, N. L. and Salisbury, G. W. (1950) The relation of the post-partum breeding interval to the reproductive efficiency in the dairy cow. *J. Anim. Sci.* **9,** 307.

Van de Weil, D. F. M., Kalis, C. H. J. and Nassir Hussain Shah (1979) Combined use of milk progesterone profiles, clinical examination and oestrus observaiton for the study of fertility in the post-partum period of dairy cows. *Br. Vet. J.* **135,** 568–577.

Wagner, W. C. and Hansel, W. (1969) Reproductive physiology of the post-partum cow. I. Clinical and histological findings. *J. Reprod. Fert.* **18,** 493–500.

Wagner, W. C. and Oxenreider, S. L. (1971) Endocrine physiology following parturition. *J. Anim. Sci.* **32** (Suppl.), 1–16.

Webb, R., Lamming, G. E. Haynes, N. B., Hafs, H. D. and Manns, J. G. (1977) Response of cyclic and post-partum suckled cows to injections of synthetic LH-RH. *J. Reprod. Fert.* **50,** 203–210.

Webb, R., Lamming, G. E., Haynes, N. B. and Foxcroft, G. R. (1980) Plasma progesterone and gonadotrophin concentrations and ovarian activity in post-partum dairy cows. *J. Reprod. Fert.* **59,** 133–143.

Wetteman, R. P., Turman, E. J., Wyatt, R. D. and Totusek, R. (1976) Suckling intensity and reproduction in range cows. *J. Anim. Sci.* **42,** 267–268.

Whitmore, H. L., Tyler, W. J. and Casida, L. E. (1974) Effects of early post-partum breeding in dairy cattle. *J. Anim. Sci.* **38,** 339–346.

Williams, G. L. and Ray, D. E. (1980). Hormonal and reproductive profiles of early post-partum beef heifers after prolactin suppression or steroid-induced luteal function. *J. Anim. Sci.,* **50,** 906–918.

Williams, G. L., Butler, J. G. and Ray, D. E. (1980) Estrous response of early post-partum beef heifers to progesterone and estradiol.17β during restricted dietary energy. *Theriogen.* **14,** 13–20.

Williamson, N. B., Quinton, F. W. and Anderson, G. A. (1980). The effect of variations in the interval between calving and first service on the reproductive performance of normal dairy cows, *Aust Vet. J.,* **56,** 477–480.

Wiltbank, J. N. (1970) Research needs in beef cattle reproduction. *J. Anim. Sci.* **31,** 755–762.

Wiltbank, J. N. (1978) Management of heifer replacements and the brood cow herd through the calving and breeding periods. In, *Commercial Beef Cattle Production*, Ed. O'Mary, C. C. and Dyer, C. C., pp. 156–208., pp. 156–208. Lea & Febiger, Philadelphia.

Wiltbank, J. N. and Mares, S. (1977) Breeding at a predetermined time following Syncromate-B. treatment. *Adv. Anim. Breed* **25**.

Wiltbank, J. N. and Spitzer, J. C. (1978) Recent research on controlled reproduction in beef cattle — practical applications. *Wld. Anim. Rev. (FAO)* **27,** 30–35.

Wyatt, R. D., Gould, M. B. and Totusek, R. (1977) Effects of single vs. simulated twin rearing on cow and calf performance. *J. Anim,. Sci.* **45,** 1049–1414.

Zaied, A. A., Humphrey, W. D., Kaltenbach, C. C. and Dunn, T. G. (1976) Fertility of beef females following controlled estrous cycles and ovulation. *J. Am. Sci.* **43,** 311–312.

Zaied, A. A., Bierschwal, D. J., Elmore, R. G., Youngquist, R. S., Sharp, A. J. and Garverick, H. A. (1979) Concentrations of progesterone in milk as a monitor or early pregnancy diagnosis in dairy cows. *Theriogen.* **12**(1), 3–11.

Zaied, Abdalla, A., Garverick, H. A., Bierschwal, C. J., Elmore, R. G., Youngquist, R. S. and Sharp, A. J. (1980) Effect of ovarian activity and endogenous reproduction hormones on Tn-RH induced ovarian cycles in post-partum dairy cows. *J. Anim. Sci.* **50,** 508–513.

Zolman, J., Convey, E. M., Britt, H. H. and Ringer, R. K. (1973) Relationships between the LH response to Gn-RH and endogenous ovarian steroids. *Fed. Am. Socs Exp. Biol.* **32**(3,1), 282.

CHAPTER 7

Embryo Transfer in Cattle

7.1 INTRODUCTION

It was not until after World War II that agricultural scientists in several countries began seriously to consider the possibility of using embryo* transfer in cattle breeding improve-ment schemes. At that time, it may be recalled, cattle AI was spreading rapidly around the world as a cheap and hopefully effective means of bringing about genetic improvement in dairy

*Up to the blastocyst stage (Day-7), the organism is usually referred to as an egg and after that time as an embryo.

cattle; embryo transfer tended to be viewed as a feasible female counterpart of this artifical insemination. The efforts of Pincus and Chang in the United States and Dowling at Cambridge with rabbits had shown that about 80% of eggs would develop after transfer to suitable recipients and this raised expectations about the application of embryo transfer in the farm animal species, especially cattle.

In the mood of optimism existing at the time, the first Egg Transfer Conference was held in Texas in 1949; several papers dealing with transfer attempts in farm animals were either reported at that meeting or appeared in the literature around that time (Dowling, 1949; Pincus, 1949; Umbaugh, 1949, 1951; Warwick and Berry, 1949; 1951; Rowson and Dowling, 1949; Chang, 1951; Willett et al., 1951; Lamming and Rowson, 1952; Dracy, 1953). A few lambs and one or two calves were born after some of these early transfer efforts, but embryo survival and pregnancy rate among the recipients was very low. It became clear that the eggs of the farm species could not be manipulated in the same way as those of rabbits; it also appeared, to the workers at that time, that thoughts of an easy non-surgical transfer technique for cattle, somewhat akin to the method employed in AI, were premature. It was to be 30 years into the future before that hope became a reality.

Making greater use of the egg cells in the ovaries of the genetically superior animal remains one of the main objectives of research in animal reproduction. Although the dream of maturing at will the many thousands of egg cells in the ovaries has not yet been realized, there are likely to be many interesting developments in this area to permit greater use of the female. On the cattle front, Thibault (1977) notes that whereas in 3 years one bull may sire a million calves by AI, a cow, during the same 3 years, gives birth to no more than three calves naturally or perhaps a dozen calves if embryo transfer techniques are used.

7.1.1 Possible advantages of cattle embryo transfer

Various authors have drawn attention to some of the ways in which cattle embryo transfer can be

applied on the farm. There is the obvious question of getting more calves from the genetically superior dairy cow. Currently, as noted by Seidel (1981), most female calves must be kept as possible replacements for cows removed from the herd by death, old age, disease, injury, infertility and so forth; if all replacements could be obtained from the top 10% of the herd, then genetic progress from this source would be between 3 and 4 times more rapid than with the normal selection intensity (Bradford and Kennedy, 1980). However, with good AI programmes at work in a country, nearly all genetic progress comes from bull selection rather than cow selection and the cost of the embryo transfer is likely to be the deciding factor with the farmer.

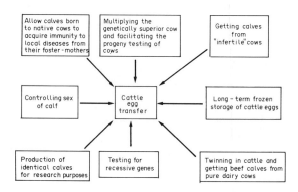

Fig. 7.1. Ways in which cattle egg transfer may be useful.

The transfer technique may be the means of getting calves from old cows no longer able to bear them; aged cows would often have ovaries which produce normal eggs but they are incapable of maintaining a normal pregnancy (Seidel, 1981). Another consideration is in employing the technique for the rapid multiplication of a small population of imported animals, thereby enabling the genetic effect of the importation to be substantially increased. On the international front, embryos are obviously much cheaper to transport than live cattle; the risk of introducing contagious diseases should also be lower and simpler to deal with. When cattle embryos are transferred to indigenous recipients, the transplant calf would get appropriate passive immunity from the dam's colostrum and

Visit to Arran October 5th
1984 in Phoebe with
George, Eileen & Sarah.

COLOURMASTER
INTERNATIONAL

IA 143

Photo Precision Limited, St. Ives, Huntingdon

its own developing immune system would become able to deal with pathogens in the new environment. As noted by Seidel (1981), there may be other physiological and behavioural adaptations that are facilitated when a calf is born in a particular environment rather than being placed there at an older age.

The use of embryo transfer to help in the preservation of rare breeds is another aspect; the idea here is to build up a bank of frozen embryos from cattle breeds that otherwise might become extinct and which could be thawed out at a later date as required. There is also the possibility of obtaining young from genetically superior pre-pubertal calves; by taking fertilized eggs and transferring these to older recipients, calves would be born long before they would otherwise be available.

For the Cattle AI Stations, embryo transfer technology should be useful in increasing selection pressure in bull testing programmes. There is also the use of the technique to screen the dams of AI bulls for specific undesirable recessive genes or to directly check the bulls themselves. The use of the technique to prove that cows and bulls are not carriers of undesirable traits has been reported in the U.S.A. (Baker et al., 1980; Johnson et al., 1980); proving that bulls are not carriers of defects (such as syndactyly) can often be difficult, because cows with homozy-gous recessives are extremely rare. However, if a single homozygous cow is available, she can be superovulated and used to test the bull; for many traits, there is no need to wait until calves are born and it can be a matter of slaughtering recipients to check on the 60-day foetus. In the meantime, the rare homozygous female is kept for further work. Embryo transfer has also been used by Cruz et al. (1980) to check whether certain defects are genuinely of genetic origin or whether they were acquired in the uterus, the specific defect under examination being the pulmonary hypertensive trait.

Apart from possible uses of transfer technology in cattle breeding programmes, there may well be a future for the technique in cattle twinning. At this moment in time, it is as well to consider the whole area of cattle embryo transfer as being in its infancy; by the end of the century developments may well have brought about a situation in which embryo transfer rather than artificial insemin-ation is standard farm practice.

7.2 HISTORICAL BACKGROUND

In England after the second war, the Agricultural Research Council set up a Unit of Animal Reproduction at Cambridge, with the late Sir John Hammond as its Director. The primary objective of this Unit was to investigate embryo transfer in cattle; the efforts of its staff over the 5 years of its existence laid the foundations for subsequent work that resulted in many valuable contributions to knowledge in this area of research (reviews by Hammond, 1950a, b; Rowson, 1971, 1974, 1979; Polge and Rowson, 1973; Trounson and Rowson, 1977; Polge, 1978; Newcomb, 1979; Willadsen and Polge, 1980). Much of the early Cambridge work was with sheep, which were both cheaper and easier to handle than cattle; the various procedures first reported by Hunter et al. (1955) in sheep transfer paved the way to many later successful developments in the other farm species.

In the late 1960s, the Cambridge group, led by Rowson, in reporting the outcome of several important studies in cattle, were the first to demonstrate clearly that acceptable pregnancy rates could be achieved after embryo transfer in that species (Rowson et al. 1969, 1971, 1972). This proved to be a great encouragement to those who had grown accustomed to the monoton-ously low pregnancy rates among recipient cattle in the previous 20 years.

7.2.1 Developments in the seventies
In the early 1970's the commercial exploitation of the embryo transfer procedure as a means of multiplying the number of young produced by the so-called "exotic" breeds of cattle developed at a rapid rate, especially in the U.K. and North America. The extremely encouraging pregnancy rate (91%) achieved by Rowson et al. (1969) was undoubtedly responsible for much of the interest, although it soon became clear that this level of achievement could not always be matched by other groups. Indeed, a survey of

results coming at that time from several commercial embryo transfer units in North America by Graham (1974) showed a figure of 1.6 pregnancies per donor animal treated. As a result of improvements during the seventies, the corresponding figure today would be nearer four pregnancies per donor (Seidel and Seidel, 1978; Moffitt, 1979; Seidel, 1981) with the possibility of repeating the procedure on several occasions without detriment to the donor.

In the United States and Canada, a multi-million dollar industry has developed in the embryo transfer field during the 1970s with about 30 000 pregnancies being produced in 1979 (Seidel, 1981); most effort is in trying to increase the reproductive rate of valuable cows, but in other directions, the procedure is being used to deal with infertile cows, exporting embryos and testing potential carriers for Mendelian recessive genes.

7.3 SUPEROVULATION TECHNIQUES

An obvious and primary consideration in any commercial embryo transfer programme in cattle is that reliable methods should be available for providing a predictable supply of fertilized eggs. Two approaches have been exploited in getting a supply of eggs; the first involves the hormonal induction of superovulation in post-pubertal heifers and cows, occasionally calves; the second approach entails the recovery, maturation and fertilization of eggs taken directly from the ovaries. The first method is still the one universally employed, but it may well be superseded by the second (or modifications of it) in the years ahead.

7.3.1 Early studies

Earliest reports in cattle superovulation came from the Wisconsin group in the United States (Casida et al. 1940, 1943); subsequently, the induction of superovulatory response in heifers and cows, using pituitary and placental gonadotrophins has been investigated by numerous workers employing a wide variety of techniques. Much of this work has already been dealt with in review articles (Foote and Onuma, 1970; Gordon,

1975; Betteridge, 1977, 1980). The first step in most cattle superovulation treatments is the administration of an appropriate FSH-type preparation several days in advance of oestrus (natural or predetermined oestrus) in doses sufficient to to grow 10–20 follicles to maturity. Anything less than three ovulations cannot be considered a superovulatory response; although it is possible to stimulate on occasions the release of more than 100 eggs in individual animals with exogenous gonadotrophins, problems in recovery and fertilization generally follow ovulation rates greatly in excess of 20 (Betteridge, 1980). In the early survey of cattle transfer units in North America already mentioned (Graham, 1974), a figure of less than four fertilized eggs per donor treated was quoted; although current reports (Betteridge, 1977; Marshall and Struthers, 1978; Schneider et al. 1980; Seidel, 1981) would put this figure at eight rather than four, the yield of fertilized eggs per donor remains one of the major factors limiting the progress of cattle embryo transfer technology.

Table 7.1. *Superovulatory response to PMSG — oestradiol – hCG treatment*

Heifers	
In oestrus	183 (94.8%)
Mean follicular response*	21.6
Mean ovulation rate	15.9
Mean no. eggs recovered	9.6
Mean no. eggs fertilized	8.3

*Ovulations + follicles > 10 mm

Data in this table are taken from U.C.D. studies conducted with beef heifer donor cattle, using 2500 iu of PMSG administered on day-16 of the natural oestrous cycle.

7.3.2 Superovulation and the ovary

Part of the problem in superovulation is a lack of precise quantitative information on many of the hormonal factors involved in the cow's oestrous cycle and in follicular growth and development. This difficulty is now rapidly being overcome with the availability of RIA and other procedures for dealing with the steroid and polypeptide hormones, but it is the factors affecting the complement of oocytes within the vesicular follicles which is of special interest; it is only these structures that are able to undergo development in response to the superovulation treatment applied. Available information shows that the number of these vesicular follicles in the bovine ovaries remains fairly constant from about 2 months of age until 8–10 years, after which it slowly declines (Erickson, 1966). Most of these follicles are lost as a result of follicular atresia and an understanding of the complex cellular interactions that exist within the micro-environment of each follicle is only beginning to emerge (Richards, 1979); investigators are still some way from understanding why 99% of follicles atrophy in the normal course of events.

It is possible, on the basis of some lines of evidence, that the superovulatory response in cattle may be influenced by the follicle population present in the ovaries (Mariana et al. 1970); this, in turn, can vary markedly among individual animals (Erickson, 1966; Choudary et al. 1968; Summers and Campbell, 1974). As a result of the continuous process of follicular atresia, the ovaries of the cow will become depleted of follicles if the animal lives long enough. The number of follicles becomes very low in cows after 15 years (Erickson, 1966) and it has been found that ovarian function becomes erratic well before all follicles disappear (Erickson et al., 1976) the indications are that a "critical mass" of growing follicles may be required to maintain normal follicle development due to essential intraovarian factors (Seidel and Niswender, 1980).

7.3.3 Gonadotrophin preparations

It is more than 50 years since Cole and Hart (1930) discovered the presence of a powerful gonadotrophin in the serum of pregnant mares during early pregnancy; the substance was termed PMSG and it was found to have an unusually long biological half-life in mares and in other experimental animals (estimated at 50–120 h in cattle; Schams et al., 1978) due to its sialic acid content. The gonadotrophin has been extensively used as a stimulator of follicle development by animal scientists and veterinarians and is unique in possessing LH — as well as FSH-like properties. It is now firmly established that PMSG is secreted by specialized trophoblast cells which invade the maternal endometrium between 36 and 40 days; the term equine chorionic gonadotrophin (eCG) rather than PMSG has been proposed for that reason (Farmer and Papkoff, 1979) but whether it becomes accepted is another matter. The name notwithstanding, the ability of PMSG to induce superovulation has led to the widespread use of this placental gonadotrophin in cattle embryo transfer work.

The outcome of many superovulation studies makes it clear that the larger the dose of PMSG the greater the average superovulatory response and the greater the variability in the number of ovulations (Dowling, 1949; Rowson, 1951; Gordon et al., 1962; Hafez et al., 1963; Scanlon et al., 1968; Lamond, 1970). For commercial applications, PMSG has the virtue of being available in quantity and at low cost (relative to FSH and LH preparations of pituitary origin); administering the agent in multiple rather than single doses is not apparently necessary (Hafez et al., 1963). As already noted, PMSG is not readily inactivated in the body; this can be shown by the fact that measurable amounts are still present in the cow 10 days after administration (Schams et al., 1978).

7.3.4 Use of anti-PMSG serum

As a result of the many studies involving PMSG during the 1970s, it was felt by some researchers that the presence of PMSG in the circulation of the cow after the time of ovulation might have an adverse effect, particularly on the quality of the developing fertilized eggs (Saumande, 1978; Schams et al., 1978). In an effort to interrupt the otherwise prolonged action of PMSG, several workers have reported on the use of serum containing antibodies against PMSG, administering the anti-serum around the start of oestrus in the superovulated donor (Bindon and Piper, 1977; Dhondt et al., 1978; Kummer et al., 1980). Although results have not always been very conclusive, some authors do report that the anti-serum increased the number of good quality embryos collected (from 1.9 to 3.7 in the heifers reported by Saumande and Chupin, 1981).

7.3.5 Pituitary preparations

Pituitary extracts of FSH were employed in many early cattle superovulation studies and comparative trials showed them to be as effective or more so than PMSG in terms of the yield of fertilized eggs (Dowling, 1949). However, in the years since then, cost and availability were always considerations favouring PMSG. A crude horse pituitary preparation (HAP) has been reported by Moore (1976) and by workers in Ireland (Boland et al., 1981) the latter obtaining superovulatory responses after a single dose in beef heifers comparable to those after 2500 i.u. PMSG; however, in terms of egg quality and fertilization rates, no obvious advantage in favour of the crude preparation was noted.

In North America, the general trend has been to use FSH and LH preparations (5:1 ratio, FSH:LH) rather than PMSG, and several reports would indicate that the FSH–LH regimen gave superior results to PMSG in terms of yield of transferable embryos (Elsden et al., 1978; Seidel et al., 1978). The FSH preparations are regarded as having a short period of activity and for that reason have usually been administered over a period of 5 days with 2 doses per day often being employed (i.e. total of 10 doses). However, there are those who report that the standard twice-daily FSH injection regimen often used by commercial transfer units over 5 days could be simplified without detriment to response (Looney et al., 1981); as well as reducing labour costs and treatment stress on donor, the once daily schedule gave a significantly greater ovulation rate (8.1 vs 6.4).

There have been suggestions, among these attempting repeated superovulation applications, that there may be some merit in alternating between PMSG and other gonadotrophins. Using human menopausal gonadotrophin (HMG) in a comparison with PMSG, Newcomb (1980) found response after a second superovulation treatment to be similar for the two preparations (3000 i.u. PMSG, 11.1 ± 2.0; HMG, 10.6 ± 1.7) and suggested that HMG may be a useful alternative, capable of superovulating some cattle that do not always respond to PMSG.

7.3.6 Timing of gonadotrophin in cycle

Regardless of the particular gonadotrophin employed, the timing of the agent's administration, relative to the occurrence of oestrus, may be an important factor determining ovarian response. Attempts to employ FSH in the main luteal phase of the oestrous cycle were seldom effective and the greatest success in inducing multiple ovulations and obtaining an acceptable yield of transferable embryos followed application of gonadotrophin treatment in the follicular phase (from day-16 onwards). Although a certain measure of control over the cow's oestrous cycle was achieved in early superovulation studies by enucleation of the corpus luteum (Dowling, 1949; Avery et al., 1962), there was evidence subsequently that fertilization of eggs released after PMSG could be influenced by the completeness or otherwise of the enucleation process (Hafez et al., 1963); much more effective than enucleation is the use of prostaglandin $F_{2\alpha}$ (or one of its analogues) to induce luteolysis.

7.3.7 Gonadotrophin and prostaglandin

Part of the variation observed in the response of cattle to PMSG or FSH in early studies was probably due to an inability to anticipate with sufficient accuracy the time at which oestrus would occur after gonadotrophin treatment, regardless of whether the preparation was given in the follicular phase of the cycle or after expressing the corpus luteum by manipulation per rectum. The availability of $PGF_{2\alpha}$ overcame this particular difficulty. Currently, the generally accepted method of superovulating cattle involves administering gonadotrophin (2000–250 i.u. PMSG in a single dose; or divided doses of FSH) during the mid-luteal phase of the oestrous cycle, followed 48–72 h later by a luteolytic dose of $PGF_{2\alpha}$ or an analogue (e.g. 30 mg $PGF_{2\alpha}$; 0.5–1.0 mg Cloprostenol); this type of regimen has been employed in Ireland and elsewhere with successful results (Sreenan et al., 1975; Betteridge, 1977; Marshall and Struthers, 1978; Seidel et al., 1978).

With PG administered 48 h after the gonadotrophin, donors can be expected to show heat symptoms 2 days later, providing an interval of 4 days between gonadotrophin and the onset of oestrus. In aligning donors and recipients for carrying out transfers, account is taken of the fact that the interval between PG and oestrus is substantially shortened in gonadotrophin-trea-

Table 7.2 *Ovarian response in superovulated beef heifers (U.C.D. Studies).*

Treatment	PMSG—Oestradiol—hCG	PMSG—Prostaglandin
No. donors	18	18
No. in oestrus	18	16
Mean follicular response*	20.1	18.8
Mean ovulation rate	16.3	15.6
Mean no. eggs recovered	9.2	10.1
Mean no. eggs fertilized	7.9	9.6
Fertilized eggs per donor treated	7.9	8.6

*Ovulations + follicles >10 mm

With the availability of prostaglandins for superovulation work in the mid-1970s, treatment of beef heifer cattle was compared with the standard method (PMSG on day-16 of natural cycle) employed up to that time. The PMSG-PG regiment was found to yield fertilized eggs at a rate similar to the existing routine.

ted cattle, oestrus commencing on the second rather than the third day after the prostaglandin (Tervit *et al.,* 1973).

Evidence that the day of administering the gonadotrophin may be an important consideration, with lower superovulatory responses being evident when gonadotrophin is given in the early luteal phase (Days 3–8 of cycle) than in the midluteal stage (days 9–12) is documented in several reports (Phillipo and Rowson, 1975; Newcomb and Rowson, 1976; Sreenan and Gosling, 1977). Regardless of whether FSH (multiple-doses) or PMSG (single dose) is employed, the interval between gonadotrophin administration and ovulation can markedly influence the superovulatory response (Scanlon *et al.,* 1968).

7.3.8 Ovulating hormone preparations

Although it is now clear that an ovulating hormone, such as hCG, administered to PMSG-treated donors at the onset of oestrus does not increase the superovulatory response by reducing the incidence of unovulated follicles (Moore, 1975; Gordon and Boland, 1978; Newcomb, 1980), there is some evidence of a favourable effect on egg recovery rate which may indicate an influence on the transport or retention of embryos. The employment of Gn-RH at the time of oestrus in donors was not found to influence superovulatory response in work reported by Newcomb (1980).

7.3.9 Ovulation in superovulated animals

There is still doubt about the duration of the ovulation process in cattle stimulated to release many eggs rather than just the usual one. In Germany, Angel (1979) used laparoscopy to examine the ovulation process in donor cattle subjected to orthodox gonadotrophin treatment (PMSG/FSH + $PGF_{2\alpha}$) and recorded that ovul-

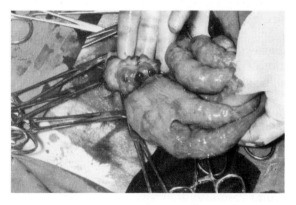

Fig. 7.2. Ovary and corpora lutea in the superovulated cow. The use of gonadotrophins in cattle can induce more than 100 ovulations in certain instances, but the general aim is to get somewhere between 10 and 20 eggs shed as a result of the superovulation regimen. There is still some argument as to whether most of the additional follicles ovulate within a reasonably short time or whether the process may extend over a day or so. For many years in work at Lyons Farm, a dose of HCG was administered early in oestrus intravenously in an effort to get ovulation of follicles occurring in a reasonably compact period. With the current PMSG-PG regimen as used by many operators, ovulating hormone is not employed and there would appear to be no real need for it.

ations extended over a period of 24 h or more; what is not clear, is the possible effect of the examination process itself. Generally, it has been held that the superovulated donor has ample endogenous LH to bring about the rupture of the additional follicles and that ovulation occurs within a few hours.

7.3.10 Repeated superovulation treatments

Conflicting reports appeared in the early literature on cattle superovulation about the feasibility of inducing superovulation in the same donor animal on more than one occasion; although some encouraging evidence was reported (Scanlon, 1972) the results of other studies were less hopeful, and it was thought that there may be problems from the production of antibodies against PMSG. The most thorough and encouraging evidence came in the report of Christie et al. (1979) who took a small group of 14 heifers (mixed breeds) and subjected them repeatedly and at intervals of 6 weeks to a standard superovulation treatment (2000 i.u. PMSG and PGF$_{2\alpha}$ after 48 h); they showed that most heifers responded satisfactorily to the repeat treatments and that even at the tenth application the response was comparable to that recorded after the second treatment. The Cambridge results were more encouraging than those reported by French workers around this time (Saumande and Chupin, 1977; Saumande et al., 1978) who applied PMSG/PG treatments at 7–9 week intervals on several occasions; the results of Christie et al. (1979) were in agreement, however, with several reports showing that ovarian response after a second PMSG treatment could be comparable to that after the first (Gordon and Boland, 1978; Newcomb et al., 1979; Newcomb, 1980). In considering the potential of repeat superovulation treatments, the assumption is that non-surgical procedures will be employed in recovering embryos; even so, there are those employing surgical techniques who report acceptable superovulatory responses after four successive treatments (Marshall and Struthers, 1978).

The evidence that satisfactory superovulatory responses can be maintained after several PMSG applications agrees with the findings of Schams

et al. (1978); they showed that production of antibodies against PMSG poses virtually no problem in cattle, even after repeated doses. Saumande and Chupin (1977), in reporting their general lack of success with repeated treatments, found that ovulation rate declined substantially after the second application, remained low until the sixth treatment and then apparently improved; the conclusion is that this variable ovarian response was the result of factors other than an immunological one.

7.4 FACTORS AFFECTING RESPONSE TO SUPEROVULATION

As a result of the many studies reported on the outcome of superovulation treatments, some amount of information is now available to show what factors can influence the ovarian response in donor cattle.

7.4.1 Dose level and batch of PMSG

The question of the most appropriate dose of PMSG for inducing superovulation was examined in the early years of research in this area; the conclusion reached was that 3000 i.u. was the upper limit (Folley and Malpress, 1944; Hafez et al., 1963). In practice, most regimens in which PMSG in used now employ doses of 2000–2500 i.u. (Betteridge, 1977), although on occasions there may be justification for going to 3000 i.u. (e.g. dealing with Friesians; Newcomb, 1980).

Apart from dose level considerations, reports have occasionally appeared in the literature suggesting that the superovulatory effect of PMSG may vary with the particular batch employed (Baker, 1973; Bowen, 1973; Rowson, 1973). The PMSG molecule certainly possesses both FSH- and LH-like properties and it was this that led some to suggest that the ratio of these components may differ among the batches of the preparation available to laboratories and thereby influence ovarian response (Lamond, 1970). When batches of PMSG were analysed for their FSH and LH activity by several investigators, no significant difference in the FSG/LH ratio was evident (Stewart et al., 1976; Schams et al., 1978); controlled comparisons of batches used in superovulation studies also failed to reveal evidence of any real difference in the ovarian response of cattle (Gordon, 1975; Beehan and Sreenan, 1977; Newcomb et al., 1979).

7.4.2 Controlling interval to oestrus by synchronizing treatments

Follicles in the ovary of the cow apparently require 4 or 5 days to mature under the influence of exogenous gonadotrophins before they are ready to ovulate; employing $PGF_{2\alpha}$ or other synchronizing agents can be the means of adjusting the PMSG to oestrus interval, thereby providing some degree of control over the number of follicles which mature and ovulate. Probably the most comprehensive work in this area was that reported by Sreenan et al. (1978); they compared the three synchronizing agents, $PGF_{2\alpha}$, Norgestamet implants and intravaginal sponge pessaries (impregnated with progesterone or FGA) as the means of controlling oestrus in donors that received a dose of PMSG 2 days prior to withdrawal of progestagen or administration of $PGF_{2\alpha}$. Although the average ovulation and fertilization rates were similar, regardless of synchronizing treatment employed, the oestrous response was higher and the ovulatory response less variable with the PMSG–PG regimen than with the progestagen treatments.

7.4.3 Breed and age effects

Evidence does exist to show that cattle breeds, even strains within a breed, can differ markedly in sensitivity to a given dose of PMSG. Data from several studies show a tendency for Friesians to respond less well to a given dose of gonadotrophin than either Charolais or Hereford/Angus cattle (Scanlon, 1969; Sreenan, 1969; Mariana et al., 1970; Saumande et al., 1978). Studies reported by the Cambridge group in Friesian heifers and milking cows do indicate that the breed will respond satisfactorily to PMSG if given at an appropriate dosage (Newcomb et al., 1979; Newcomb, 1980); their data suggest that for Friesians, 2000 i.u. rather than 1500 i.u. should be regarded as the minimum PMSG dose for superovulation.

Moore (1975) was one worker who examined response to superovulation treatments in relation to age, finding evidence of a greater ovulatory response in heifers than in cows; on the other hand, an analysis of data for 422 superovulated holsteins, ranging in age from 16 months to 17 years, reported by Hasler et al. (1981) showed no significant difference in ovulation rate with age nor in the survival rate of the embryos produced. In other work, Erickson (1966) did show evidence of a general decrease in the number of vesicular follicles from the fourth year of life to a virtual absence in cows at 15–20 years of age.

7.4.4 Nutritional and seasonal effects

There is clear evidence that fasting the donor cow in the period immediately after PMSG administration can markedly reduce the subsequent ovulatory response (Lamond, 1972). The effect of undernutrition on the development of vesicular follicles in cattle was reported by Hill et al. (1970); low plane feeding produced no evident effect on vesicular follicles up to day-15 of the oestrous cycle, but beyond that time it did influence the number of large follicles. Studies reported by Maurasse et al. (1980) led them to conclude that the vesicular follicle population in the bovine ovary can be influenced by energy levels imposed within the one oestrous cycle. Research findings apart, those engaged in cattle embryo transfer work are unlikely to be dealing with donors other than those on an adequate level of feeding although there could be occasions when valuable cows are in poor body condition because of some debilitating disease, injury or old age. Dunn (1980), reviewing the effect of nutrition on ovarian responsiveness to superovulation regimens concluded that it was safe enough to assume that donors should always be kept on adequate feed.

On the matter of seasonal effects, there was some suggestion of this in reports from Denny (1964) in South Africa and Church and Shea (1976) in North America, but there are also those who have failed to find any evidence of this nature (Critser et al., 1980). The reason for differing reports on seasonal effects may not always be apparent in view of the complex of nutritional and environmental factors associated with a particular season. In untreated cattle, Rajakoski

(1960) in Finland found the vesicular follicle population to be greater in the winter and spring periods than in the summer and autumn and this presumably reflects variations which could affect the outcome of superovulatory regimens. Nutrition and season aside, it would be expected that the physiological status of donor cattle, in terms of being dry or lactating or perhaps even nursing calves, would influence superovulatory response although as yet comparative data on which to assess these effects are not available.

7.4.5 Repeat breeder cows as donors

As mentioned earlier, embryo transfer is occasionally attempted in an effort to get young from an otherwise infertile (repeat breeder) cow. A study reported by Greve (1980) in Denmark indicated that the superovulatory capacity of repeat breeder cattle could be the same as in normal cows; the difference lay in the number of eggs fertilized, which was significantly lower in the repeat breeders (41 vs 82% fertilization rate) although the reasons for this were not clear.

7.4.6 Predicting outcome of superovulation treatments

In human fertility work, it is well accepted that prior hormone analysis in those receiving treatment leads to a better understanding and control of the quality and quantity of ovulations and a similar approach in cattle has been attempted in France by Saumande (1980); this worker found that the hormone analysis approach provided a better understanding of the reasons underlying failures in superovulation. It is suggested that in using hormone profiles, superovulation treatment may be modified to take account of the existing physiological situation; Saumande (1980) notes that reducing the number of non-responding cattle would be a useful step in cutting down on the extent of variability in the number of ovulations.

7.5 BREEDING THE DONOR ANIMAL

After superovulation treatment, the next step is for donors to be checked for oestrus and bred; 10% or more of cattle may not exhibit oestrus,

regardless of the particular superovulatory treatment regimen (Gordon, 1975). Although in early superovulation studies there was a tendency to regard normal breeding and insemination procedures as being adequate in achieving a high fertilization rate in donors (bred on the detection of oestrus), later recommendations usually called for AI at 12-h intervals during and immediately after oestrus. An initial report by McKenzie and Kenny (1973) did show evidence of a higher fertilization rate among donors bred with fresh rather than frozen semen (67 vs 20%) but subsequent studies clearly show that it is possible to achieve satisfactory results with frozen semen (Betteridge, 1977). The current widespread use of $PGF_{2\alpha}$ in embryo transfer clinics to control the timing of the heat period permits more precise recommendations for AI to be made.

Fig. 7.3. Breeding the donor cow or heifer. The general rule in breeding donor cows during the heat period that follows application of superovulation treatment is for insemination at 12 h intervals until the end of oestrus. In using frozen semen, there seems to be some evidence that some bulls achieve higher fertilization rates with donor cows than others. It would seem worth having some assessment of a bull's AI record in selecting for use with donors.

Donors can be expected to come in oestrus about 2 days after prostaglandin and it would be normal practice to breed in the morning and again in the evening if they exhibit heat early in the day; if oestrus occurs later, then insemination in the afternoon and again the next morning would be the rule. Frozen semen AI would generally be on the basis of using two straws (20

million live sperm/straw) in the initial breeding at
heat onset and an additional one or two straws
after 12–24 h. When fresh semen is employed,
one insemination rather than two during oestrus
appears sufficient (Rowson, 1979), presumably
because fresh sperm may survive longer in the
bovine reproductive tract than those that are
frozen.

The fertilization rate in donor cattle after AI
with frozen semen may be markedly influenced
by choice of bull (Newcomb et al., 1978;
Callaghan and King, 1980; Newcomb, 1980;
Miller et al., 1981); although there normally is
variation in the fertility of bulls standing at any AI
centre, it would appear that such differences are
greatly accentuated in breeding superovulated
cattle. In fact, it has been suggested that potential
AI bulls with above average fertility may be
selected on the basis of fertilization rates
achieved in superovulated cattle (Callaghan and
King, 1980). Further points that might be noted
about breeding donors include the fact that
semen mixtures from two or three bulls are
occasionally employed (Seidel, 1981) and the
progeny are sorted out after birth on the basis of
blood type and the need to avoid inseminating
donors late after the end of standing oestrus as
this may adversely affect the recovery rate of
embryos at a later stage (Newcomb, 1980).

7.5.1 Fertilization in non-oestrous cows

Dealing largely with data derived from studies
in the pre-prostaglandin era, Gordon (1975) did
note marked differences in fertilization rates
between donors exhibiting oestrus after gonadotrophin treatment and those that did not, even
though the non-oestrous cattle were induced to
ovulate with hCG and inseminations carried out
subsequently at 12 h intervals. The use of $PGF_{2\alpha}$ to
control oestrus and ovulation now permits
donors to be bred at predetermined times (e.g.
48, 60 and 72 h after PG) so that animals failing to
show heat can be bred alongside the oestrous
cattle; it is still not clear if fertilization rate is
satisfactory in the non-oestrous category.

7.6 THE CALF AS A DONOR

Superovulation of the young heifer calf could
have merit as a means of providing supplies of
bovine embryos for research purposes. In
breeding programmes, there might be some
genetic advantage in reducing the generation
interval and initiating the early progeny testing of
females. Heifer calves are born with many
vesicular follicles already evident in their ovaries;
Erickson (1966) records the highest number at
about 4 months of age with a decline as the heifer
approaches puberty. Gonadotrophins have
been employed in many studies by workers in the
U.K. and North America to induce multiple
ovulations and although such treatments were
not successful in animals a few days old,
superovulation did occur in calves 1 month of age
and older (Marden, 1953; Black et al., 1973; Howe
et al., 1962; Jainudeen et al., 1966; Onuma and
Foote, 1969; Onuma et al., 1969, 1970; Seidel
et al., 1970, 1971,). Marked variability in the
superovulatory responses induced with low
recovery and fertilization rates were a common
feature of these reports. Although young calves
will respond readily enough to exogenous
gonadotrophins and often show higher ovulation rates than older cattle, fertilization and
recovery rates tend to be very unsatisfactory.

French efforts (Testart, 1972; Testart and Arrau,
1973) involved treating calves with progestagens
(intravaginal route) to try and establish greater
ovarian uniformity prior to administering the
FSH-preparation. Michelsen et al. (1978), using
an LH-preparation after an initial treatment with
PMSG or FSH report better results, in terms of egg
recovery and fertilization rates. As yet, however,
it has to be said that very few pregnancies have
followed the transfer of embryos derived from
calves (Seidel et al., 1970; Betteridge, 1977);
degeneration of bovine embryos recovered from
the prepubertal reproductive tract has also been
observed.

It is relevant to mention here that in sheep,
embryos from prepubertal ewe-lambs do not
have the same potential for continued development when cultured in vitro as those from adult
sheep (Wright et al., 1976); in Ireland, embryo
transfer studies by Quirke and Hanrahan (1977)

have shown evidence of substantial differences in the survival rate of embryos from adult sheep and ewe-lambs (73 vs 33%) when transferred to the uteri of adult ewes. It may be that questions of embryo mortality arise in using prepubertal animals that are not found among most-pubertal cattle and sheep. Other than for research purposes, the practical utilization of calves remains very limited at this time.

7.7 UTILIZATION OF FOLLICULAR OOCYTES AND *IN VITRO* FERTILIZATION

An eventual alternative to superovulation as a source of bovine embryos, especially for research purposes, may prove to be in the maturation and utilization of the follicular oocyte. The main stimulus for work in oocyte maturation *in vitro* was provided by the discovery, some 45 years ago, by Pincus and Enzmann (1935) that the resumption of meiosis in the mammalian oocyte is initiated by the simple expedient of removing and culturing oocytes outside the follicle. The value of this finding, however, was diminished by subsequent observations, especially those of Thibault (1977) and associates showing that such extra-follicular oocytes are almost totally incapable of undergoing normal embryonic development after fertilization. It appears that most of the defects arise because of the failure to synthesize the correct sequence and range of proteins during maturation, proteins that are required for essential processes such as decondensation of the sperm's DNA, growth of the male pronucleus and support during the early cleavage divisions. Cran and Moor (1980), reviewing the problems in utilizing the follicular oocyte, conclude that techniques which will permit the maturation of these will be developed over the next several years.

In work already reported for cattle, Sreenan (1969) confirmed and extended an earlier report of Edwards (1965) that nuclear maturation can be achieved by culture of the extra-follicular bovine oocyte in an appropriate medium; others have subsequently reported similar findings (Hunter et al., 1972; Shea et al., 1973 Iritani and Niwa, 1977; Sato et al., 1977; Motlik et al., 1978; Fukui

and Sakuma, 1980). Evidence provided by these studies show that about 80% of cultured oocytes can be expected to reach metaphase II after 20–24 h in incubation; the nuclear membranes disappear after some 5–6 h and after 12 h or so, the chromosomes are in metaphase I.

7.7.1 Culture of intact follicles

The growing awareness that there is a complex regulatory system operating within the Graafian follicle, involving hormonal and other factors, has led to the intact follicle rather than the oocyte itself being cultured, using suitable media and gas phases (Thibault et al., 1975). There is evidence that a normal pattern of cytoplasmic protein synthesis does occur in oocytes matured in the intact follicle (Warnes et al., 1977) but not necessarily in those liberated from the follicle and cultured directly (Thibault, 1977). Nevertheless, there is one report on the birth of two calves after the transfer of embryos derived from such liberated oocytes fertilized *in vivo* after maturation *in vitro* (Newcomb et al., 1978); although success rate was very low, the possibility exists, as noted earlier, that refinements and modifications to culture techniques can made this approach much more effective.

Studies with cattle and sheep oocytes matured within intact preovulatory follicles have achieved both normal nuclear and cytoplasmic maturation, the developmental capacity of the oocytes being confirmed subsequently by their fertilization in the oviduct of the species in question and in the development of normal young (Moore and Trounson, 1977; Trounson et al., 1977). In the cattle studies, follicular oocytes were recovered 6–24 h after administration of hCG to animals previously treated with PMSG and then placed in the oviducts of previously inseminated oestrous heifers.

7.7.2 Culturing the oocyte in vitro

Culture systems that can be employed to produce extra-follicular oocyte showing normal cytoplasmic maturation as well as nuclear maturation are under investigation in several laboratories; there may be ways in which the culture system needs to be enriched either with hormones or with granulosa cells isolated from preovulatory follicles. McLaren (1980) notes that only 50% of the proteins in the mature mouse egg have been synthesized within the oocyte itself, the remaining proteins having been taken in from the intra-follicular environment. Several authors (Thibault et al., 1975; Moor et al., 1980) note that the action of steroid hormones is probably important for the synthesis of the so-called male pronucleus growth factor (MPGF) and Fulka and Motlik (1980), working with rabbit oocytes, showed that granulosa cells from preovulatory follicles, introduced into their in vitro culture system, helped to produce oocytes with apparent full physiological integrity. Increased energy metabolism in the mammalian oocyte after resumption of meiosis has been recorded by Magnusson et al. (1981) this being part of the maturation process occurring in the oocyte involving changes in the pattern and rate of protein synthesis (Warnes et al., 1977).

7.7.3 In vitro fertilization

Only a few preliminary reports which claim in vitro fertilization of cow eggs appear in the literature (Edwards, 1973; Von Bregulla et al., 1974; Brackett et al., 1977, 1978; Iritani and Niwa, 1977). Efforts to achieve fertilization in vitro by combining cow eggs, recovered near the expected time of ovulation from follicles or oviducts, with bull sperm treated with a high ionic strength medium resulted in sperm penetration and development to the 2 to 4-cell stage (Brackett et al., 1980); it is claimed that about 50% of eggs were fertilized normally in this work. In talking about in vitro fertilization, some have drawn attention to the fact that the mechanics of sperm entry into the egg may differ quite markedly between the in vitro and the usual in vivo situation (Shalg and Phillips, 1980); this may be a factor influencing success rate, which may be low in some attempts because of the unnatural sperm–egg interactions. It should be noted that only one pregnancy has yet been reported after cattle in vitro fertilization attempts (Brackett et al., 1980); this was confirmed by the birth of a 43 kg bull calf in summer 1981. However, as Seidel (1981) points out, production of young from oocytes fertilized in vitro has been reported in only four other mammalian species, rabbit, mouse, rat and human.

7.7.4 Capacitation of bull sperm

Capacitation of bull sperm in the uterus of the rabbit has been reported (Iritani and Niwa, 1977); artificially matured extra-follicular cattle oocytes were readily penetrated by such sperm in vitro. In subsequent studies, Iritani (1980) reported evidence of sperm penetration of artificially matured cow oocytes in vitro, using sperm preincubated in the isolated cow oviduct, cow uterus or rabbit uterus; these in vitro fertilized eggs cleaved to the 2–4 cell stage by in vitro culture or in the rabbit oviduct. The artificial capacitation of bovine sperm, such as that reported by Brackett et al. (1980) by brief high ionic strength treatment (developed in course of rabbit studies; Brackett and Oliphant, 1975) would seem to be the preferred approach, if it proves successful.

7.7.5 Xenogenous fertilization

Fertilization of cattle oocytes has been attempted in the oviduct of the oestrous ewe (Sreenan, 1969, 1970), oestrous rabbit (Sreenan, 1970), prepubertal gilt (Bedirian et al., 1975) and pseudopregnant rabbit (Trounson et al., 1977) but success has only been claimed for the oestrous ewe and prepubertal gilt. DeMayo et al. (1980) reported fertilization rates of 60% and 36% in hamster and squirrel monkey oocytes in the pseudopregnant rabbit oviduct and later in the same laboratory successful work was reported with cattle and pig oocytes (Hirst et al., 1981). In the cattle studies, a fertilization rate of about 13% was found, and 2-cell eggs were recovered 50–70 h after insemination; according to the authors, earlier attempts by others probably failed because of the use of oestrous rabbits and the concomitant rapid rate of egg transport through the oviduct and because the site of sperm deposition had been vaginal rather than oviducal as employed in their studies. Hirst et al. (1981) suggest that their technique of xenogenous fertilization of cow oocytes may be of use in screening the fertility of bulls at AI centres, if it could be shown that fertilization of cattle eggs in the rabbit oviduct was correlated with the non-return rates of bulls.

A less optimistic report on xenogenous fertilization was that of Meinecke and Meinecke-Tillman (1979) who artificially matured 285 cattle oocytes and transferred them to the oviducts of rabbits, pigs and sheep, some of which had been inseminated with bull sperm; about 47% of the oocytes were subsequently recovered without any evidence of fertilization, although partheno-getic development was noted.

7.7.6 Releasing oocytes from ovaries

The fact that the oocyte population in each ovary of the heifer or cow runs into tens, if not hundreds of thousands, makes it an intriquing question how best to obtain these cells for use in reproduction. One possibility may be liberating oocytes, not only from the tertiary (vesicular) follicles but from secondary follicles as well. Strickland et al. (1977) employed a technique, which involved trypsin digestion, to liberate substantial numbers (110±35 per trial) of oocytes which had the ability to survive in vitro up to 72 h in culture medium. It may well be possible eventually to devise methods which would enable the recovery of a much higher number of the total oocyte population, but much more work is required in this area.

7.7.7 Oocyte fusion

It has been shown by Soupart (1980) to be possible to fuse two mice oocytes and obtain embryonic development up to the blastocyst stage; no young has yet been produced but the oocyte fusion method would be one means of producing 100% female offspring. In the fusion technique, mouse zona-free oocytes are coated with Sendai virus and brought together in pairs to establish contact between their vitelline membranes; fusion activates the fertilization process and two female pronuclei form, with first cleavage occurring within 24 h. Oocyte fusion products are encased in empty rabbit zonae pellucidae to force a tri-dimensional arrange-ment of the blastomeres. Development of the embryos formed by this process to term would provide a method for producing all-female offspring and would demonstrate that no sperm

is necessary to ensure normal embryonic development.

7.8 CLONING POSSIBILITIES IN CATTLE

The prospect of producing multiple copies of higher organisms, such as mice and sheep, has aroused a great deal of interest over the years. It is only in recent times, however, that much headway has been made in this area on the cattle front.

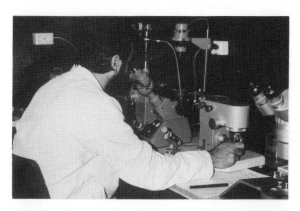

Fig. 7.4 Production of identical twin embryos by micro-manipulation techniques. There are likely to be many interesting developments in cattle embryo transfer tech-nology between now and the end of the century. The use of micromanipulation techniques, whether as a means of dividing a cattle embryo to give identical twins or attempting to introduce a nucleus from a somatic cell into a suitably prepared egg cell, is likely to become commonplace. Already a form of genetic engineering has been carried out in mice and it may eventually become possible to introduce genes for desirable cattle characteristics by injecting a fragment of DNA into the pronucleus of a fertilized bovine egg.

7.8.1 Use of isolated blastomeres

Single blastomeres from early cleavage eggs of the rat, mouse, rabbit, pig and sheep were shown in a number of studies to be capable of continued development (Nicholas and Hall, 1942; Seidel, 1952; Tarowski, 1959; Moore et al., 1969); single blastomeres of two, four and eight-cell rabbit and sheep eggs have developed into apparently normal young after transfer to recipients (Seidel, 1952; Trounson and Moore, 1974); this was in work in which all but one blastomere in the early cleavage egg was destroyed by mechanical means. Mullen et al. (1970) were the first to produce a pair of identical twins by culturing single mouse blastomeres to morulae *in vitro* and then transferring these to a mouse recipient to carry them to term. Success rate was not encouraging until the work of Moustafa and Hahn (1978) which resulted in eight sets of identical twin mice, simply by cutting morulae in half and transferring these "half" embryos to recipients. Similar work, this time with rat and rabbit morulae, has also been reported from Japan (Nagasima and Ogawa, 1981).

Cambridge workers have now reported the production of monozygotic twins from pre-selected parents in cattle, sheep, pigs and horses (Willadsen, 1979; Willadsen *et al.*, 1981; Willadsen and Polge, 1980, 1981; in all instances, such twins have been produced from embryos containing 8-cells or less collected surgically within the first few days after fertilization.

Working with these early cleavage eggs has been of interest in establishing the efficiency of techniques and the developmental potential of single blastomeres. A further step has been in using cattle eggs at the 5–6 day stage, when they are at the morula stage, and taking either half or a quarter of these cells to produce the new embryo; rate of survival of "half" embryos on transfer has been as good (75%) as that found with whole embryos and much above the rate of survival of the "quarter" eggs (41%) in the work reported by Willadsen *et al.* (1981); elsewhere it has been shown that survival of "quarter" embryos produced as 2-blastomeres of an 8-cell cattle egg (Willadsen and Polge, 1981) is below that of "half"-embryos derived from 4-blasto-meres.

One advantage of using 5–6 day cattle embryos is the fact that they can be collected non-

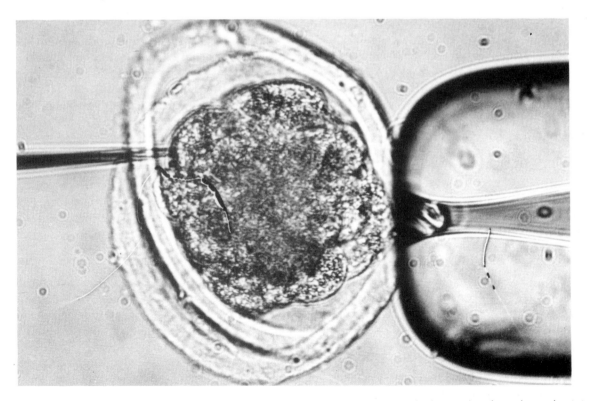

Fig. 7.5. Cutting open the 5-day morula under the microscope. French, American and other workers have shown that it is possible to take cattle embryos at the morula and early blastocyst stage and after division to transfer the two "halves" inside host zona pellucidas directly into recipients. Work at Lyons Farm has included the use of 5-day morulas with transfer to recipients after splitting. Using eggs older than the 2, 4 or 8 cell stages means that the agar technique can be dispensed with. The ability to split eggs under the microscope is an important advance — and for cattle research, it may mean a considerable saving in the cost of certain lines of work.

surgically from the animal. According to Willadsen *et al.* (1981) it should be possible for one person to micromanipulate about 20 cattle morulae in a day, making this a useful adjunct to routine embryo transfer in doubling the number of possible offspring from a given donor; the authors also mention the possibility of being able to use a simple culture procedure for a few hours to permit compaction of cells in the "half" embryo to occur (rather than using the current tedious agar imbedding/sheep oviduct procedure). There is much yet to be explored in following up the efforts of the Cambridge workers; already reports are appearing from work in the U.S.A. and France showing that it is possible to transfer day-6 day-7 embryos soon after splitting the embryo into two (Ozil *et al.,* 1981).

7.8.2 Nuclear transplantation possibilities

A further step along the road from using isolated blastomeres would be the transfer of the nucleus from a cell of a bovine embryo to a previously enucleated egg. Nuclear transplantation in amphibians dates back to the work of Briggs and King (1952) when they reported the first successful transplants in frog eggs. Since then, they and others, notably John Gurdon at Oxford/Cambridge, have greatly extended the amphibian work and shown that it is possible to produce clones of animals by nuclear transplantation techniques. Despite the long history of work in amphibians, successful cloning with mammals has been slow to perfect, mainly because of the many technical difficulties in working with the much smaller mammalian eggs (thousand times less in volume than the frog egg). It should be noted that the prime motivation for developing nuclear transplants in amphibians is to study the relative contributions of nucleus and cytoplasm to the developmental patterns of the embryo, in showing how the genes are turned on and off during the course of development as cells become committed to producing one type of tissue and not another.

Nuclear transplanting is still a tedious and uncertain process, even in frogs (McKinnell, 1978) and there may be the problem that most nuclei in adults are irreversibly differentiated (Talmage, 1979); some evidence shows, however, that somatic nuclei can reversibly respond to cytoplasms directing either meiotic or mitotic events and that somatic nuclei from differentiated frog cells may be reversed by conditioning in oocytes (Hoffner and Diberardino, 1980).

In mammals, early attempts were made to introduce somatic nuclei into unfertilized mouse oocytes or blastomeres with the aid of Sendai virus-mediated cell fusion (Graham, 1969; Lin *et al.,* 1973) but the fate of the transferred nucleus was not followed. Working with rabbits, transfer of somatic nuclei into unfertilized eggs from embryonic cells, both by virus-mediated fusion and by micromanipulation, was reported by Bromhall (1975); there was some evidence that successful transfer was achieved by microsurgery and that development up to the morula stage took place.

In recent times, successful cloning in mice has been achieved by inserting the nucleus of a somatic cell into a fertilized one-cell egg and then removing the original genetic complement (male and female pronuclei) of the egg (Illmensee and Hoppe, 1981). According to Marx (1981) in a review of the most recent work, true cloned mice have been produced at the University of Geneva by Illmensee using the nuclei of 7-day old mouse embryos rather than the 3-4 day old embryos used previously; a total of eight mice were born after successful nuclear transplants. It would appear that nuclei from only two embryonic tissues, the ectoderm and the proximal endoderm retain the potential to produce whole mice and of these, the ectodermic nuclei were found to be the better. From the cattle breeding viewpoint, it may eventually prove possible to mature extra-follicular cattle oocytes, fertilize these *in vitro* and then insert by microsurgery somatic nuclei from genetically desirable cattle embryonic tissue, after removing or destroying the original genetic complement of the cow egg; as noted by Seidel (1981), embryo transfer technology is likely to be crucial for producing cloned mammals.

Although the technical problems associated with the micromanipulation of the very small and delicate mammalian egg are formidable, it is well within the realms of possibility to think of a future in which calves can be produced from eggs provided with transplanted somatic nuclei, a procedure which would also determine sex according to the gender of the embryonic donor tissue.

7.8.3 Producing homozygous embryos

A procedure for the production of homozygous mice, which may have applications in other mammals, has been reported by Market and Petters (1977). They showed that microsurgical removal of one pronucleus from a fertilized mouse egg was technically feasible; this then results in a haploid egg containing either the sperm or egg nucleus. When treated with cytochalasin B, nuclear division occurs; the two identical haploid nuclei form the first cleavage spindle and a homozygous diploid egg begins development, with normal cleavage and development thereafter. Only females can be produced by this method; haploid pronuclei containing the Y chromosome (and no X) cannot develop very far when converted to the diploid state because genes on the X chromosome are apparently essential for basic metabolism.

7.9 EGG RECOVERY PROCEDURES

Surgical means were employed in recovering fertilized eggs in the first successful cattle embryo transfer studies (Rowson *et al.*, 1969); the methods employed by the Cambridge team have been modified by investigators over the years to meet changing needs. In the mid-ventral laparotomy procedure as originally employed at Cambridge, suitably fasted and tranquillized donor cattle are anaesthetized, using an initial intravenous "knockdown" injection (e.g. sodium thiamylal) followed by intubation and closed circuit anaesthesia (e.g. halothane/oxygen mixture). The animal is positioned on her back, an area along the mid-line shaved and the skin prepared for surgery; a 15 cm incision is made in the midline just anterior to the udder. The uterus is exteriorized and retained by a ligature passed around the body of the uterus and tied to a stainless steel bar. A fine cannula is introduced into the ovarian end of the oviduct and flushing fluid gently forced through from the uterus.

Newcomb and Rowson (1975) subsequently reported an alternative method of simultaneously flushing the oviduct and the uterus, which resulted in an efficient recovery of eggs. In this, flushings from the donor's breeding tract are collected into specially designed vacuum collecting cups, which are then examined under the microscope for the eggs. Strict aseptic conditions and a stable temperature environment are regarded as contributing towards the survival of the embryos, which are stored in a light-proof incubator held at 30°C–37°C until time of transfer.

Whether eggs are recovered from the oviducts or the uterus will depend on the timing of collection relative to ovulation. The bovine egg enters the uterus some four days after the end of standing oestrus (Hamilton and Laing, 1946) and most surgical recovery attempts would now be timed for about 7 days after heat. When it is a matter of trying to recover blastocysts which have hatched from the zona pellucida and expanded (about 9 days and more after fertilization) then the recovery rate may be markedly lower than when dealing with the early cleavage eg (Gordon, 1975); similar findings were reported by Baker and Jillella (1978) who thought the problem may have been caused by the expanding blastocysts partially occluding the utero-tubal junction. Those who have compared recovery rates on different days after oestrus have shown a drop from day-3 to days-7/8 but no further decline from then on (Sreenan and Beehan, 1976; Newcomb and Rowson, 1976; Seidel *et al.*, 1978).

Milking cows are not regarded as good candidates for surgical recovery, quite apart from the fact that they may respond less well to the superovulation treatment; they may become ketotic when fasted prior to surgery and their recovery from the intervention may be prolonged and occasionally complicated by hypocalcaemia for reasons that are not clear (Betteridge, 1980). At surgery, the mammary gland needs retracting posteriorly and care must be taken to avoid the large milk veins (subcutaneous-abdominal) at time of incision.

7.9.1 Non-surgical procedures

Several workers during the early years of cattle embryo transfer described devices for the non-surgical recovery of eggs (Rowson and Dowling, 1949; Dracy and Petersen, 1950; Dziuk et al., 1958). In the late 1960's, one active worker in this field was Tadashi Sugie in Japan, who reported encouraging results on several occasions (Sugie, 1970; Sugie et al., 1972). However, it was the fact that the problem of adhesions places a definite limit on the number of surgical opportunities which are available for the recovery of cattle embryos (no more than about three) that mainly concentrated attention in the mid-1970's on the need to develop alternative non-surgical techniques. Apart from animal welfare considerations, it was also generally recognized that non-surgical atraumatic methods would greatly augment the practicability of cattle embryo transfer, especially with certain categories of donors. As already mentioned, in high-yielding dairy cows, there is some danger in pre-surgical fasting as well as dificulties in exteriorizing the reproductive tract surgically in cows with considerable udder development.

The reports of many workers now show that non-surgical egg recovery procedures have found ready application, providing such techniques are reliable, simple to perform, call for a minimum of special equipment, avoid risk of injury to the donor and the risk of contamination of the flushings with blood cells (Drost et al., 1976; Elsden et al., 1976; Rowe et al., 1976; Greve et al., 1977; Lampeter, 1977, 1978; Brand et al., 1978; Newcomb et al., 1978; Sreenan, 1978; Shelton et al., 1979; Critser et al., 1980; Pugh et al., 1980; Seidel, 1981). Results in general support the view that egg recovery rates comparable to those achieved by surgery can be achieved once the appropriate manipulative experience and skills have been developed. In contrast to the situation with surgical recoveries, the precise egg recovery rate may not always be accurately determined because palpation of corpora lutea per rectum is the method of estimating the number of ovulations induced. Most commercial cattle transfer units favour collection around day-7, at which time the eggs would still be in the upper reaches of the uterine

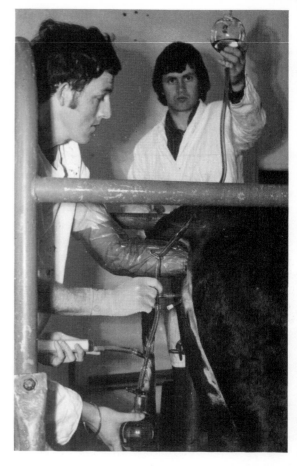

Fig. 7.6. Non-surgical egg recovery in the cow. In recent years, one of the most important steps forward in cattle embryo transfer has been the development of efficient methods for non-surgical recovery of embryos which are harmless to the donor animal and can be applied repeatedly with no ill effects. Here, Dr. Maurice Boland is carrying out recovery at 7 days after breeding when it should be possible to recover 6 or so embryos per flush. The fact that embryos recovered non-surgically can be "split" into two viable embryos increases the number of young which can now be obtained from the superovulated animal.

horns. It should also be mentioned that repeated non-surgical collections have been made in non-superovulated donors with considerable success (around 70% or so of eggs recovered) and this can be an accurate measure of the efficiency of the recovery technique (Elsden et al., 1976; Sreenan, 1978; Shelton et al., 1979; Critser et al., 1980; Linares and King, 1980).

One feature with the non-surgical procedure is that it can lead to a significant shortening of the oestrous cycle after recovery; Elsden et al. (1976) found a mean oestrous cycle length of 18.4 days for 54 heifers, as against 20.6 days for the cycle prior to collection; Critser et al. (1980) record corresponding figures of 18.1 and 20.4 days.

7.9.2 Locating the embryo

A sedimentation funnel or a conical cylinder is usually employed as a collection vessel for flushings coming from the donor's reproductive tract; aliquots are removed from the vessel after a period of settling and searched for embryos, a process which can be rather time-consuming. A filtration system using nylon plankton net was employed by Pugh et al. (1980) in an attempt to reduce the time normally taken to search for embryos; these workers concluded that the plankton net sieve is a simple and rapid technique for locating cattle embryos that can be adapted to all systems of non-surgical collection.

7.9.3 Dilating cervix

A problem which can face non-surgical recovery attempts is the passage of catheters through the cervix of the donor animal during the luteal phase of the oestrous cycle, particularly in heifers. Simple, mechanical dilation with a cervical expander does not always provide an answer and there may be risk of trauma; for such reasons, there have been attempts to dilate the cervix with relaxin (Graham and Dracy, 1953), prostaglandin (Von Hoppen et al., 1978) and carbachol (Zraly et al., 1980). Of the various possibilities, carbachol may have certain advantages over relaxin and PG, the agent being effective, easy to administer and cheap (Zraly et al., 1980).

7.9.4 Premature regression of corpora lutea

Morphological and functional regression of corpora lutea in superovulated donors has either been directly observed (Brand et al., 1978; Bouters et al., 1980), inferred from progesterone levels in blood (Lamond and Gaddy, 1972; Booth et al., 1975; Rajamahendron et al., 1976) or confirmed by both methods (Schams et al., 1978). The incidence (less than 10% generally) is low in cattle as compared with sheep (up to 40% incidence in PMSG–PG treated ewes) but

presumably regression would not often be obvious in cattle flushed within a week of breeding; when recovering at late stages, however, luteal regression may adversely affect the process (Bouters et al., 1980).

7.9.5 Dye test for donor cows

One factor reported by Coulthard (1980) as a problem in obtaining fertilized eggs from donors is that of uterine infection in the post-partum cow; the same worker suggested that this condition can be diagnosed and rectified by applying the phenosulphophtalein dye test (Kothri et al., 1978) on all prospective donors before undertaking superovulation. However, there is some evidence that this dye test may not always reveal cows which have tubal problems that may interfere with the normal transport of the egg (Kelly et al., 1981).

7.10 EVALUATION OF EGG AND EMBRYO

As part of the developing technology in cattle embryo transfer in the 1970s, it was recognized that to achieve optimal pregnancy rates in recipient animals it is essential that meaningful information on the chronological and morphological development of the cow egg should be available. Cattle eggs and embryos were first described in the report of Hartman et al. (1931) and information on the chronological development of the egg in its early stages was provided by workers in the U.K. and France (Hamilton and Laing, 1946; Thibault, 1966, 1967); in recent times, a great deal of information is presented in reviews (Betteridge, 1977, 1980). A study of cattle eggs and embryos using light and electron microscopy is also reported by Brackett et al. (1980), which also deals with the group's attempts to achieve in vitro fertilization.

The cow egg remains capable of fertilization for about 24 h following ovulation (Thibault, 1967); pronuclear eggs can be found within 5–12 h after ovulation. After superovulation in cattle, as already mentioned, there can be a spread in the egg stages that are recovered at any one time, and part of this is presumably a result of the prolonged process of ovulation; Brackett *et al.* (1980) using orthodox PMSG–PG treatment in superovulation, records that ovulation occurred over a period of 59 h in certain of the animals studied.

In terms of size, eggs from the one-cell stage to the early blastocyst (7–8 days after oestrus) are between 120 and 140 μ in diameter, exclusive of the zona pellucida; between days 8 and 110, embryos can be expected to double in diameter, hatch from the zona pellucida, and then grow to 20 cm in length by day-18 (Northey and French, 1980). Enormous variability has been recorded in the size of cattle embryos recovered at late stages (days 10–16). One report instances a size range of 4–40 mm from the same day-14 donor (Betteridge *et al.*, 1980); this is to be expected with embryos collected at different stages of their logarithmic elongation growth phase but it does make it difficult to decide whether the small embryos are likely to be less viable than the larger ones. Time lapse cinematography has been employed with cattle eggs to study blastocyst formation and hatching from the zona pellucida (Massip and Mulnard, 1980); the embryo was observed to escape by an active process through a slit formed by rupture of the zona pellucida.

An early attempt to provide evaluation criteria which could be employed with the cattle egg was that of Shea (1976) and Shea *et al.* (1976). It is not difficult to distinguish between unfertilized and fertilized eggs, but beyond that it can become a matter of experience and subjective judgement in assessing the normality of the egg or embryo on the basis of its development at a particular age. As noted by Shea (1981), the single most reliable morphological characteristic used to evaluate the cattle embryo remains the extent of its development, relative to its age.

There is evidence supporting the view that the incidence of abnormalities in eggs shed after superovulation in cattle may be higher than in the spontaneously ovulated egg (Church and Shea, 1976; Betteridge, 1977; Elsden, 1977). Although there have been reports recording less good quality eggs with higher ovulation rates (Hafez *et al.*, 1963; Church and Shea, 1976; Boland *et al.*, 1978), there are others showing that pregnancy rates after transfer did not differ regardless of whether eggs originated from donors showing low, moderate or high superovulation responses (Betteridge, 1977).

Although the phenomenon of "fragmentation" of unfertilized eggs can sometimes pose a problem in evaluating pig eggs (Dziuk, 1960), it is extremely rare for this to occur in cattle. In contrast to what is known to occur in horses, the unfertilized eggs may be found in the uterus for up to 2 weeks after ovulation (Bindon, 1969; Skehan, 1974).

7.10.1 Egg abnormalities after superovulation

Several reports show that the uterine environment of superovulated donors can adversely affect egg development, as shown in an increase in the incidence of morphologically abnormal eggs after day-4 or so, when the eggs enter the uterus (Gordon, 1976; Newcomb *et al.*, 1976; Boland *et al.*, 1978; Schilling *et al.*, 1980). It is also recognized that grossly abnormal blood steroid levels can exist in such superovulated cattle and it has been suggested that higher levels of oestrogen in particular might be responsible for accelerated transport of eggs into the uterus (Booth *et al.*, 1975). Reports may differ on the time at which sharp increases in the incidence of abnormals have been noted; Newcomb *et al.* (1976) and du Mesnil du Buisson *et al.* (1977) record the greatest increases between day-6 and day-8. In work elsewhere, Boland *et al.* (1978) found the sharpest increase between day-4 and -5; in Germany, Schilling *et al.* (1980) found that almost 50% of eggs recovered from their donors were unsuitable for transfer and there was some evidence of a relationship between progesterone levels at days 4- to 6- after breeding and the incidence of degenerated eggs recovered at days-6 to 8. There is no reason to believe that the incidence of abnormal eggs is any different after current PMSG–PG treatments than it was after previously employed procedures which did not involve prostaglandin (Gordon and Boland, 1978).

It is worth noting that in using non-surgical egg recovery techniques a week after breeding, recovery is being carried out after the eggs have been exposed to the donor's uterine·environment for several days. The yield of transferable embryos, due to the somewhat lower recovery

Table 7.3. *Incidence of major morphological abnormalities in egg from superovulated beef heifers according to day of recovery.*

Day of recovery after breeding	2	3	4	5
Number of superovulated donor heifers	8	28	14	31
Mean number of fertilized eggs recovered	14.4	7.7	7.4	9.4
Incidence of major* egg normalities	Nil	2.3%	17.5%	45.9%

*Refers to fertilized eggs showing marked evidence of blastomers degeneration. From Gordon (1976).

rate when uterine eggs are involved and the higher incidence of abnormalities, may therefore be lower with non-surgical techniques than when surgical intervention at an early stage after oestrus is employed.

7.10.2 Assessing the quality of the embryo

Although rapid morphological evaluation is the only practical method when conducting embryo transfer under normal commercial conditions, other procedures have been examined. Linares and King (1980) reported on a method of assessing the living bovine blastocyst with phase contrast microscopy; the mean number of cells was greater in normal than in abnormal blastocysts and the degree of cellular organization was also greater. Others have attempted to evaluate quality from the embryo's ability to continue development *in vitro* (Trounson *et al.*, 1976; Renard *et al.*, 1978), by measuring embryonic metabolic activity (Renard *et al.*, 1978) and the use of certain dye tests.

7.10.3 Fluorescent dye tests

It has been suggested that short-term incubation of week-old cattle embryos with fluorescein diacetate (FDA) may be useful as a rapid test for viability and developmental capacity (Schilling *et al.*, 1980); similar conclusions were reached by Mohr and Trounson (1980) in studies with pre-implantation mouse embryos. The dye FDA is a non-fluorescent compound, first employed by Rotman and Papermaster (1960) in tests to distinguish between living and dead mammalian cells; these authors showed that the activity of living cells resulted in the conversion of FDA into a fluorescent compound. Loss of fluorochromasia (accumulation of intracellar fluorescein in living cells) by embryonic cells can result from aging, freezing, thawing or mechanical injury which damages the cells without destroying their morphological integrity.

In a further report by Schilling *et al.* (1979), it was claimed that the viability of cow eggs and embryos could be rapidly and accurately diagnosed by using another fluorescent dye (4,6-diamidino-2-2phenylindole; DAPT); this compound has a highly sensitive affinity for DNA and the test works on the basis that the nuclei of dead blastomeres show a positive fluorescence whereas living embryos or blastomeres do not. Schilling *et al.* (1980) believe that the FDA and DAPT tests can be very useful in the evaluation of early embryonic stages, especially of frozen-thawed embryos.

7.11 FREEZING AND SEXING EMBRYOS

It has long been recognized that the effective frozen storage of cattle embryos would have numerous applications. It can render synchronization of recipients with donor cattle unnecessary; embryos are held and transferred as suitable recipients become available. Already mentioned is the fact that frozen storage would provide a method of cheap and rapid transport of cattle and of preserving potentially valuable strains or breeds of cattle for future use; in breeding programmes, while embryos are stored prior to use, their parents or sibs, or both, could be tested for production characteristics.

Some of the earliest efforts in the frozen storage of mammalian embryos were those of

Averill and Rowson (1959) working with sheep but it was not until the birth of two calves after transfer of blastocysts previously stored in liquid nitrogen (Wilmut, 1973; Wilmut and Rowson, 1973) that hopes were raised that cattle embryos might soon be shipped around the world in flasks of liquid nitrogen in much the same way as bull semen. Work at Cambridge subsequently showed that in the early stages of embryonic development, up to the morula stage, cattle eggs are particularly sensitive to cooling and do not survive well after exposure to temperatures around 0°C; by contrast, embryos at the blastocyst stage will tolerate cooling much better and are therefore more suitable for freezing (Trounson et al., 1976a, b,).

Based on methods evolved for the freezing of sheep embryos (Willadsen et al., 1974, 1976a) succcessful freezing and thawing of cattle embryos was reported by Willadsen et al. (1976b) at Cambridge. Although the first succcessful storage of blastocysts from the cow was obtained after slow cooling and rapid thawing, survival rate was low (>10%) in the work of Wilmut and Rowson (1973). It was initially thought that rapid thawing was deleterious to embryo survival, whatever the rate of cooling, until later work with sheep and cattle embryos showed that these could survive rapid thawing, provided that slow cooling is terminated between -30°C and -45°C by direct transfer to liquid nitrogen (Willadsen, 1977; Willadsen et al., 1978; Willadsen and Polge, 1980). As well as the efforts of the Cambridge group, studies were reported around the same time by investigators in Australia (Bilton and Moore, 1976, 1977), Denmark (Lehn-Jensen and Greve, 1977; Lehn-Jensen, 1978; Lehn-Jensen and Greve, 1978), Holland (Trounson et al., 1978) and North America (Shea et al., 1977; Trounson et al., 1978).

Enriched phosphate buffers (PBS) similar to those used for fresh storage have been employed in frozen storage, and in most of the early studies, 1.5–2.0 M dimethyl sulphoxide (DMSO) was the cryoprotectant used. Work reported by Bilton and Moore (1979) showed that 1.0 M glycerol was as good as DMSO at 1.5 M, a finding already established for the mouse (Whittingham et al., 1972) and goat (Bilton and Moore, 1976). As well

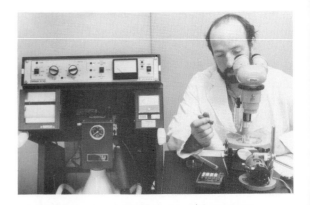

Fig. 7.7. Freezing and the frozen storage of cattle embryos. Freezing techniques applicable to cattle embryos have improved markedly over the past decade. The first calf born in 1973 after being frozen as an embryo was the only survivor out of about 40; today it can be expected that 50% or more of frozen embryos can develop on into calves on transfer to recipient cows. For the frozen storage of embryos to become really useful, it is necessary for the present complex and time-consuming procedures to be simplified. The hope is that it will prove practicable to freeze the embryo in the straw, using methods that will dilute out cryoprotectants when the straw is thawed out prior to making transfers. It would seem likely that freezing in straws will become as commonplace with embryos as it is with bull semen.

as DMSO and glycerol, studies elsewhere have shown that other cryoprotectants, including 1.2-propanediol, can be effective in the preservation of cow embryos (Renard et al., 1981).

As freezing investigations continue, the conditions during freezing and thawing that affect embryonic survival are becoming better known. It is no longer necessary, as already mentioned, to adhere to the strict requirements of slow thawing in order to obtain maximum survival of embryos. By freezing eggs rapidly to –196°C from about –30°C, the survival rate is high after rapid thawing. As noted by Bilton and Moore (1979), rapid cooling may require rapid thawing, because rapid cooling may mean incomplete dehydration and rapid thawing prevents growth and rearrangement of ice crystals in the cell. Why slow cooling requires slow thawing is not well understood. There are undoubtedly many ways in which procedures for low temperature preservation will become better understood so that they may be simplified and practical applications made easier.

Kanagawa et al. (1979) drew attention to the

fact that the freezing methods for cattle embryos were much the same as those employed very successfully in mice, despite the cattle egg being much larger (80% larger) in volume and having a much thicker zona pellucida (70% thicker) than the mouse egg; these workers tried to speed up the diffusion rate through the zona pellucida (the barrier preventing rapid osmotic equilibrium between blastomeres and medium) of the cattle egg by puncturing the membrane by micro-manipulation.

Cattle embryos have usually been frozen in glass ampoules, but plastic straws (as used in cattle AI) were used by Massip et al. (1979) who showed that the survival and development of cattle embryos frozen and thawed in 0.25 ml plastic straws was comparable to that achieved with glass ampoules. The 0.25 ml straw was seen to be attractive because it is the smallest container available and it could be used in the nonsurgical transfer of the cattle embryo once it was thawed. However, removing the cryoprotectant after thawing out the embryo is one of the aspects that needs simplifying; current procedures involve removing the DMSO, glycerol or other agent by a reverse of procedures employed for its addition. The survival rate in embryos in the absence of removal of DMSO from the thawed organism is known to be substantially decreased (Willadsen et al., 1978). In work elsewhere, Schneider and Hahn (1979) attempted removing DMSO more rapidly by employing a hypertonic PBS solution; a procedure involving rapid dilution of the DMSO cryoprotectant was found to work well with mice eggs (Whittingham et al., 1979) and may prove useful with cattle embryos.

7.11.1 Survival after transfer

It is still unknown why there should be differences between mammalian species (cattle and pigs) and between developmental stages of the same egg (day-3 vs day-7) in sensitivity to cooling 0°C. On the basis of present evidence, it would appear that the optimal stage for freezing cattle embryos is the blastocyst prior to hatching (day-7/8 embryos) when survival rates up to 80% have been achieved; there is evidence that frozen-thawed cattle embryos may need an intact zona pellucida at transfer for achieving

satisfactory pregnancy rates (Tervit et al., 1981). In general, current experience suggests that pregnancy rates after thawing and transferring unselected frozen embryos are about half those with unfrozen eggs (Seidel and Seidel, 1978; Tervit et al., 1981). This means that twice as many embryos must be transferred in order to achieve the same number of pregnancies as without freezing. As noted by Schneider et al. (1980), commercial results from frozen–thawed embryos may occasionally be low because of a tendency to freeze any embryo that looks as though it may survive and for eggs to be selected after freezing rather than before. It is only to be expected that freezing techniques will become increasingly effective in future years with the growth of knowledge and experience in this area of research.

7.11.2 Storage of oocytes

The frozen storage of the unfertilized cattle egg would provide the opportunity of making various crosses at some point in the future; already there have been reports dealing with the freezing and thawing of unfertilized mice, rat, hamster and gerbil eggs. With the mouse, there was a claim that live young had been produced from oocytes frozen in mouse ovarian tissue, according to one report in the 1960s. In more recent times, live offspring have resulted from the transfer on in vitro fertilized eggs (Tsunoda et al., 1976; Whittingham, 1977); the overall survival rate of eggs to birth was found to be very low (<10%) which the investigators thought may have been due to the induction of aneuploidy caused by the disruption of the second meiotic spindle during cooling and thawing. This would seem to be an aspect deserving further investigation if unfertilized cattle eggs are to be stored for breeding purposes.

7.11.3 Sex control by embryo transfer

One intriguing possibility which lies in the future is in using embryo transfer technology to enable the cattle producer to specify whether his animals are to produce bull or heifer calves. All attempts thus far at separating male and female cattle sperm have failed and there are those who feel that such separation may prove a particularly difficult undertaking (Beatty, 1972). Sex control by embryo transfer, on the other hand, was first demonstrated in rabbits by Gardener and Edwards (1968) who "sexed" the embryo by identifying the presence or absence of the sex chromatin mass. Around the same time, Rowson and Moore (1966) had observed that the removal of a small piece of trophoblast from 13-day old sheep embryos did not prevent most of these subsequently developing to term as normal lambs in recipient ewes; this finding was made use of in later work by Canadian investigators in cattle. Successful sexing and transfer of 2-week-old cattle embryos, using excised trophoblast cells for sex determination, was reported in due course (Hare et al., 1976; Mitchell et al., 1976); it was found possible to sex 68% of the biopsied embryos (using chromosomal analysis) with a 45% pregnancy rate in the recipients of these biopsied embryos.

The Canadian technique and modifications of it have been used in other laboratories and, on average, it is possible to determine sex in about 70% of the cattle embryos at the 12–15 day stage (Brand et al., 1978; Wintenberger-Torres and Popescu, 1979). An inability to sex the embryo can be attributed to poor quality or the fact that metaphase spreads were not obtained from the biopsied trophoblast. In testing the method further, there was a 15% reduction in pregnancy rate compared with controls in the Canadian work (Hare et al., 1978). A serious disadvantage in carrying out sex determination as late as day-12/15 is that the cattle embryo cannot be frozen effectively at that stage; this means that collection, sexing and transfer all have to be carried out during a very short time-span, which can make the procedure costly.

7.11.4 Sexing the week-old embryo

As already mentioned, by day-7 it is possible to freeze the cattle embryo very effectively; Moustafa et al. (1978) aroused interest when they reported being able to sex cattle embryos at the day-6/7 stage with a succcess rate similar to that obtained by others for the day-12/15 embryos and with a pregnancy rate of 71%. However, in a subsequent report by Singh and Hare (1980), in which they attempted to sex morula stage cattle embryos, the findings of Moustafa et al. (1978) could not be confirmed and the Canadian workers concluded that the very low success rate in sexing week-old cattle embryos did not warrant consideration of freezing sexed embryos at that stage. The difficulty with trying to sex at 7 rather than at 14 days is that the mitotic activity of the cells in so low, making the chromosomal analysis procedure that much more difficult than with older embryos. Even with 2-week old embryos, the sexing may severely reduce survival rate; only 21% of recipients proved to be pregnant after two-egg transfers of sexed embryos in work with day-13 embryos reported by Wintenberger-Torres and Popescu (1980).

7.11.5 Future sexing possibilities

Present procedures based on chromosomal analysis are tedious and time-consuming and before sexing can be applied on any general scale, it must be made simple, fast, cheap and non-damaging to embryos, as noted by several authors (Wilmut, 1980; Seidel, 1981); it may be that it becomes a question of detecting the gene product of the Y chromosome, ie. the H-Y antigen, on the cattle embryo, as can be done for some mammalian species (Kcro and Goldberg, 1976). A more immediate possibility would be in linking up sexing techniques with those employed for the production of identical multiples in cattle (Willadsen and Polge, 1981); three of four "quarter" embryos could perhaps be frozen stored while the fourth is sexed as a late embryo to provide information on the gender of the three identicals.

7.12 SHORT TERM CULTURE AND STORAGE TECHNIQUES

In any cattle embryo transfer programme, it is clearly essential that fertilized eggs remain viable, in vitro, for a period of several hours. A number of the early authors reported limited success in storing sheep embryos at refrigerator temperatures and in Ireland workers used a temperature of 10°C (Sreenan, 1968; Sreenan et al., 1970) which was sufficient to arrest cleavage of cattle eggs; embryos stored for 1 day at this temperature resumed what appeared to be normal development when transferred to the rabbit oviduct. However, it is now known that the cooling of day-5/6 cattle eggs below 10°C can substantially reduce their chances of survival and rapid cooling can decrease survival rate to a greater degree than slow cooling (Trounson et al., 1976); it would seem that resistance of cattle embryos to cooling to 0°C does not develop until they approach the day-7 blastocyst stage.

7.12.1 Media employed in recovery and transfer

In work at body temperature, early efforts at culturing cattle eggs in homologous blood serum met with very little success (Dowling, 1949; Pincus, 1949; Brock and Rowson, 1952; Hafez et al., 1963). It was later reported, however, that bovine follicular fluid would support limited cleavage of cattle eggs (Thibault, 1966; Sreenan, 1968) and shortly afterwards Rowson et al. (1969) successfully employed Tissue Culture Medium (TCM) 199 as a recovery and transfer medium. Although TCM 199 was used in the early and mid-1970s by the Cambridge group, as well as by Betteridge and Mitchell (1974), Sreenan and Beehan (1974), Sreenan et al. (1975) and many others, it was by no means regarded as an ideal medium. During the second half of the 1970s, workers started using Dulbecco's phosphate buffered saline (PBS) either supplemented according to Whittingham (1971) with glucose, sodium pyruvate and bovine serum albumin (BSA) or supplemented with foetal calf serum (FCS); the medium has come to be recognized as a particularly effective one (Boland et al., 1975; Trounson et al., 1976; Brand et al., 1978). Heat inactivated FCS (or even ordinary cattle or sheep serum) is added in volumes of 1% for flushing and 10–20% for storage; as a source of macro-molecules, homologous or heterologous heat inactivated blood serum or its albumin-fraction has come to be an essential component of most culture media (Kane, 1978).

7.12.2 Culture systems

As noted by Anderson (1978), culture systems designed for storing cattle embryos temporarily before transfer may be quite different from those necessary to support cleavage in vitro. The use of TCM 199 with Hepes buffer and supplemented with 5% heat inactivated bovine serum proved to be satisfactory for storing cattle embryos for several hours before transfer, either at 37°C or room temperature (Seidel, 1974; Drost et al., 1975) but the medium does not support continued development in vitro for long periods. Cattle and sheep embryos cultured by Tervit et al. (1972) in a synthetic fluid medium and with a specific gas phase (5% CO_2/5% O_2/90% N_2) cleaved readily enough and lambs were born after culture of sheep eggs in the medium for up to 6 days (Tervit and Rowson, 1974); the same culture system, however, gave very poor pregnancy rates with cattle eggs (Tervit, 1973).

After examining the effectiveness of a number of culture media (including TCM 199, synthetic oviduct fluid, Brinster's mouse ova culture medium (BMOC) and Whitten's mouse ova culture medium) in maintaining cattle embryos in a viable condition, Peters et al. (1978) found the most acceptable to be Ham's F 10 medium supplemented with 10% heat-treated foetal calf serum; embryos were cultured from the early cleavage stage to that of the hatched blastocysts (7-days) and were tested successfully for usability after 24 h culture. Comparing PBS and the modified Ham's F 10 medium, Hahn et al. (1978) found the survival rate of eggs to be much less in PBS than in the F 10. Boone et al. (1978) described techniques using the BMOC-3 medium containing α-ketoglutarate which were effective; a high percentage (92%) of 6–8-day eggs cultured in BMOC-3 plus 10% FCS for 24 h were normal and on transfer gave pregnancy rates comparable to those after transfer on the day of recovery (Schneider et al., 1980). Work elsewhere by Kanagawa (1980) reported culturing 6-day embryos in BMOC for 24 h at either 20–25°C or at 4–5°C; good survival rates were observed on transfer to recipients after 24 h but not after 48 h. Further studies by Japanese workers, using the BMOC medium are reported by Takahashi (1981) and Takahashi and Suzuki (1981).

The media most commonly employed in current embryo transfer in cattle (PBS or TCM 199) can be considered satisfactory for short-term storage (i.e. between recovery and transfer of embryos). An acceptable medium for in vitro culture for more than about 2 days has still to be reported. It should be noted that one important consideration is that the survival rate of transferred embryos may be adversely affected when they have undergone a period of culture prior to transfer; Renard et al. (1980) records evidence that the proportion of embryos surviving at day-60 of pregnancy was less with those cultured for 24 h before transfer than in those transferred within a few hours of recovery from the donor. Bon Durant et al. (1981) deal with pregnancy rates after transfer of cattle embryos stored at 4°C for periods up to 48 h and record that these were comparable to those for frozen–thawed embryos.

7.12.3 Storage in the rabbit

Early attempts to store cattle eggs in the rabbit did not succeed (Hafez and Sugie, 1963) but later efforts were successful (Sreenan and Scanlon, 1968) when it became evidence that blood serum was probably not a satisfactory medium for the recovery and transfer of cattle eggs to the rabbit (Sreenan et al., 1968). These observations were extended by Cambridge workers (Adams et al., 1968; Rowson et al., 1969; Tervit and Rowson, 1972); not only did it become clear that early-cleavage cattle eggs continue developing satisfactorily for several days (4 days regarded as limit), but that a high percentage are capable of continuing on as normal embryos after re-transfer to the cow (Lawson et al., 1972; Gordon, 1976).

7.13 SYNCHRONIZING OESTRUS IN DONOR AND RECIPIENT

Over the years, studies in the farm species have clearly shown that the survival of embryos depends on their stage of development corresponding closely to the developmental stage of the recipient's uterus. At the same time, much remains in determining the precise nature of many factors involved in the survival of cattle embryos after transfer; there may occasionally be circumstances, as noted later, when exact synchrony between donor and recipient may not always result in optimum pregnancy rates. There

is also the fact that early work in cattle transfer almost always involved recipient animals selected on the basis of a naturally occurring oestrus; since the mid-1970's, the selection of recipients has widened to include animals that have their oestrous cycles modified by exogenous hormones. Clearly, the use of synchronizing agents ($PGF_{2\alpha}$ or progestagens) must not result in an adverse effect on pregnancy rates. It should also be mentioned that one great advantage of working with frozen rather than fresh cattle embryos is that it becomes a matter of embryos waiting for the recipient to arrive at the appropriate stage rather than the converse.

7.13.1 Importance of synchrony

Experiments directed specifically towards elucidating the importance of exact synchrony between donor and recipient in the successful establishment of pregnancy in cattle have been few; nevertheless, a considerable body of less controlled evidence has accumulated in course of the commercial exploitation of the embryo transfer technique. Rowson et al. (1969) were among the first to show that exact synchrony resulted in the highest pregnancy rate and that a degree of variation between donor and recipient cycles of ± 2 days could be tolerated; it should be mentioned that it has usually been the start of oestrus rather than the end that has been used as the reference point in matching animals although it is really ovulation (which occurs after heat) which is the crucial physiological event calling for alignment.

Cambridge work subsequently provided evidence of a marked decline in the pregnancy rate of recipients for each day they were out of exact synchrony with their respective donors over the range ±3 days; there were strong indications in these data that the synchronization requirements for successful embryo transfers in cattle may be more acute than in sheep (Rowson et al., 1972). Although this work showed that pregnancy rate dropped sharply between recipients at exact synchrony and those at ±1 day (91 vs 52–57%), there was a question mark over the exceptionally high value recorded for the cattle exactly aligned. The studies of Sugie et al. (1972) in Japan around the same time revealed much less of a difference pregnancy rates between cattle at exact synchrony and those out-of-phase by ±1 day, although in all categories the pregnancy rates in recipient cattle were on a much lower level than those of the Cambridge workers. Later studies at Cambridge, however, reported differences no more than about 10% between recipients exactly aligned and those out-of-phase by ±1 day (Newcomb and Rowson, 1975).

7.13.2 Irish studies and others

Work in Ireland, which reported high pregnancy rates after surgical transfer, also observed a greater proportion of pregnancies among the exactly synchronized cattle than in those out-of-phase by ±1 day (Sreenan and Beehan, 1974; Sreenan et al., 1975). Although there had been a suggestion by Trounson et al. (1976) that cattle out-of-phase by ±1 day might show higher pregnancy rates when the donor was in advance of the recipient, more extensive Canadian data did not support this (Shea et al., 1976), showing a 63% pregnancy rate in 1126 cattle at exact alignment, 60% in 334 recipients which had shown oestrus 1 day ahead of donors (−1) and 49% in 556 cattle exhibiting heat 1 day after their respective donors (+1). Further evidence along similar lines was apparent in data generated in Texas in commercial applications (Schneider et al., 1980); on the basis of 2556 transfers, exactly synchronized cattle showed a pregnancy rate of 67%, those in oestrus 12 h earlier than donors 66% and those in heat 12 h later than donors 61% (significantly lower). The Texan workers note that in practice, recipients that exhibit oestrus 12 h after a donor can often be employed as recipients for donors collected from on the next day. A report by Wright (1981) also noted that recipients in heat 12 h before donors showed good pregnancy rates.

7.13.3 Asynchronous recipients

Selection of recipients in large commercial transfer units favours animals either in exact synchrony or in heat before the donors. On certain occasions, however, there may be merit in asynchrony rather than exact alignment of donor and recipient; thus, cattle in oestrus 1 day earlier than donors in studies reported by Halley et al. (1979) in Brahman cattle showed a significantly higher pregnancy rate (42%) than those at exact synchrony (26%). The same authors do note, however, that metabolic and developmental differences between the embryos of Bos taurus and Bos indicus cattle may be a factor explaining such results.

7.13.4 Frozen embryos

With increasing knowledge and experience in the area of low temperature preservation of cattle embryos, it will become commonplace to arrange such exact synchrony on the basis of thawing the frozen embryo when the recipient reaches the appropriate stage of her cycle. In the early days of transfer work in cattle, when early cleavage stage eggs (3- to 4-day old) were usually employed, the hazards of asynchrony may have tended to be greater than they are today when the older 7-day embryo is used; early cleavage eggs are now recognized as being much more susceptible to adverse effects, whether these take the form of reduced temperatures (Trounson et al., 1976a) or premature exposure of the early cleavage egg to the uterine environment. Newcomb and Rowson (1975), for instance, recorded that the transfer of day-4 eggs to the uterus of day-3 recipients resulted in a significantly higher pregnancy rate than when the day-3 donor was exactly synchronous with the day-3 recipient.

7.13.5 Effects of synchronizing treatments

In sheep, it was well established some time ago that pregnancy rates after embryo transfer were not adversely affected by progestagen/progesterone treatments employed in the synchronization of recipients (Hunter et al., 1955; Moore et al., 1960; Shelton and Moore, 1966); evidence along the same lines for cattle has been provided by Sreenan et al. (1976) and Sreenan and Beehan (1976). It is also clear that when $PGF_{2\alpha}$ or one of its analogues is employed as the synchronizing agent in recipients, pregnancy rates after transfer have also been no different from those found in recipients showing a spontaneous oestrus (Rowson et al., 1972; Sreenan et al., 1975).

Before the advent of effective synchronization

treatments for cattle, it was necessary for commercial transfer units to maintain a large herd of potential recipients so that the required number could be found in alignment with the donors; for various reasons, this may still be the preferred system with some transfer units. The usual rule is to have 10–20 potential recipients available and in synchrony with each donor animal (Seidel and Seidel, 1978). This can often represent the major cost in operating a transfer unit, when it may be a matter of maintaining hundreds of potential recipients in prime reproductive condition, as well as those recipients that have received eggs and are waiting until the 3-month stage of pregnancy before being moved out of the unit. Currently, there are transfer units in North America operating with anything up to 2000 recipients on hand at all times; other units may prefer being mobile and conducting recovery/transfer operations on the farm itself, employing synchronizing agents to align donors and recipients.

There are obvious practical difficulties in transfer units recruiting and maintaining large groups of recipients in prime reproductive condition. Quite apart from ensuring that recipients are of acceptable quality and that their feeding and management is of suitably high standard, there is some likelihood that such animals may not always be capable of functioning at peak reproductive efficiency for other reasons. In the U.K., Williams (1960) drew attention more than 20 years ago to a temporary form of sub-fertility that may operate among cattle recruited from several sources and grouped together in unfamiliar surroundings.

7.14 TRANSFER TECHNIQUES, SURGICAL AND NON-SURGICAL

The work of Rowson et al. (1969, 1971, 1972) marked an important turning point in cattle transfer prospects by showing, not only that an acceptable pregnancy rate could be achieved by a surgical technique, but that these rates could be substantially above those regarded as normal in the untreated cow (90% + as compared with 60% or so). Although there was a suggestion that the exceptionally high pregnancy rates achieved may have stemmed from the elimination of abnormal and retarded eggs and the maintenance of exact synchrony between donor and recipient, part of the explanation may have been the fact that two eggs rather than one were used in transfers. It would seem probable that one means of achieving a higher pregnancy rate in cattle lies in using two egg transfers; data that were summarized by Betteridge (1977) from several reports would appear to support this view. This would seem to be in contrast to the situation in sheep, where pregnancy rates are not necessarily improved by increasing the number of embryos transferred.

7.14.1 Mid-ventral and flank procedures

In carrying out surgical transfers, workers may use the mid-ventral approach (as previously described for collection of embryos); having brought the uterine horn to the incision and confirmed the location of the corpus luteum, the uterus is punctured with a suitable instrument directed towards the tip of the ipsilateral horn and the embryo subsequently deposited by Pasteur pipette in a minimum volume of medium. Although the mid-ventral procedure can be carried out quickly on heifer cattle, it is both labour and capital intensive and is not at all suitable for use on the farm.

Consequently, much of the commercial embryo transfer work in cattle has been done using the flank approach with the recipient standing sedated and under local anaesthetic. The method was used in early studies by Avery et al. (1962) in the U.S.A. and Baker (1973) in Australia was one of the first to report on it in the 1970s. The site of incision is the sublumbar fossa and the embryo is transferred into the uterine lumen towards the tip of the horn as in the mid-ventral method. Prior to surgery, the location of the corpus luteum is established by palpation per rectum to show the side on which the transfer should be made. Compared with the mid-ventral technique, the flank approach is seen by many to be a highly successful, practical and rapid means of performing surgical transfers with a minimum of equipment, facilities and labour (Evans et al., 1979; Schneider and Hahn, 1979); clearly, in dealing with lactating recipient animals or others in which mammary development would present problems, the flank method would have an advantage. There have been those who suggest that the method may be more practicable in dairy heifers than among less tractable range cattle (Elsden, 1977); certainly, Schneider and Hahn (1979) prefer it because the technique is easy to employ in the docile type of cow they deal with in Germany.

Several groups have attempted to make comparisons between the mid-ventral and flank approaches (Newcomb, 1979; Rowe et al., 1980; Shelton et al., 1980); as well as recording the fact that results with the flank approach were equal to those with the mid-ventral technique (59% pregnancy rate for flank method, 57% for mid-ventral), Shelton et al. (1980) found they could employ the flank approach over a much wider range of conditions than the mid-ventral.

7.14.2 Early efforts at non-surgical transfers

Although some small degree of success with transfer after mid-ventral laparotomy in cattle was reported by workers in the United States in the early 1950s (Willett et al., 1951, 1953), most efforts at that time were concentrated on transcervical non-surgical transfer (Dowling, 1949; Umbaugh, 1949; Rowson, 1951; Lamming and Rowson, 1952; Dracy, 1953; Dziuk et al., 1958; Avery et al., 1962). No success was achieved with this mode of transfer in the 1950s; with hindsight, it is evident that several factors, quite apart from the transfer method itself, precluded the possibility of pregnancy in these early attempts.

At that time, it was generally believed that the susceptibility of the bovine uterus to infection in the luteal phase posed a serious problem to any thought of a transcervical transfer approach (Lamming and Rowson, 1953; Rowson et al., 1953). There was also the somewhat unexpected finding that artificial resin "eggs" were ejected from the cow's uterus with ease and speed after cervical transfer (Bennett and Rowson, 1961; Harper et al., 1961) and that such ejection was not prevented by any of the obvious drug treatments (Rowson et al., 1964). However, studies in the U.S.A. by Dziuk et al. (1958) did suggest that the

addition of trace amounts of antibiotics to the medium might control uterine infection and that cervical transfer per se need not necessarily interfere with the progress of a normal pregnancy.

7.14.3 Attempts to circumvent the cervix

Efforts in non-surgical transfer continued sporadically through the 1960s, although pregnancy rates achieved were far below the level necessary for any commercial interest. An isolated instance of success after a cervical transfer was reported by Mutter et al. (1964) but is of historic interest only. Hafez and Sugie (1963) devised a set of transfer instruments designed to by-pass the cervix (thereby, hopefully, avoiding the ejection phenomenon) and to be guided into the uterus by manipulation per rectum; carbon dioxide was used to distend the uterus and enable the lumen to be defined. Sugie (1965), reporting on the first use of this equipment, recorded establishing two pregnancies. Rowson and Moor (1966), at about the same time, reported three pregnancies in fourteen recipients; their procedure involved transcervical transfer with subsequent inflation of the uterus with CO_2, supposedly to inhibit myometrial activity. Later studies at Cambridge, using TCM 199 rather than blood serum as the recovery and transfer medium, resulted in four pregnancies among twenty recipients (20% pregnancy rate) and up to 40% when later stage embryos were transferred (Lawson et al., 1975). Japanese workers continued with their approach into the early seventies, with Sugie et al. (1972b) transferring eggs to sixty-eight recipients to achieve an 18% calving rate; as well as the unacceptably low pregnancy rate, the need to maintain recipients in an immobile condition and the considerable manipulative expertise required ruled out the feasibility of using this approach on any scale.

7.14.4 Transfer with Cassou Gun

Although earlier attempts at transfer via the cervix with inseminating pipettes did not meet with success in Ireland (Sreenan, 1969), by the mid-1970s two groups in the country were able to report pregnancies after embryo transfer with the Cassou artificial inseminating "gun" (Boland *et al.,* 1975; Sreenan, 1975). The method involved drawing an embryo into an 0.5 ml or 0.25 ml plastic straw, placing the straw in the AI gun and covering it with an outer plastic sheath; the gun was then introduced directly through the cervix and the embryo expelled into the uterus Boland *et al.* (1975) used the technique in mated beef heifers and achieved a 25% embryo survival rate; Sreenan (1975) reported a 50% pregnancy rate and a 25% embryo survival rate in eight unmated heifers that received two embryos each. Around this time, reports were appearing in the literature showing that transfers via the cervix at day-5 and beyond of the cow's cycle were likely to be much more successful than those attempted earlier. Apart from the older egg being less susceptible to damage through temperature fluctuations, there now was evidence that spontaneous activity of the myometrium died away after about day 4/5 (Brand *et al.,* 1976) and that this would alleviate the egg ejection phenomenon. There was further evidence against egg ejection occurring at day 5 or later in the report of Rowson *et al.* (1972) who were unable to demonstrate oxytocin release after vaginal and cervical stimulation on day-5; work by Newcomb *et al.* (1977) also showed that higher levels of $PGF_{2\alpha}$ were released in response to oxytocin treatment on day-3 than on day-6, the implication being that the situation for transfers was more favourable at day-6. In the U.S.A. there was a report by Seidel *et al.* (1975) showing that fertility was not impaired by sham non-surgical transfers on day-6 to previously bred heifers, providing aseptic precautions were taken.

7.14.5 Non-surgical vs surgical transfers

Although instruments designed specifically for the non-surgical transfer of cattle embryos have been described in the literature (Hahn *et al.,* 1975 Brand, 1975; Hahn and Hahn, 1976; Rasbech, 1976, 1978), most transfers via the cervix are presently carried out with the *Cassou* inseminating gun or modifications of it. Brand and Drost (1977) provided a survey of the results achieved with the method up to that time, showing an average embryo survival rate of 24% for non-surgical transfer and 55% for surgical transfers. Probably a more realistic appraisal of the current situation is that of Hahn *et al.* (1980) who provide

comparative data (57% surgical vs 49% non-surgical) and express the view that with further improvements to the transfer instrument, it should be possible to replace surgical methods with the non-surgical approach. A comparison between non-surgical transfer (0.25 ml straw) and flank surgical is given by Takahashi (1980) in Japan; a pregnancy rate of 57% was achieved by surgery as against 32% using the inseminating gun.

7.14.6 Experience of technicians

A feature of several reports dealing with *Cassou* "gun" transfer has been the fact that the success rate has varied according to the experience of the workers conducting the transfers. Rowe *et al.* (1980) found that an experienced operator achieved a 58% pregnancy rate as against 35% for a person with no previous non-surgical experience; Schneider *et al.* (1980) and Curtis *et al.* (1981) also reported a significant difference in pregnancy rates achieved by different technicians, indicating a degree of dexterity or experience required to perform successfully non-surgical transfers.

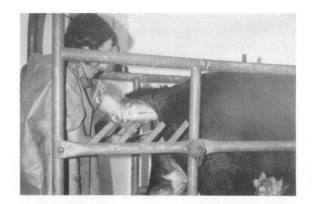

Fig. 7.8. Transfer of a cattle embryo into the ipsilateral horn of the recipient cow by way of the *Cassou* gun. Attempts to induce pregnancy in cattle by non-surgical transfer of eggs go back more than 30 years. A major step came in 1975 when Irish workers reported success using the *Cassou* inseminating gun as the method of placing the embryo into the uterus. Although pregnancy rates with non-surgical transfer are lower than those after surgical transfer, there is every reason to believe that techniques can be refined and improved to the point where the two procedures give comparable pregnancy rates.

7.14.7 Heifer or cow recipient

In most embryo transfer reports, heifers rather than cows have served as recipients, although it is well established that cervical penetration of a heifer during the luteal phase is more difficult than in the cow. Greve (1976) and Boland and Gordon (1978) used milking cows as recipients rather than heifers, but without any obvious improvement in pregnancy rates beyond those expected in the maiden animal. Newcomb (1979) and Greve and Lehn-Jensen (1979), on the other hand, using cows as recipients did record higher than average pregnancy rates (56–80%) and ascribe part of their success to the atraumatic deposition of the embryo in the uterus. The ease with which the embryo is transferred, using the *Cassou* gun, was noted by Gordon (1976) as a possible factor affecting the ensuing pregnancy rate and several reports subsequently provided some support for this view (Newcomb, 1979; Greve and Lehn-Jensen, 1979; Tervit *et al.*, 1980; Wright, 1981); this may be taken as evidence of the desirability of employing an atraumatic transfer technique.

7.14.8 Age of embryo at transfer

Newcomb and Rowson (1975) were the first to show clearly that the stage of development of the transferred cattle egg was a most important consideration; the percentage of recipient heifers that became pregnant rose from 10% in these receiving day-3 eggs to 55% with day-4 eggs, 73% with day-5 and 82% pregnant with day-6/7 embryos. Evidence from other sources also became available to show that survival rate may be markedly lower with day-3 or day-4 eggs than with the week-old embryo (Nelson *et al.*, 1975; Hahn and Hahn, 1976; Trounson *et al.*, 1976); as already noted, the recognition of the suscepti-bility of the early stage cattle egg to low temperature constitutes one of the important milestone in cattle transfer work. The studies of Newcomb (1979) would indicate that day-7 embryos survive as readily as day-8 or day-10 embryos, so that in deciding on a particular stage for carrying out cattle transfers, the week-old embryo has much to commend it.

7.14.9 Placement of the embryo

Although the deposition of the embryo in the upper reaches of the ipsilateral uterine horn poses no problem when the transfer is performed surgically, there is a definite limit in what can be achieved using the non-surgical transfer appro-ach. The curvature of the horn imposes a limit to the depth to which the *Cassou* inseminating "gun" can be inserted. There is ample evidence to show that the embryo should be deposited in the ipsilateral horn. Newcomb and Rowson (1976) and Sreenan (1976) were among the first to show marked evidence of a higher survival rate in embryos transferred to the ipsilateral as compared to the contralateral horns; there are others who recorded differences in favour of the ipsilateral horn, although not so clearcut (Del Campo *et al.*, 1977; Tervit *et al.*, 1977).

At a week-old, the bovine embryo is still in the upper reaches of the uterine horn (Newcomb and Willadsen, 1975; Newcomb *et al.*, 1976), presumably several inches distant from the site of deposition likely to be achieved by the *Cassou* "gun" method of non-surgical transfer. There have been those who have made direct comparisons between the *Cassou* "gun" and a catheter device designed to place the embryo as near as possible to the tip of the horn. Wilmut *et al.* (1978), using day-8 embryos, recorded seven calves born after *Cassou* "gun" transfer to thirty-seven suckler cattle but no pregnancy after thirty transfers with a catheter device.

Elsewhere, Bowen *et al.* (1978), using a catheter to transfer to ninety-five heifers, reported a 19% pregnancy rate, a figure much below the average for their surgical transfers; no pregnancy was established when difficulty was experienced in gaining entry to the uterus through the cervix. As already mentioned, acceptable pregnancy rates do follow placement of the egg in the tip of the uterine horn by surgical means and the indications are that catheter devices may cause damage to the endometrium such that embryo survival is jeopardized, perhaps as a result of the escape of blood (which is embryotoxic) from ruptured capillary vessels.

In examining the outcome of non-surgical transfers using catheter devices, it should be noted that Seidel *et al.* (1975) did perform sham transfers by this means in cattle already bred a week earlier without adversely affecting pregnancies. Although there have been one or two favourable reports from those attempting to place the embryo close to the tip of the uterus (Jillella et al., 1977; Jillella and Baker, 1978), the general consensus would seem to be that there is no advantage over the lower horn placement; this is all the more likely to hold true for embryos a week-old or beyond.

7.14.10 Modification to Cassou Gun

It is essential to ensure that the embryo is safely deposited in the lumen of the cow's uterus and that it remains in situ after the Cassou "gun" is withdrawn. With transfers performed by surgery, it is easier to be definite about the placement of the embryo than when this is done non-surgically; the possibility always exists that embryos are occasionally lost in the non-surgical process. Making quite certain that the embryo is safely located in the lumen of the uterus may be one aspect of transcervical transfer which should be better examined.

There are probably many ways in which relatively minor adjustments to the Cassou "gun" transfer technique may result in an improvement in the results achieved. German workers have employed a modified Cassou "gun" and examined uterine tracts after sham transfers, observing that injury to the uterine mucosa may occasionally occur due to the sharp tip of the outer plastic sheath (Schneider and Hahn, 1979); Cambridge modifications have included a Cassou "gun" with a larger diameter stainless steel sheath which is carefully rounded at its free end to make for atraumatic passage along the uterine horn (Newcomb, 1979). In Japan, Takahashi et al. (1981) used an AI instrument covered with a paper sheath to achieve a pregnancy rate of 59% in thirteen recipients which they transferred to.

7.14.11 Aseptic precautions

The general view is that introduction of infectious agents into the uterus by way of the Cassou "gun" technique is not likely to be a source of pregnancy failure, provided aseptic precautions are taken (Brand et al., 1976; Trounson et al., 1978); as an additional measure, Cambridge workers protected the Cassou "gun" from contamination in the recipient's vagina by a plastic sleeve. Nevertheless, as Brand and Akabwau (1978) point out, even if bacteriological examination of instruments after non-surgical transfer yields negative results, viral contamination during transfer may still occur and be a source of difficulty later; these same authors mention the possibility of increasing the volume of the transfer medium when using non-surgical transfer in order to dilute serum (resulting from endometrial damage) and thus minimise any embryotoxic effect.

7.14.12 Recipient considerations

Far and away the largest single cost in cattle embryo transfer operations is in getting a supply of suitable recipients and maintaining them in a non-pregnant state until embryos are available for transfer. As mentioned by Seidel (1981), recipients should certainly not be recruited from undesirable cattle rejected for other purposes. Although obviously genetically less valuable than the donor cattle, recipients must be highly fertile, free from disease and able to give birth to a calf without complications. It may also be considered desirable that the recipient is capable of producing sufficient quantities of milk that the calf grows at an optimal rate.

There have been efforts to look at the hormone levels in potential recipients to see if the most suitable cattle could be screened to increase pregnancy rates after embryo transfer (Hasler et al., 1980), but there was no evidence that progesterone levels in the luteal phase could be used as a guide to subsequent capability as a host cow. On the feeding front, Dunn (1980) points out that the provision of adequate nutrition, but avoiding either extremely high or extremely low levels, is the prudent course; he recommends that in order to provide adequate nutrients for foetal growth and body maintenance of the recipient, cattle should be fed to gain 0.6–0.7 kg per day during the last trimester of gestation.

7.14.13 Attempts to improve pregnancy rates in recipients

There is evidence to show that the administration of massive doses of hCG treatment might be a means of improving pregnancy rates, particularly after non-surgical or contralateral surgical transfer. More than 20 years ago, some evidence was reported that the administration of progesterone could be used in early pregnancy to increase first service conception rate in normal cows (Johnson et al., 1958); in cattle transfer studies, progesterone treatment has also been found to have a beneficial effect on survival of the embryo (Kinkel et al., 1977), although it remains to be seen whether this is likely to be a practical procedure in dealing with recipients.

7.14.14 Embryo mortality and foetal loss

Studies reported by Sreenan and Beehan (1976) among heifer recipients after two-egg surgical transfers, suggested that the extent of embryonic and subsequent foetal loss between day-27 and full-term was quite small (5%); this was in agreement with an earlier report by Rowson et al. (1971). Surveying the literature on this aspect, Sreenan (1978) concluded that rectal palpation for pregnancy diagnosis or other experimental reasons may be one of the causes of the high embryonic or foetal loss recorded in many reports (Hahn and Hahn, 1976; Betteridge, 1977; Brand et al., 1978) and that the incidence of this mortality is no different after surgical or non-surgical transfers or AI. There may, as already noted, be some grounds for believing that cattle embryos cultured beyond 24 h or so in vitro may be more at risk during embryonic and foetal life than is usually the case with fresh or frozen–thawed embryos (Hahn et al., 1978; Betteridge et al., 1980).

7.15 FUTURE DEVELOPMENTS

Embryo transfer over the years has been an area of reproductive physiology which has excited the imagination of researchers and farmers alike in pointing towards an era in which cows of superior genetic merit may be superovulated and embryos taken one by one and transferred to the uteri of other, genetically less distinguished, host mothers. As mentioned earlier, commercial interests in the U.K., North America and Australasia started working primarily as a result of the 1969 Cambridge success and the explosion of interest in the "exotic" beef breeds (Charolais, Simmental, Limousin, etc.). It was probably a fortunate coincidence that advances in cattle embryo transfer occurred at the very time when the "exotics" were most sought after. Research in cattle embryo transfer is extremely costly and this has been one of the main reasons for the slow progress towards anything of commercial interest in this species during the past 30 years. There is, perhaps, a certain irony in the fact that the first to benefit from this high cost area of research should be those who can best afford to exploit the possible financial gains; in this regard, cattle embryo transfer has commenced its commercial career rather differently from artificial insemination.

Animal breeders, for some number of years, have drawn attention to the possible impact that technical developments such as embryo transfer and sex control may have upon the way that farm livestock are bred (Land and Hill, 1975; Cunningham, 1976). Artificial insemination remains the classic example in farming of a physiological technique capable of being widely applied and achieving substantial breeding improvements. It is not possible, however, to regard embryo transfer as a serious contender to AI in breeding improvement programmes for the general run of farmers until radical improvements in the present technology have been made.

It is exciting to look ahead at the many opportunities yet to be explored in making embryos for transfer available, running all the way up to the possibility of successfully applying nuclear transplantation technology on the farm.

7.16 REFERENCES

Adams, C. E., Moor, R. N. and Rowson, L. E. A. (1968) Survival of Cow and Sheep eggs in the rabbit oviduct. Proc. 6th Conf. Anim. Reproduc. A. I. (Paris) **1**, 573–574.

Anderson, G. B. (1978) Advances in large mammal embryo culture. In, Methods in Mammal Reprod., J. C. Daniel Jr., Ed. Ch. 13, pp. 224–283. Acad. Press, N.Y.

Angel, A. H. M. (1979) Endoscopic examinations in cattle with special reference to superovulation. *Inaugural Dissert. Tierarztliche Hochschule, Hannovec.*

Averill, R. L. W. and Rowson, L. E. A. (1959) Attempts at storage of sheep ova at low temperatures. *J. Agric. Sci.* **52,** 392–395.

Avery, T. L., Fahning, M. L., Pursel, V. G. and Graham, E. F. (1962) Investigations associated with the transplantation of bovine ova. IV. Transplantation of ova. *J. Reprod. Fert.* **3,** 229–238.

Avery, T. L., Fahning, M. L. and Graham, E. F. (1962) Investigations associated with the transplation of bovine ova. II. Superovulation. *J. Reprod. Fert.* **3,** 212–217.

Baker, A. A. (1973) Ovum transfer in the cow. *Aust. Vet. J.* **49**(9), 424–426.

Baker, A. A. and Jillella, D. (1978) Techniques of surgical and non-surgical ova collection of superovulated cows. *Vet. Rec.* **103,** 558–562.

Baker, R. D., Snider, G. W., Leipoid, H. E. and Johnson, J. L. (1980) Embryo transfer tests for bovine syndactyly. *Theriogen.* **13,** 100.

Beatty, R. A. (1972) Sex determination in farm and laboratory animals: a review. *Vet. Rec.* **90,** 243.

Bedirian, K. N., Shea, B. F. and Baker, R. D. (1975) Fertilization of bovine follicular oocytes in bovine and porcine oviducts. *Can. J. Anim. Sci.* **55,** 251.

Beehan, D. and Sreenan, J. M. (1977) Factors affecting superovulation response to PMSG in the cow. *Proc. Soc. Study. Fertil. (Dublin).* **11**(abs).

Bennett, J. P. and Rowson, L. E. A. (1961) The use of radioactive eggs in studies of egg transfer and transport in the female reproductive tract. *Proc. 4th Int. Congr. Amin. Reprod. (The Hague),* **2,** 360–366.

Betteridge, K. J. (1977) Embryo transfer in farm animals. *Monograph 16, Can. Dept. Agric. (Ottawa),* 1–10.

Betteridge, K. J. (1980) Procedures and results obtainable in cattle. In, *Current Therapy in Theriogen.* Morrow, D. A., Ed. pp.74–88.

Betteridge, K. H. and Mitchell, D. (1974) Embryo transfer in cattle; experience of twenty-four completed cases. *Theriogen.* **1,** 69–82.

Betteridge, K. J., Englesome, M. D., Randall, G. C. G. and Mitchell, D. (1980) Collection, description and transfer of embryos from cattle 10–16 days after oestrus. *J. Reprod. Fert.* **59,** 205–216.

Bilton, R. J. and Moore, N. W. (1976) Storage of cattle embryos. *J. Reprod. Fert.* **46,** 537–538.

Bilton, R. J. and Moore, N. W. (1977) Successful transport of frozen cattle embryos from N.Z. to Australia. *J. Reprod. Fert.* **50,** 363–364.

Bilton, R. J. and Moore, N. W. (1979) Factors affecting the viability of frozen stored cattle embryos. *Aust. J. Biol. Sc.* **32,** 101–107.

Bindon, B. M. (1969) Fate of the unfertilized sheep ovum. *H. Reprod. Fert.* **20,** 183–184.

Bindon, B. N. and Piper, L. R. (1977) Induction of ovulation in sheep and cattle by injection of PMSG and ovine anti-PMSG Immune Serum. *Theriogen.* **8**(4), 17.

Black, W. G., Ulberg, L. G., Christian, R. D. and Casida, L. E. (1953) Ovulation and fertilization in the hormone-stimulated calf. *J. Dairy Sci.* **36,** 274.

Boland, M. P. and Gordon, I. (1978) Twinning in lactating Fresian cows by non-surgical egg transfer. *Vet. Rec.* **103,** 241

Boland, M. P., Crosby, T. F. and Gordon, I. (1975) Twin pregnancy in cattle established by non-surgical egg transfer. *Brit. Vet. J.* **131,** 738–740.

Boland, M. P., Crosby, T. F. and Gordon, I. (1978) Morphological normality of cattle embryos following superovulation using PMSG. *Theriogen.* **10,** 175–180.

Boland, M. P., Kennedy, L. G., Crosby, T. F. and Gordon, I. (1981) Superovulation in the cow using PMSG or HAP. *Theriogen.* **15,** 110 (Abs).

Bon Durant, R. H., Anderson, G. B., Boland, M., Cupps, P. T. and Hughes, M. A. (1981) Pregnancy rates and embryo survival following transfer of bovine embryos stored at 4°C. *Theriogen.* **15,** 122 (Abs).

Boone, W. R., Dickey, J. F., Luszcz, L. J., Dantzler, J. R. and Hill, J. R. Jr. (1978) Culture of ovine and bovine ova. *J. Anim. Sci.* **47,** 808–913.

Booth, W. D., Newcomb, R., Strange, H., Rowson, L. E. A. and Sacher, H. B. (1975) Plasma oestrogen and progesterone in relation to superovulation and egg recovery in cow. *Vet. Rec.* **97,** 366–369.

Bouters, R., Moyaert, I., Coryn, M., Spincemaille, J. and Vandeplassche, M. (1980) Premature regression of the corpora lutea in superovulated cows. *Theriogen.* **14,** 207–216.

Bowen, J. M. (1973) Problems associated with ovum transplants. *Vet. Rec.* **92,** 17.

Bowen, J. M., Elsden, R. P. and Seidel, G. E. Jr. (1978) Non-surgical embryo transfer in the cow. *Theriogen.* **10**(1), 89–95.

Brackett, B. G. and Oliphant, G. (1975) Capacitation of rabbit spermatozoa *in vitro. Biol. Reprod.* **12,** 260–274.

Brackett, B. G., Oh. Y. K., Evans, J. F. and Donawick, W. J. (1977) Bovine fertilization and early development *in vivo* and *in vitro. 10th Ann. Meet. Soc. Study Reprod.* 56–57.

Brackett, B. G., Oh. Y. K., Evans, J. F. and Donawick, W. J. (1978) *In vitro* fertilization of cow ova. *Theriogen.* **9,** 89.

Brackett, R. G., Oh, Y. K., Evans, J. F. and Donawick, W. J. (1980) Fertilization and early development of cow ova. *Biol. Reprod.* **23,** 189–205.

Bradford, G. W. and Kennedy, B. W. (1980) Genetic aspects of embryo transfer. *Theriogen.* **13**(1), 13–16.

Brand, A. and Akabwai, D. (1978) Some aspects of non-surgical embryo transfer in cattle. *Vet. Sci. Commun.* **2,** 23–37.

Brand, A., Aarts, M. H., Zaayer, D. and Oxender, W. D. (1978) Recovery and Transfer of embryos by non-surgical procedures in lactating dairy cattle. In, *Control of Reprod. in the Cow.* Galway, Sreenan, J., Ed.) C. E. C., Luxembourg.

Brand, A., Drost, M., Aarts, M. H. and Gunnink, J. E. (1976) A device for non-surgical transfer in bovine embryos and its effect on uterine contamination. *Theriogen.* **6**(5), 509–514.

Brand, A., Taverne, M. A. M., vazn der Weyden, G. C., Aarts, M. H., Dielman, S. J., Fontijone, P., Drost, M. and de Bois, C. H. W. (1976) Non-surgical embryo transfer in cattle. Myometrial activity as a possible cause of embryo expulsion. *Proc. Seminar on Egg Transfer in Cattle (Camb.).* pp. 41–56. E.E.C. Publ.

Briggs, R. and King, T. J. (1952) Transplantation of living nuclei from blastula cells into enucleated frogs eggs. *Proc. Natn. Acad. Sci. (U.S.A.).* **38,** 455–63.

Bromhall, J. D. (1975) Nuclear transplantation in the rabbit egg. *Nature Land.* **258,** 719–721.

Callaghan, B. D. and King, G. J. (1980) Determination of the fertilization rate of A.I. sires. *Theriogen.* **14,** 403–410.

Casida, L. E., Meyer, R. K., McShann, W. H. and Wisnicky, W. (1943) Effects of pituitary gonadotrophins on the ovaries and the induction of superfecundity in cattle. *Amer. J. Vet. Res.* **4,** 76.

Casida, L. E., Nalbandov, A., McShann, W. H., Meyer, P. J. and

Wisnicky, W. (1940) Potential fertility of artifically matured and ovulated ova in cattle. *Proc. Am. Soc. Anim. Prod.* 302.

Chang, M. G. (1951) The problems of superovulation and egg transfer in cattle. *Proc. 1st Nat. Egg Transfer Breed Conf. San Antonio, Texas.* p. 39. Foundation for Applied Research.

Choudary, J. B., Gier, H. T. and Marion, G. B. (1968) Cyclic changes in bovine vesicular follicles. *J. Anim. Sci.* **27**, 468–471.

Christie, W. B., Newcomb, R. and Rowson, L. E. A. Ovulation rate and egg recovery in cattle, treated repeatedly with pregnant mare serum gonadotrophin and prostaglandin. *Vet. Rec.* **104**, 281–283.

Church, R. B. and Shea, B. (1976) Some aspects of bovine embryo transfer. *Proc. Seminar on Egg Transfer in Cattle (Camb.).* pp. 73–86 E.E.C.

Cole, H. H. and Hart, G. H. (1930) The potency of blood serum of mares in progressive stages of pregnancy in effecting the sexual maturity of the immature rat. *Am. J. Physiol.* **93**, 57–68.

Coulthard, H. (1980) Embryo transfer can be successful. *Livestock Int.* **37**, 10–12.

Cran, D. G. and Moor, R. M. (1980) The development of oocytes and ovarian follicles of mammals. *Sci. Prog.* **66**, 371–383.

Critser, J. K., Rowe, R. F., Del Campo, M. R. and Ginther, O. J. (1980) Embryo transfer in cattle: Factors affecting superovulatory response, number of transferable embryos and length of post-treatment estrous cycles. *Theriogen.* **13**, 397–406.

Cruz, J. C., Reeves, J. R., Russell, B. E., Alexander, A. F. and Will, D. H. (1980) Embryo transplanted calves: The pulmonary hypertension trait is genetically transmitted. *Proc. Soc. Exp. Biol. Med.* **164**, 142–145.

Cunningham, E. P. (1976) The use of embryo transfer techniques in genetic improvement. In, *Egg Transfer in Cattle, C.E.C. Conf. (Camb.).* 345–354.

Curtis, J. L., Elsden, R. P. and Seidel, G. E., Jr. (1981) Non-surgical transfer of bovine embryos. *Theriogen.* **15**, 124 (Abs).

DeMayo, F. J., Mizoguchi, H. and Dukelow, W. R. (1980) Fertilization of squirrel monkey and hamster ova in the rabbit oviduct (xenogenous fertilization) *Science.* **208**, 1468–1469.

du Mesnil du Buisson, F., Renard, J. P. and Levasseur, M. C. (1977) Factors influencing the quality of ova and embryos. In. *Embryo Transfer in Farm Animals,* K. J. Betteridge, Ed. Monograph 16, Canada Dept. Agriculture.

Denny, J. E. F. M. (1964) Ovulation control as a first step in the induction of twin births in dairy cattle. *Proc. S. Afr. Soc. Anim. Prod.* **57.**

Dhondt, D., Bouters, R., Spincemaille, J., Coryn, M. and Vandeplassche, M. (1978) The control of superovulation in the bovine with a PMSG-Antiserum. *Theriogen.* **9**(6), 529–534.

Dowling, D. F. (1949) Problems of the transplantation of fertilized ova. *J. Agric. Sci. Camb.* **39**, 374.

Dracy, A. (1953) The future of ova transfer. *Iowa St. Coll. J. Sci.* **28**, 101.

Dracy, A. E. and Petersen, W. E. (1950) Isolation of ova from the living bovine. *J. Dairy Sci.* **33**, 979.

Drost, M., Brand, A. and Aarts, M. H. (1976) A device for non-surgical recovery of bovine embryos. *Theriogen.* **6**(5), 503–507.

Drost, M., Anderson, G. B., Cupps, P. T., Horton, M. B., Warner, P. V. and Wright, R. W. (1975 A field study on embryo transfer in cattle. *J. Am. Vet. Med. Ass.* **166**, 1176–1179.

Dunn, T. G. (1980) Relationship of nutrition to successful embryo transplantation. *Theriogen.* **13**(1), 27–39.

Dziuk, P. J. (1960) Frequency of spontaneous fragmentation of ova in unbred gilts. *Proc. Soc. Exp. Biol. Med.* **103**, 91–92.

Dziuk, P. J., Donker, F. D., Nichols, J. P. and Petersen, W. E. (1958) Problems associated with the transfer of ova between cattle. *Univ. Minn. Agr. Sta. Tech. Bull.* 222.

Edwards, R. G. (1965) Maturation in vitro of mouse, sheep, cow, pig, rhesus monkey and human ovarian oocytes. *Nature Lond.* **206**, 349.

Edwards, R. G. (1973) Physiological aspects of human ovulation, fertilization and cleavage. *J. Reprod. Fert. Suppl.* **18**, 87–101.

Elsden, R. P. (1977) Embryo collection by surgical methods. In, *Embryo Transfer in Farm Animals.* Betteridge, K. J., Ed. pp. 10–13. *Canada Dept. Agric. Monograph.* 16.

Elsden, R. P., Hasler, J. F. and Seidel, G. E., Jr. (1976) Non-surgical recovery of bovine eggs. *Theriogen.* **6**(5), 523–532.

Elsden, R. P., Nelson, L. D., Seidel, G. E., Jr. (1978) Superovulation cows with follicle stimulating hormone and pregnant mare's serum gonadotrophin. *Theriogen.* **9**(1), 17–26.

Erickson, B. H. (1966) Development and senescence of the post-natal bovine ovary. *J. Anim. Sci.* **25**, 800–805.

Erickson, B. H., Reynolds, R. A. and Murphree, R. L. (1976) Ovarian characteristics and reproductive performance of the aged cow. *Biol. Reprod.* **15**, 555–650.

Evans, J. F., Hesseltine, G. R. and Kenney, R. M. (1979) Standing paralumbar approach for surgical embryo transfer in cattle. *Theriogen.* **11**(1), 97 (Abs).

Farmer, S. W. and Papkoff, H. (1979) Immunochemical studies with PMSG. *Biol. Reprod.* **21**, 425–431.

Folley, S. J. and Malpress, F. H. (1944) The response of the bovine ovary to pregnant mare's serum and horse pituitary extract. *Proc. R. Soc.* **132**, 164.

Foote, R. H. and Onuma, H. (1970) Superovulation, ovum collection culture and transfer — a review. *J. Dairy Sci.* **53**, 1681–1692.

Fukui, J. and Motlik, J. (1980) In vitro maturation. *Proc. 9th Int. Congr. Anim. Reprod. A.I. (Madrid).* **2**, 55–62.

Gardner, R. L. and Edwards, R. G. (1968) Control of the sex ratio at full term in the rabbit by transferring sexed blastocysts. *Nature, Land.* **218**, 346–349.

Gordon, I. (1975) Problems and prospects in cattle egg transfer; Part I. *Ir. Vet. J.* **29**, 21–30.

Gordon, I. (1975) Problems and prospects in cattle egg transfer; Part II. *Ir. Vet. J.* **29**, 39–62.

Gordon, I. (1976) Cattle twinning by an egg transfer approach. *Proc. E.E.C., Seminar Egg Transfer in Cattle (Cambridge)* 305–319.

Gordon, I. and Boland, M. P. (1978) Cattle Twinning by non-surgical egg transfer. *Control of Reproduction in the Cow.* Galway, Sreenan, J., Ed., pp. 336–355. C.E.C., Luxembourg.

Gordon, I., Williams, C. and Edwards, J. (1962) The use of serum gonadotrophin in the induction of twin pregnancy in the cow. *J. Agric. Sci. Camb.* **59**, 143–198.

Graham, C. F. (1969) The fusion of cells with one- and two-cell mouse embryos. *The Wistar Inst. Symposium on Hetereospecific Genome Interaction.* Defendi, V. Ed. **9**, 19–35.

Graham, E. F. (1974) Ova Transfer. *Proc. 5th Tech. Conf. A.I.*

and Reprod., Chicago., Feb. 15–16, 1974. Columbia, U.S.A. pp. 21–28. Nat. Assoc. Anim. Breed. Inc.

Graham, E. F. and Dracy, A. E. (1953) The effect of relaxin and mechanical dilation on the bovine cervix. *J. Dairy Sci.* **36,** 772.

Greve, R. (1976) Non-surgical egg transfer in the cow. *Proc. 27th Ann. Meet. European Assoc. Anim. Prod. Zurich, Aug. 23–26, 1976.* 1–7.

Greve, T. (1980) Embryo transplantation in cattle. Non-surgical recovery of embryos from repeat breeders. *Acta. Vet. Scand.* **21,** 26–33.

Greve, T. and Lehn-Jensen, H. (1979) Embryo transplantation in cattle. Non-surgical transfer of $6\frac{1}{2}$–$7\frac{1}{2}$ day old embryos to lactating dairy cows under farm conditions. *Acta. Vet. Scand.* **20,** 135–144.

Greve, T., Lehn-Jensen, H. and Rasbech, N. O. (1977) Non-surgical recovery of bovine embryos. *Theriogen.* 7(4), 239–250.

Hafez, E. S. E. and Sugie, T. (1963) Reciprocal transfer of cattle and rabbit embryos. *J. Anim. Sci.* **22,** 30–35.

Hafez, E. S. E., Sugie, T. and Gordon, I. (1963) Superovulation and related phenomena in the beef cow. I. Superovulatory responses following PMS and HCG injections. *J. Reprod. Fert.* **5,** 359–379.

Hafez, E. S. E., Sugie, T. and Hunt, W. L. (1963) Superovulation and related phenomena in the beef cow. II. Effect of oestrogen administration on production of ova. *J. Reprod. Fert.* **5,** 381–388.

Hahn, J. and Hahn, R. (1976) Experiences with non-surgical transfer techniques. In, *Egg Transfer in Cattle* Rowson, L. E. A., Ed. pp. 199–204. Commission of the European Communities, Luxembourg.

Hahn, J., Hahn, R., Baumgartner, G., Lorrmunn, W. and Zoder, H. F. (1975) Successful non-surgical transfer of ova in cattle (in German; Eng. Summary). *Dtsch. Tieraerztl. Wochen.* **82,** 429–431.

Hahn, J., Moustafa, L. A., Schneider, U., Hahn, R., Romanowski, W. and Roselius, R. (1978) Survival of cultured and transported bovine embryos following surgical and non-surgical transfers. In, *Control of Reprod. in the Cow.* (Galway, Sreenan J., Ed., pp. 356–362. C.E.G. Luxembourg.

Hahn, J., Roselius, R., Romanowski, W. and Schneider, U. (1980) Non-surgical collection and transfer of bovine embryos. *Arch. Androl.* **5,** 106.

Halley, S. M., Rjodes, R. C. III., McKeller, L. D. and Randel, R. D. (1979) Successful superovulation, non-surgical collection and transfer of embryo from Brahman Cows. *Theriogen.* 12(2), 97, 108.

Hamilton, W. J. and Laing, J. A. (1946) Development of the egg of the cow up to the stage of blastocyst formation. *J. Anat.* **80,** 194.

Hammond, J. (1950a) Problems concerning the transplantation of fertilized ova or "artificial pregnancy". *Ann. Fac. Med. Montevideo.* **35,** 810.

Hammond, J. (1950b) The possibility of artificial pregnancy in cattle. *J. Min. Agric. (Lond.).* 57–67.

Hare, W. C. D. and Betteridge, K. J. (1978) Relationship of embryo sexing to other methods of prenatal sex determination in farm animals: a review. *Theriogen.* 9(1), 27–43.

Hare, W. C. D., Mitchell, D., Betteridge, K. H., Eaglesome, M. D. and Randall, G. C. B. (1976) Sexing 2-week old bovine embryos by chromosomal analysis prior to surgical transfer; preliminary methods and results. *Theriogen.* **5,** 243–253.

Harper, M. J. K., Bennett, J. P. and Rowson, L. E. A. (1961) A possible explanation for the failure of non-surgical ovum transfer in the cow. *Nature Lond.* **190,** 789.

Hartman, C. G., Lewis, W. H., Miller, F. W. and Sivett, W. W. (1931) First findings of tubal ova in the cow together with notes on estrus. *Anat. Rec.* **48,** 267–275.

Hasler, J. F. Bowen, R. A., Nelson, L. D. and Seidel, G. E., Jr. (1980) Serum progesterone concentrations in cows receiving embryo transfers. *J. Reprod. Fert.* **58,** 71–77.

Hasler, J. F., Brooke, G. P. and McCauley, A. D. (1980) The relationship between age and response to superovulation in Holstein cows and heifers. *Theriogen.* **15,** 109 (Abs).

Hill, J. R., Lamond, D. R. Henricks, D. M., Dickey, J. F. and Niswender, G. D. (1970) Effect of undernutrition on ovarian function and fertility in beef heifers. *Biol. Reprod.* 2, 78.

Hirst, P. J., DeMayo, F. J. and Dukelow, W. R. (1981) Xenogenous fertilization of laboratory and domestic animals in the oviduct of the pseudo-pregnant rabbit. *Theriogen.* **15,** 67–75.

Hoffner, N. J. and Diberardino, M. A. (1980) Developmental potential of somatic nuclei transplanted into meiotic oocytes of rana pipiens. *Science* **209,** 517–519.

Howe, G. R., Black, D. L., Foley, R. C. and Black, W. G. (1962) Ovarian activity in prepuberal dairy calves. *J. Anim. Sci.* **21,** 82.

Hunter, G. L., Adams, C. E. and Rowson, L. E. A. (1955) Interbreed ovum transfer in sheep. *J. Agric. Sci.* **46,** 143–149.

Hunter, R. H. F., Lawson, R. A. S. and Rowson, L. E. A. (1972) Maturation transplantation and fertilization of ovarian oocytes in cattle. *J. Reprod. Fertil.* **30,** 325.

Illmensee, K. and Hoppe, P. C. (1981) Nuclear transplantation in *Mus Musculis*; developmental potential of nuclei from preimplantation embryos. *Cell* **23,** 9–18.

Iritani, A. (1980) Fertilization *in vitro* of follicular oocytes matured in culture in cattle, pig and human. *Arch. Androl.* **5,** 77–78 (Abs).

Iritani, A. and Niwa, K. (1977) Capacitation of bull spermatozoa and fertilization in vitro of cattle follicular oocytes matured in culture. *J. Reprod. Fertil.* **50,** 119.

Iritani, A. and Niwa, K. (1977) Fertilization *in vitro* of cattle follicular oocytes matured *in vitro.* *Fert. Ster.* **28,** 350.

Jainudeen, M. R., Hafez, E. S. E. and Lineweaver, J. A. (1966) Superovulation in the calf. *J. Reprod. Fertil.* **12,** 149.

Jillella, D. and Baker, A. A. (1978) Transcervical transfer of bovine embryos. *Vet. Rec.* **103,** 574–576.

Jillella, D., Eaton, R. J. and Baker, A. A. (1977) Successful of a bovin embryo through a cannulated fallopian tube. *Vet. Rec.* **100,** 385–386.

Johnson, K. R., Ross, R. H. and Fourt, D. L. (1958) *J. Anim. Sci.* **17,** 386.

Johnson, J. L., Leipold, H. W., Snider, G. W. and Baker, R. D. (1980) *J. Am. Vet. Med. Asso.* **176,** 549.

Kane, M. T. (1978) Culture of mammalian ova. In, *Control of Reproduction in the Cow,* Galway, Sreenan, J., Ed. pp. 383–397. C.E.C., Luxembourg.

Kanagawa, H. (1980) One to two-day preservations of bovine embryos. *Jpn. J. Vet. Res.* **28,** 1–6.

Kanagawa, H., Frim, J. and Kruuv, J. (1978) The effect of puncturing the Zona Pellucida on freeze–thaw survival of bovine embryos. *Can. J. Anim. Sci.* **59,** 623–626.

Kelly, E. F., Renton, J. P. and Munro, C. D. (1981) Assessment of oviduct potency in the cow. *Vet. Rec.* **108,** 357–360.

Kothari, B., Renton, J. P., Munro, C. D. and MacFarlane, J. (1978). *Vet. Rec.* **103,** 229.

Kummer, V., Zraly, Z., Holcak, V., Veznik, Z., Schlegelova, J.

and Hruska, K. (1980) Superovulation in cattle: Effect of goat anti-PMSG seruserum. *Theriogen.* **14,** 383–390.

Krco, C. J. and Goldberg, E. H. (1976) *Science* **193,** 1134.

Lamming, G. E. and Rowson, L. E. (1952) Superovulation and ovum transfer in cattle. *Proc. 2nd Int. Congr. Anim. Reprod. A.I. (Copenhagen),* **1,** 144–153.

Lamming, G. E. and Rowson, L. E. A. (1953) Ovarian hormones and uterine infection in cattle. *Proc. R. Soc. Med.* **46,** 387–392.

Lamond, D. R. (1970) The effect of pregnant mare serum gonadotrophin (PMS) on ovarian function of beef heifers, as influenced by progestins, plane of nutrition and fasting. *Aust. J. Agric. Res.* **21,** 153–156.

Lamond, D. R. (1972) Hormonal induction of multiple ovulations in the bovine. *J. Anim. Sci.* **34,** 901 (Abs).

Lamond, D. R. and Gaddy, R. G. (1972) Plasma progesterone in cows with multiple-ovulations. *J. Reprod. Fert.* **29,** 307–311.

Lampeter, Von W. W. (1977) Practice of non-surgical collection of bovine embryos. *Zuchthygiene* **12**(1), 8–13.

Lampeter, W. W. (1978) Non-surgical recovery of bovine embryos under farm conditions. In, *Control of Reprod. in the* Cow Galway, Sreenan, J., Ed., pp. 305–311. C.E.C., Luxembourg.

Land, R. B. and Hill, W. G. (1975 The possible use of superovulation and embryo transfer in cattle to increase response to selection. *Amin. Prod.* **1,** 1–12.

Lawson, R. A. S., Rowson, L. E. A. and Adams, C. F. (1972) The development of cow eggs in the rabbit oviduct and their viability after re-transfer to heifers. *J. Reprod. Fert.* **28,** 313–315.

Lawson, R. A. S., Rowson, L. E. A., Moor, R. N. and Tervit, H. R. (1975) Experiments on egg transfer in the cow and ewe; dependence of conception rate on the transfer procedure and stage of the oestrous cycle. *J. Reprod. Fert.* **45,** 101–107.

Lehn-Jensen, H. and Greve, T. (1977) Successful transfer of deep frozen bovine embryos. *Dansk. Vettidsskr.* **60,** 17, 768–769.

Lehn-Jensen, H. and Greve, T. (1978) Freezing of cattle blastocysts– and future prospects. *Dansk. Vet. Tidsskr.* **61,** 21, 11.

Lehn-Jensen, H. and Greve, T. (1978) Low temperature preservation of cattle blastocysts. *Theriogen.* **9**(4), 313–322.

Lin, T. P., Forence, J. and Oh, J. O. (1973) Cell fusion induced by a virus within the zona pellucida of mouse eggs. *Nature Lond.* **242,** 47–49.

Linares, T. and King, W.A. (1980) Morphological study of the bovine blastocyst with phase contrast microscopy. *Thereiogen.* **114,** 123–133.

Linares, T., King, W. A., Larsson, K., Gustavsson, I and Bane, A. (1980) Successful, repeated non-surgical collection of blastocysts from virgin and repeat breeder heifers. *Vet. Res. Commun.* **4,** 113–118.

Looney, C. R., Boutte, B. W., Archibald, L. F. and Godke, R. A. (1981) Comparison of once daily and twice daily FSH injections for superovulating beef cattle *Theriogen.* **15,** 13–22.

McKenzie, B. E. and Kenny, R. N. (1973) *In vitro* culture of bovine embryos. *Am. J. Vet. Res.* **34,** 1271–1275.

McKinnell, R. G. (1978) *Cloning: Nuclear Transplantation in Amphibia.* Univ. Minneapolis. Minnosta Press.

McLaren, A. (1980) Folliculogenesis and ova production. *Prof. 9th Int. Congr. Anim. Reprod. A.I. (Madrid),* **2,** 63–70.

Magnusson, C., LeMarie, W. J. and Hillensjo, T. (1981) Stimulation by hCG in vivo of oxygen consumption by rabbit oocytes in vitro. *J. Reprod. Fert.* **61,** 185–188.

Marden, W. G. R. (1953) The hormonal control of ovulation in calf. *J. Agric. Sci. Camb.* **43,** 381.

Mariana, J. G., Mauleon, P., Benoit, M. and Chupin, D. (1970) Variability and repeatability of the number of ovulations obtained after injection of 1,600 i.u. in PMSG and 1,500 i.u. hCG. *Ann. Biol. Anim. Biochem. Biophys.* **10**(1), 47.

Markert, C. L. and Petters, R. M. (1977) Homozygous mouse embryos produced by microsurgery. *J. Exp. Zool.* **201,** 295–302.

Marshall, D. P. J. and Struthers, G. A. (1978) Commercial embryo-transfers in cattle. *N.Z. Vet. J.* **26,** 92–95.

Marx, J. L. (1981) Three mice cloned in Switzerland. *Science,* **211,** 375–376.

Massip, A. and Mulnard, J. (1980) Time lapse cinematographic analysis of hatching of normal and frozen–thawed cow blastocysts. *J. Reprod. Fert.* **58,** 475–478.

Massip, A., van der Zwalmen, P., Ectors, F., de Coster, R., D'Ieteren, G. and Hanzen, C. (1979) Deep freezing of cattle embryos in glass ampules or French straws *Theriogen.* **12**(2), 79–84.

Meinecke, B. and Meinecke-Tillmann, S. (1979) Experimental studies on fertilization of extracorporal matured oocytes of cattle in heterologueous recipients. *Dtsch. tierarztl. Wschr.* **86,** 477–479.

Mickelsen, W. D., Wright, R. W., Jr., Menino, A. R., Zamora, C. S. and Paisley, L. G. (1978) Superovulation fertilization and embryo recovery in gonadotropin treated prepuberal calves. *Theriogen.* **10,** 167.

Miller, D. M., Johnson, W. J., Cates, W. F. and Mapletoft, R. J. (1981) Superovulation studies in heifers to determine fertilization rates of bulls with high levels of certain sperm defects. *Theriogen.* **15,** 112 (Abs).

Mitchell, D., Hare, W. C. D., Betteridge, K. J., Eaglesome, M. D. and Randall, G. C. B. (1976) Sexing and transfer of bovine embryos. *Proc. 9th Int. Congr. Anim. Reprod. A.I. (Krakow).* **3,** 258–261.

Moffit, J. E. (1979) World situation with regard to embryo transfer. *Br. Cattle Breed. Club Dig.* **34,** 5.

Mohr, L. R. and Trounson, A. O. (1980) The use of fluorescein diacetate to assess embryo viability in the mouse. *J. Reprod. Fert.* **58,** 189–196.

Moor, R. M. and Trounson, A. O. (1971) Hormonal and follicular factor affecting maturation of sheep oocytes *in vitro* and their subsequent developmental capacity. *J. Reprod. Fert.* **49,** 101.

Moor, R. M., Polge, C. and Willadsen, S. M. (1980) Effect of follicular steroids on the maturation and fertilization of mammalian oocytes. *J. Embryo. Exp. Morph.* **56,** 319–335.

Moore, N. W. (1975) The control of time of oestrus and ovulation and the induction of superovulation in cattle. *Aust. J. Agric. Res.* **25**(2), 295–304.

Moore, N. W, Polge, C. and Rowson, L. E. A. (1969) The survival of single blastomeres of pig eggs transferred to recipient gilts. *Aust. J. Biol. Sci.* **22,** 979.

Moore, N. W., Rowson, L. E. A. and Short, R. V. (1960) Egg transfer in sheep. Factors affecting the survival and development of transferred eggs. *J. Reprod. Fert.* **1,** 332–349.

Motlik, H., Koefoed-Johnsen, H. H. and Fulka, J. (1978) Breakdown of the germinal vesicle in bovine oocytes cultivated *in vitro. J. Exp. Zool.* **205,** 377–384.

Mourrasse, C., Matton, P. and Dufour, J. J. (1980) Effects of feeding regimes on ovarian follicular population in heifers. *J. Anim. Sci.* **51,** (Suppl. 1.) 302–303 (Abs).

Moustafa, L. A. and Hahn, J. (1978) Experimental production of identical twin mice. *Dtsch. Tierarztl. Woch.* **85,** 242–244.

Moustafa, L. A. Linares, T., Gustavsson, I. and Bane, A. (1978) Versuche zur geschlechts bestimmungan tagbund alten rinderembryoneu. *Ber Munch. Tierarztl. Wschr.* **91,** 236–238.

Mullen, R. J., Whitten, W. K. and Carter, S. C. (1970) In, *Ann. Rept. Jackson Lab, Bar Arbor, Maine, U.S.A.*.

Mutter, L. R., Graden, A. P.and Olds, D. (1964) Successful non-surgical bovine embryo transfer. *A.I. Dig.* **12,** 3.

Nelson, L. D., Bowen, R. A. and Seidel, G. E. Jr. (1975) Factors affecting bovine embryo transfer. *J. Anim. Sci.* **41,** 371–372. (Abs.)

Newcomb, R. (1979) Surgical and non-surgical transfer of bovine embryos. *Vet. Rec.* **105,** 432–434.

Newcomb, R. (1980) Investigation of factors affecting superovulation and non-surgical embryo recovery from lactating British Friesian cows. *Vet. Rec.* **106,** 48–52.

Newcomb, R. and Rowson, L. E. A. (1975) Conception rate after uterine transfer of cow eggs in relation to synchronization of oestrus and age of eggs. *J. Reprod. Fert.* **43,** 539–541.

Newcomb, R. and Rowson, L. E. A. (1975 A technique for the simultaneous flushing of ova from the bovine oviduct and uterus. *Vet. Rec.* **96,** 468–469.

Newcomb, R. and Rowson, L. E. A. (1976) Multiple ovulation, egg transplantation: towards twinning. In, *Principles of Cattle Prod.* Swan, H. Ed., and Broster, W. H. Ed., pp. 59–83. Proc. 23rd Easter Sch. in Agr. Sci. Univ. of Nottingham, Butterworths, London.

Newcomb, R., Booth, W. D. and Rowson, L. E. A. (1977) The effect of ozytocin treatment on the levels of prostaglandin F. in the blood of heifers. *J. Reprod. Fert.* **49,** 17–24.

Newcomb, R., Christie, W. B. and Rowson, L. E. A. (1978) Birth of calves after in vivo fertilization of oocytes removed from follicles and matured in vitro. *Vet. Rec.* **102,** 461.

Newcomb, R., Christie, W. R. and Rowson, L. E. A. (1978) The non-surgical recovery and transfer of bovine embryos. In, *Control of Reprod. in the cow.* Galway, Sreenan, J., Ed., pp. 398–417, C.E.C. Luxembourg.

Newcomb, R., Christie, W. B., Rowson, L. E. A., Walters, D. E. and Bousfield, W. E. D. (1979) Influence of dose, repeated treatment and batch of hormone on ovarian response in heifers treated with PMSG. *J. Reprod. Fert.* **56,** 113–118.

Newcomb, R., Rowson, L. E. A. and Trounson, A. O. (1976) The entry of superovulated eggs into the uterus. *Proc. Sem. Egg Transfer in Cattle (Camb.)* EEC. 1–15.

Newcomb, R., Rowson, L. E. A. and Trounson, A. O. (1978) The Sacrewell project; An on-farm demonstration of potential of egg transfer *Vet. Rec.* **130,** 415–418.

Nicholas, J. S. and Hall, B. V. (1942) Experiments on developing rates. II. The development of isolated blastomeres and fused eggs. *J. Exp. Zool.* **90,** 441.

Northey, D. L. and French, L. R. (1980) Effect of embryo removal and intrauterine infusion of embryonic homogenates on the lifespan of the bovine corpus luteum. *J. Anim. Sci.* **50,** 298–302.

Onuma, H. and Foote, R. G. (1969) Superovulation in prepuberal calves on two levels of nutrition intake. *J. Anim. Sci.* **28,** 771.

Onuma, H. and Foote, R. H. (1969) *In vitro* development of ova from prepuberal cattle. *J. Dairy Sci.* **52,** 1085.

Onuma, H, J. and Foote, R. H. (1970) Factors affecting superovulation, fertilization and recovery of super-ovulated ova in prepuberal cattle *J. Reprod. Fert.* **21,** 119.

Onuma, H., Hahn, J., Maurer, R. R. and Foote, R. H. (1969) Repeated superovulation in calves. *J. Anim. Sci.* **28,** 634.

Ozil, J. P., Heyman, Y, and Renard, J. P. (1981) Production of monozygotic twins in cows by micromanipulation and cervical transfer. Soc. Study of Fertility (Cambridge) Abstracts, p. 10.

Peters, D. F., Anderson, G. B., Bondaurant, R., Cupps, P. T. and Drost, M. (1978) Transfer of cultured bovine embryos. *Theriogen.* **10**(4), 337–342.

Phillipo, M. and Rowson, L. E. A. (1975) Prostaglandins and superovulation in the bovine. *Ann. Biol. Anim. Biochim. Biophys.* **15,** 233–240.

Pincus, G. (1949) Observations on the development of cow ova in vivo and in vitro. *Proc. Natl. Egg Transfer and Breeders Conf. (San Antonio), Texas.* **1,** 18.

Pincus, G. and Enzmann, E. V. (1935) The comparative behaviours of mammalian eggs *in vivo* and *in vitro* I. The activation of ovarian eggs. *J. Exp. Med.* **62,** 665–675.

Polge, C. (1978) Embryo transfer and embryo preservation. Artificial breeding of non-domestic animals: *Symp. Zool. Soc. Lond.* **43,** 303–316.

Polge, C. and Rowson, L. E. A. (1973) Recent progress in techniques for increasing reproductive potential in farm animals. *3rd World. Conf. Anim. Prod. (Melbourne),* Pre Conf. Vol. **3,** 6.

Pugh, A., Trounson, A. O., Aarts, M. H. and McPhee, S. (1980) Bovine embryo recovery by filtration on non-surgical flushings. *Theriogen.* **13,** 281–285.

Quirke, J. F. and Hanrahan, J. P. (1977) Comparison of the survival in the uteri of adult ewes of cleaved ova from adult ewes and ewe lambs. *J. Reprod. Fert.* **51,** 487–489.

Rajakoski, E. (1960) Ovarian follicular system in sexually mature heifers with special reference to the seasonal cyclical and left to right variations. *Acta. Endocr.* **34,** (Suppl), 52, 1.

Rajamahendran, R., Logue, P. G. and Baker, R. D. (1974) Progesterone levels in normal and superovulated heifers. *Can. J. Anim. Sci.* **54,** 715 (Abs).

Rasbech, N. D. (1976) Non-surgical instruments for recovery and transfer of bovine embryos. *Arsberet. Inst. Sterilitets-forsk.* **19,** B74–B80.

Ratman, B. and Papermaster, B. W. (1966) Membrane properties of living mammalian cells as studied by enzymatic hydrolysis of fluorogenic esters. *Proc. Natn. Acad. Sci. (USA),* **55,** 134–141.

Renard, J. P., Heyman, Y and Ozil, J. P. (1981) Freezing bovine blastocysts with 1.2 propanediol as cryoprotectant. *Theriogen.* **15,** 113 (Abs).

Renard, J. P., Menez, O. Y., Saumande, J. and Heyman, Y. (1978) Attempts to predict the viability of cattle embryos produced by superovulation. In, *Control of Reprod. in the Cow,* Galway, X. X. Ed., pp. 398–417, C.E.C. Luxembourg.

Richards, J. A. (1979) Hormonal control of ovarian follicular development. A 1978 perspective. *Rec. Prog. Hormone Res.* **35,** 343–373.

Rowe, R. F., Critser, J. K. and Ginther, O. J. (1979) Non-surgical embryo transfer in cattle. *Theriogen.* **11**(1), 17 (Abs).

Rowe, R. F., Del Campo, M. R., Eilts, C. L., French, L. R., Winch, R. P. and Hinther, O. J. (1976) A single cannula technique for non-surgical collection of ova from cattle. *Theriogen.* **6**(5), 471–483.

Rowson, L. E. A. (1951) Methods of inducing multiple ovulation in cattle. *J. Endocr.* **7,** 260–270.

Rowson, L. E. A. (1971) The role of reproductive research in animal production. *J. Reprod. Fert.* **26,** 113–126.

Rowson, L. E. A. (1973) The use of egg transfer in practice and research. *Br. Cattle Breed. Club Dig.* **23,** 19–22.

Rowson, L. E. A. (1974) The role of research in animal reproduction. *Vet. Rec.* **95,** 276–280.

Rowson, L. E. A. (1979) Embryo transfer. *Br. Cattle Breed. Club Digest.*

Rowson, L. E. A. and Dowling, D. F. (1949) An apparatus for the extraction of fertilized eggs from the living cow. *Vet. Rec.* **61,** 191.

Rowson, L. E. A. and Moor, R. M. (1966) Non-surgical transfer of cow eggs. *J. Reprod. Fert.* **11,** 311–312.

Rowson, L. E. A. and Moor, R. M. (1966) Embryo transfer in the sheep; The significance of synchronizing oestrus in the donor and recipient animal. *J. Reprod. Fert.* **11,** 207–212.

Rowson, L. E. A., Bennett, J. P. and Harper, M. J. K. (1964) The problem of non-surgical egg transfer to the cow uterus. *Vet. Rec.* **76,** 21.

Rowson, L. E. A., Lamming, G. E. and Fry, R. M. (1953) The relationship between ovarian hormones and uterine infection. *Vet. Rec.* **65,** 335–340.

Rowson, L. E. A., Lamming, G. E. and Fry, R. M. (1953) Influence of ovarian hormones on uterine infection. *Nature Land.* **17,** 749–750.

Rowson, L. E. A., Lawson, R. A. S. and Moore, R. M. (1971) Production of twins in cattle by egg transfer. *J. Reprod. Fert.* **25,** 261–268.

Rowson, L. E. A., Lawson, R. A. S. and Moor, R. M. (1971) Twinning in cattle. *Vet. Rec.* **88,** 210.

Rowson, L. E. A., Lawson, R. A. S., Moor, R. M. and Baker, A. A. (1972) Egg transfer in the cow: synchronization requirements. *J. Reprod. Fert.* **28,** 427–431.

Rowson, L. E. A., McNeilly, A. S. and O'Brien, C. A. (1972) The effect of vaginal and cervical stimulation on oxytocin release during the luteal phase of the cow's oestrous cycle. *J. Reprod. Fert.* **30,** 287–288.

Rowson, L. E. A., Moor, R. N. and Lawson, R. A. S. (1969) Fertility following egg transfer in the cow: effect of method, medium and synchronization of oestrus. *J. Reprod. Fert.* **18,** 517–523.

Sato, E., Iritani, A. and Nishikawa, Y. (1977) Factors involved in maturation of pig and cattle follicular oocytes cultured in vitro. *Jap. J. Amin. Reprod.* **23,** 12.

Saumande, J. (1978) Relationship between ovarian stimulation by PMSG and steroid secretion. In, *Control of Reproduction in the Cow.* Galway, Sreenan, J., Ed., pp. 169–194. C.E.C. Luxembourg.

Saumande, J. (1980) Concentrations of luteinizing hormone, oestradiol-17$_B$ and progesterone in the plasma of heifers treated to induce superovulation. *J. Endocr.* **84,** 425–437.

Saumande, J. and Chupin, D. (1977) Superovulation: A limit to Egg Transfer in cattle. *Theriogen.* **3,** 141–149.

Saumande, J. and Chupin, D. (1982) Production of PMSG anti-serum in cattle: Assay of inhibitory activity and use in superovulated heifers. *Theriogen.* **15,** (Abs).

Saumande, J., Chupin, D., Mariana, J. C. Ortavant, R. and Mauleon, P. (1978) Factors affecting the variability of ovulation rates after PMSG stimulation. In, *Control of Reproduction in the Cow.* Galway, Sreenan, J., Ed., pp. 195–224. C. E. C., Luxembourg.

Scanlon, P. F. (1969) Studies in reproduction in the cow. Ph.D. Thesis, N.U.I. Dublin.

Scanlon, P. F. (1972) Ovarian response of cows following PMSG treatment during two successive estrous cells. *J. Dairy Sci.* **55,** 527.

Scanlon, P. F., Sreenan, J. and Gordon, I. (1968) Hormonal induction of superovulation in cattle. *J. Agric. Sci. Camb.* **70,** 179–182.

Schams, D., Menzer, Ch., Schallenberger, E., Hoffman, B., Hahn, J. and Hahn, R. (1978) Some studies on pregnant mare serum gonadotrophin (PMSG) and on endocrine responses after application for superovulation in cattle. In, *Control of Reproduction in the Cow.* Galway, Sreenan, J., Ed., pp. 122–143. C.E.C., Luxembourg.

Schilling, E., Sacher, B. and Smidt, D. (1980) Quality of eggs and embryos from superovulated cows. *Zuchthyg.* **15,** 30–34.

Schilling, E., Smidt, D., Sacher, B., Petac, D. and El Kaschab, S. (1979) Diagnosis of the viability of early bovine embryos by fluorescence microscopy. *Ann. Anim. Biol. Anim. Bioch. Biophys.* **19**(5), 1625–1629.

Schneider, U. and Hahn, J. (1979) Recent results of frozen and thawed bovine embryos. *Theriogen.* **11**(1), 108 (Abs).

Schneider, U. and Hahn, J. (1979) Bovine embryo transfer in Germany. *Theriogen.* **11**(1), 63–80.

Schneider, H. J. Jr., Castleberry, R. S. and Griffin, J. L. (1980) Commercial aspects of bovine embryo transfer. *Theriogen.* **13**(1), 73–85.

Seidel, F. (1952) The development potential of an isolated blastomere in the 2-cell stage mammalian egg. *Naturvissen,* **15,** 355.

Seidel, G. E., Jr. (1974) Maintaining the viability of bovine embryos outside the cow. *Proc. Soc. Study Breed.* 9.

Seidel, G. E., Jr. (1981) Superovulation and embryo transfer in cattle. *Science.* **211,** 351–358.

Seidel, G. E., Jr. Browen, J. M., Homan, N. R. and Okun, M. E. (1975) Fertility of heifers with sham embryo transfer through the cervix. *Vet. Rec.* **97,** 307–308.

Seidel, G. E., Jr. Elsden, R. P., Nelson, L. D. and Bowen, R. A. (1978) Superovulation of cattle with pregnant mare's serum gonadotrophin and follicle stimulating hormon. In, *Control of Reproduction in the Cow.* Galway, Sreenan, J., Ed., pp. 159–168. C.E.C., Luxembourg.

Seidel, G. E., Jr. Elsden, R. P., Nelson, L. D. and Hasler, J. F. (1978) Methods of ovum recovery and factors affecting fertilization of superovulated bovine ova. In, *Control of Reproduction in the Cow.* Galway, Sreenan, J., Ed., pp. 268–280. C.E.C., Luxembourg.

Seidel, G. E., Jr. Larson, L. L., Spilman, G. H., Hahn, J. and Foote, R. H. (1970) Transfer of superovulated calf ova. *J. Anim. Sci.* **31,** 230.

Seidel, G. E., Jr. Larson, L. L., Spilman, C. H., Hahn, J. and Foote, R. H. (1971) Culture and transfer of calf ova. *J. Dairy Res.* **54,** 923.

Seidel, G. E., Jr. Larson, L. L. and Foote, R. H. (1971) Effects of age and gonadotrophin treatment on superovulation in the calf. *J. Anim. Sci.* **33,** 617.

Seidel, G. E., Jr. and Niswender, G. D. (1980) Control of folliculogenesis and ovulation in domestic animals: Puberal and adult function. *Proc. 9th Int. Congr. Anim. Reprod. A.I. (Madrid).* **2,** 11–16.

Seidel, G. E. and Seidel, S. M. (1978) Bovine embryo transfer: costs and success rates. *Adv. Anim. Breeder,* November, 1978.

Sequin, B. E., Oxender, W. D. and Britt, J. H. (1977) Effect of hCG and Gn-RH on corpus luteum function and estrous cycle duration in dairy heifers. *Am. J. Vet. Res.* **38,** 1153–1156.

Shalgi, R. and Phillips, D. M. (1980) Mechanics of *in vitro* fertilization in the hamster. *Biol. Reprod.* **23**, 433–444.

Shea, B. F. (1981) Evaluating the bovine embryo. *Theriogen.* **15**, 31–42.

Shea, B. F., Bedirian, K. N. and Baker, R. D. (1973) Sperm penetration of bovine follicular oocytes following *in vitro* and *in vivo* maturation. *Biol. Reprod.* **9**, 84.

Shea, B. F., Hines, D. J., Lightfoot, D. E., Ollis, G. W., and Olson, S. M. (1976) The transfer of bovine embryos. *Proc. EEC Seminar Egg Transfer in Cattle (Cambridge)*, 145–152.

Shea, B. F., Ollis, G. W. and Jacobson, M. E. (1977) Pregnancies following long distance transport and transfer of frozen bovine embryos. *Can. J. Anim. Sci.* **57**, 801–802.

Shelton, J. N. and Moore, N. W. (1966) Survival of fertilized eggs transferred to ewes after progesterone treatment. *J. Reprod. Fert.* **11**, 149–151.

Shelton, J. N., Heath, T. D., Old, K. G., and Turnbull, G. E., (1979) Non-surgical recovery of eggs from single ovulating bovines. *Theriogen.* **11**(2), 149–151.

Singh, E. L. and Hare, W. C. D. (1980) The feasibility of sexing bovine morula stage embryos prior to embryo transfer. *Theriogen.* **14**, 421–427.

Skehan, B. N. (1974) Factors affecting survival of cattle embryos in an egg transfer programme. M. Agri. Sci. Thesis, N.U.I. Dublin.

Soupart, P. (1980) Initiation of mouse embryonic development by oocyte fusion. *Arch. Androl.* **5**, 55—57.

Sreenan, J. (1968) *In vivo* and *in vitro* culture of cattle eggs. *Proc. 6th. Int. Congr. Anim. Reprod. A.I. (Paris).* **1**, 577.

Sreenan, J. M. (1969) Studies related to ovum transfer in cattle. Ph. D. Thesis. N.U.I. Dublin.

Sreenan, J. (1970) *In vitro* maturation and attempted fertilization of cattle follicular oocytes. *J. Agric. Sci. Camb.* **75**, 393.

Sreenan, J. M. (1975) Successful non-surgical transfer of fertilized cow eggs. *Vet. Rec.* **96**, 490–491.

Sreenan, J. M. (1978) Non-surgical egg recovery and transfer in the cow. *Vet. Rec.* **102**, 58–60.

Sreenan, J. M. and Beehan, D. (1974) Egg transfer in the cow; pregnancy rate and egg survival. *J. Reprod. Fert.* **41**, 497–499.

Sreenan, J. M. and Beehan, D. (1976) Methods of induction of superovulation in the cow and transfer results. In, *Egg Transfer in Cattle*, pp. 19–34., C.E.C. Luxembourg.

Sreenan, J. M. and Beehan, D. (1976) Embryonic survival and development at various stages of gestation after bilateral egg transfer in the cow. *J. Reprod. Fert.* **47**, 127–128.

Sreenan, J. M. and Beehan, D. (1976) Effect of site of transfer on pregnancy and twinning rates following bilateral egg transfer in the cow. *J. Reprod. Fert.* **48**, 233–224.

Sreenan, J. M. and Gosling, J. P. (1977) The effect of cycle stage and plasma progesterone level on the induction of multiple ovulations in heifers. *J. Reprod. Fert.* **50**, 367–369.

Sreenan, J. M., Beehan, D. and Mulvehill, P. (1975) Egg transfer in the cow: factors affecting pregnancy and twinning rates following vilateral transfers. *J. Reprod. Fert.* **44**, 77–85.

Sreenan, J. M., Beehan, D. and Gosling, J. P. (1978) Ovarian responses in relation to endocrine status following PMSG stimulation in the cow. In, *Control of Reproduction in the Cow*, Galway, Sreenan, J., Ed., pp. 144–158., C.E.C., Luxembourg.

Sreenan, J. M. and Scanlon, P. (1968) Continued cleavage of fertilized bovine ova in the rabbit. *Nature, Lond.* **217**, 867.

Sreenan, J. M., Scanlon, P. and Gordon, I. (1968) Culture of fertilized cattle eggs. *J. Agric. Sci., Camb.* **70**, 183–185.

Sreenan, J., Scanlon, P. and Gordon, I. (1970) Storage of fertilized cattle ova *in vitro*. *J. Agric. Sci., Camb.* **74**, 593–594.

Stewart, F., Allen, W. R. and Moor, R. M. (1976) PMSG: Ratio of FSH and LH activities measured by radio-receptor assay. *J. Endocr.* **71**, 371–382.

Strickland, J. D., Stallings, C. M., Dorgan, W. J. and Moody, E. L. (1977) Recovery rate, size and viability of trypsin liberated bovine oocytes. *Proc. West. Sect., Am. Soc. Anim. Sci.* **28**, 158–159.

Sugie, T. (1965) Successful transfer of a fertilized bovine egg by non-surgical techniques. *J. Reprod. Fert.* **10**, 197–201.

Sugie, T. (1970) Reciprocal ova transfer between different breeds in cattle. *Ann. Rpt. Mat. Int. Ind. Chiba-ski, Jpn.* **8**, 56.

Sugie, T. (1970) Non-surgical ova collection in cattle. *Ann. Rpt. Nat. Inst. Anim. Ind., Chiba-ski, Jpn.* **8**, 55.

Sugie, T., Soma, T., Fukumitsu, S. and Otsuki, K. (1972a) Studies on the ovum transfer in cattle, with special reference to collection of ova by means of non-surgical techniques. *Nat. Inst. Anim. Ind. Bull.* **25**, 27–34.

Sugie, T., Soma, T., Fukumitsu, S. and Otsuki, K. (1972b) Studies on the ovum transfer in cattle with special reference to transplantation of fertilized ova by means of non-surgical techniques. *Nat. Inst. Anim. Ind. Bull.* **25**, 35–40.

Summers, P. M. and Campbell, R. S. F. (1974) A histological study of ovarian function in infertile beef cows. *Res. Vet. Sci.* **17**, 131.

Takahashi, Y. (1980) Comparative studies on bovine embryo transfer for three different techniques of transcervical, flank surgical and cervical bypass methods. *Jap. J. Anim. Reprod.* **26**(4), 155–157.

Talmage, D. W. (1979) Recognition and memory in the cells of the immune system. *Am. Sci.* **67**, 173–177.

Tarowski, A. K. (1959) Experiments on the development of isolated blastomeres of mouse eggs. *Res. Vet. Sci.* **17**, 131.

Tervit, H. R. (1973) Culture and transfer of sheep and cattle ova. Ph. D. Thesis. Univ. of Cambridge.

Tervit, H. R. and Rowson, L. E. A. (1972) The viability of fertilized ova recovered from slaughtered cattle. *Proc. Int. Congr. Anim. Reprod. A.I. (Munich)*, **1**, 489–492.

Tervit, H. R. and Rowson, L. E. A. (1974) Birth of lambs after culture of sheep ova *in vitro* for up to 6 days. *J. Reprod. Fert.* **38**, 177.

Tervit, H. R., Cooper, M. W., Goold, P. G. and Hazard, G. M. (1980) Non-surgical embryo transfer in cattle. *Theriogen.* **13**(1), 63–71.

Tervit, H. R., Elsden, R. P. and Ferand, G. D. (1981) Deep freezing 7- to 8- and 10- to 11 day old cattle embryos. *Theriogen.* **15**, 115 (Abs).

Tervit, H. R., Havik, P. G. and Smith, J. F. (1977) Egg transfer in cattle. Pregnancy rate following transfer to the uterine horn ipsilateral or contralateral to the functional corpus luteum. *Theriogen.* **7**(1), 3–10.

Tervit, H. R., Rowson, L. E. A. and Brand, A. (1973) Synchronization of oestrus in cattle using a prostaglandin $F_{2\alpha}$ analogue (ICI 79939). *J. Reprod. Fert.* **34**, 179–181.

Tervit, H. R., Whittingham, D. G. and Rowson, L. E. A. (1972) Successful culture *in vitro* in sheep and cattle ova. *J. Reprod. Fert.* **30**, 493–497.

Testart, J. (1972) Follicular response of immature heifers to various treatments with serum gonadotrophin, with or without progestin. *Ann. Biol. Anim. Biochim. Biophys.* **12**, 397.

Testart, J. (1972) Synchronization of induced ovulation in the perpuberal female calf. *Proc. 7th Int. Congr. Anim. Reprod., A.I. (Munich).* **1,** 493.

Testart, J. and Arrau, J. (1973) Oocyte maturation following follicle stimulation in the calf. *Ann. Biol. Anim. Biochim. Biophys.* **13,** (Suppl.) 157.

Thibault, C. (1967) A comparative analysis of fertilization and its anomalies in the ewe, cow and rabbit. *Ann. Biol. Anim. Biochim. Biophys.* **7,** 5–23.

Thibault, C. (1977) Are follicular maturation and oocyte maturation independent processes? *J. Reprod. Fert.* **51,** 1–15.

Thibault, C., Gerard, M. and Menezo, Y. (1975) In vitro acquired ability of rabbit and cow oocyte to ensure sperm nucleus decondensation during fertilization (MPGF). *Ann. Biol. Anim. Biochim. Biophys.* **15,** 704–714.

Thibault, C., Gerard, M. and Menezo, Y. (1975) Preovulatory and ovulatory mechanism in oocyte maturation. *J. Reprod. Fert.* **45,** 605–610.

Trounson, A. O. and Moore, N. W. (1974) Attempts to produce identical offspring in the sheep by mechanical division of the ovum. *Aust. J. Biol. Sci.* **27,** 505.

Trounson, A. O. and Rowson, L. E. A. (1977) Research in embryo transfer in domestic animals. *J. R. Agric. Soc.* **137,** 77–85.

Trounson, A. O., Brand, A. and Aarts, M. H. (1978) Non-surgical transfer of deep-frozen bovine embryos. *Theriogen.* **10**(1), 111–115.

Trounson, A. O., Shea, B. F., Ollis, G. W. and Jacobson, M. E. (1978) Frozen storage and transfer of bovine embryos. *J. Anim. Sci.* **47**(3), 677–681.

Trounson, A. O., Rowson, L. E. A. and Willadsen, S. M. (1978) Non-surgical transfer of bovine embryos. *Vet. Rec.* **102,** 74–75.

Trounson, A. O., Willadsen, S. M. and Rowson, L. E. A. (1976a) The influence of in vitro culture and cooling on the survival and development of cow embryos. *J. Reprod. Fert.* **47,** 367–370.

Trounson, A. O., Willadsen, S. M., Rowson, L. E. A. and Newcomb, R. (1976b) The storage of cow eggs at room temperature and at low temperatures. *J. Reprod. Fert.* **46,** 173–178.

Trounson, A. O., Willadsen, S. M., Rowson, L. E. A. and Newcomb, R. (1977) Fertilization and development capacity of bovine follicular oocytes matured in vitro and in vivo and transferred to the oviducts of rabbits and cows. *J. Reprod. Fert.* **51,** 321.

Tsunoda, Y., Parkening, T. A. and Chang, M. C. (1976) In vitro fertilization of mouse and hamster eggs after freezing and thawing. *Experienta.* **32,** 223–224.

Umbaugh, R. E. (1949) Superovulation and ovum transfer in cattle. *Am. J. Vet. Res.* **10,** 295–305.

Umbaugh, R. E. (1951) Superovulation and ovum transfer in cattle. *Fert. Ster.* **2,** 243.

Von Bregulla, K., Gerlach, U. and Hahn, R. (1974) Versuche zur extrakorporalen Rei fung, Befruchtung and embryo-enzucht mit Rinderkeimzellen. *Dtsch. Tierarztl. Wochenschr.* **81,** 465–470.

Von Hoppen, H. O., Unshelm, J. and Haupt, P. (1978) Cervix-weiterung und luteal funktion nach intracervicaler injektion cines synthetischen prostaglandin E_2-Derivats beim Rind *Zuchtrhgy.* **13,** 68.

Warnes, G. M., Moor, R. M. and Johnson, M. H. (1977) Changes in protein synthesis during maturation of sheep oocytes in vivo and in vitro. *J. Reprod. Fert.* **49,** 331–335.

Warwick, B. L. and Berry, R. O. (1949) Inter-generic and intra-specific embryo transfers. *J. Hered.* **40,** 297–303.

Warwick, B. L. and Berry, R. O. (1951) Embryo transfers in sheep and goats. *Egg Transfer Breeding Conf.* Found of Applied Res., San Antonio.

Whittingham, D. G. (1971) Survival of mouse embryos after freezing and thawing. *Nature, Lond.* **233,** 125.

Whittingham, D. G. (1977) Fertilization in vitro and development to terms of unfertilized mouse oocytes previously stored at $-196°C$. *J. Reprod. Fert.* **89,** 94.

Whittingham, D. G., Wood, M., Ferrant, J., Lee, H. and Hasley, J. A. (1979) Survival of frozen mouse embryos after rapid thawing from $-196°C$. *J. Reprod. Fert.* **56,** 11–21.

Willadsen, S. M. (1977) Factors affecting the survival of sheep and cattle embryos during deep-freezing and thawing. In, *Freezing of Mammalian Embryos.* Ciba Foundation Symp. 52 (New Series Elliott, K. and Whelan, J. Eds., pp. 175–194. Excerpta Medica, Amsterdam.

Willadsen, S. M. (1979) A method for culture of micro-manipulated sheep embryos and its use to produce monozygotic twins. *Nature, Lond.* **277,** 298.

Willadsen, S. M. and Polge, C. (1980) Embryo transplantation in the large domestic species: applications and perspectives in the light of recent experiments with eggs and embryos. *J. R. Agric. Soc. Eng.* 115–126.

Willadsen, S. M. and Polge, C. (1981) Attempts to produce monozygotic quadruplets in cattle by blastomere separation. *Vet. Rec.* **100,** 211–213.

Willadsen, S., Polge, C. and Rowson, L. E. A. (1978) The viability of deep-frozen cow embryos. *J. Reprod. Fert.* **52,** 391–393.

Willadsen, S. M., Lehn-Jensen, H., Fehilly, C. G. and Newcomb, R. (1981) The production of monozygotic twins of preselected parentage by micromanipulation of non-surgically collected cow embryos. *Theriogen.* **15,** 23–29.

Willadsen, S. M., Polge, C., Rowson, L. E. A. and Moor, R. M. (1974) Preservation of sheep embryos in liquid nitrogen. *Cryobiol.* **11,** 560 (Abs).

Willadsen, S. M., Polge, C., Rowson, L. E. A. and Moor, R. M. (1976a) Deep freezing of sheep embryos. *J. Reprod. Fert.* **46,** 151–154.

Willadsen, S. M., Trounson, A. O., Polge, C., Rowson, L. E. A. and Newcomb, R. (1976b) Low temperature preservation of cow eggs. In, *Transfer in Cattle.* Rowson, L. E. A. Edd., pp. 117–124., C,E.C. Luxembourg.

Williams, G. L. (1960) Observations on the fertility of newly established herds. *Vet. Rec.* **72,** 197.

Willett, E. L., Black, W. G., Casida, L. E., Stone, W. H. and Buckner, P. J. (1951) Successful transplantation of a fertilized bovine ovum. *Science.* **113,** 247.

Willett, E. L., Buckner, P. J. and Larson, G. L. (1953) Three transplantations of fertilized bovine eggs. *J. Dairy Sci.,* **36,** 520.

Wilmut, I. (1973) Animal Breeding; a role for embryo preservation?. *Span,* **16,**(3), 99.

Wilmut, I. (1980) Embryo transfer in cattle breeding. *Wld. Anim. Rev.* **35,** 30–35.

Wilmut, I. and Hume, A. (1978) The value of embryo transfer to cattle breeding in Britain. *Vet. Rec.* **103,** 107–110.

Wilmut, I. and Rowson, L. E. A. (1973) Experiments on the low-temperature preservation of cow embryos. *Vet. Rec.* **92,** 686–690.

Wilmut, I., Sales, D. I., Manson, C. and Newell, G. (1978) Non-surgical transfer of cattle embryos — a field trial. *Ann. Rpt. A.B.R.O.* **1978,** 41.

Wintenberger-Torres, S. and Popescu, P. C. (1980) Transfer of cow blastocysts after sexing. *Theriogen.* **14,** 309–318.

Wright, J. M. (1981) Non-surgical embryo transfer in cattle embryo recipient interactions. *Theriogen.* **15,** 43–56.

Wright, R. W. (Jr.)., Anderson, G. B., Cupps, P. T., Drost, M. and Bradford, G. E. (1976) *In vitro* culture of embryos from adult and prepuberal ewes. *J. Anim. Sci.* **42,** 912–917.

Zraly, Z., Kummer, V. and Veznik. Z. (1980) Use of carbachol for dilation of the cervix in heifers. *Theriogen,* **13,** 217–220.

CHAPTER 8

Induction of Twin Births

8.1 INTRODUCTION

For the most efficient systems of animal production, a high reproduction rate is a basic requirement. For most countries, the constantly rising costs of feed, labour and land make this more true today than at any time in the past. Without entering into arguments about the world's expanding human population and the need for adequate animal protein supplies, there can be few who would deny that the long-term solution is a matter of research and technology applied world-wide to increase both crop and animal production, allied to determined efforts to keep the human population at a figure that can be provided for.

The development of some simple and reliable technique for getting twin calves from beef and dairy cattle may well have a useful part to play, both in making beef production economically more attractive and in making possible an increase in world beef supplies. It could also have merit in enabling the annual production of calves for beef rearing in a country such as Ireland to be increased without this involving additions to the breeding cow population. For Ireland, in which beef is the single most important product of the agricultural industry, the availability of a commercially viable twinning technique could be of special importance in increasing the supply of desirable beef calves.

The fact remains, however, that the amount of research effort which has gone into cattle twinning would seem to be small, relative to the potential economic value of an effective technique. Part of the reason is the high cost of large animal research and the fact that cattle twinning is probably not seen as a potential source or reward by pharmaceutical companies; certainly in comparison to the money spent by such companies in developing prostaglandins and progestagens for oestrus control in cattle, the amount spent on twinning is negligible.

Looking at the North American scene, Seidel (1981) notes that almost 80% of the cows are beef animals whose sole function is to provide one calf each year. Certainly, it can be argued that, in terms of converting feedstuffs into beef, the process would be much more efficient with cows producing twins; about 70% of the nutrients consumed by each cow go towards her maintenance whereas only the remaining 30% or so goes towards growth and maintenance of the calf during pregnancy and lactation. In many countries around the world, beef cattle producers usually operate on a low-input low-output basis with their present-day production methods differing little from those of their forebears several generations ago. Nevertheless, an effective twinning procedure might be of advantage to cattle producers, both small and large, as a means of increasing their incomes as well as updating their production systems.

8.1.1 Twins in dairy and beef cattle

Although it is usually held that twinning is likely to be of greatest interest to farmers with beef suckler cattle, this need not necessarily be the direction an effective twinning method would take in practice. The fact is that suckler cows tend to be kept under conditions in which nutrition and management may be serious limiting factors; certainly, this is more likely to be true for beef cattle than for dairy animals. In Ireland, by far the greater number of calves for beef rearing come from the dairy herds; the majority of cattle are Friesians whose milk goes either to the manufacturing industry or for direct human consumption. Accordingly, in this country it is of interest to examine the possibilities and implications (nutritional, endocrinological, physiological) of induced twinning in such cattle.

In national terms, twinning in dairy cattle could be one positive way of increasing cattle numbers for beef in the Irish Republic without this causing additional milk supply problems within the E.E.C. Traditional objections to twins in cattle are often based on their present record, where the performance of cows and calves is assessed under

feeding and management conditions favouring singles. Indeed, as observed by Lamond (1974), one advantage of work in developing induced cattle twinning may be in encouraging new systems of cattle husbandry which may be required in coping with the greater flow of calves. Certainly, twinning for beef rearing, perhaps for other reasons as well, such as veal production, could offer impressive economic advantages in countries where nutrition is not a limiting factor and intensive management is possible.

8.1.2 Incidence of natural twins

Twins are not uncommon in cattle, especially among those kept in favourable environmental conditions with good feeding and management; information on this has been reviewed in several reports over the years (Johansson, 1932; Gordon et al., 1962; Hendy and Bowman, 1970; Scanlon et al., 1974; Johansson et al., 1974; Rutledge, 1975). Isolated instances of cattle giving rise to as many as seven calves have been recorded and quintuplet and quadruplet births are mentioned in several reports in the literature (review by Scanlon et al., 1974) although precise information on their incidence in the cattle population is limited. Richter (1955) reports an incidence of 3.23% twins, 0.01% triplets and 0.002% quadruplets in 59 557 calvings. Referring to the available literature at the time on cattle multiples, Cook (1948) estimated the frequency of quintuplets at not less than one in every 3–5 million births.

Table 8.1. *Incidence of twin births and twin ovulations in cows*

	Gordon et al. (1962)	Scanlon et al. (1974)
Total calvings	3826	2323
With twins	108	64
With twins (%)	2.82%	2.76(%)
	Gordon et al. (1962)	Scanlon et al. (1974)
Total cattle examined	436	3136
With twin ovulations	18	107†
With twin ovulations (%)	4.13%	3.41%

†Includes 4 animals with more than 2 ovulations.
Data from studies conducted in Wales and Ireland.

The percentage of twin births in cattle varies among breeds and according to factors such as age and environment. In some reports, it is almost negligible, in others, an incidence as high as 10% has been reported. In Ireland and the U.K., the incidence recorded in various surveys is somewhere from 2 to 3% (Gordon et al., 1962; Scanlon et al., 1974). It follows from this that most cattle producers in the British Isles have had some experience of naturally-occurring twins, a fact which inevitably colours the views expressed on the possible advantages and disadvantages of such calves. Veterinarians are not always kindly disposed to twinning but perhaps this may partly reflect the fact that they are often called to those twinning occasions in which difficulties have arisen at parturition or subsequently. In a survey conducted in Wales, Gordon et al. (1962) found that most sets of natural twins born to beef suckler cows were delivered unaided and that professional assistance in dealing with retained foetal membranes was required in less than 10% of calvings.

8.1.3 Feeding and twins

It is well accepted that there is virtually nothing that can be done in the feeding and/or management of the cow to raise the twinning percentage to any figure of practical value, certainly not in the way that this is possible in sheep with "flushing" them around the time of mating. However, it may be mentioned that in certain circumstances, sheep may produce multiples no more frequently than cattle or horses. In a study of 14 930 births in a heathland breed of sheep in Germany, Luhr (1936) reports no more than 2.7% of twins. A report by Nel et al. (1960) for Karakul ewes in South West Africa gives an incidence of twins no greater than 2–5%. Under conditions operating in India, Bhattacharya et al. (1956) reported 0.22% cattle twins in 22 949 calvings, a value much below that usually reported in West European and North American studies. A similarly low incidence of twins in British breeds was observed in areas such as South Africa where nutritional and other environmental limitations could be expected (Joubert, 1961).

8.1.4 Age, season and breed

Although good feeding cannot produce any noticeable effect on the incidence of twins, it is generally accepted that the frequency of twins is higher in dairy herds on a good plane of nutrition (Wettstein, 1947; Auran, 1974). There is a well-established relationship between the incidence of twinning and age of cow; Butz and Schmahlsteig (1953) and Scanlon et al. (1973) are among authors recording the highest incidence of twins at the fifth pregnancy. Data from the MMB of England and Wales (Anon, 1976, 1979) show an increase in the twinning percentage from first to fifth lactation for all breeds examined with the highest incidence in the Canadian Holstein breed.

The effect of season on twinning is less clearcut, although Auran (1974) in Norway found a peak frequency of births in June which agrees well with the much earlier Scandinavian results of Johansson (1932). As noted earlier, breed differences in the frequency of multiple births certainly exist, with dairy breeds showing a higher incidence of twin births than beef breeds (Scanlon et al., 1974).

8.1.5 Identical twins in cattle

It has been recognized for some time that monozygotic twins occur in cattle, in contrast to the situation in the other farm species; the incidence of identicals has been estimated as about 10% of the like-sexed twins (Meadows and Lush, 1957; Johansson, 1961). The factors responsible for the occurrence of one-egg cattle twins are not known, but there apparently is no hereditary basis for the phenomenon. It has been suggested that identicals may occur more frequently after some bulls than others and that this might be a matter of factors associated with the sperm (Hancock, 1950).

Asdell (1955) considered that the incidence of monozygotic twins was higher than usual in herds suffering from Vibrio foetus infection and speculated on this arising from changes in the oviducal environment of the infected animals. The artificial induction of cattle identicals has not been attempted by any form of drug treatment,

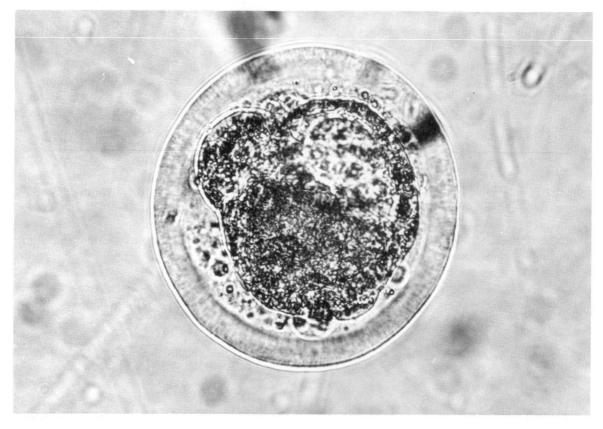

Fig. 8.1. Monozygotic cattle twins, at the start of their development in a blastocyst. Of the various farm animals, cattle are the only ones to produce monozygotic twins — and here they would be expected at the rate of one set per 1000 calvings for Irish cattle. This photo is a rare one of an 8-day bovine embryo which on transfer to a recipient developed into a set of conjoined twins (Siamese twins). The factors that are responsible for the occurrence of identical twins are not known. In some species, the incidence of congenital abnormalities is much higher in identical twins than in single born offspring and this would indicate that genetic factors probably play a part in the phenomenon.

but in mice there now is an experimental method, involving the agent vincristine sulphate (Oncovin, Lilly) by which a low incidence of such twinning can be induced (Kaufman and O'Shea, 1978); the technique permits examination of the early stages in the development of monzygotic twins to be made under controlled conditions. As noted earlier, a new experimental approach to the production, not only of identical twins, but even identical triplets and quadruplets in cattle was opened up with the report of Willadsen and Polge (1981), who employed micromanipulation techniques to separate blastomeres in the early developing egg.

8.2 BREEDING FOR TWINS

The possibility of developing a twinning strain in cattle, despite the low heritability of the trait, has been discussed in some number of reports over the years (Bowman et al., 1970; Hendy and Bowman, 1970; Rutledge, 1975; Cady and Van Vleck, 1978; Piper and Bindon, 1979; during the 1970's, there was a revival of interest in the subject which led to a number of herds practising genetic selection for the twinning trait being established in several countries. Those breeding schemes which have been reported on already apparently met with little success (Mechling and Carter,

1964; Donald and Gibson, 1974). Nonetheless, there is the view that an intense selection programme for increased twinning could be expected to make better progress; there is also the suggestion that it would be possible to produce cattle that are better adapted to multiple births than those existing today (Johansson *et al.*, 1974). In Finnish cows, an analysis of 600 000 calvings by Maijala and Syvajarvi (1977) led them to conclude that a strain capable of 20% twin births could be developed within 10 years, using modern data processing technology allied to an artificial insemination programme.

In high yielding Holstein dairy cows, although Rutledge (1975) concluded that reasonably rapid progress could be made towards twinning by selection, others tended to the view that such selection, even if it were likely to be of commercial advantage, would be difficult and time-consuming (Cady and Van Vleck, 1978). Looking at the situation in the U.K., Bowman (1976) concluded that there was not likely to be any economic advantage in selecting Friesian dairy cattle for twinning, since it would pay better to concentrate on selection for milk production rather than for additional calves; he suggested, under the economic conditions operating in the U.K. at that time, that the most promising area for twinning work would be in a beef breed such as the Charolais.

8.2.1 Twin-births and twin ovulations

It should be noted that selection for twin-births in cattle involves more than just selection for twin-ovulating animals. One rather unusual consideration, which makes selection more difficult in cattle than in sheep is the fact that one egg must be shed from each ovary if a high twin pregnancy rate is to be achieved (Gordon *et al.*, 1962). Confirmation of this observation came later from surgical embryo transfer studies by Rowson *et al.* (1969, 1971) who showed that a high twinning rate was achieved after bilateral transfer of single embryo to each uterine horn, but not after the unilateral transfer of two embryos to the horn ipsilateral to the corpus luteum. This apparently was the result of competition between embryos within the one uterine horn. Unlike the situation in sheep and pigs, transuterine migration of eggs rarely occurs in the cow (Perkins *et al.*, 1954; Gordon *et al.*, 1962; Scanlon, 1972); thus, even if selection for twin ovulations was fully successful, both eggs would be ovulated from the one ovary in 50% of cases and the outcome would often be one calf rather than twins (Table 8.2).

8.2.2 Problems in natural twinners

Although it is possible to build up twinning strains of cattle by selective breeding, for various reasons, including the failure of unilateral twins to survive as readily as bilateral twins, the success rate using the breeding approach may be limited to a figure of 20% or so, despite the best efforts. There may also be the need to keep a watchful eye that such selection does not in itself result in certain breeding difficulties. Attention was first drawn, almost a half century ago, to the fact that twinning rate was high in herds in which there

Table 8.2 *Survival rate in cattle/sheep embryos according to location of twin-ovulations*

Species	Method of examination	No. of animals	Percentage of animals carrying twins when both ovulations occur:		Reference
			In a single ovary	One ovulation in each ovary	
Cattle	Rectal exam. at 6 weeks after breeding	67	28.6	61.5	Gordon *et al.* (1962)
Sheep	Slaughter	51	58.1	75.0	Smyth (1965)
Sheep	Slaughter	418	76.3	80.3	Scanlon (1972)

was a high incidence of cystic ovaries (Clapp, 1934). In a later study among Holstein cattle, Erb et al. (1959) presented evidence indicating that several factors, including cystic follicles, abnormal oestrous cycle lengths, retained foetal membranes and multiple births, may have a genetic relationship arising from the one endocrine peculiarity. Bar-Anan and Bowman (1974), in an analysis of Israeli-Friesian calving data, drew attention to a bull whose daughters not only showed an unusually high incidence of twinning (12%) but also evidence of a major endocrine disturbance.

One final aspect which might be mentioned, in contemplating possible breeding approaches to twinning, is the selection of cattle strains in which the artificial induction of multiples may be somewhat easier to accomplish than in the normal run of cattle. Rowson (1971), for instance, drew attention to the considerable variation that exists in the number of uterine caruncles among cattle and suggested it might be worth examining the inheritance of this characteristic as part of any move towards multiple-births. Mauleon (1974), on the basis of work among French breeds of cattle, noted that cows of the Normandy breed apparently possessed an ability to sustain gonadotrophin-induced multiples more readily than Friesian cattle.

8.3 TWINS BY HORMONE TREATMENT

It was not until the years of World War II that attention turned to the possibility of hormonally inducing twins; Hammond and Bhattacharya (1944) were among the first to use PMSG and horse pituitary extracts with the express purpose of inducing twin pregnancy. In most instances, the gonadotrophin treatment was allied to enucleation of the corpus luteum, but the procedure did not have a high success rate. Later work, in which PMSG was given in the follicular phase of the normal oestrous cycle, appeared more promising (Hammond, 1949) but numbers were too few to permit a critical assessment, either of the procedures involved or the results obtained.

One attempt to explore the hormonal

approach to cattle twinning was the large-scale trial undertaken by the MMB in the 1959–61 period in the Welsh border counties. The technique which the MMB sought to test involved a single dose of PMSG given on day-16/17 of the cow's oestrous cycle; this type of treatment had been used with some success in boosting the twinning percentage in low fertility breeds of sheep in the south of England in the fifties (Gordon, 1955). The MMB trial dealt with upwards of 500 cattle which were given PMSG and thereafter kept under close observation through until calving (Gordon et al., 1962); results from the work drew attention to certain aspects of cattle twinning which had not previously been evident. One problem revealed was the fact that even when the cow releases two eggs in response to exogenous gonadotrophin, the animal could still end up producing a single calf. There was evidence, however, that a much higher percentage of twin pregnancies survived when one ovulation occurred in each ovary rather than when both eggs were released from one ovary (61.5% twins vs 28.6% in cattle becoming pregnant after treatment). Such findings have been confirmed subsequently, either as a result of embryo transfer studies or in other investigations; an abattoir survey, involving 8000 cattle reproductive tracts, reported on by Al-Dahash and David (1977) in the U.K., showed that unilateral twins occurred much less frequently than bilateral twins, although twin ovulations in one ovary were observed to occur as frequently as single ovulations in each ovary. One useful feature of the MMB trial was the fact that it provided some evidence, albeit limited, that the adverse effects of twin births in dairy cattle might be overcome by appropriate modification of feeding levels during late pregnancy; subsequent studies have tended to confirm this.

A major drawback to PMSG approach to cattle twinning, as shown in the data of Gordon et al. (1962), was the marked individual variation in ovulatory response which occurred, together with the fact that the treatment not uncommonly resulted in triplet, quadruplet and even quintuplet births; under most farm conditions, litters in excess of twins in cattle can only be considered highly undesirable. With dairy and

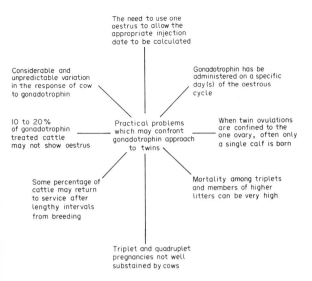

The need to use one oestrus to allow the appropriate injection date to be calculated

Considerable and unpredictable variation in the response of cow to gonadotrophin

Gonadotrophin has be administered on a specific day(s) of the oestrous cycle

10 to 20% of gonadotrophin treated cattle may not show oestrus

Practical problems which may confront gonadotrophin approach to twins

When twin ovulations are confined to the one ovary, often only a single calf is born

Some percentage of cattle may return to service after lengthy intervals from breeding

Mortality among triplets and members of higher litters can be very high

Triplet and quadruplet pregnancies not well sustained by cows

Fig. 8.2. Problems in the hormonal induction of twins in cattle.

beef cows under suitable feeding and management, however, there is the possibility that triplet calves may be dealt with satisfactorily; it remains for experimental work to clarify the point.

8.3.1 Multiple dose gonadotrophin treatment

Schilling and Holm (1963) were the first to report on the possibility of inducing twins by limiting the number of eggs ovulated to two or three. The most promising results followed a single injection of 1000–1500 i.u. PMSG on the fifth day after oestrus, enucleation of the corpus luteum between the 16th and 18th day and injection of a second dose of 2000 i.u. PMSG at that time; cattle came in heat, 3–5 days later, and were given a dose of 4000 i.u. hGC intravenously. This treatment was effective in limiting the extent of the multiple-ovulation to two to three eggs in the 8/11 cattle responding. This type of regimen, with certain modifications, was subsequently used by Turnman et al. (1971) in the U.S.A.; 1500 i.u. PMSG was given in the early luteal phase of the cycle (days 5 to 6), a further 2000 i.u. in the follicular phase (days 16 to 18) followed by 2500 i.u. hCG immediately after breeding by natural service. Of the 81 beef cows treated, 23 sets of multiples were produced, these including 12 sets of twins, 8 triplets, 2 quadruplets and a set of quintuplets; less than half the triplets and members of larger sets survived at birth process.

In a later report, the Oklahoma workers reported on a further 65 beef cattle treated with the double PMSG dose regimen; 21 conceived at first service and produced 9 singles, 7 sets of twins, 4 sets of triplets and a set of quadruplets (Johnson et al., 1973). It is evident that the occurrence of triplet births is a major hazard in this form of treatment and the low first service conception rate is an unwelcome feature.

According to French studies on the growth of Graafian follicles in the ovaries of the cow during the oestrous cycle (Mariana and Nguyen Huy, 1973), the aim of the double PMSG dose regimen (days 6 and 16) is to make these injections coincide with the phases of maximum follicular growth in such a way that the number of large vesicular follicles able to respond to gonadotrophin in the follicular phase is limited. French researchers have also shown that certain breeds or even particular strains within a cattle breed may respond differently to gonadotrophin treatment (Mauleon et al., 1970); they suggest that it may be feasible to arrange PMSG dosage and timing schedules to achieve limited superovulation in an acceptable proportion of the animals (Mauleon et al., 1970; Mauleon, 1974).

Nearer home, work in Northern Ireland reported by McCaughey and Dow (1977) involved two spaced doses of PMSG (800 i.u.) and a single dose of 2000 i.u. hCG at oestrus; although less than 50% of the 15 cows conceived at the post-treatment oestrus, five sets of twins without triplets or larger litters were recorded.

8.3.2 Gonadotrophins and synchronizing agents

There have been several reports dealing with the use of gonadotrophins to induce multiple ovulations in cattle whose oestrous cycles have been synchronized with oral progestagens such as MAP (Bellows et al., 1969; Bellows and Short, 1972) or CAP (Lamond, 1972); there were indications that variability in response to gonadotrophins was somewhat less than that after the use of PMSG on day-16 of the oestrous cycle.

Work in Ireland, which involved low doses of PMSG (750–800) i.u.) after short-term progestagen treatment for oestrus synchronization in beef suckler cattle, showed 10–20% of twins in animals calving to first service with no litter in excess of two (Mulvehill and Sreenan, 1977; Sreenan, 1977b, 1979). French workers, using similar PMSG doses (800 i.u.) in conjunction with their synchronization applications, have reported 5% triplets and quadruplets among the multiples (Mauleon et al., 1978).

8.3.3. Gonadotrophins employed

The type of gonadotrophin preparation used can be expected to have some influence on ovulatory response. Anterior pituitary FSH preparations are known to give rise to less variability than PMSG, but on the debit side, they have to be given in a series of injections and are expensive (Bellows et al., 1969; Bellows and Short, 1972). Attempts to get a longer duration of action with FSH preparations have included administering the gonadotrophin in gelatin capsules (Vincent et al., 1973) or using carboxymethyl cellulose or polyvinyl pyrrolidone as an injectable carrier (Reynolds et al., 1970; Mills et al., 1971; Johnson and Rich, 1973; Smith et al., 1973). The fact that such a wide selection of agents and regimens have been employed in experiments makes critical assessment, either of the procedures themselves or the results obtained, difficult.

8.3.4 Prostaglandin and gonadotrophins

In an attempt to achieve a less variable interval between gonadotrophin treatment and oestrus, investigators have occasionally combined PMSG or FSH with enucleation of the corpus luteum by manipulation per rectum (Hammond and Bhattacharya, 1944). Regression of the corpus luteum can now be readily achieved by prostaglandin $F_{2\alpha}$ or one of its analogues and one way in which the PG has been employed is in conjunction with short-term progestagen and PMSG, the PG being given at progestagen withdrawal and two days after low-dose (500–600 i.u.) PMSG; Friesian cows allowed to go to term gave 34% twin pregnancies and suckler cattle examined for ovulations showed 33% with two to four ovulations and none with more than four (Chupin and Saumande, 1979). There are indications that when PG-PMSG is allied to short-term progestagen treatment, the effectiveness of a low dose of PMSG may be increased. The PG in this type of regimen is given in order to ensure that the cyclic corpus luteum is no longer functional after terminating the progestagen treatment, in view of evidence suggesting that PMSG can otherwise maintain the corpus luteum in some circumstances (Saumande, 1978). In noting the above value of 33% twinning in Friesians, it should be borne in mind that this figure relates to cattle holding pregnant to first service; assuming a pregnancy rate of 66%, this would provide no more than about 20% twins relative to the number of cattle treated. However, there is ample scope for following up the possibilities of these progestagen–PMSG–PG regimens; certainly, among beef suckler cattle, there may well be particular merit in combining oestrus synchronization with a mild degree of superovulation.

The availability of Gn-RH or one of its potent analogues held out some hope at one time of an additional approach to the induction of two ovulations rather than one; the hope was that extra gonadotrophin might be released after its use around the time of oestrus. Lamond (1973) dealt with the possibility at the date and concluded, on the basis of studies reported for Gn-RH, that hopes for its use in inducing multi-ovulations should not be exaggerated; nothing has appeared in more recent times to change that view.

8.3.5 Maintenance of pregnancy

Lamond (1973) drew attention to the fact that one of the difficulties in the induction of additional ovulations was the production of high levels of progesterone by the several corpora lutea formed. Plasma levels of progesterone in some cows with two to four ovulations were found to be much above those usual for cattle (Lamond and Gaddy, 1972). There would seem to be indications that unlike the ewe, in which progesterone concentrations are kept within tolerable limits when more than one corpus luteum is in the ovary, the cow's output of progesterone may be much above normal after the induction of extra corpora lutea. This sort of evidence might fit in with some observations on pregnancy failure in PMSG-treated cows by Gordon et al. (1962) and Testart et al. (1970). It has also been taken as further evidence that cattle may not be well-adapted to carry twins (Dawson, 1979). In the U.S.A., several reports dealing with hormonally induced twins and multiples refer to embryonic and foetal losses (Bellows *et al.*, 1974, 1979). There has been some evidence that the survival rate of multiple embryos could be significantly increased by feeding an orally-active progestagen (Bellows and Short, 1972; Christensen *et al.*, 1972) but other work showed that foetal loss in later pregnancy continued even when progestagen was fed (Bellows *et al.*, 1973).

8.3.6 Problems in hormonal approach

There is ample evidence in the literature to show that twin and multiple-pregnancies can be induced hormonally by a wide range of techniques. It is also clear that among cattle becoming pregnant with multiples some proportion may be expected to carry triplets and even larger litters; such calves would not be welcome on the normal farm. Even given a technique affective in confining ovulations to two, no control is possible over the site of ovulation; because of the lack of transuterine migration and the occurrence of unilateral twin-ovulations, a high rate of twin pregnancy would not seem likely. There may be the added problem of the cow not managing to keep its progesterone level under control.

Although it may appear desirable to view cattle twinning as attainable by way of a simple injection procedure rather than requiring a more complex approach, the basic difficulties to the hormonal solution still remain; it is not possible to avoid unwelcome triplet births nor to induce more than a limited percentage (20% or so) of multiples.

8.4 EMBRYO TRANSFER FOR TWINS

Reviewing a number of possibilities for continued efforts in cattle twinning, in the light of their 3-year MMB trial programme, Gordon *et al.* (1962) suggested that efforts might be directed towards using embryo transfer to introduce a second egg into the cow's uterus a few days after breeding. The cow could then carry twins in the

form of her own calf and one which originated in an appropriate donor animal. One unknown factor, at that time, was whether twin-pregnancy could be successfully sustained by just the one corpus luteum. The results of Rowson *et al.* (1971), in which they recorded a 73% incidence of twins when an egg was placed in each uterine horn, made it clear that a high incidence of twinning could be induced in the absence of a second corpus luteum; these findings have been amply confirmed by other groups (Sreenan, 1977; Anderson, 1978).

Fig. 8.3. Twins born as a result of the transfer of one embryo to the contralateral horn of the uterus of the mated cow. Research in cattle twinning by embryo transfer was started in the Irish Republic at the University Farm in 1966. The objective was to develop a method which could be applied to beef and dairy cows under the particular conditions that obtain in that country. By 1976, several sets of twins had been produced by non-surgical transfer of a beef egg into the empty horn of a mated recipient cow. In the west of Ireland, workers in the state research organization (An Foras Taluntais) led by Dr. Joe Sreenan have obtained very encouraging results with the same type of procedure.

Although Rowson *et al.* (1971), reporting the first successful production of twins by bilateral two-egg transfer, did allude to the alternative possibility of twinning by one-egg transfer to a previously mated animal, it was Boland *et al.* (1975, 1976) who eventually showed that this approach might be the basis of a commercially feasible technique. Reviewing Cambridge efforts at the time, Rowson (1971) mentioned various attempts to produce twins of differing breeds by transfer of an embryo to the uterus of the previously mated animal; apparently, results in

Table 8.3 *Calving and twinning rates after contralateral non-surgical transfer to mated recipients*

	Mated recipients				
	U.C.D. Studies	Sreenan and McDonagh (1979)	Renard et al. (1979)	Sreenan et al. (1981)	Holy et al. (1981)
Cattle receiving one egg by transfer	52	25	63	84	95
Pregnant calved to first service	34 (65%)	15 (60%)	36 (57%)	49 (58%)	58 (62%)
Produced twins	18 (53%)	9 (60%)	16 (44%)	20 (41%)	28 (48%)

By 1981, data from four independent sources — total of 319 animals, gave pregnancy or calving rate of 60% and a twinning rate of 47%.

both sheep and cattle suggested that an obscure physiological or immunological effect operated in the recipient's uterus, resulting in the loss of either the native or transferred egg in a higher than expected proportion of cases.

Although it is possible that certain physiological and immunological aspects of cattle embryo transfer need more precise definition, work in France (Testart et al., 1975; Renard et al., 1979) the U.S.A. (Anderson et al., 1977) and elsewhere in Ireland (Sreenan, 1978, 1979; Sreenan et al., 1981) has amply confirmed that one-egg transfers can be made successfully to recipients which are already pregnant. In following the embryo transfer approach to twins, one important consideration is that the technique can avoid the risk of cows carrying more than two calves, as well as ensuring that bilateral and not unilateral twin-pregnancy is established.

8.4.1 Bos indicus + Bos taurus twins

One unusual application of one-egg transfer to the mated recipient cow has been that made by Morris (1981) in Australia who has transferred Friesian embryos into Brahman cows bred to a Brahman bull to produce sets of Friesian–Brahman twins. The production of cattle twins of different species in this way is of interest because of the fact that most bovine twins are also blood cell-chimeras and have their immune systems in common; resistance to tickborne infections is characteristic of Brahman cattle but not of Friesians and the possibility exists that blood-borne features of the Brahman twin may be transferred to the Friesian. The practical hope in all this is to produce a Friesian with the production characteristics of that breed with the tick-immunity characteristic of the Brahman.

8.4.2 Production of identical twins

As a result of the efforts of Cambridge workers (Willadsen, 1979; Willadsen and Polge, 1981; Willadsen et al., 1981) it is now possible to contemplate producing identical sets by way of micromanipulation. This should be of great value in providing identicals for research purposes. Macmillan (1980), dealing with the natural occurrence of identicals in New Zealand, estimated that in the average dairy herd in that country, a set of identical twin heifers would be born once every 50 years. In dairy cattle research, identical twins have been used in management studies, such as stocking rates, and in trials dealing with the effects of udder stimulation or milking frequency; the general view is that identical twins will continue to be important research animals with new uses being found for them in dealing with problems in the dairy industry. In countries other than New Zealand, monozygotic cattle twins have been used in several areas of research in animal production (Hansson and Claesson, 1961; Witt, 1961); they provide a means of greatly increasing the precision of experiments without necessarily increasing the number of cattle used. At a research station, this has the advantage that a limited number of cattle can effectively be used on a greater number of experiments. However, the collection of naturally occurring indenticals can be a costly and difficult exercise; Foot et al. (1961) noted that despite a widespread publicity campaign in the U.K., they were only able to collect about 25 heifer sets of dairy cattle twins in course of a year. The availability of the micromanipulation means of producing cattle, possibly sexed according to requirements, should prove a valuable asset.

8.4.3 One-egg transfer technique

The outcome of current efforts with one-egg transfers to mated recipients suggests that about 50% of recipients that become pregnant to first service will sustain twins. However, the twinning technique itself is still in the early stages of its development and it could eventually prove capable of providing a 70% pregnancy rate and a 70% twinning rate in those recipients that hold to first service. There are probably reasonable grounds for believing that a higher pregnancy rate may follow the application of the twinning technique (70% conceptions to first service against the usual 60% or so) as a result of the transferred embryo's ability to maintain pregnancy in some occasions when the native egg fails to survive; this belief would become all the stronger if two-egg transfers were made to the contralateral horn of the mated cow rather than a one-egg transfer. Assuming that the twinning technique could eventually operate at the level

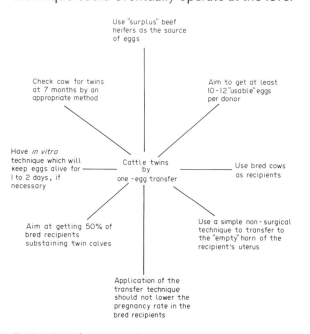

Fig. 8.4. Considerations in the induction of twin-pregnancy in cattle by one-egg transfer.

envisaged, the possibility would be that the number of calves produced to first service would be about double that expected in the normal way (119 vs 60).

8.4.4 The mated recipient cow

When attempting twinning by one-egg transfer to the contralateral uterine horn, it is clearly essential that the recipient cow's own egg should be fertilized and pregnancy established by that means. Already mentioned is the fact that most eggs are likely to be fertilized in healthy cattle after normal breeding procedures, whether these take the form of AI or natural service. For success in twinning, however, not only must the breeding method be adequate, but the fertility status of the recipient cow needs consideration. Clearly, there is little point in trying to establish twin-pregnancy in cattle likely to suffer from poor conception and pregnancy rates. As mentioned earlier, in discussing cattle fertility, there is ample evidence that conception rate can be influenced by factors such as the *post-partum* interval and the nutritional status of the cow over the service period.

The one-egg transfer technique does not necessarily require recipient cows to be synchronized for oestrus. Assuming that in future years it will be possible for frozen embryos to be employed in twinning, then these can be taken prior to the start of the inseminator's normal day and twinning transfer performed as required during the course of the usual farm visits. There would, of course, probably be many instances in which the recipients would be synchronized to permit both inseminations and twinning transfers to be applied on predetermined days.

8.4.5. Embryo survival rates

Studies using non-surgical transfer of embryos to the ipsilateral horn of recipients have shown that it is possible to get up to a 40% survival rate; with transfers to the contralateral horn of the mated recipient, embryo survival rates of the order of 25% are usual (Sreenan, 1977; Gordon and Boland, 1979). The reason for the lower survival rate among embryos transferred to the contralateral horn is not clear and it is essential to have clearer evidence on this in arriving at improvements in the twinning technique. There is some evidence that the survival rate of cattle embryos may be higher after transfer to mated rather than to unmated recipients and that conditions for survival of the transferred embryo may be more favourable among recipients that have their own embryo present (Gordon, 1976). This might also suggest that the transferred embryo in the unbred recipient is sometimes less able to prevent luteolysis than the native embryo in the mated recipient. In view of current evidence that luteolysis is probably prevented in the pregnant animal by virtue of a hormonal signal emanating from the embryo, this would seem possible.

In cattle, as already mentioned, the presence of an embryo around day-16 changes the way in which $PGF_{2\alpha}$ operates; the process of luteolysis is not permitted and the PG is probably associated with the secretion of the uterine histotrophe (an exocrine action rather than an endocrine one). Certainly, in the pig, unless transferred embryos are allowed to distribute themselves within the uterine horn at the appropriate age, luteolysis can occur in the same way as in the non-pregnant animal (Dziuk et al., 1964). This may not be without a certain relevance to the outcome of cattle embryo transfer; there have been studies showing that the survival rate of transferred embryos in mated recipients may be higher in those receiving two embryos rather than one in the contralateral horn (Gordon and Boland, 1978). It may be that the anti-luteolytic action of two embryos in the non-pregnant horn may be that much greater than when one embryo is transferred and this may help to maintain the uterus in a condition which will adequately sustain the embryos. There is also recent evidence from the micromanipulation studies of Willadsen and Polge (1981) that embryos formed after dividing up early-cleavage cattle eggs into "quarters" may not have the anti-luteolytic ability of the normal embryo.

8.4.6 Bilateral two-egg transfers

Although most effort in the induction of twin-pregnancy by way of bilateral two-egg transfers to unmated recipients has been by surgical procedures, there are reports dealing with such transfers performed non-surgically; Renard et al. (1977) recorded a pregnancy rate of 60% with 50% of these sustaining twins. Inevitably, however, such two-egg transfers call for a higher degree of manipulative skill and it remains to be seen whether it could become a feasible alternative to the one-egg transfer to the mated cow approach.

On the basis of a high incidence of embryo migrations when 2-egg transfers to the ipsilateral horn of unmated recipients were made by Newcomb et al. (1980), the authors did suggest that one-egg transfers to the ipsilateral horn of the bred recipient might be worth considering as a twinning approach; the assumption was that the transferred egg would be better able to establish pregnancy in instances where the bred recipient was not sustaining a viable embryo of its own.

8.4.7 Supply of eggs

The twinning by egg-transfer approach inevitably depends for its successful application on a ready supply of eggs. In Ireland, it has been envisaged that these would be obtained on a routine basis from beef heifers that go for

Fig. 8.5. Recovering embryos from heifer cattle tracts for eventual use in twinning transfers. If twinning by embryo transfer is to be commercially effective, then a cheap and ready source of embryos must be available. Each year, some 400 000 heifers are slaughtered at abattoirs in the Republic for beef and the hope is that they could provide the embryos that are needed. Eventually, it should be possible to think in terms of collecting the ovaries of these animals, maturing a crop of oocytes from them and then inserting a nucleus from a high quality beef embryo so as to provide a ready supply of eggs for transfer on the farm. The development of techniques for freezing embryos in the straw would mean that twinning transfers could be readily carried out on the farm in the same way as with frozen semen.

slaughter for meat (Gordon and Boland, 1979). Certainly, there would be ample opportunity to build up information on the merits or otherwise of twinning in dairy and beef cattle in Ireland on the basis of that egg source. If the commercial prospects for twinning were seen to be good, then beef eggs could be made available in due course in quantity by way of *in vitro* oocyte maturation and fertilization techniques. There are many biologists, animal scientists and medical scientists engaged in ovum physiology research on a worldwide basis and the future should see reasonably rapid developments in maturing and fertilizing the ovarian egg; this would mean the starting point for cattle twinning embryos could well be the ovaries of recently slaughtered beef heifers in the abattoir.

8.5 TWIN-BEARING CAPACITY OF CATTLE

There is no great amount of evidence in the literature on the extent of prenatal loss at different stages of pregnancy in twin-bearing cattle. Gordon et al. (1962) did report a foetal loss rate of about 10% after pregnancy diagnosis at 6 weeks, but this may have been influenced to an unknown extent by the rectal examination. After bilateral surgical transfers, Rowson et al. (1971) reported an embryo survival rate of 82% at day-90. Sreenan and Beehan (1976) examined embryo survival rates at different stages of pregnancy through to calving after bilateral transfers; they found no difference in survival rate at any stage between day-27 and calving. Such evidence suggested that once twin-pregnancy is established, foetal loss is likely to be of minor importance.

8.5.1 Attempts to aid embryo survival

It has previously been noted that much remains unknown about factors influencing the survival of twin embryos in the uterus of the cow. Although the studies of Christie et al. (1979, 1980) suggested that the survival rate of a single embryo, transferred to the contralateral horn of the unmated recipient, might be improved by hCG treatment in early pregnancy, such an effect was not observed by Newcomb et al. (1980) in

recipients in which two-egg bilateral transfers were made. It seems possible that the luteo-trophic/antiluteolytic effect of two embryos may have been adequate in itself to replace the beneficial action of hCG on foetal survival.

8.5.2 Choosing recipient cattle

As well as the embryo transfer technique itself, the farmer can influence the outcome of twinning by his selection of the recipient animal. Although a great deal of work in cattle twinning has been with the heifers as the experimental animal, it would seem desirable that twinning transfers on the farm should be restricted to cows which have the size and capability of dealing with two calves; for several reasons, it would not seem appropriate to encourage maiden heifers to start their breeding careers with twins.

Evidence that the twin-bearing capacity of the cow's uterus may differ markedly as between heifers and cows is provided in the evidence of Vandeplasse et al. (1979). Working with the Red and White breed of dual-purpose cattle, they observed that whereas there was no great difference in the incidence of twin-ovulations between maiden heifers and cows (3.8 vs 5.0%) there was a marked difference in the actual twin-calving rate (1.04 vs 3.77%); the results were taken to indicate that growth of the bovine reproductive tract during pregnancy, which results in a persisting hyperplasia, may play an important part in permitting twin-pregnancy to go ahead. There is also some evidence indicating that artificially induced twin-pregnancies (hormonally or by embryo transfer) have been sustained rather more readily in cows than in heifers (Bellows et al., 1974; Anderson et al., 1977).

8.5.3 Re-breeding the twin-bearing cow

From the farmer's point of view, it is clearly desirable that induced twin-pregnancy should not result in an increase in the calving interval beyond that usual for single-bearing animals. Data derived from studies with naturally-occurring twins in dairy cows have suggested that there may be a decrease in fertility after the birth of two calves (Pfau et al., 1948; Bowman and Hendy, 1970; Hendy and Bowman, 1970; Wood, 1975). However, it should be remembered that in the case of natural twins, there has occasionally been a suggestion that they may be associated with endocrine disturbances in the cow which may interfere with normal fertility (Erb et al., 1959). Working with induced twins, several authors have presented evidence indicating that with appropriate management during the *pre-partum* and *post-partum* periods reduced fertility in cattle producing twins need not occur (Gordon et al., 1962; Sreenan, 1977; Wheeler et al., 1979).

On the question of difficulties around the time of calving, it might be mentioned that large birth-weight of calves is one of the most important causes of dystocia; the birth of twins, as a result of their smaller size can be easier to deal with than the one large single calf. In considering the pro's and cons of twinning in beef cattle, one consideration worth keeping in mind is that with two calves on the cow, there may well be an extended *post-partum* interval arising from the greater suckling stimulus (Wyatt et al., 1977), although this need not always be true (Wheeler et al., 1979).

8.6 TWINNING AND RETAINED FOETAL MEMBRANES

It is well established in reports dealing with cattle twins, whether induced (Gordon et al., 1962) or naturally occurring (Macmillan and Curnow, 1976), that the gestation period on average is reduced by about a week; in the matter of retained foetal membranes (RFM) reports for induced and natural twins alike show that this can and does occur. As observed by Roberts (1971), the problem of retained foetal membranes has been considered to exist if the membranes are not expelled within 12 h of delivery of the calves. The etiology of RFM in the cow is complex but is believed to be due to the failure of the villi of the foetal cotyledons to separate from the crypts of the maternal caruncle. The real difficulty with RFM is probably one of keeping metritis under control subsequently, rather than any direct impairment of fertility arising from the condition itself. The effect of RFM on fertility has been the subject of several reports with some authors recording no significant effect (Muller and Owens, 1974) and others observing impaired fertility (Morrow et al., 1966; Pelissier, 1972); in fact, it seems likely that RFM itself does not reduce fertility but may predispose the cow to metritis, which certainly will affect reproductive performance adversely (Sandals et al., 1979).

Certainly, in the context of twin calvings, the problems of RFM deserves close attention, particularly the endocrinological and physiological aspects. It might be mentioned that calf suckling is believed to have a definite stimulatory effect on myometrical activity; prompt suckling of the recently calved cow apparently exerts a favourable influence on the expulsion of the membranes, presumably due to the release of oxytocin.

8.6.1 Oxytocin treatment

Whether the use of oxytocin, immediately after calving, when blood levels of oestrogen are still elevated, would be beneficial with twin-bearers, is something that might be examined more fully. The amplitude and frequency of myometrical contractions diminish rapidly beyond 24 h *post-partum* and after about 48 h there is a complete absence of any marked contraction rhythm (Arthur, 1979); according to this, prompt action after calving is required if oxytocin is to be of value.

8.6.2 Progesterone treatment

Alternatives to oxytocin, or perhaps $PGF_{2\alpha}$ treatment, immediately after calving may include hormonal treatment prior to parturition. There is the suggestion of Dawson (1979) that in a high-yielding, relatively infection-free population, a major cause of retained membranes may be a deficiency of progesterone in late pregnancy. If this is so, then exogenous progesterone may have a possible application in induced twin pregnancy; whether or not there is any future for this type of approach, the fact remains that several possibilities do exist for minimising the problem of retained membranes.

8.7 TWINNING AND MILK PRODUCTION

The economic effect of twinning on lactation performance in dairy cattle has not always been clear; Hendy and Bowman (1970), reviewing the literature at that time, refer to reports of reduced conception rates and lowered milk yields but at the same time pointed to contrary lines of evidence. In a direct study of 38 000 calvings, Bowman and Hendy (1970) found that increased milk production followed the birth of twins but attributed this mainly to a longer lactation associated with delayed breeding. Kay (1978) found that milk yields both preceding and following twins were higher than usual. In the U.S.A., work with Holsteins (Chapin and Van Vleck, 1980) has shown a negative effect of twinning on milk and fat production in the lactation initiated by natural twinning, but what occurs in high yielding dairy animals under one particular set of feeding and management conditions may not necessarily apply in all situations.

There is certainly a general tendency for the incidence of natural twins to rise with increasing production level of the dairy herd (Auran, 1974; Syrstad, 1977); presumably this can be due to the particular combination of breeding, feeding and management associated with high producing cattle. Although Syrstad (1974, 1977) has suggested that milk yield may be depressed both before and after twin calving, examination of data by Wood (1975) for recorded Friesians in the U.K. did not appear to support this view. Extensive data analysed by the MMB for milk recorded dairy cattle in the U.K. have also shown evidence of a consistent increase in milk yield with twins in all lactations studied without there being any significant change in the duration of lactation (Anon, 1976, 1979); such findings do appear to be reconcilable with hormonal effects which are now known to operate during the twin-pregnancy.

8.7.1 Pregnancy and the concurrent lactation

The drying-off effect of the normal single pregnancy on the dairy cow is well-known and has been accurately measured (Hammond and Sanders, 1923; Gaines and Davidson, 1926). Initially, pregnancy has little effect on the rate of milk secretion and up to the fifth month, milk yields are usually unaffected. After this time, the effect is increasingly evident and by the eighth month of pregnancy, the "drying off" effect is usually very evident. It seems more likely that the depressing effect of pregnancy on lactation is the result of inhibitory hormonal action, as suggested by Gaines and Davidson (1926) rather than to any competition from the rapidly growing foetus for nutrients in the maternal blood. In fact, the effect of pregnancy on food requirements of the cow is remarkably small. In the first half of pregnancy, the additional energy required for the developing foetus is negligible; even in the later stages of gestation, the cow requires only about 2% more food for its maintenance than an animal of the same weight without a developing foetus.

8.7.2 Pregnancy and subsequent lactation

It is now recognized that factors associated with the foetal calf can have an effect on the cow's ability to produce milk in the lactation that follows the birth of that foetus. Skjervold and Fimland (1975) in Norway provided some evidence that the bull employed in breeding could influence the cow's milk yield in the subsequent lactation; the authors estimated that

Fig. 8.6. Twins from the dairy cow and its effect on milk production. The nutritional and physiological implications of twinning in dairy cows has yet to be adequately examined. Dairy farmers are concerned with milk yield and quality and are not going to be attracted to methods which adversely affect this side of their business. With suitable feed and management, it may be possible to get additional calves and additional milk yields but the farmer needs to see this fact for himself in order to be convinced.

1.2% of variation in milk yield was due to the particular sire employed. Elsewhere, Adkinson *et al.* (1977) reported an even greater influence of the cow's mate on subsequent milk production. Such effects are believed to arise from foetal hormones, which can be influenced by the particular genotype of the calf; when it is a matter of twin-foetuses rather than one, then foetal effects may be even more pronounced.

Far from twin-pregnancy leading to a depression in milk yield, there would seem to be some reasonable grounds for believing that milk yield might increase rather than decrease in the lactation subsequent to twins. A certain amount of evidence is now building up about the role of bovine placental lactogen (bPL) and its action on mammary function. Placental lactogen is a peptide hormone of foetal origin, similar in its amino acid sequence to growth hormone and prolactin, which interacts with prolactin binding sites in the mammary gland.

The fact that bPL may play an important part in influencing subsequent milk production has been suggested in the studies of Bolander *et al.* (1976); they found evidence that dairy breeds of cattle show higher concentrations of bPL than beef breeds and that high yielding dairy animals show higher levels of placental lactogen than do lower yielding cows of the same breed. They have measured bPL with a sensitive RIA procedure and have shown that there is a marked increase in circulating hormone in the last 100 days of pregnancy in the cow and that the bPL concentration in cattle bearing twins is about double that in cows with singletons. Evidence in sheep also suggests strongly that the concentration of placental lactogen is related to the number of foetuses (Martal and Djiane, 1977; Taylor *et al.*, 1980) and the same is true in goats (Hayden *et al.*, 1979).

In the U.S.A., Bolander *et al.* (1976) suggest that bPL may induce prolactin receptors in mammary tissue, rendering the milk secretory tissue more responsive to the concentrations of prolactin by the cow *post-partum*. This view appears to be supported by the fact that significantly higher concentrations of bPL have been found in dairy cows than in beef and by the tendency of high yielding dairy cows to have greater than average bPL concentrations. There is also evidence found in goats that those producing triplets or twins yield 47 and 27% more milk, respectively, than those with singles (Hayden *et al.*, 1979).

It would not seem unreasonable that in twin-bearing cows, in which the level of bPL is reported to be markedly elevated, an increase in milk yield after the birth of the calves might be expected on the basis of the endocrinological evidence presently available. If this is so, and there is a genuine increase in milk yield after twins, this would tend to support the interpretation of Wood (1975) in his treatment of data from dairy cattle producing natural twins. It would not seem to agree so well with the contention of Syrstad (1977) that twins depress milk yield both during the lactation concurrent with the twin-pregnancy and in the subsequent lactation as well.

8.8 INDUCED vs NATURAL TWINS

Cattle twins induced by embryo transfer could be expected to possess several important advantages over many natural twin sets. In the first place, arranging to have one embryo in each horn of the uterus, should give rise to a more acceptable form of twin-pregnancy than can occasionally occur in nature, when both calves are located in the one uterine horn (unilateral twins). In France, Testart and du Mesnil du Buisson (1966) showed that in bilateral twin pregnancy, each uterine horn of the cow contributes equally to the placental area; when the pregnancy is unilateral, the non-gravid horn may contribute less than 10% of the placental area. The French workers also observed, in unilateral twin-pregnancies, the occurrence of "giant" placentomes, double the size of any found during single or bilateral twin-pregnancies. Calf size is related to placental area, and the "giant" placentomes may be a factor determining the incidence of RFM, a possibility mentioned by Kay (1978) in considering problems arising with natural twins.

A second possible advantage of induced twinning is the fact that cows can be prepared for the event by additional feed and attention; Gordon *et al.* (1962) suggested that problems

Table 8.4 *Twins and triplets as affected by pre-calving treatment of cow* (from Gordon et al., 1962)

	Pre-calving feed	Cows that calved	Calves born alive	Gestation period (days)		Birth-weight (lb)	
				Range	Mean	Range	Mean
Cows with Singles	Fed in accord with normal custom	129	125	188–290	283.1	56–98	78.6
Cows with Twins	Cows prepared for twins Limited extra Feed provided	10	20	278–283	280.3	59–89	71.3
		10	18	262–283	275.6	55–75	63.8
	Fed in accord with normal custom	8	11	210–278	260.6	50–60	56.3
Cows with Triplets	Cow carefully prepared for twins	6	9	223–274	262.8	40–90	56.1
	Fed in accord with normal custom	2	2	241–279	260.0	40–50	43.3

associated with twin-pregnancy in cattle may be largely overcome by an appropriate feeding regime. Much the same view has been expressed by workers elsewhere (Turman *et al.*, 1971; Chupin *et al.*, 1976). In Ireland, Sreenan (1977, 1979) has reported evidence indicating that the level of feeding of pregnant cattle during the final trimester affects the incidence of RFM and the survival rate in calves after birth.

Given reasonable *pre-partum* feeding, the size nd weight of twin calves should be at least 80% that of singles (Gordon *et al.*, 1962; Scanlon *et al.*, 1974); this order of difference between twins and singles is much the same as that in sheep.

A third advantage when dealing with induced rather than natural twins is that the farmer can be prepared at the time of calving to assist, if necessary, in the birth of the calves. A couple of months prior to this time, he should have learnt which of the cows were probably carrying twins (by oestrogen assay or otherwise). In the light of evidence in Ireland and elsewhere with induced twins, the incidence of difficult calvings can be expected to be low (Gordon *et al.*, 1962; Sreenan, 1977; Anderson *et al.*, 1978). This would seem to be in contrast to some reports for natural twins, where dystocia has been mentioned as a serious

problem (Cady and Van Vleck, 1978). The farmer should be on the outlook for twins coming about a week earlier than single calves (276 days gestation length vs 283 days).

Table 8.5 *Incidence of RFM in cattle bearing singles or twins in relation to level of feeding provided*

Reference	Without supplementation	With supplementation
Gordon et al. (1962)	13/23 (54.2%)	2/11 (18.2%)
Bosc and Chupin (1975)	4/9 (44.4%)	3/18 (16.6%)
Sreenan (1979)	4/5 (80.0%)	0/18 (nil)

8.9 FREEMARTINS

A review by Marcum (1974) put the incidence of freemartins in naturally occurring cattle twins of unlike sex at 92%; it was noted among hormonally-induced twins that the incidence of freemartins was greater in unilateral than in bilateral twins (Williams *et al.*, 1963). This effect, had it been confirmed, might have been an additional factor in favour of the embryo transfer approach to twinning. As it is, more recent studies by Horton *et al.* (1980) showed the incidence of freemartins to be the same after bilateral transfer of embryos as with naturally occurring twins. However, in the context of an induced twinning programme, the freemartin need not present a problem; such animals are destined for slaughter and not breeding. Nevertheless, for dairy farmers looking for replacement dairy heifers as well as a beef calf by transfer, the eventual solution would be in employing pre-sexed beef heifer embryos.

8.9.1 Explanation of the freemartin

The bovine freemartin remains the classic example of abnormal sexual differentiation in mammals, having been mentioned in the literature as long ago as Hunter in the 18th century. Unlike the situation in sheep or goats, twinning in cattle is marked by the establishment of chorionic vascular anastomoses between the two partners and it has been suggested that the freemartin gonad is induced to organize as a testis by agents originating in the foetal bull and carried via the blood to the heifer co-twin. Over the years, two main theories have been put forward in explanation of the freemartin, the hormonal or humoural theory (Lillie, 1916) and the later cellular theory (Fechheimer et al., 1963).

There is now evidence to show that the initial transformation of the freemartin gonad is probably due to H–Y antigen secreted by the foetal bull. It is known that H–Y antigen is secreted by testicular Sertoli cells (Zenzes et al., 1978) and it is thought that in unlike twins, H–Y is synthesized in the testis of the foetal bull calf, disseminated in the blood and borne via vascular anastomoses to target cells in the ovary of the heifer. When the concentration of H–Y reaches a certain critical threshold in the female gonad, differentiation is inhibited. Testicular differentiation occurs at about day-40 in the foetal bull and the initial phase of inhibition of the co-twin heifer's tract begins at about day-50, followed by a phase of masculinization that may begin as early as day-75 (Vigier et al., 1977). It is still accepted that there may be other factors than H–Y antigen in the development of the cattle freemartin; extensive chorionic vascular anastomoses occur in marmosets and humans, presumably H–Y antigen is present and yet sexual development is unimpaired.

8.9.2 Detecting the freemartin

The economic importance of being able to diagnose the freemartin condition has been highlighted by workers such as David et al. (1976) who showed that a substantial proportion of heifers sold in the U.K. markets, for breeding, were in fact freemartins; farmers should not, of course, be buying cattle for breeding in the open market, unless it is an emergency situation. In any induced twinning programme, the ability to diagnose the condition is obviously important when the farmer is thinking of using the animal

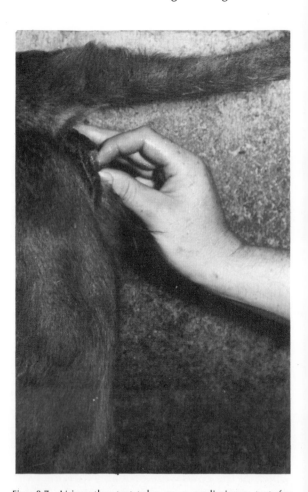

Fig. 8.7. Using the test-tube as a preliminary test for freemartinism in a calf. Studies have been made on the cattle freemartin going back to the days of John Hunter in 1779 and even earlier. To all intents and purposes, the farmer can regard any heifer born twin to a bull to be a freemartin. For those who may wish to check out the chances of a fertile heifer, then the "test-tube" test will show whether it is worth proceeding on to some of the more accurate methods of positive identification.

for breeding. The principal means that have been used for diagnosis are the measurement of the vaginal depth and the detection of sex chromosome chimaerism.

Swett et al. (1940) and Goss (1950) are among those who have described clinical signs of the freemartin such as abnormal development of clitoris, the small vulva and the short length of the vagina; it has to be recognized that early diagnosis of freemartinism by clinical signs is by no means completely reliable. For practical purposes, many freemartins can often be distinguished at age 3 to 6 weeks by a simple test based on features of the vagina (Eldridge and Blazak, 1977; Kastli and Hall, 1978). The absence of the external os of the cervix and the fact that the length of the vagina is but 5–5 cm or less can be readily confirmed. The insertion of a lubricated test-tube (15 cm x 3 cm) should reveal the short vagina of the freemartin, the tube only reaching about one-third of the full distance. According to some authors, vaginal depth should not be accepted as highly reliable until puberty (Marcum et al., 1972; Greene et al., 1979); some freemartins can possess a vagina of approximately normal length but show sex chromosome chimaerism (Miyake et al., 1980).

The analysis of sex chromosome constitution of cultured leucocytes from twins of unlike sex is regarded as an effective and reliable test for the early diagnosis of the freemartin (Eldridge and Blazak, 1977); it can be used in checking on potential freemartins whose reproductive tracts appear to be normal by other forms of examination (Wilkes et al., (1981).

Cytogenetic tests have led to the suggestion that single-born cattle freemartins may exist at about 1% of the heifer population and that they arise from the demise of the bull co-twin at some stage after the anastomoses of chorionic blood vessels (Wijeratne et al., 1977); there are others, however, who do not agree (Hare, 1977).

8.9.3 Fertility of bulls in hetereosexual twins

The reproductive normality of bulls born co-twin to freemartins was accepted until some researchers produced evidence suggesting the presence of X–X germ cells in the testes of newborn bull calves (Ohno et al., 1962). This was apparently supported by later reports showing that germ cells entered the circulation of the 25–34-day-old cattle embryo at a time when chorionic vascular anastomoses had been established between twins (Ohno and Gropp, 1965; Teplitz et al., 1967; Jost et al., 1972). Apart from its biological interest, an understanding of germ-cell chimaerism is of practical importance because of evidence clearly suggesting that certain bulls born co-twin to freemartins may be either sterile or below average in semen quality and fertility (Dunn et al., 1968; Stafford, 1972).

Although it has been suggested that a co-twin bull can be used successfully for breeding if his semen picture is normal (Long, 1979), the studies of Dunn et al. (1979) shows that more than 50% of chimaeric bulls are likely to be culled for poor fertility in the first 10 years of life compared with a figure of 5% for a single-born bull.

There has even been debate as to whether germ cells that migrate from the heifer into the bull testes are capable of giving rise eventually to spermatozoa (Ford and Evans, 1977; Dunn et al., 1979). Although this seems most unlikely, there have been reports of individual bulls born co-twin to a freemartin producing excess female offspring (Dunn et al., 1968). As observed by Long (1979), there are also reports of bulls born co-twin to bulls producing an excess of heifer calves whereas others have produced an excess of male offspring; the reasons for such deviations are not apparent.

8.10 GROWTH OF TWINS

There is evidence that freemartins show good growth potential and a positive response to exogenous steroid growth promoters (Greene et al., 1979). This characteristic, together with the freemartins lack of sexual activity (Greene et al., 1977) can be regarded as encouraging to the possibility of using the freemartin to a greater extent in meat production. Additional to the question of growth and behavioural characteristics, it would be desirable to check that the particular conformation of the freemartin at marketing age is not such that any price discrimination would operate against it if these animals were coming forward in large numbers.

Apart from the freemartin consideration, there is every reason to believe that calves born and reared as twins produce carcases similar in composition to those of single-born calves (Hallford et al., 1976).

8.11 FUTURE DEVELOPMENTS

Of the various techniques which may be employed in manipulating cattle reproduction, the availability of an effective twinning method would seem to have considerable potential. Progress in elucidating the various problems that must be solved in getting the procedure into a form that can be applied on the farm would seem to be much too slow, given the possible rewards that would flow from an effective technique.

8.12 REFERENCES

Adkinson, R. W., Wilcox, C. J. and Thatcher, W. W. (1977) Effects of sire of fetus upon subsequent production and days open of the dam. *J. Dairy Sci.* **60,** 1964–1969.

Al-Dahash, S. Y. A. and David, J. S. E. (1977) The incidence of ovarian activity, pregnancy and bovine genital abnormalities shown by an abattoir survey. *Vet. Rec.* **101,** 296–299.

Anderson, G. B. (1978) Methods for producing twins in cattle. *Theriogen.* 9(1), 3–16.

Anderson, G. B., Cupps, P. T. and Drost, M. (1977) Twinning in beef cattle following unilateral and bilateral embryo transfer. Proc. 69th Ann. Meet. Amer. Soc. Anim. Sci., 332 (Abs).

Anderson, G. B., Curro, P. T., Drost, N. and Horton, M. B. (1978) Induction of twinning in beef heifers by bilateral embryo transfer. *J. Anim. Sci.* **46,** 449–452.

Asdell, S. A. (1955) *Cattle Fertility and Sterility.* Little, Brown, Boston.

Anon. (1976) Incidence of multiple-births in N.M.R. herds. *MMB Rpt. 25, Breeding and Production Div.,* 34–35.

Anon. (1979) Incidence of multiple births in N.M.R. herds. *MMB Rpt. 28, Breeding and Production Div.,* 94–95.

Arthur, G. H. (1979) Retention of the afterbirth in cattle: a review and commentary. *Vet. Ann.* **18,** 26–36.

Auran, T. (1974) Multiple births in Norwegian cattle. *Acta. Agric. Scand.* **24,** 207–210.

Bar-Anan, R. and Bowman, J. C. (1974) Twinning in Israeli-Friesian herds. *Anim. Prod.* **18,** 109–115.

Bellows, R. A. and Short, R. E. (1972) Superovulation and multiple births in beef cattle. *J. Anim. Sci.* **34** (Suppl), 67–77.

Bellows, R. A., Anderson, D. C. and Short, R. E. (1969) Dose-response relationship in synchronized beef heifers treated with follicle stimulating hormone. *J. Anim. Sci.* **28,** 628–644.

Bellows, R. A., Kitto, G. P., Randel, R. D., Short, R. E. and

Varner, L. W. (1974) Conceptus development in super-ovulated beef heifers. *J. Anim. Sci.* **39,** 198 (Abs).

Bellows, R. A., Short, R. E., Randel, R. D., Christensen, D. S. and Pahnish, O. F. (1973) Calving rates in superovulated heifers fed MGA during gestation *J. Anim. Sci.* **37,** 301 (Abs.).

Bellows, R. A., Short, R. E. AND Staigmillar, R. B. (1979) Research areas in beef cattle reproduction. In, *Anim. Reprod.* (BARC. Symp. 3, H. Hawks, Ed.) pp. 413–421. Allenheld, Osman, Montclair.

Bhattacharya, P., Prabhu, S. S. and Chatterjee (1956) Twin and multiple births in Indian cattle. *Z. Tierz. Zucht. Biol.* **66,** 301–305.

Boland, M. P., Crosby, T. F. and Gordon, I. (1975) Twin pregnancy in cattle established by non-surgical egg transfer. *Br. Vet. J.* **131,** 738–740.

Boland, M. P., Crosby, T. F. and Gordon, I. (1976) Birth of twin calves following simple transcervical non-surgical egg transfer technique. *Vet. Rec.* **99,** 274–275.

Bolander, F. F., Jr., Ulberg, L. G. and Fellows, R. D. (1976) Circulating placental lactogen levels in dairy and beef cattle. *Endocrin.* **99,** 1273–1278.

Bowman, J. C. (1976) Management and economic aspects of twinning. In, *Egg Transfer in Cattle,* L. E. A. Rowson Ed., pp. 54–91. Comm. Europ. Commun. Luxembourg.

Bowman, J. C., Frood, I. J. M. and Wood, P. D. P. (1970) A note on the variation and heritability of twinning in British Friesian Cattle. *Anim. Prod.* **12,** 531–533.

Bowman, J. C. and Hendy, C. R. C. (1970) The incidence, repeatability and effect on dam performance of twinning in British Friesian cattle. *Anim. Prod.* **12,** 52–55.

Butz, H. and Schmahlsteig, R. (1953) Recent results of twin research in cattle and horses. *Berl. Munch. Tierarztl. Wschr.* **66,** 222–225.

Cady, R. A. and Van Vleck, L. D. (1978) Factors affecting twinning and effects of twinning in Holstein dairy cattle. *J. Anim. Sci.* **46,** 950–956.

Chapin, C. A. and Van Vleck, L. D. (1980) Effects of twinning on lactation performance in Holstein dairy cattle. *Prog. Am. Dairy Sci. Assoc. 75th Ann. Meet.,* 97.

Christensen, D. S., Bellows, R. A., Short, R. E. and Wiltbank, H. N. (1972) Embryo survival in superovulated heifers. *J. Anim. Sci.* **34,** 902 (Abs).

Christie, W. B., Newcomb, R. and Rowson, L. E. A. (1979) Embryo survival in heifers after transfer of an egg to the uterine horn contralateral to the corpus luteum and the effect of treatments with progesterone or hCG on pregnancy rates. *J. Reprod. Fert.* **56,** 701–706.

Christie, W. B., Newcomb, R. and Rowson, L. E. A. (1980) Non-surgical transfer of bovine eggs: Investigation of some factors affecting embryo survival. *Vet. Rec.* **106,** 190–193.

Clapp, H. (1934) Cystic ovaries and twinning in Holsteins. *Cornell Vet.* **24,** 309.

Chupin, D., Nguyen, Huy., Azan, M., Mauleon, P. and Ortavant, R. (1976) Hormonal induction of multiple-births; the main consequence for breeding performance. *Ann. Zootech.* **25,** 79–94.

Chupin, D. and Saumande, J. (1979) New attempts to decrease the variability of ovarian response to PMSG in cattle. *Ann. Biol. Anim. Bioch. Biophys.* **19,** 1489–1498.

Cook, R. (1948) The Bucks County quintuplets. *J. Hered.* **39,** 346–348.

Dawson, F. L. M. (1979) Reproduction and infertility. *Vet. Ann.* **19,** 13–25.

Donald, H. P. and Gibson, D. (1974) Twinning in cattle. *A.R.C. Anim. Breed. Res. Organ. Ann. Rpt.*

Dunn, H. O., Kenney, R. M. and Lein, D. H. (1968) XX/XY chimerism in a bovine true hermaphrodite: An insight into the understanding of freemartinism. Cytogenetics 7, 390–402.

Dunn, H. O., Kenney, R. M., Stone, W. H. and Bendel, S. (1968) Cytogenetic and reproductive studies of XX/XY chimeric twin bulls. Proc. 6th Int. Congr. Anim. Reprod. A.I. (Paris) 2, 877–879.

Dunn, H. O., McEntee, K., Hall, C. E., Johnson, R. J. Jr. and Stone, W. H. (1979) Cytogenetic and reproductive studies of bulls born co-twin with freemartins. J. Reprod. Fert. 57, 21–30.

Dziuk, P. J., Polge, C. and Rowson, L. E. A. (1964) Intrauterine migration and mixing of embryos in swine following egg transfer. J. Anim. Sci. 23, 37–42.

Eldridge, F. E. and Blazak, W. F. (1977) Chromosomal analysis of fertile female heterosexual twins in cattle. J. Dairy Sci. 60, 458–463.

Erb, R. E., Hinze, P. M. and Gildow, E. M. (1959) Factors influencing prolificacy of cattle. II. Some evidence that certain reproductive traits are additively inherited. Tech. Bull. Wash. Agric. Exp. Sta. No. 30. 18 pp.

Fechheimer, N. S., Herschler, M. S. and Gilmore, L. O. (1963) Sex chromosome mosaicism in unlike-sexed cattle twins. Genetics to-day. Proc. 11th Int. Congr. Genet. (The Hague), 265 (Abs).

Foot, A. S., Dodd, F. H. and Soffe, D. W. (1961) Collection and use of MZ twins at the N.I.R.D. (1952–1960) Proc. E.A.A.P. 7th study Mt. (Stockholm) Publ. No. 9, 119–128.

Ford, C. E. and Evans, E. P. (1977) Cytogenetic observations on XX/XY chimaeras and reassessment of the evidence for germ cell chimaerism in heterosexual twin cattle and marmosets. J. Reprod. Fert. 49, 25–33.

Gaines, W. L. and Davidson, F. A. (1926) Rate of milk secretion as affected by advance in lactation and gestation. Bull. Ill. Agr. Exp. Sta. No. 272.

Gordon, I. (1955) The hormonal augmentation of fertility in sheep. Proc. Br. Soc. Anim. Prod. 55.

Gordon, I. (1976) Cattle twinning by egg transfer. In, Egg Transfer in Cattle, pp. 305–319. E.E.C. Seminar, Camb.

Gordon, I. and Boland, M. P. (1978) Towards cattle twins by egg transfer. Wld. Rev. Anim. Prod. 14(2), 9–23.

Gordon, I. and Boland, M. P. (1979) Embryo transfer and twinning in cattle Vet. Sci. Commun . 3(3), 177–186.

Gordon, I. and Boland, M. P. (1979) Cattle twins by egg transfer. Ir. Vet. J. 33, 79–94.

Gordon, I., Williams, G. L. and Edwards, J. (1962) The use of PMS in the induction of twin pregnancy in the cow. J. Agric. Sci. Camb. 59, 143–198.

Goss, L. W. (1950) The early diagnosis of freemartins. N. Amer. Vet. 31, 653–655.

Greene, W. A., Dunn, I. O. and Foote, R. H. (1977) Sex-chromosome ratios in cattle and their relationship to reproductive development in freemartins. Cytogenet. Cell. Genet. 18, 97–105.

Greene, W. A., Mogil, L. G., Lein, D. H., McCauley, A. D. and Foote, R. H. (1979) Growth and reproductive development in freemartins: Hormonally treated from 1 to 79 weeks of age. Cornell Vet. 69, 248–261.

Halford, D. N., Turman, E. J., Selk, G. E., Walters, L. E. and Stephens, D. F. (1976) Carcase composition in single and multiple birth cattle. J. Anim. Sci. 42, 1098–1103.

Hammond, J., Jr. (1949) Induced twin ovulations and multiple pregnancy in cattle. J. Agric. Sci. Camb. 39, 222–225.

Hammond, J., Jr. and Bhattacharya, P. (1944) Control of ovulation in the cow. J. Agric. Sci. Camb. 34, 1–15.

Hammond, J. and Sanders, H. G. (1923) Some factors affecting milk yield. J. Agric. Sci. Camb. 13, 74.

Hancock, J. J. (1950) Studies in monozygotic cattle twins. N.Z. Sci. Tech. Agric. 30, 257.

Hansson, A. and Claesson, O. (1961) Research with monozygotic cattle twins. Proc. E.A.A.P. 7th Study Mt. (Stockholm) Publ. No. 9, 21–75.

Hare, W. C. D. (1977) Heifer sterility and freemartinism. Vet. Rec. 100, 536.

Hayden, T. G., Thomas, C. R. and Forsyth, I. A. (1979) Effect of number of young born (litter-size) on milk yield of goats: role for placental lactogen. J. Dairy Sci. 62, 53–57.

Hendy, C. R. C. and Bowman, J. C. (1970). Twinning in cattle Anim. Breed Abstr. 38, 22–37.

Holy, L., Jiricek, A., Vanatka, F. Vrtel, M. and Fernandez, V. (1981). Artificial induction of twinning in cattle by means of supplemental embryo transfer. Theriogenology, 16, 483–488.

Horton, M. B., Anderson, G. B., Bon Durant, R. H. and Cupps, P. T. (1980) Freemartins in beef cattle twins induced by embryo transfer. Theriogen. 14, 443–451.

Johansson, I. (1932) The sex ratio and multiple births in cattle. Z. Zucht. Reihe. B. 24, 183–260.

Johansson, I. (1961) The diagnosis of monozygosity of cattle twins and the use of such twins for different types of research. Tijdsch. Diergen. 86. 1332–1340.

Johansson, I., Lindhe, B. and Pirchner, F. (1974) Causes of variation in the frequency of monozygous and dizygous twinning in various breeds of cattle. Hereditas. 78(2), 201–234.

Johnson, G. L. and Rich, T. D. (1973) Evaluation of carboxy-methyl cellulose as an injectable carrier for FSH. J. Anim. Sci. 36, 375.

Johnson, M. R., Turman, E. J., Magee, J. G., Stephens, D. F. and Cothren, J. E. (1973) The production of multiple births in beef cows by gonadotrophic hormone injection timed from a synchronised oestrus. Res. Rpt. Agric. Exp. Sta. Oklahoma State Univ. Publ. 90, 10 pp.

Jost, A., Vigier, B. and Prepin, J. (1972) Freemartins in cattle: the first steps of organogenesis J. Reprod. Fert. 29, 349–379.

Joubert, D. M. (1961) Twin births in cattle in South Africa. Tydskr. Natuurwet. 1, 33–39.

Kastli, F. and Hall, J. G. (1978) Cattle twins and freemartin diagnosis. Vet. Rec. 102, 80–83.

Kaufman, M. H. and O'Shea, K. S. (1978) Induction of monozygotic twinning in the mouse. Nature Lond. 276, 707–708.

Kay, R. M. (1978) Changes in milk production, fertility and calf mortality associated with retained placentae or the birth of twins. Vet. Rec. 102, 477–479.

Lamond, D. R. (1972) Hormonal induction of multiple ovulation in the bovine. J. Anim. Sci. 34, 901–902.

Lamond, D. R. (1973) The role of the bovine practitioner in synchronization and twinning in cattle. Bovine Pract. 8, 2–8.

Lamond, D. R. (1974) Multiple births in cattle: As assessment. Theriogen. 1, 181–212.

Lamond, D. R. and Gaddy, R. G. (1972) Plasma progesterone in cows with multiple-ovulations. J. Reprod. Fert. 29, 307–311.

Lillie, F. R. (1916) The theory of the freemartin. Science 43, 611.

Long, S. E. (1979) The fertility of bulls born twin to freemartins: A review. *Vet. Rec.* **104,** 211–213.

Luhr, O. (1936) Twin and multiple births in the Heath sheep of the Luneburger Heide. Diss. Univ. Leipzig, 44 pp.

Macmillan, K. L. (1980) The research value of identical twin heifers. *N.Z. Dairy Exporter,* **55,** 75.

Macmillan, K. L. and Curnow, R. J. (1976) Aspects of reproduction in New Zealand Dairy herds. I. Gestation length. *N.Z. Vet. J.* **24,** 243–252.

McCaughey, W. L. and Dow, G. (1977) Hormonal induction of twinning in cattle. *Vet. Rec.* **100,** 29–30.

Maijala, K. and Syvajarvi, J. (1977) On the possibility of developing multiparous cattle by selection. *Z. Tierarzuchtg. Zuchr.* **94,** 126–150.

Mariana, J. G. and Nguyen, Huy, N. (1973) Folliculogenesis in the cow. *Ann. Biol. Anim. Biochim. Biophys.* **13,** 211.

Marcum, J. B. (1974) The freemartin syndrome. *Anim. Breed. Abstr.* **42,** 227–242.

Marcum, J. B., Lasley, J. F. and Day, B. N. (1972) Variability of sex chromosome chimerism in cattle from hetereosexual multiple births. *Cytogenetics* **11,** 388–399.

Martal, j., Djiane, J. and Dubois, M. P. (1977) Immuno-fluorescent localization of ovine placental lactogen. *Cell. Tiss. Res.* **184,** 427–433.

Mauleon, P. (1974) New trends in the control of reproduction in the bovine. *Livest. Prod. Sci.* **1,** 117–131.

Mauleon, P., Bosc, M. J., Courot, M., Pelot, J., Schneberger, J. and Ortavant, R. (1970) Twin births after restricted super-ovulation and production characters of the cows and their twin calves. *Ann. Biol. Anim. Biochim. Biophys.* **10,** 113–122.

Mauleon, P., Chupin, D., Pelot, J. and Aguer, D. (1978) Modifying factors of fertility after different oestrous treatments in beef cattle. In, *Control of Reproduction in the Cow.* E.E.C. Seminar (Galway) 531–545.

Mauleon, P., Mariana, J. C., Benoit, M., Solari, A. and Chupin, D. (1970) The effect of different PMSG and hCG doses, injected during the follicular phase of the oestrous cycle, on the number and yield of ovulations in French Friesian cattle. *Ann. Biol. Anim. Biochim. Biophys.* **10,** 31–46.

Meadows, C. E. and Lush, J. L. (1957) Twinning in dairy cattle and its relation to production. *J. Dairy Sci.* **40,** 1430–1436.

Mechling, E. A. and Carter, R. C. (1964) Selection for twinning in a Grade Aberdeen Angus herd, *J. Hered.* **55,** 73–75.

Miyake, Yoh-Ichi, Ishikawa, Tsune and Kawata, Kelichiro (1980) The relationship between sex chromosomal chimerism and vaginal length in bovine heterosexual twin females. *Jap. J. Anim. Reprod.* **26,** 9–31.

Morris, B. (1981) Personal communication.

Morrow, D. A., Roberts, S. J., McEntee, K. and Gray, H. G. (1966) *Post-partum* ovarian activity and uterine involution in dairy cattle. *J. Am. Vet. Med. Assoc.* **149,** 1596–1609.

Muller, L. D. and Owens, M. J. (1974) Factors associated with the incidence of retained placentas. *J. Dairy Sci.* **57,** 725–728.

Mulvehill, P. and Sreenan, J. M. (1977) Improvement of fertility in *post-partum* beef cows by treatment with PMSG and progestagen. *J. Reprod. Fert.* **50,** 323–325.

Nel, J. A., Moslert, L. and Steyn, M. G. (1960) Karakul breeding and research in S.W. Africa with special reference to the Neudam Karakul stud. *Anim. Breed. Abs.* **28,** 89–101.

Newcomb, R., Christie, W. B. and Rowson, L. E. A. (1980) Fetal survival rate after the surgical transfer of two bovine embryos. *J. Reprod. Fert.* **59,** 31–36.

Newcomb, R. and Rowson, L. E. A. (1980) Investigation of physiological factors affecting non-surgical transfer. *Theriogen.* **13**(1), 41–49.

Ohno, S. and Gropp, A. (1965) Embryological basis for germ chimerism in mammals. *Cytogenetics* **4,** 251–260.

Ohno, S., Trujillo, J. M., Stenius, C., Cjristian, L. C. and Teplitz, R. L. (1962) Possible germ cell chimeras among newborn dizygotic twin calves. Possible germ cell chimeras among newborn dizygotic twin calves. (Bos Taurus). *Cytogenics* **1,** 258–265.

Pelissier, C. L. (1972) Herd breeding problems and their consequences. *J. Dairy Sci.* **53,** 936–944.

Perkins, J. R., Olds, D. and Seath, D. M. (1954) A study of 1000 bovine genitalia. *J. Dairy Sci.* **37,** 1158.

Pfau, K. O., Bartlett, J. W. and Stuart, C. E. (1948) A study of multiple births in a Holstein-Friesian herd. *J. Dairy Sci.* **31,** 241–254.

Piper, L. R. and Bindon, B. M. (1979) Selection for increased cow fecundity: A review. *Proc. N.Z. Soc. Anim. Prod. (39th Ann. Conf.)* **39,** 224–232.

Renard, J. P., Heyman, Y. and du Mesnil du Buisson, R. (1977) Unilateral and bilateral cervical transfer of bovine embryos at the blastocyst stage. *Theriogen.* **7,** 189–194.

Renard, J. P., Ozil, J. P. and Heyman, Y. (1979) The use of embryo transfer in the field for increased calf crops in beef and dairy cattle. *Anim. Reprod. Sci.* **2,** 353–361.

Richter, F. (1955) The disposal of the progeny of Register of Performance Highland cattle. *Z. Tierz. Zucht. Biol.* **65,** 223–242.

Roberts, S. J. (1971) *Veterinary Obstetrics and Genital Diseases. Ithaca, N.Y.*

Rowson, L. E. A. (1971) The role of reproductive research in animal production. *J. Reprod. Fert.* **26,** 113–126.

Rowson, L. E. A., Lawson, R. A. S. and Moor, R. M. (1969) Twinning in cattle. *Vet. Rec.* **85,** 583.

Rowson, L. E. A., Lawson, R. A. S. and Moor, R. M. (1971) Production of twins in cattle by egg transfer. *J. Reprod. Fert.* **25,** 261–268.

Rutledge, J. J. (1975) Twinning in cattle. *J. Anim. Sci.* **40,** 803–815.

Sandals, W. C. D., Curtis, R. A., Cote, J. F. and Martin, S. D. (1976) The effect of retained placenta and metritis complex on reproductive performance in dairy cattle — a case control study. *Can. Vet. J.* **20,** 131–135.

Saumande, J. (1978) Relationships between ovarian stimulation by PMSG and steroid secretion. In, *Control of Reproduction in the Cow.* Galway, J. Sreenan.; Ed., pp. 169–194. E.E.C., Luxembourg.

Scanlon, P. F. (1972) Frequency of transuterine migration of embryos in ewes and cows. *J. Anim. Sci.* **34,** 791–794.

Scanlon, P. F., Gordon, I. and Sreenan, J. M. (1974) Multiple ovulations, multiple pregnancies and multiple births in Irish cattle. *J. Dept. Agric. Irish Republic* **70,** 45–61.

Schilling, E. and Holm, W. (1963) Investigation on induction of limited Multiple-ovulation in cattle. *J. Reprod. Fert.* **5,** 283–286.

Seidel, G. E., Jr. (1981) Superovulation and embryo transfer in cattle. *Science* **211,** 351–358.

Skjervold, H. and Fimland, E. (1975) Evidence for a possible influence of the fetus on the milk yield of the dam. *Z. Tieruchtg. Zuchtgsbiol.* **92,** 245–251.

Smith, L. E., Sitton, G. D. and Vincent, C. K. (1973) Limited injections of follicle stimulating hormone for multiple births in beef cattle. *J. Anim. Sci.* **37,** 523–527.

Sreenan, J. M. (1977a) Embryo transfer for the induction of twinning in cattle. In, *Embryo Transfer in Farm Animals.*

K. J. Betteridge, Ed.,Canada Dept. Agric. Monograph **16,** 62–66.

Sreenan, J. M. (1977b) New breeding techniques in the suckler herd. *Ir. Fmrs. J.* **29**(16), 28–29.

Sreenan, J. M. (1978) Non-surgical egg recovery and transfer in the cow. *Vet. Rec.* **102,** 58–60.

Sreenan, J. M. (1978) Non-surgical embryo transfer in the cow. *Theriogen.* **9**(1), 69–83.

Sreenan, J. M. (1979) Increasing the calf crop: synchronization and twin calving. *Ir. Fmrs. J.* **31**(7), 46–47.

Sreenan, J. M. (1979). Possibilities for the improvement of reproductive efficiency in cattle. In, *The Future of Beef Production in the European Community,* E.E.C. Seminar, Abano-Terme, Italy, 191–217.

Sreenan, J. M. and Beehan, D. (1976) Embryonic survival and development at various stages of gestation after bilateral egg transfer in the cow. *J. Reprod. Fert.* **47,** 127–128.

Sreenan, J. M., Diskin, M. G. and McDonagh, T. (1981) Induction of twin-calves by non-surgical embryo transfer. A field trial. *Vet. Rec.* **109,** 77–80.

Sreenan, J. M. and McDonagh, T. (1979). Comparison of the embryo survival rate in heifers following artificial insemination, non-surgical blastocyst transfer or both, *J. Reprod. Fert.,* **56,** 281–284.

Stafford, M. J. (1972) The fertility of bulls born co-twin to heifers. *Vet. Rec.* **90,** 146–148.

Swett, W. W., Mathews, C. A. and Graves, R. R. (1940) Early recognition of the freemartin condition in heifers twin born with bulls. *J. Agric. Res.* **61,** 587–623.

Syrstad, O. (1974a) Relationship between twin births and milk production in dairy cattle. *Meld. Norg. Landbr. Hogsk.* 53(5), 1–8.

Syrstad, O. (1974b) Genetic aspects of twinning in dairy cattle. Acta. Agric. Scand. **24,** 319–322.

Syrstad, O. (1977) Effects of twinning on milk production in dairy cattle. *Livest. Prod. Sci.* **4,** 255–261.

Taylor, M. J., Jenkin, G., Robinson, J. S., Thorburn, G. D., Friesen, H. and Chan, J. S. D. (1980) Concentrations of placental lactogen in chronically catheterized ewes and fetuses in late pregnancy. *J. Endocr.* **85,** 27–34.

Teplitz, R. L., Moon, Y. S. and Basrur, P. K. (1967) Further studies of Chimerism in heterosexual cattle twins. *Chromosoma,* **24,** 202–209.

Testart, R. L., Bosc, M. J. and du Mesnik F. (1970) A study of embryonic survival after induced superovulation in the cow. *Annals. Biol. Anim. Biochim. Biophys.* **10,** 99–104.

Testart, J. and du Mesnil du Buisson, F. (1966) Biometric study of placentomes in single or twin bovine pregnancies. *Anim. Biol. Anim. Biochim. Biophys.* **6,** 483–493.

Testart, J., Godard-Siour, C. and du Mesnil du Buisson, F. (1975) Transvaginal transplantation of an extra egg to obtain twinning in cattle. *Theriogen.* **4,** 163.

Turman, E. J., Laster, D. B., Renbarger, R. E. and Stephens, D. F. (1971) Multiple births in beef cows treated with equine gonadotrophin (PMS), and chorionic gonadotrophin (HCG). *J. Anim. Sci.* **32,** 962–968.

Vandeplasse, N., Butaye, R. and Bouters, R. (1979) Twin bearing capacity of the uterus in heifers and cows. *Dtsch. tierarztl. Wschr.* **86,** 470–473.

Vigier, B., Prepin, J., Perchellet, J. P. and Jost, A. (1977) Development de l'effet freemartin chez la foetus de veau. *Ann. Med. Uct.* **121,** 521–536.

Vincent, C. K., Ladd, H. W., Pittman, S. L. and Smith, L. E. (1973) Superovulation of cattle with FSH in Gelatin capsules. *J. Anim. Sci.* **36,** 212–213 (abs).

Wettstein, F. (1947) Herd book records of twinning in cattle. *Agrartud. Szle.,* **1,** 326–338.

Wheeler, M. B., Scheer, J. W., Anderson, G. B. and Bondurant, R. H. (1979) *Post-partum* fertility in beef cattle producing twins. *Theriogen.* **12,** 383–387.

Wijeratne, W. V. S., Munro, I. B. and Wilkes, P. R. (1977) Heifer sterility associated with single-birth freemartinism. *Vet. Rec.* **100,** 333–336.

Wilkes, P. R., Wijeratne, W. V. S. and Munro, I. B. (1981) Reproductive anatomy and cytogenetics of freemartin heifers. *Vet. Rec.* **108,** 349–353.

Willadsen, S. (1979) A method for culture of micro-manipulated sheep embryos and its use to produce monozygotic twins. *Nature, Lond.* **277,** 298–300.

Willadsen, S. M., Lehn-Jensen, H., Fehilly, C. B. and Newcomb, R. (1981) The production of monozygotic twins of preselected parentage by micro-manipulation of non-surgically collected cow embryos. *Theriogen.* **15,** 23–29.

Willadsen, S. M. and Polge, C. (1981) Attempts to produce monozygotic twins in cattle by blastomere separation. *Vet. Rec.* **108,** 211–213.

Williams, G., Gordon, I. and Edwards, J. (1963) Observations on the frequency of fused foetal circulations in twin calves. *Brit. Vet. J.* **119,** 467–472.

Witt, M. (1961) The use of monozygotic twins for research projects. *Proc. E.A.A.P. 7th Study Mt. (Stockholm)* Publ. No. 9, 179–186.

Wood, P. D. P. (1975) A note on the effect of twin births on production in the subsequent lactation. *Anim. Prod.* **20,** 421–424.

Wyatt, R. D., Gould, M. B. and Totusek, R. (1977) Effects of single vs. simulated twin rearing on cow and calf performance. *J. Anim. Sci.* **45,** 1409–1414.

CHAPTER 9

Breeding Cattle at Younger Ages

9.1 INTRODUCTION

Factors affecting puberty in cattle have not received a great deal of attention in the past, although clearly there is much to be said, both in dairy and beef cattle, in favour of reducing the non-productive phase of the animal's life, i.e. the period which ends at the time of first breeding. In his classic work on cattle reproduction, Hammond (1927) estimated the average age at puberty in heifers of dairy breeds, maintained under normal conditions of feeding and management, as being about 9 months, with a range from about 3–15 months; data from the U.S.A. which was reviewed at the time for dairy cattle showed ages at puberty to average 8 months (Jerseys), 11 months (Friesians) and 13 months (Ayrshires). More recent reports for American dairy and beef cattle quote averages varying from 319 days for the Jersey bred to 390 days for the Hereford breed (Laster et al., 1972). Crossbreeding in beef cattle tends to decrease age at puberty in addition to the effect of hetereosis expressed through daily liveweight gain (Wiltbank et al., 1966).

9.2 AGE AND LIVEWEIGHT AT FIRST OESTRUS

The onset of puberty in heifers is primarily determined by age and weight, although these will obviously differ according to breed. If it is a beef heifer, and she is to calve at 2 years, she must be cycling and fertile at 15 months of age and there is ample evidence to show that many beef animals may not have reached puberty at that time (Wiltbank et al., 1969; Arije et al., 1971; Laster et al., 1972; Gonzalez-Padilla et al., 1975a,b,c). Under certain conditions, the economic feasibility of having beef heifers reach the liveweight at which a high proportion may be expected to attain puberty by 13–16 months of age, may be questionable. It would be under such circumstances that artificial induction of puberty might have some practical appeal. Under most American conditions, age at puberty, date of conception and conception rate to first service are largely determined by the feeding and management of beef heifers during the winter period immediately after weaning (Short and Bellows, 1971). Age at puberty and time of year at which the beef heifer has her first calf, i.e. early or late in the calving season, are of considerable importance in determining her lifetime production potential Lesmeister et al., 1973, Zimmerman et al., 1975; the tendency is for beef heifers calving early for the first time to continue calving early in subsequent years and to wean heavier calves.

Work in the U.K. has shown a relationship between liveweight and age at first oestrus in Hereford heifers (Cohen et al., 1980); calculations suggest that 5, 50 and 95% of heifers would show oestrus at weights of 187, 231 and 280 kg, respectively.

9.2.1 Feeding at puberty

There has always been plenty of evidence to show the profound effect of nutrition on the age of puberty and conception in heifers (Sorensen et al., 1959; Wiltbank et al., 1966; Short and Bellows, 1971). Cattle fed to gain 1 lb/day (from 7 to 12 months of age) have shown satisfactory fertility, whereas increasing the daily liveweight gain to 1½ lb was not justified in terms of improvements in the pregnancy rate (Wiltbank et al., 1966); in heifers gaining at the lower rate of ½ lb daily, however, a marked effect on the age at puberty was observed. Certainly, the evidence shows puberty as being related to size and weight and not to age. According to Robinson (1977), under good nutritional conditions, a heifer may be expected to reach puberty at about two-thirds adult size; Swanson (1975) referring to the same relationship, puts the figure at about 50% of mature size. There may be the point that the question of puberty is not so much one simply of weight and size but may involve the fat content of the heifer reaching a certain value as well (Smith et al., 1979).

Further evidence on the effect of feeding is in the report of Fleck et al. (1980) dealing with Hereford beef heifers calving at 2-years old; these authors found that heifers with high gains during the first winter as weanlings had higher breeding efficiency when bred as yearlings, had larger pelvic areas as 2-year-olds, had less calving difficulties at first parturition and higher breeding efficiency at the subsequent breeding.

9.2.2 Nutritional and hormonal interactions

Some evidence has become available in recent years on the way in which energy intake, reproductive function and endocrine involvement operate. Moseley et al. (1978) were able to show that heifers fed monensin sulphate (a feed additive which alters fermentation processes in the rumen) reached puberty earlier than control animals. There is also information showing that heifers fed protein-protected lipid (a feedstuff in which the major energy source is protected from degradation in the rumen) may reach puberty significantly later than control heifers. Such studies and others (McCartor et al., 1979; Bushmich et al., 1980) have led to the view that an integral relationship exists between ruminal volatile fatty acid (VFA) production, reproductive performance and reproductive hormone secretion and/or synthesis. This view is further supported by the studies of Gombe and Hansel (1973) and others (Turner et al., 1977; Beal et al., 1978; Chew et al., 1978) who have shown changes in reproductive hormone levels related to changes in dietary energy and ruminal fermentation patterns. Studies reported by Randel and Rhodes (1980) provided further evidence that the feeding of dietary monensin can enhance the reproductive function of prepubertal heifers.

9.3 ENDOCRINOLOGY OF PUBERTY IN CATTLE

The ovaries of heifer calves show evidence of follicular activity long before the onset of puberty and the establishment of oestrous cycles (Desjardins and Hafs, 1969). As noted earlier, even in very young calves, the ovaries are capable of responding to exogenous gonadotrophins and use is made of this fact in attempting to get eggs for use in embryo transfer studies. According to Staigmiller et al. (1979), the major components of the endocrine mechanisms necessary for normal oestrous cycles in beef heifers appear to be present after about 5 months of age; at that time it can be demonstrated that the hypothalamic-pituitary mechanisms can respond to exogenous oestradiol with a surge release of LH, that results in blood levels of this gonadotrophin similar to those required for ovulation.

Unlike events in the mature cow, the peaks of oestradiol and LH that occur in the heifer before puberty are not synchronized but rather take place at inconsistent and unrelated intervals. However, it would seem that synchrony between the two peaks, which can lead to normal cyclical oestrous patterns can be induced at an earlier than usual age by the application of short-term progestagen treatments. The naturally occurring endocrine mechanisms that result in the synchrony of the events leading to the onset of puberty remain to be defined.

9.3.1 Puberty and conception

There have been those who have presented data on pituitary and ovarian hormone levels in post-pubertal cattle showing that maturation of the bovine reproductive system continues well beyond the first heat; in practical terms, this may mean that breeding a heifer after she has passed through several oestrous cycles may result in a higher conception rate than after the first heat period. In one study of puberty and ovarian activity, Dufour (1975) reported that about 80% of Friesian heifers ovulated prior to puberty without showing oestrus and that some proportion had an oestrous cycle of less than 10 days; this would suggest that endocrinological events around puberty can be abnormal.

The ability of dairy and beef heifers to conceive after artificial insemination has been noted by some as being somewhat below the level observed in older cattle whereas slighter differences between ages have been reported after natural service (Swanson, 1975). The insemination of maiden heifers is usually more difficult than in older cattle because of the tighter cervix; there may well be a case for looking at an AI routine specifically developed for this category of animal.

9.4 EFFECT OF ENVIRONMENTAL FACTORS

Roy et al. (1980) reported on several factors affecting puberty and produced evidence that Friesian heifer calves born during the period of increasing daylength reached puberty about 2 months earlier than those born at other times; these authors even mention the possibility of the moon having an influence on the occurrence of oestrus. Elsewhere, authors have looked at management factors as well as questions of feeding and environment. Varner et al. (1973) reported on the effect of separating light and heavy beef heifer calves at weaning and wintering them in two groups. This management practice significantly reduced the average age of puberty compared with heifers that were handled in just the one group.

9.5 HORMONAL INDUCTION OF OESTRUS

Age at first oestrus can be controlled to a certain extent by breeding, feeding and management, but these approaches may not always be possible or the most economical. Although there is still a lack of knowledge regarding endocrine mechanisms involved in puberty, sufficient is known to provide a basis for a treatment which will induce oestrus in prepubertal heifers (Gonzalez-Padilla et al., 1975c); the regimen consisted of a 9-day progestagen (Norgestamet) implant (6 mg SC-21009) with an initial progestagen/oestrogen dose (3 mg oestradiol valerate + 3 mg SC-21009) given at the time of implantation. Results have been confirmed by other workers (Short et al., 1976; Burfening, 1979) but in the studies of Smith et al. (1979) the technique was not able to induce a fertile oestrus in many lightweight heifers, although the reason for this was not known. The age of the heifer for a given liveweight has been found to be important in determining the success of the inducing treatment (Burfening, 1979).

9.6 DAIRY CATTLE

In dairy cattle, the possibility of improving the economic efficiency of milk production by the early mating of heifers is clearly a valid objective, but problems associated with dystocia and with possible reduced lifetime milk yield might outweigh any possible advantages. In the U.K., the general recommendation has been that Friesian heifers should not be bred before 60 weeks of age, but depending on the season of calving, as soon as possible after that (ADAS, 1973). A study by Little and Kay (1979) showed that Friesian-type dairy heifers, reared at a rapid rate of growth on a cereal diet, had reduced milk yields in first and later lactations, whether they were first mated at 43 or 78 weeks of age; those bred at 43 weeks produced significantly lower first lactation yields and showed a higher incidence of dystocia than those bred at the older age.

Fig. 9.1. Considerations in the breeding of the dairy heifer. There could be some circumstances in which it would be useful to breed dairy heifers so that they would calve between 20 and 24 months of age — but this is rarely attempted because it is known that heifers reared very rapidly during their first year of life have tended to produce poor milk yields regardless of their age at calving, not only in the first lactation but in later ones as well. On the research front, there is need to find out just how rapidly heifers can be reared in their first year without depressing their milk yields. The use of artificially produced identical cattle twins could be of much value in this type of study.

Fig. 9.2. Breeding the beef heifer for earlier calving. A great deal of very useful work was carried out in Ireland by Dr. Sean Crowley and colleagues into systems of production aimed at taking a calf from the beef heifer before slaughter — but such systems have not yet been adopted in practice. The main farmer objection to the once-calved heifer is the price differential between maiden heifer and calved heifer beef — and there is the further reason that it is more difficult calving young heifers and older cows. In truth, there is really no difference in meat quality between maiden and calved heifers and it should be possible to use existing knowledge to get once-calved heifer systems contributing usefully to the supply of calves within the country.

9.7 BEEF CATTLE

The present trend, in the U.S.A. and elsewhere, is towards getting beef heifers in-calf at earlier ages. In the case of range cattle, which are bred each year within a relatively short breeding season, this means a change to calving at 2 years; according to Lemenager et al., (1980), calving heifers at 2 years of age has become a widely accepted practice among beef producers in the U.S.A.

The wisdom of breeding beef heifers to calve at 2 years involves considerations beyond those of inducing oestrus and getting the animal pregnant on time. In beef cattle, calf mortality has been reported as ranging from 5 to 20% (Randall, 1978); it is well accepted that losses at calving are usually much higher in the maiden heifer than in older cows (Donald, 1963). The high incidence of dystocia and calf mortality are often major considerations explaining why farmers may be slow to adopt early calving systems (Swanson, 1975). There is plenty of justification for research into approaches which may ease calving problems in the young heifer; the animal's body

condition at calving appears to be of considerable importance, with fit rather than fat heifers being associated with a lower incidence of calving difficulties.

For several reasons, there is probably justification for an acceptable hormonal technique for the initiation of cyclical breeding activity in cattle, providing an acceptable conception rate follows treatment. Additional to the feeding, breeding and management considerations that apply to puberty in beef cattle, it would be useful to have this aspect of reproduction under more positive control.

9.8 REFERENCES

ADAS (1973) Profitable Farm enterprises Booklet 1. Rearing Friesian Dairy Heifers. Ministry of Agric., Fish., Food, Pinner.

Arije, G. F. and Wiltbank, J. N. (1971) Age and weight at puberty in Hereford heifers. J. Anim. Sci. 33, 401–406.

Beal, W. E., Short, R. E., Staigmiller, R. B., Bellows, R. A., Kaltenbach, C. C. and Dunn, T. G. (1978) Influence of dietary energy intake on bovine pituitary and luteal function. J. Anim. Sci. 46, 181.

Bushmich, S. L., Randel, R. D., McCartor, M. M. and Carroll, L. H. (1980) Effect of dietary monensin upon ovarian response following gonadotrophin treatment in prepuberal heifers. *J. Anim. Sci.* **51**, 692.

Burfening, P. H. (1979) Induction of puberty and subsequent reproductive performance. *Theriogen.* **12**, 215–221.

Chew, B. P., Randel, R. D., Rouquette, F. M. and Erb, R. E. (1978) Effects of dietary monensin and sex of calf on profiles of serum progesterone and estrogen in late pregnancy of first cross Braham–Hereford cows. *J. Anim. Sci.* **46**, 1316.

Cohen, R. D. H., Garden, D. L. and Langlands, J. P. (1980) A note on the relationship between live weight and the incidence of oestrus in Hereford heifers. *Anim. Prod.* **31**, 221–222.

Desjardins, G. and Hafs, H. D. (1969) Maturation of bovine female genitalia from birth through puberty. *J. Anim. Sci.* **28**, 502–507.

Donald, H. P. (1963) Perinatal deaths among calves in a crossbred dairy herd. *Anim. Prod.* **5**, 87–95.

Dufour, J. J. (1975) Influence of postweaning growth rate on puberty and ovarian activity in heifers. *Can. J. Anim. Sci.* **55**(1), 93–100.

Fleck, A. T., Schalles, R. R. and Kiracofe, G. H. (1980) Effect of growth rate through 30 months of reproductive performance of beef heifers. *J. Anim. Sci.* **51**, 816–821.

Gombe, S. and Hansel, W. (1973) Plasma LH and progesterone levels in heifers on restricted energy intake. *J. Anim. Sci.* **37**, 728.

Gonzalez-Padilla, E., Wiltbank, J. N. and Niswender, G. D. (1975a) Puberty in beef heifers. I. The interrelationship between pituitary. hypothalamic and ovarian hormones. *J. Anim. Sci.* **40**(6), 1091–1104.

Gonzalez-Padilla, E. M. Niswender, G. D. and Wiltbank, J. N. (1975b) Puberty in beef heifers. II. Effect of injections of progesterone and Estradiol.17$_B$ on serum LH, FSH and ovarian activity. *J. Anim. Sci.* **40**, 1105–1109.

Gonzalez-Padilla, E., Ruiz, R., LeFever, D., Denham, A. and Wiltbank, J. N. (1975c). Puberty in beef heifers. III. Induction of fertile estrus. *J. Anim. Sci.* **40**, 1110–1118.

Hammond, J. (1927) The Physiology of Reproduction in the Cow. *Camb. Univ. Press, London.*

Laster, D. B., Glimp, H. A. and Gregory, K. E. (1972) Age and weight at puberty and conception in different breeds and breed-crosses of beef heifers. *J. Anim. Sci.* **34**, 1031–1036.

Lemenager, R. P., Smith, W. H., Martin, T. G. Singleton, W. L. and Hodges, J. R. (1980) Effects of winter and summer energy levels on heifer growth and reproductive performance. *J. Anim. Sci.* **51**, 837–843.

Lesmeister, J. L., Furfening, P. J. and Blackwell, R. L. (1973) Date of first calving in beef cows and subsequent calf production. *J. Anim. Sci.* **36**, 1.

Little, W. and Kay, R. M. (1979) The effects of rapid rearing and early calving on the subsequent performance of dairy heifers. *Anim. Prod.* **29**, 131–142.

McCartor, M. M., Randel, R. D. and Carroll, L. H. (1979) Dietary alteration of ruminal fermentation of efficiency of

growth and onset of puberty in Brangus heifers. *J. Anim. Sci.* **48**, 488.

Moseley, W. M., McCartor, M. M. and Randel, R. D. (1978) Effects of monensin on growth and reproductive performance of beef heifers. *J. Anim. Sci.* **45**, 961.

Randall, G. C. B. (1978) Perinatal mortality: some problems of adaptation at birth. *Adv. Vet. Sci. Comp. Med.* **22**, 53–81.

Randell, R. D. and Rhodes, R. C. (1980) The effect of dietary monensin on the LH response of prepuberal heifers given a multiple Gn-RH challenge. *J. Anim. Sci.* **51**, 925–931.

Robinson, T. J. (1977) Reproduction in cattle. In, *Reproduction in Domestic Animals*, 3rd Ed. Cole, H. H. and Cupps, P. T., Eds. pp. 433–454.

Roy, J. H. B., Gillies, C. M., Perfitt, M. W. and Stobo, I. J. F. (1980) Effect of season of the year and phase of the moon on puberty and on the occurrence of oestrus and conception in dairy heifers reared on high planes of nutrition. *Anim. Prod.* **31**, 13–26.

Short, R. E. and Bellows, R. A. (1971) Relationships among weight gains, age at puberty and reproductive performance in heifers. *J. Anim. Sci.* **37**, 551.

Short, R. E., Bellows, R. A., Carr, J. B., Staigmiller, R. B. and Randel, R. D. (1976) Induced or synchronized puberty in heifers. *J. Anim. Sci.* **43**, 1254–1263.

Smith, M. F., Burrell, W. C., Broadway, J. and Wiltbank, I. N. (1979) Estrus and pregnancy in beef heifers following use of the synchromate B. treatment (SMB). *Theriogen.* **12**, 183–195.

Sorensen, A. M., Hansel, W., Hough, W. H., Armstrong, D. T., McEntee, K. and Bratton, R. W. (1959) Influence of under feeding and overfeeding on growth and development of Holstein heifers. *Cornell Univ. Agr. Exp. Sta. Bull.* 936.

Staigmiller, R. B., Short, R. E. and Bellows, R. A. (1979) Induction of LH surges with estradiol in beef heifers and age dependent response. *Theriogen.* **11**(6), 453–459.

Swanson, E. W. (1975) Future research on problems of increasing meat production by early calving. In, *The Early Calving of Heifers and its Impact on Beef Production.* pp. 281–288. C.E.C., Luxembourg.

Turner, H. A., Ralieghi, R. J. and Young, D. C. (1977) Effect of monensin on feed efficiency for maintaining gestating mature cows wintered on meadow hay. *J. Anim. Sci.* **44**, 339.

Varner, L. W., Bellows, R. A. and Christensen, D. S. (1973) Winter management of replacement heifers. *Proc. West. Sec. Amer. Soc. Anim. Sci.* **24**, 240–245.

Wiltbank, J. N., Gregory, K. E., Swinger, L. A., Ingalls, J. E., Rothlisberger, J. A. and Koch, R. M. (1966) Effects of heterosis on age and weight at puberty in beef heifers. *J. Anim. Sci.* **25**, 744–751.

Wiltbank, J. N., Kasson, C. W. and Ingalls, J. E. (1969) Puberty in crossbred and straight bred beef heifers on two levels of feed. *J. Anim. Sci.* **29**, 602.

Zimmerman, J. E., Pope, L. S., Stephens, D. and Waller, G. (1975) Effect of feeding different levels of winter supplement and age at first calving on the performance of range beef cows and replacement heifers. *Okl. Agr. Exp. Stn. Misc. Publ. No.* 48.

PART II

The Control and Manipulation of Reproduction in Sheep

CHAPTER 10

Introduction to Controlled Breeding in Sheep

10.1 INTRODUCTION

For about 50 years, research workers around the world have examined the possibility of employing hormones in the control of oestrus and fertility in sheep. The fact that most ewes in the agriculturally productive countries are seasonal breeders and often produce smaller lamb crops than the farmer may actually desire has made sheep a rather obvious target for the reproductive physiologist's attention.

Authors have drawn attention to the fact that low lamb output per ewe is a major factor limiting the energetic efficiency of sheep meat production (Blaxter, 1964); it has also been observed that with an estimated "biological ceiling" of five lambs per ewe per pregnancy and a lambing interval of 6 months (Wilson, 1968) the sheep has further to go than any of the farm animals towards realizing its full reproductive potential.

From the farmer's viewpoint, it is probably fortunate that over the past two decades, the ewe has become one of the animals preferred by the biologist for research in mammalian reproduction, particularly in understanding more of the detail of the endocrinological mechanisms which mammals use to turn their reproductive systems on and off (Karsh, 1980); there are also many areas of interest in human medicine (e.g. foetal physiology) which have been advanced using the ewe as the experimental animal. Progress towards commercially acceptable controlled breeding techniques in sheep was greatly accelerated in the 1950s with the elucidation of the role of progesterone in facilitating the induction of co-incident oestrus and ovulation (Robinson, 1952, 1954, 1955; Robinson et al., 1956) and with the availability of the highly potent progesterone analogues.

An event of major significance in the development of controlled breeding in sheep was the report of Robinson (1965) showing that progesterone and progestagens can be administered in physiologically effective doses over a period of about 2 weeks by the intravaginal route. Without recourse to needless historical detail, most attempts in controlled breeding up to that time had centred around a series of progesterone injections or oral administrations, with or without serum gonadotrophin (PMSG); quite apart from the fact that oestrous response and conception rate left much to be desired, the time and labour which was involved remained a major factor militating against their acceptance in commercial sheep farming. Much of the work in controlled breeding in sheep in the U.K. and Ireland in the

1950s and early sixties was concerned with attempts to simplify the progesterone/progestagen administration procedures down to the point at which techniques might be useful to farmers (Gordon, 1958, 1963; Crowley, 1964).

10.1.1. Maximum reproductive potential

Sheep are among those farm species whose production methods can still be profitably and greatly intensified, right from the point of breeding the ewe through until the time of dispatching the lamb at the abattoir; it is also a species that is capable of coping with difficult terrains and hardy environments. Although in theory it is possible to talk about sheep producing two litters of five lambs each year, the more realistic target to keep in mind is increasing the annual output of the lowland ewe to four lambs by improvements to litter-size and lambing frequency; as noted by Robinson (1979), such a lamb output could result in a considerable improvement in the efficiency of feed utilization.

10.2 AREAS OF CONTROLLED BREEDING

Controlled breeding in sheep, as the term might be applied to conditions in Ireland, could be expected to cover the full spectrum of lowland lamb production systems; it may mean breeding sheep towards the end of the normal anoestrous period (early-lamb production); it may mean breeding ewes to permit an extremely compact spring lambing period or even getting most of the lambs in a flock born on almost the same day; it may mean breeding ewes to top quality rams by artificial insemination and it may even mean a rapid build-up of stocks of certain breeds of sheep by embryo transfer.

The scope for certain controlled breeding applications can be expected to vary with flock size and environment. A New Zealand farmer with a thousand or more breeding ewes would view compact lambings in quite a different light from an Irish farmer with 50 ewes or so. In some countries, out-of-season breeding may hold no great interest, either because of the adverse effects of high summer temperatures on ram fertility and lamb viability or because autumn and

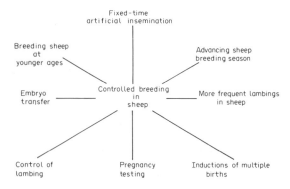

Fig. 10.1. Areas of controlled breeding in sheep.

winter climatic conditions are quite inappropriate for low-cost lamb rearing.

For the Irish sheep producer, and for farmers elsewhere, the technology for the control of reproduction, including control of oestrus, fixed time-AI, early pregnancy diagnosis and synchronization of lambings is now available in basic form; this offers possibilities in allowing lamb production to be planned from A to Z in a way which is just not feasible under nature. In many parts of the world, including Ireland, the approach to sheep farming is still very traditional; lowland sheep suffer from the handicap that they are usually regarded as a sideline to the dairy or other enterprises and do not always command the physical and mental effort which is called for if they are to improve their comparative efficiency.

Controlled breeding can be important in saving time and labour, especially on the small farm at critical periods such as lambing, and in permitting the use of breeding methods (e.g. AI from rams of a particular breed and quality) which would otherwise be debarred on the grounds of the high costs involved; using the new technology as an essential ingredient, sheep systems have now been developed which can permit the annual output per ewe to be doubled, even trebled. However, it should also be emphasized that successful controlled breeding in sheep is not only a matter of an appropriate hormonal technique but also in ensuring that it is used in situations where it can give an acceptable result. Difficulties in the past in some areas of controlled breeding have undoubtedly arisen, not only from inadequacies in the hormone techniques themselves, but in trying to pursue unnecessarily ambitious objectives, such as two lamb crops within the calendar year.

10.3 FACTORS AFFECTING FERTILITY AND BREEDING ACTIVITY

As a background to a discussion of the techniques employed in controlled breeding in sheep, some mention is desirable on conception rates and breeding activity as they may be expected to occur in the normal sheep.

When the farmer introduces the ram among lowland sheep, of the breeds native to Ireland and the U.K., he can expect that about 80% of ewes conceive at first service (Averill, 1955; Gordon, 1955, 1958, 1963, 1967); this is talking of adult sheep exposed to a ram of good fertility in the full breeding season. The conception rate of 80% or so in the ewe is in contrast to the 65% or less in the cow, and is presumably the result, among other things, of the fact that sheep tend to shed two eggs rather than one. With exotic breeds, such as the Finn Landrace, which are exceptionally prolific, conception rates of the order of 90% and better may be achieved, and this would be largely due to the greater number of ovulations occurring. Thus, a farmer may be able to apply controlled reproduction to breed a small flock of Finn or Finn-cross sheep simultaneously and by the application of cortico-steroid treatment for controlled parturition at the other end of pregnancy get almost all the lambs born on a predetermined date; this would work less well with breeds or conditions in which 80% or less conceive at first service.

Between first and later services, it can be expected that most sheep become pregnant.

Constitutional barrenness in sheep is rare, a fact recorded at the turn of the century by Heape (1899); in a comprehensive analysis of lowland sheep records at the time, he only found 6.8% to be barren. Much the same evidence was reported by Marshall (1905). At a later stage, a study of several breeds in the U.K. and Ireland recorded that 6–7% of adult breeding ewes exposed to the ram failed to give birth (Gordon, 1958, 1967); elsewhere, Lees (1978) dealing with data for the U.K., quotes a barren rate of 7.6% in lowland sheep.

To be commercially acceptable, as opposed to technically possible, controlled breeding methods need to be simple to apply, cheap (relative to the product involved) and highly effective. In assessing the effectiveness of controlled breeding measures, conception rate to first service should be of the same order (i.e. 80% or so) as that expressed by the average cyclic sheep in its natural breeding season. The number of lambs produced per conception (litter-size) is also of great practical interest; this can be expected to vary in ewes subjected to most forms of controlled breeding in the same way as it does in the untreated sheep in the autumn breeding season. Breed, age and body condition of ewe, as well as several well-recognized environmental influences (feed, daylength, temperature) may all contribute towards the incidence of multiple-births in sheep under treatment.

10.3.1 Seasonal breeding activity

All native breeds of sheep in Ireland show a well-defined breeding and non-breeding season in the case of the ewe; for most lowland breeds, the breeding season would span the 6 month period running from September to February. Although some reports in the literature contend

Table 10.1. *Lambing outcome in 51 sheep flocks bred in the autumn season* (From Gordon (1975))

	Ewes bred	Gave birth	Lambs born	Conception rate (%)*	Lambs per conception
First services		1608	2266	80.8	1.41
	1991				
First and second services		1845	2564	92.7	1.39

*Ewes that gave birth as p. 100 of those bred.

that rams as well as ewes are seasonal breeders, this would not seem to apply to any of the sheep breeds in Ireland; this is not to say that seasonal fluctuations in semen quality and libido do not occur, but simply that if they do, they do not interfere with the mating process in any clear way.

It is widely accepted that the breeding season of sheep is regulated by changes in daylength, the photoperiodic effect acting via the hypo-thalamic–pituitary axis and possibly mediated by way of the pineal gland; much of this acceptance stems from the work of Yeates (1949), working with Suffolk-cross sheep in the U.K., who reversed the seasonal breeding activity of the animals by artificially controlling the light environment. Later studies with ewes of the Merino breed in Australia showed that the breeding season of these sheep was regulated by seasonal fluctuations in daylength, although breeding activity was less decisively separated from the anoestrous season compared with sheep of British origin (Yeates, 1956). It also became evident around this time and later that environmental temperature can influence the onset of the breeding season quite markedly (Dutt and Bush, 1955; Lees, 1964, 1966; Neville and Neathery, 1970).

The precise role of temperature as it may operate under natural, as opposed to contrived experimental conditions, is not clear. It is known, however, that on a long-term basis seasonal fluctuations in temperature do not override seasonal changes in photoperiodicity (Robertson, 1977); ewes kept in a light environment 6 months out of phase with normal seasonal lighting showed their breeding season during the warm weather of late spring and early summer and a period of anoestrus during the colder autumn and winter months.

As observed by Radford (1966) some years ago, no explanation of the sheep breeding season based solely on light can cover the facts that are presently available. Even on the question of light itself, there may be questions of moonlight as opposed to sunlight; in Czechoslovakia, there has been a suggestion, based on a 10-year study involving about 10 000 ewes, that the start of cyclical breeding was associated with the

occurrence of the full moon (Horak and Potucek, 1978). It should be mentioned that in equatorial regions of the world, where seasonal variations in daylength do not occur as they do in the more temperate regions, sheep breeds may have no distinct breeding season (Mittal, 1980; Mittal and Ghosh, 1980).

Fig. 10.2. Irish breeds are seasonal breeders. Information on the time of onset and duration of the breeding season is essential for the selection of optimal mating and lambing dates for ewes flocks which are to be used in out-of-season and accelerated lamb production systems. In the early 1970s work on the University farm with groups of adult Galway, Cheviot and other breeds showed that it was the end of August before Galways were coming in oestrus and into September before Cheviots (seen here) responded. Without controlled breeding, there is just no easy way of getting Cheviots pregnant during the summer months of June, July and August.

It certainly need not be a question of the sheep breeding season being determined by a change-over from lengthening daylight to decreasing daylength; Watson and Radford (1955) drew attention to instances in which Merino ewes started breeding while natural daylength was still increasing and similar evidence has been noted with other breeds elsewhere (Thimonier and Mauleon, 1969). Other studies with Merinos in Australia, in which ewes were exposed for prolonged periods either to continuous or equinoctial lighting clearly showed that seasonal variations in breeding activity developed in the absence of changes in the duration of light (Radford, 1961); the breeding of Mérinos can also vary markedly according to the particular locality in which they are found (Watson, 1962). In New South Wales, some Merino flocks can show maximum breeding activity in spring and may go into anoestrus in autumn, a complete reversal of the breeding pattern to be expected on the basis of daylength changes (Robinson et al., 1970).

10.4 STRESS AND EWE REPRODUCTION

There has been a growing amount of evidence in the 1970s of the adverse effects of stress on sheep reproduction and this is a consideration when plans are being made for the application of controlled breeding techniques. In the U.K., Doney et al. (1976a, b) have shown that the stress of handling ewes in normal husbandry operations can influence ovulation rates adversely and increase the incidence of embryonic loss; similar effects could be induced experimentally, using exogenous ACTH doses. In New Zealand, the effect of shearing as a factor inducing stress has been the subject of several reports. Shearing, which is widely practised throughout New Zealand during or shortly after the mating season, is regarded as one of the most stressful events that can happen to sheep (Kilgour and de Langen, 1970); it involves forcing them into strange situations, handling and isolation from other sheep, as well as the stresses associated with shearing itself and consequent readjustments in their body metabolism. Welch et al. (1979) has shown that shearing carried out 10 days after mating exerted a dramatic effect on the lambing pattern subsequently shown by the flock; shearing markedly reduced the proportion of ewes lambing at the expected time, although the ewes did become pregnant at a later stage.

Although much has yet to be precisely defined, any form of stress should be avoided as far as possible during the mating period (Gunn and Doney, 1979). Looking at feeding in terms of a possible nutritional stress factor, the usual recommendation is that extremes of body condition or nutritional levels should be avoided around the mating period (Gunn and Doney, 1979); in early pregnancy in the ewe, the evidence indicates that a sustained moderate degree of undernutrition, resulting in a 3–4% loss in liveweight during the first month of gestation is

unlikely to have any significantly harmful effect in ewes which are in good body condition at mating (Russell, 1979).

10.5 RAM FERTILITY AND ACTIVITY

The success or otherwise of many controlled breeding techniques is not alone a question of influencing the reproductive processes of the ewe; the outcome also depends on the capability of the ram (mating activity and semen quality) when natural service is the method of breeding, and on semen quality and insemination procedures when AI is the chosen method.

Where rams are joined with ewes for natural service, semen quality and the sperm doses that operate must be such as to ensure a high fertilization rate in the ewe. In normal commercial practice, two or three rams are usually joined for every 100 ewes in the flock; with one ram for every 30–50 ewes, the male has three ewes or so to work with each day, based on a 17-day cycle. However, the normal servicing ability of the ram is high (Mattner et al., 1967; Blockey ,1980) and New Zealand workers have shown that the proportion of rams to ewes can be reduced to about 1% and still remain adequate (Edgar, 1965; Allison, 1975); this means that a ram would be covering on average, some 6 ewes per day. Elsewhere, however, studies have suggested that individual rams are not always capable of this level of performance (Synott et al., 1981).

10.5.1 Assessing ram mating performance
Although the importance of the ram in determining the lambing performance of the flock is widely accepted, relatively few efforts have been made to quantify and assess ram mating performance. On the assumption that an average ram must be capable of two or more services for every ewe that comes in oestrus, a pen mating test was devised by Mattner et al. (1971); in this, rams were placed in a pen with five oestrous ewes for 20 min and the number of services recorded. It was found that a relationship existed between the total number of services in three such tests and the service performance of the ram

in a flock situation; other workers, however, did not find any relationship between the test results and flock fertility (Cahill *et al.*, 1975; Kelly *et al.*, 1975; Fletcher, 1976; Walkley and Barber, 1976; Allison, 1978).

In subsequent studies, Kilgour (1979) reported using service tests of longer duration, occupying periods of 1 or 3 h rather than 20 min; he showed that it was possible to arrange rams into high and low serving categories and that these could be related to the performance of males under flock conditions. An additional aspect of this ram testing work was in finding that high performing rams tend to have daughters of higher than usual fertility (Wilkins and Kilgour, 1978). Other work reported by Kilgour and Wilkins (1980) showed that ram serving performance (measured by a 1-h pen-test in the morning and one in the afternoon) affected ewe reproductive performance when the rams were employed in flock matings during the early weeks after joining; service tests were regarded as important when the mating load was to be higher than usual or when matings were to be completed in a short time-span.

Age of sheep, whether talking of rams or ewes, can be a relevant consideration in assessing fertility under certain conditions. Several Australian reports dealing with Merino sheep have emphasized the importance of age of rams and ewes for fertility (Lightfoot and Smith, 1968; Croker and Lindsay, 1972; Dawe *et al.*, 1974); ewes and rams mated for the first time at 1½ years of age consistently gave lower lambing percentages than mature animals.

Although sheep farmers have always recognized that rams differ in their mating capabilities and in their fertility, it is only in fairly recent times that it has become evident that rams may contribute to variation in the litter-size of their mates via differences in the fertilizing capacity of their semen or in the pre-natal survival of their offspring (Parker and Bell, 1965; Cunningham *et al.*, 1967; Barr *et al.*, 1968; Newton and Betts, 1968; Turner, 1969; Bradford, 1972). It has also been found that selection for high fertility in ewes has been accompanied by an enhanced ability of semen from related rams to fertilize eggs (Moore and Whyman); the implication here is that the ram can exert a direct effect on litter-size.

10.5.2 Seasonal variations in ram activity

In the British Isles, despite one report suggesting markedly inferior ram performance in the ewe anoestrus (Yeates, 1949), the bulk of evidence for rams accumulated since that time would indicate that they are quite capable of maintaining high mating vigour and acceptable semen quality during the spring and summer months (Gordon, 1958, 1963; Smyth and Gordon, 1967; Jennings, 1972). In Australia, Braden and Baker (1973) noted that there was no distinct breeding season in the ram as in the ewe, although the rate of sperm production may be decreased in the spring months. Among environmental factors (daylength, feed, altitude) likely to reduce the effectiveness of the ram markedly, elevated temperature would seem to be one of the most important. In Australia (Gunn *et al.*, 1942) and North America (McKenzie and Terrill, 1937; Dutt and Hamm, 1957) several studies have shown that high summer temperature is often responsible for temporary infertility.

Fig. 10.3. Rams in Ireland are capable of breeding in all seasons of the year. In the 1950s, it was commonly believed that rams were often incapable of breeding during the spring and summer months of the year and that they experienced something akin to the ewe's non-breeding season. With the development of effective methods for inducing oestrus in sheep in all months of the year, it has become quite clear that rams, certainly of the Suffolk breed, are perfectly capable of acceptable breeding performance at all times of the year.

10.5.3 Need for information on ram ability

With the development of more intensive lamb production systems, especially those calling for more frequent lambings and lambings throughout the year, it is clearly essential to assess the nature and extent of seasonal changes in ram fertility. The availability of new methods for overcoming the seasonal anoestrus in the ewe (e.g. use of sheep with extended seasons; induction of oestrus and ovulation by hormone treatment or even photoperiodic manipulation) does make it necessary that rams on high fertility should be available at all times of the year. There is also the question of devising methods of improving ram performance, if it is considered that this is necessary.

10.5.4 Light manipulations

Several authors have drawn attention to the relationship between decreasing photoperiod, i.e. short days, and increased reproductive activity in rams; on this basis, peak fertility in the male occurs in the autumn (Yeates, 1949; Ortavant, 1977). It is considered that decreasing daylength influences the synthesis and release of gonadotrophins in the ram (Pelletier and Ortavant, 1964, 1975; Lincoln and Peet, 1977; Lincoln et al., 1977); this results in increased testosterone and sperm production (Ortavant, 1956; Katongole et al., 1974) and enhanced mating activity (Lees, 1965; Lincoln and Davidson, 1977).

There is no doubt that considerable seasonal variation in testis size and semen production is evident in rams of primitive breeds such as the Soay, as used by Lincoln (1976); although a case could possibly be made for employing photoperiodic manipulations if a farmer was faced with using Soay rams to breed ewes throughout the year, the need for light treatment in dealing with

Fig. 10.4 Use of light-treatments to influence the breeding capabilities of rams. Much research over the years has been conducted on the effect of different light regimes on the breeding response of sheep. On the University farm, light treatments designed to give short (8 h) or long (16 h) days have been applied to Suffolk, Texel and Dorset rams in a controlled environment house. This is part of efforts to maintain high quality ram semen for sheep AI at all times of the year. Although the application of light treatments to a flock of ewes poses considerable problems, a small number of rams can be managed readily enough. Although French workers maintain that ram semen quality shows evidence of marked deterioration in the spring months, this has not been found in work at Lyons Farm as yet.

improved breeds, such as the Suffolk, is much less evident. One report from the U.S.A. (Schanbacher, 1979) has maintained that considerable seasonal variations occur in the testicular volume of Suffolk rams and that application of short-day (8 h light + 16 h darkness) light treatments over a period of 3–10 weeks resulted in increases of 40–50% in the volume of the testes; however, as already mentioned, there is ample evidence from work in the U.K. and elsewhere that Suffolk rams are able to perform satisfactorily in all seasons. If it was a matter of dealing with Suffolks which were incompetent breeders in the ewe anoestrus, then light manipulations would have to be considered. As it is, there may be a case for using light control in keeping rams in peak breeding condition when they are supplying semen for breeding ewes by AI in the spring and summer months of the year. Those who have employed light treatments report that rams respond to light changes faster than do ewes (Evans and Robinson 1980); however, it should be kept in mind that decreasing light or a constant short daylength environment is not capable of maintaining a ram in peak fertility indefinitely (Ortavant et al., 1964).

10.5.5 Detecting low fertility rams

Clearly, ram fertility is important in determining the proportion of ewes that conceive; methods of distinguishing rams of good fertility from those of poor fertility have been the subject of some number of studies. It is either a matter of examining or measuring the ram's reproductive organs, especially the testes, taking semen samples for microscopic examination or employing a combination of clinical examination and semen testing. On the question of semen testing, Crowley and Walsh (1971), in work in Ireland, did find that semen testing could be useful for detecting the small proportion of rams of inherently very low fertility, but its general use as a screening procedure was not satisfactory.

Examining semen prior to using rams for breeding may not always detect those rams which subsequently suffer from temporary infertility, nor does it permit discrimination between the best and the moderate fertility males. The fertility examination of rams before sale or the start of mating has been common practice in countries

such as New Zealand (Bruere, 1971) and it is desirable that such examinations become accepted practice. It is perhaps noteworthy that New Zealanders take a careful note of the size and tone of the testes rather than paying too much attention to the examination of semen samples.

Sperm output is proportional to testis size, and a ram possessing large symmetrical testes free from defects is likely to produce semen of good quality (Kilgour, 1979). It has been shown that a good estimate of semen production can be obtained by measuring the size of the testes; Knight (1972) showed that semen is produced at a rate of about 20×10^6 sperm per gram per testis per day and in later work demonstrated that measurement of scrotal volume, scrotal circumference (scrotal wool removed) and mean diameter of the testis could all give equally good measures of semen production (Knight, 1977). In Ireland, a survey of lowland rams indicated that the incidence of constitutional infertility in rams is very low (Crowley and Walsh, 1971) as it is with ewes.

10.6 PLACE OF ARTIFICIAL INSEMINATION

The first serious efforts with sheep AI were in Soviet Russia during the 1920s and the number of ewes bred by this method has increased through the years to the point that now 42–44 million ewes are inseminated each year in that country, which represents 72–76% of all ewes (Jheltobruch, 1979); in certain sheep regions, 90–95% of ewes are bred by AI. The development of sheep AI on this scale in Russia was part of a massive grading-up programme applied in native sheep which started after World War I, when Australian Merinos were imported into the country. The AI procedures adopted at that time were simple and have remained basically unchanged over the years, the ram semen being collected and used immediately, occasionally with some degree of dilution. Thus, although Soviet Russia may have a reputation for world leadership in the application of sheep AI, in terms of ram semen processing technology, it has not been associated with any great advances.

According to Ryder (1981), the sheep industry

in the Soviet Union has made considerable progress since World War II not only in expanding sheep numbers, but in moving rapidly towards a predominance of Merino types by the extensive use of AI. Most sheep in Russia are on large-scale farms carrying from 3000 to 60 000 sheep. The usual arrangement is for breeding ewes to be kept in flocks of 600 to 800; for AI, heat periods among ewes are checked by running 8–10 "aproned" rams with the flock, and selecting out those marked, once daily, in the morning. About 70% of ewes are inseminated using fresh undiluted semen, the AI being carried out within 20–30 min of semen collection, using 0.05 ml volumes and doses of 120–150 million sperm; the "load" on any one ram is usually not more than 400–500 ewes in a breeding season and it is claimed that conception rates of 75–80% are achieved (Jheltobruch, 1979).

Despite its extensive use in Russia and several other eastern and central European countries and in some centres in South America, sheep AI is not a common practice in many other sheep producing countries, including Australia, New Zealand, Western Europe and North America. This results from several problems relating to the management of the ewe flock, the costs involved in AI and the handling procedures necessary for ram semen. The fact that most AI, as currently applied in Soviet Russia, is still based on fresh, undiluted semen, as it was more than 50 years ago, serves very clearly to show that methods of dilution and frozen storage of semen applicable in cattle do not necessarily hold good for sheep.

For any thought of applying AI economically under the small farm and flock conditions found in countries such as Ireland, the need for oestrus detection must be eliminated completely and all members of the selected group inseminated at a predetermined hour. This involves the precise control of oestrus and ovulation, using controlled breeding techniques, not only among cyclic ewes in the full breeding season but also in sheep during other seasons of the year when they would normally be anoestrous. It is only during the past decade that methods, both of controlled breeding and ram semen processing, have become available to enable the application of the new fixed-time approach to sheep AI; France is

the country in which these developments have proceeded the furthest.

10.6.1 Chilled storage of ram semen

There have been many reports on the storage of diluted ram semen at refrigerator temperature ($+5°C$), but the important practical objective of achieving satisfactory fertility after such "chilled" storage has not often been recorded. Although the motility of ram semen can apparently be maintained during several days of chilled storage, the lambing rate after AI declines after 24 h (Salamon and Robinson, 1962; Rabocev, 1965, 1966; Lapwood et al., 1972; Watson 1979); in one report, Salamon et al. (1979) used semen stored at 5°C in a tris-fructose-egg yolk diluent in surgical inseminations and reported fertilization rates of 95% with semen stored up to 4 days, although a marked drop occurred after that time. Insemination into the uterus is too difficult and slow for use in commercial application.

10.6.2 Prostaglandins as semen additives

In Australia, Salamon et al. (1979) examined the addition of prostaglandin $F_{2\alpha}$ (300 μg dose) to the inseminate, but this did not increase the conception rate after AI with either fresh semen or semen stored for one day; this was in agreement with the findings of Dimov and Stefanov (1975) who also recorded no improvement in fertility of fresh semen supplemented with differing amounts of $PGF_{2\alpha}$ and PGE_2. Investigations elsewhere with prostaglandins, however, have reported that supplementation of frozen–thawed semen or injection of ewes shortly after AI with $PGF_{2\alpha}$ improved transport of sperm for cervix to oviducts (Edqvist et al., 1975) and that addition of this PG to frozen-thawed semen (Zhiltzov et al., 1974; Gustafsson et al., 1975) or of $PGF_{2\alpha}$ and PGE_2 to fresh diluted semen (Dimov and Georgiev 1977) improved the fertility.

10.7 FREEZING OF RAM SEMEN

Any consideration of sheep AI as a method of breeding would be incomplete without referring to the possibility of employing frozen semen.

Although techniques for the insemination of sheep with freshly collected semen have been available for many years (review by Emmens and Robinson, 1962); the development of frozen-storage methods has been slow and procedures are still far from being satisfactory. Although there are many reports showing that the revival of ram sperm following frozen storage can be satisfactory (Lopyrin and Loginova, 1958; Mattner et al., 1969; Lightfoot and Salamon 1970a), reports of acceptable conception rates after normal cervical insemination with such semen have been few (Visser and Salamon, 1974a; Colas, 1975).

In many comparative trials, the fertility of frozen–thawed ram semen has been much below that of fresh semen; this reduced fertility has been attributed to impaired sperm transport through the cervix, resulting in failure to establish an adequate sperm reservoir in the anterior cervix adjacent to the uterus (Lightfoot and Salamon, 1970a; Robinson, 1975). It is also established that the insemination of frozen-thawed semen directly into the uterus results in a fertilization rate comparable to that of fresh semen (Lightfoot and Salamon, 1970a); such evidence is in line with the view that the basic difficulty is that of establishing an adequate reservoir of viable sperm in the cervix. It should be mentioned that variation in fertility between individuals is regarded as even more marked in rams than in bulls (Watson, 1979).

10.7.1 Pellets and straws

Australian workers have favoured the pellet-freezing of ram semen and have been careful to observe the same principles as apply in fresh semen AI work; namely, the need to employ a dense inseminate of highly motile sperm if an adequate cervical population of sperm is to be established (Lightfoot and Salamon, 1970a; Salamon and Lightfoot, 1970). The Australian freezing method is based on the use of a tris-glucose-citric acid-egg yolk diluent, added to semen at a low dilution rate (1:2; semen to diluent ratio); ewes inseminated once or twice during oestrus with sperm doses of 360 million motile sperm have given conception rates of 50–55% or so (Salamon, 1972; Salamon and Visser, 1972; Visser and Salamon, 1974a). Work in the U.K. by

Maxwell et al. (1980) showed a 52% lambing rate for semen frozen in this way in pellets as against 29% for semen frozen in straws.

Freezing in pellets has an advantage over freezing in straws because of its simplicity and the speed at which it can be done. On the other hand, handling pellets on the farm is not easy because of the steps that have to be taken before insemination can be carried out (thawing of pellets, filling of insemination pipettes or straws).

Investigations elsewhere, mindful of some of these difficulties in using pellets under farm conditions, have used plastic straws for semen storage (Colas and Brice, 1970; Colas, 1972, 1979, 1980; Watson and Martin, 1975a). In handling semen frozen in straws, evidence clearly shows that injury to the sperm is less when ram semen is thawed rapidly (Colas, 1979); the percentage of motile sperm is higher after exposure of straws to 50°C than to 25°C and even higher temperatures could be used to advantage if the exposure time is very short (<10 s). In practice, as with bull semen, such short exposures and rapid thaws are extremely difficult to control.

Fig. 10.5. Dorset Horn rams may perform better in the ewe anoestrus than some other breeds. Various pieces of evidence from using Dorset Horn rams in either sheep AI or in natural service indicates that rams of this breed may be more fertile than those of other breeds such as the Suffolk or Texel during the spring and summer months. In terms of semen quality as revealed under the microscope, there is no explanation for this and it may not be a genuine effect. Dorset Horn ewes have been used for producing lambs in the autumn rather than the spring in the south of England for many years — at one time supplying a trade for young lamb at Christmas in London. Why the Dorset should differ from the other British breeds in its breeding characteristics is by no means clear.

10.7.2 Seasonal effects on sperm quality

French workers maintain that the fertility of frozen semen is highly dependent upon the season of collection and that during the autumn breeding season it shows the best fertility. It has been reported by Colas (1979) that the incidence of morphologically abnormal sperm (distal cytoplasmic droplets and abnormal tails) can be much greater under increasing daylength conditions than under decreasing light (22.5 vs 10.3%); fertilizing ability of fresh semen is also affected, with the poorest semen being produced under conditions of increasing daylength. Such seasonal differences in ram fertility and sperm morphology have not apparently been reported as yet by other investigators.

10.8 FUTURE DEVELOPMENTS

Without doubt, frozen semen will prove to be valuable in sheep breeding and production programmes, especially when it is a matter of importing semen for use in breeding improvement programmes (Colas, 1980). There would also be scope for building up stocks of frozen semen for use during the period of peak demand for sheep AI in the autumn season; this could be valuable for the operation of a commercially viable insemination service.

10.9 REFERENCES

Allison, A. J. (1975) Ewe and ram fertility in commercial flocks mated with differing numbers of ewes per ram. *N.Z.J. Exp. Agric.* **3**, 161–167.

Allison, A. J. (1978) Flock mating in sheep. IV. Effect of number of ewes per ram on ejaculated characteristics and libido during the mating period *N.Z.J. Agric. Res.* **21**, 187–195.

Averill, R. L. W. (1955) Fertility of the ewe. *Proc. Soc. Study Fert.* **7**, 139–148.

Barr, A. L., Cunningham, C. J., Harper, J. O. and Inskeep, E. K. (1965) *W. Virg. Univ. Agr. Exp. Sta. Bull.* No. 562.

Blaxter, K. L. (1964) Dietary factors affecting energy utilization. *Proc. Nutr. Soc.* **23**, 3–11.

Blockey, M. A. de B. (1980) Sheep and cattle mating behaviour. In, *Behaviour in Relation to Reprod. Management and Welfare of Farm Animals. Reviews of Rural Science*, Vol. 4, pp. 53–61.

Bradford, G. E. (1972) Genetic control of litter size in sheep. *J. Reprod. Fert.* Suppl. 15, 23–41.

Bruere, A. N. (1971) Practical aspects of fertility in the ram. *Sheep Farming Ann., Massey Univ. N.Z.*, 31–40.

Cahill, L. P., Blockey, M. A. de B. and Parr, R. A. (1975) Effects of mating behaviour and ram libido on the fertility of young ewes. *Aust. J. Exp. Agric. Anim. Husb.* **15**, 337–341.

Colas, G. (1975) Effect of initial freezing temperature, addition of glycerol and dilution on the survival and fertilising ability of deep frozen ram semen. *J. Reprod. Fert.* **42**, 277–285.

Colas, G. (1979) fertility in the ewe after AI with fresh and frozen semen at the induced oestrus and influence of the photoperiod on the semen quality of the ram. *Livest. Prod. Sci.* **6**, 153–166.

Colas, G. (1980) Suggested international standards for ram semen exchange. *Proc. 9th Int. Congr. Anim. Reprod. A.I. (Madrid)*, **2**, 287–296.

Croker, K. P. and Lindsay, D. R. (1972) A study of the mating behaviour of rams when joined at different proportions. *Aust. J. Exp. Agric. Anim. Husb.* **12**, 13–18.

Crowley, J. P. (1964) The extension of the breeding season of sheep. *Proc. 5th Int. Congr. Anim. Reprod. A.I. (Trento)*, **2**, 378–383.

Crowley, J. P. and Walsh, M. A. (1971) Infertility in rams in Ireland. *Ir. vet. J.* **25**, 27–30.

Cunningham, C. J., Barr, A. L., Harper, J. O. and Inskeep, E. K. (1967) *J. Anim. Sci.* **26**, 884.

Dawe, S. T., Archer, W. R., Bennett, N. W., Brunskill, A., Cahill, J. R., Donnelly, F. B., Roberts, B. C. and Trimmer, B. I. (1974) The effect of ram percentage on the fertility of maiden ewes. *Proc. Aust. Soc. Anim. Prod.* **10**, 274–278.

Dimov, V. and Georgiev, G. (1977) Ram semen prostaglandin concentration and its effect on fertility. *J. Anim. Sci.* **44**, 1050–1054.

Dimov, V. and Stefanov, G. (1975) Studies on the content of prostaglandins and fertility of sheep semen. *Proc. Int. Conf. Prostaglandins (Florence) Italy*, 108.

Doney, J. M., Gunn, R. G. and Smith, W. F. (1976a) Effects of premating environmental stress, ACTH, cortisone actate or metapone on oestrus and ovulation in sheep. *J. Agric. Sci., Camb.* **87**, 127–132.

Doney, J. M., Smith, W. F. and Gunn, R. G. (1976b). Effects of post-mating environmental stress or administration of ACTH on early embryonic loss in sheep. *J. Agric. Sci. Camb.* **87**, 133–136.

Dutt, R. H. and Bush, L. F. (1955) The effect of low environmental temperature on initiation of the breeding season in sheep. *J. Anim. Sci.* **14**, 885.

Dutt, R. H. and Hamm, P. T. (1957) The effect of high environmental temperature and shearing on semen quality of rams. *J. Anim. Sci.* **16**, 328–334.

Edgar, D. G. (1965) Talking about tupping. *Proc. Ruakura Farmers Conf. Week.* 61–69.

Edqvist, S., Einarsson, S. and Gustafsson, B. (1975) Effect of prostaglandin $F_{2\alpha}$ on sperm transport in the reproductive tract of the ewe. *Acta Vet. Scand.* **16**, 149–151.

Emmens, C. W. and Robinson, T. J. (1962) A.I. in sheep. In, *The Semen of Animals and Artificial Insemination* J. P. Maule, Ed. pp. 205–251.

Evans, G. and Robinson, T. J. (1980) The control of fertility in sheep: endocrine and ovarian responses to progestagen—PMSG treatment in the breeding season and in anoestrus. *J. Agric. Sci., Camb.* **94**, 69–88.

Fletcher, I. C. (1976) Sexual activity in Merino rams. *Proc. 1976 Int. Congr. (Murest, W. A.)* Tomes Robertson and Lightfoot, Eds. 345–351. Waite Press, Perth.

Gordon, I. (1955) The hormonal augmentation of fertility in sheep. *Proc. Brit. Soc. Anim. Prod.* 55.

Gordon, I. (1958) Studies in the extra-seasonal production of lambs. *J. Agric. Sci. Camb.* **50,** 125.

Gordon, I. (1963) The induction of pregnancy in the anoestrous ewe by hormonal therapy. *J. Agric. Sci., Camb.* **60,** 77.

Gordon, I. (1967) Aspects of reproduction and neonatal mortality in the ewe lambs and adult sheep. *J. IR. Dept. Agric.* **64,** 76–127.

Gunn, R. G. and Doney, J. M. (1979) Fertility in Cheviot Ewes. 1. The Effect of body condition at mating on ovulation rate and early embryo mortality in North and South country Cheviot ewes. *Anim. Prod.* **29,** 11–16.

Gunn, R. M. C., Sanders, R. N. and Granger, W. (1942) Studies in fertility in sheep, 2. Seminal changes affecting fertility in rams. *Bull Coun. Sci., Industr. Res. Aust.,* No. 148, 140 pp.

Gustafsson, B., Edqvist, S., Einarsson, S. and Linge, F. (1975) The fertility of deep frozen ram semen supplemented with $PGF_{2\alpha}$. *Acta. Vet. Scand.* **16,** 468–470.

Heape, W. (1899) Abortion, barrenness and fertility in sheep. *J. R. Agr. Soc.,* Ser. 111, **10,** 217.

Horak, F. and Potucek, M. (1978) The effect of the lunar phase on the sexual activity of ewes. *Sb. vys. Sk. Zemed. Brne* **23,** 743–749.

Jennings, J. J. (1972) Some factors affecting the reproductive performance of rams. *Ph. D. Thesis, N.U.I., Dublin.*

Jheltobruch, N. A. (1979) AI of sheep in the Soviet Union. In, *Sheep Breeding, 2nd ed.* Tomes et al., Ed. revised by Haresign, W. pp. 565–570. Butterworths, London.

Karsh, F. J. (1980) Seasonal reproduction: a saga of reversible fertility. *The Physiologist* **33**(6), 29–38.

Katongole, C. B., Naftolin, R. and Short, R. V. (1974) Seasonal variations in blood luteinizing hormone and testosterone levels in rams. *J. Endoc.* **60,** 101–106.

Kelly, R., Allison, A. J. and Shackell, G. H. (1975) Libido testing and subsequent mating performance in rams. *Proc. N.Z. Soc. Anim. Prod.* **35,** 204–211.

Kilgour, R. J. (1979) The importance of the ram on flock fertility. *Wool Tech. Sheep Breed.* **27,** 41–44.

Kilgour, R. J. and Wilkins, J. F. (1980) The effect of serving capacity of the ram syndicate on flock fertility. *Aust. J. Exp. Agric. Anim. Husb.* **20,** 662–666.

Kilgour, R. J. and de Langen, H. (1970) Stress in sheep resulting from management practices. *Proc. N.Z. Soc. Anim. Prod.* **30,** 65–76.

Knight, T. W. (1972) A study of factors which affect the potential fertility of the ram. *Ph. D. Thesis, Univ. W. Australia.*

Knight, T. W. (1977) Methods for the indirect estimation of testes weight and sperm numbers in Merino and Romney rams. *N.Z. J. Agr. Res.* **20,** 291.

Lapwood, K. R., Martin, I. C. A. and Entwistle, K. W. (1972) The fertility of Merino ewes artificially inseminated with semen diluted in solutions based on skim milk glucose or ribose. *Aust. J. Agric. Res.* **23,** 457–466.

Lees, J. L. (1964) Variations in the pattern of the breeding season in sheep and their effects on subsequent productivity. *Anim. Prod.* **6,** 255.

Lees, J. L. (1965) Seasonal variation in the breeding activity of rams. *Nature, Lond.* **207,** 221–222.

Lees, J. L. (1966) Variations in the time of onset of the breeding season in Clun ewes. *J. Agric. Sci., Camb.* **67,** 173–179.

Lees, J. L. (1978) Functional infertility in sheep. *Vet. Rec.* **102,** 232–236.

Lightfoot, R. J. and Salamon, S. (1970a) Transport and viability of spermatozoa within the genital tract of the ewe. *J. Reprod. Fert.* **22,** 385–000.

Lightfoot, R. J. and Salamon, S. (1970b) The effects of method of insemination on fertilization and embryonic mortality. *J. Reprod. Fert.* **22,** 399.

Lightfoot, R. J. and Smith, J. A. C. (1968) Studies on the number of ewes joined per ram for flock matings under paddock conditions. I. Mating behaviour and fertility. *Aust. J. Agric. Res.* **19,** 1029–1042.

Lincoln, G. A. (1976) Secretion of LH in rams exposed to two different photoperiods. *J. Reprod. Fert.* **47,** 351.

Lincoln, G. A. and Davidson, W. (1977) The relationship between sexual and aggressive behaviour and pituitary and testicular activity during the seasonal sexual cycle of rams and the influence of photoperiod. *J. Reprod. Fert.* **49,** 267–276.

Lincoln, G. A. and Peet, M. J. (1977) Photoperiodic control of gonadotrophin secretion in the ram. *J. Endocr.* **74,** 355.

Lincoln, G. A., Peet, M. J. and Cunningham, R. A. (1977) Seasonal and circadian changes in the episodic release of FSH, LH and testosterone in rams exposed to artificial photoperiods. *J. Endocr.* **72,** 337.

Loginova, N. V. and Zeltobrjuh, N. A. (1968) Test of different methods of freezing semen (ram). *Ovtsevodstvo,* **14**(9), 22–25.

Lopyrin, A. I. and Loginova, N. V. (1958) The method of freezing ram semen. *Ovtsevodstvo* **5**(8), 31–34.

McKenzie, F. F. and Terrill, C. E. (1937) Estrus, ovulation and related phenomena in the ewe. *Res. Bull. Mo. Agr. Exp. Sta.* No. 264.

Marshall, F. H. A. (1905) Fertility in Scottish sheep. *Proc. R. Soc.* **77,** 58.

Mattner, P. E., Braden, A. W. H. and Turnball, K. E. (1967) Studies in flock mating of sheep. Mating Behaviour. *Aust. J. Exp. Agric. Anim. Husb.* **7,** 103–109.

Mattner, P. E., Entwistle, K. W. and Martin, I. C. A. (1969) Passage, survival and fertility of deep-frozen ram semen in the genital tract of the ewe. *Aust. J. Biol. Sci.* **22,** 181–187.

Mattner, P. E., Braden, A. W. H. and George, J. M. (1971) Studies in flock mating of sheep. 4. The relation of libido tests to subsequent service activity of young rams. *Aust. J. Exp. Agric. Anim. Husb.* **11,** 473–477.

Maxwell, W. M. C., Curnock, R. M., Logue, D. N. and Reed, H. C. B. (1980) Fertility of ewes following artificial insemination with semen frozen in pellets or straws. A preliminary report. *Theriogen.* **14,** 83–89.

Mittal, J. P. (1980) Seasonal changes in semen characteristics of Marwari and Magra sheep of the Indian desert. *J. Agric. Sci., Camb.* **95,** 721–724.

Mittal, J. P. and Ghosh, P. K. (1980) A note on annual reproductive 'rhythm' in Marwari sheep of the Rajasthan desert in India. *Anim. Prod.* **30,** 153–156.

Neville, W. E. and Neathery, M. W. (1970) Effect of natural differences in atmospheric temperature on the incidence of first estrus following anoestrus in sheep. *J. Anim. Sci.* **30,** 242–249.

Newton, J. E. and Betts, J. E. (1968) The effect of superovulation synchronization and the ram on litter size. *Proc. 6th Int. Congr. Reprod A.I. (Paris),* 289.

Ortavant, R. (1956) Action de la durée d'eclairement sur les processus spermatogenetiques chez le belier. *C. R. Soc. Biol.* **150,** 471.

Ortavant, R. (1977) Photoperiodic regulation of reproduction in the sheep. In, *Management of Reproduction in Sheep and Goats.* S.I.D. Publn.

Ortavant, R., Mauleon, P. and Thibault, C. (1964) Photoperiodic control of gonadal and hypophyseal activity in domestic animals. *Ann. N.Y. Acad. Sci.* **117**, 157.

Parker, C. F. and Bell, D. S. (1965) Ram effect on ewe fertility. Sheep research and development. *Res. Sum. Ohio Agric. Res. Dev. Cen.* No. 4 17–21.

Pelletier, J. and Ortavant, R. (1964) Influence of light duration on the content of the gonadotrophin hormones FSH and ICSH in the hypophysis of the ram. *Ann. Biol. Anim. Biochim. Biophys.* **4**, 17–26.

Pelletier, J. and Ortavant, R. (1975) Photoperiodic control of LH release in the ram. *Acta. Endocr.* **78**, 435–441.

Rabocev, V. K. (1965) Comparison of the fertilising ability of ram semen preserved by different methods for various times. *Ovtsevadstvo* **11**(9), 14–16.

Rabocev, V. K. (1966) How to increase the conception rate of ewes when using stored semen. *Ovtsevodstvo* **12**(9), 33–36.

Radford, H. M. (1961) Photoperiodism and sexual activity in Merino ewes. I. The effect of continuous light on the development of sexual activity. *Aust. J. Agric. Res.* **12**, 139.

Radford, H. M. (1966) Regulation of the breeding season in mammals. *Proc. Aust. Soc. Anim. Prod.* **6**, 19–31.

Robertson, H. A. (1977) Reproduction in the ewe and the goat. In, *Reproduction in Domestic Animals, 3rd Ed.* Cole and Cupps, Ed. pp 477–498. Academic Press, London.

Robinson, J. J. (1979) Intensive systems. In, *The Management and Diseases of Sheep*, pp. 431–446, Comm. Agr. Bur. Slough.

Robinson, T. J. (1952) role of progesterone in the mating behaviour of the ewe. *Nature, Lond.* **170**, 373–374.

Robinson, T. J. (1954) Fertility of anoestrous ewes following injection of progesterone and PMS. *Aust. J. Agric. Res.* **5**, 730–736.

Robinson, T. J. (1955) Quantitative studies on the hormonal induction of oestrus in spayed ewes. *J. Endocr.* **12**, 163–173.

Robinson, T. J. (1965) Use of progestagen-impregnated sponges inserted intravaginally or subcutaneously for the control of the oestrous cycle in the sheep. *Nature, Lond.* **206**, 39–41.

Robinson, T. J., Moore, N. W. and Binet, F. E. (1956) The effect of the duration of progesterone pretreatment on the response of the spayed ewe to oestrogen. *J. Endocr.* **14**, 1–7.

Robinson, T. J., Moore, N. W., Lindsay, D. R., Fletcher, I. C. and Salamon, S. (1970) Fertility following synchronization of oestrus in the sheep with intravaginal sponges. I. Effects of vaginal douche, supplementary steroids, time of insemination and numbers and dilution of sperm. *Aust. J. Agric. Res.* **21**, 767.

Russel, A. J. F. (1979) The nutrition of the pregnant ewe. In, *The Management and Diseases of Sheep.* pp. 221–241. Comm. Agric. But., Slough.

Ryder, M. L. (1981) Sheep in the Soviet Union. *Span.* **24**(1), 36–37.

Salamon, S. (1972) Fertility of ram spermatozoa frozen stored for three years. *Proc. 7th Int. Congr. Anim. Reprod. A.I. (Munich)*, **2**, 1493.

Salamon, S. and Lightfoot, R. J. (1970) Fertilization of ram spermatozoa frozen by the pellet method. *J. Reprod. Fert.* **22**, 409.

Salamon, S. and Robinson, T. J. (1962) Studies on the AI of Merino sheep. II. The effects of semen diluents and storage on lambing performance. *Aust. J. Agric. Res.* **13**, 271–281.

Salamon, S. and Visser, D. (1972) Effect of composition of Tris-based diluent and of thawing solution on survival of ram spermatozoa frozen by the pellet method. *Aust. J. Biol. Sci.* **25**, 605–618.

Salamon, S., Maxwell, W. M. C. and Firth, J. H. (1979) Fertility of ram semen after storage at 5°C. *Anim. Reprod. Sci.* **2**, 373–385.

Schanbacher, B. D. (1979) Increased lamb production with rams exposed to short daylengths during the non-breeding season. *J. Anim. Sci.* **49**, 927–932.

Smyth, P. and Gordon, I. (1967) Seasonal and breed variations in the semen characteristics of rams in Ireland. *Ir. Vet. J.* **21**, 222–233.

Synnot, A. L., Fulkerson, W. J. and Lindsay, D. R. (1981) Sperm output by rams and distribution amongst ewes under conditions of continual mating. *J. Reprod. Fert.* **61**, 355–361.

Thimonier, J. and Mauleon, P. (1969) Variations saisonnieres du comportement d'oestrus et des activites ovariennes et hypophysaires chez les ovins, *Anim. Biol. Anim. Bioch. Biophys.* **9**, 233.

Turner, H. N. (1969) Genetic improvement of reproduction rate in sheep *Anim. Breed. Abstr.* **37**, 545.

Visser, D. and Salamon, S. (1974a) Fertility following inseminations with frozen–thawed reconcentrated and unconcentrated ram semen. *Aust. J. Biol. Sci.* **27**, 423.

Visser, D. and Salamon, S. (1974b) Effect of composition of Tris-based diluent on survival of boar spermatozoa following deep freezing. *Aust. J. Biol. Sci.* **27**, 485–497.

Watson, P. F. (1979) The preservation of semen in mammals. In, *Oxford Reviews. Reprod. Biology*, Vol. 1, pp. 283–350. Oxford University Press, Oxford.

Watson, P. F. and Martin, I. C. A. (1975a) Effects of egg yolk, glycerol and the freezing rate on the viability and acrosomal structures of frozen ram spermatozoa. *Aust. J. Biol. Sci.* **28**, 153–159.

Watson, P. F. and Martin, I. C. A. (1975b) The influence of some fractions of egg yolk on the survival of ram spermatozoa at 5°C. *Aust. J. Biol. Sci.* **28**, 145–52.

Watson, R. H. (1962) Seasonal variation in occurrence of oestrus in Merino ewes in Southern Victoria. *Aust. Vet. J.* **28**, 310.

Watson, R. H. and Radford, H. M. (1955) A note on the hours of daylight associated with the seasonal increase in sexual activity in Merino ewes. *Aust. Vet. J.* **31**, 31.

Walkley, J. R. N. and Barber, A. A. (1976) The relationship between libido score and fertility in Merino rams. *Proc. Aust. Soc. Anim. Prod.* **11**, 141–144.

Welch, R. A. S., Kilgour, R. J., Robson, G. A., Smith, M. E. and Williams, E. T. (1979) The effect of shearing ewes during the mating period on the subsequent lambing pattern. *Proc. N.Z. Soc. Anim. Prod.* **39**, 100–102.

Wilson, P. N. (1968) Biological ceilings and economic efficiency for the production of animal protein, A.D. 2000 *Chem. Ind.* 899.

Wilkins, J. F. and Kilgour, R. J. (1978) Early reproductive performance of female progeny of rams selected on serving capacity. *Proc. 10th Ann. Conf. Aust. Soc. Reprod. Biol.* 22.

Yeates, N. T. M. (1949) The breeding season of the sheep, with particular reference to its modification by artificial means using light. *J. Agric. Sci., Camb.* **39**, 1–43.

Yeates, N. T. M. (1956) The effect of light on the breeding season, gestation and birth weight of Merino sheep. *Aust. J. Agric. Res.* **7**, 440.

Zhiltzov, N. S., Bolub, V. S., Varnavskaya, V. A., Azhgikhin, I. S., Bobylev, R. V., Gandelj, V. G. and Pechennikov, V. M. (1974) Possibility of using prostaglandins for increasing the effectiveness of AI in sheep. *Zhivotnovodstvo.* **8**, 67–70.

CHAPTER 11

The Ewe's Oestrous Cycle and Seasonal Breeding Activity

11.1 INTRODUCTION

The ewe is seasonally polyoestrous with oestrous cycles usually commencing in late summer and continuing through until the start of spring, unless pregnancy intervenes. During the breeding season, the ewe shows cycles of 16–17 days (McKenzie and Terrill, 1937; Hafez, 1952; Asdell, 1964); in general, most cycles range from 14 to 18 days with an average length of between 16.5 and 17.5 days. The oestrous cycle length seems to be more variable in the second half of the breeding season as a result of the luteal phase of the cycle increasing in its duration (Hammond, 1944).

11.2 OESTRUS AND THE OESTROUS CYCLE

The duration of oestrus, looking at the reports in the literature, generally fall within the range of 1–1.5 days (Asdell, 1964); detailed observations of several British sheep breeds in a 3-year study showed the heat period to be, on average, about 35 h in length (Hafez, 1952). There have been those who have observed that long heat periods are more intense than short ones and that the first oestrus of the breeding season may be shorter and less intense than subsequent periods (Grant, 1934); oestrus is generally shortest in ewe lambs and of intermediate duration in yearling sheep (McKenzie and Terrill, 1937; Hafez, 1952).

The ewe is a spontaneous ovulator and estimates of the time at which ovulation occurs, relative to onset of oestrus have varied; reviewing the literature at the time, Robinson (1959) concluded that ovulation occurs at about the end of oestrus regardless of the duration of the receptive period. The phenomenon of oestrus in the ewe is generally recognized as being rather more complex than was at one time thought. It is now evident that the continuous presence of rams can reduce the duration of behavioural oestrus (Parsons and Hunter, 1967; Westhuysen et al., 1970; Fletcher and Lindsay, 1971) and advance the time of ovulation, relative to the onset of oestrus (Lindsay et al., 1975; Signoret, 1975) by advancing the preovulatory surge of LH; in the absence of the male, presumably the preovulatory surge of LH awaits the build-up of follicular oestradiol to an appropriate concentration before it is triggered off.

Duration of the heat period can be markedly influenced by breed (Land, 1970). It should also

Fig. 11.1. Oestrus symptoms may not be easy to detect in the ewe in the absence of the ram. Without the presence of rams or sterile teasers it is usually impossible to distinguish a ewe that is in oestrus from one that is not — using simple powers of observation. However, apart from the ram's ability to detect the oestrous ewe by his sense of smell, the female sheep herself does show ram-seeking behaviour when in heat. Such behavioural patterns are useful enough for sheep that are operating under hill and mountain conditions in bringing the two sexes together.

be noted that the interval between the start of oestrus and the time of preovulatory LH discharge varies between and within breeds (Thimonier and Pelletier, 1971); the interval is reported by Land et al. (1973) to be greater in highly prolific sheep (18 h) than in less prolific breeds (6–7 h). The maximum concentrations of preovulatory LH varies from animal but the duration of the surge is 8–12 h (Goding et al., 1969; Cunningham et al., 1975; Legan and Karsh, 1979); and ovulation itself occurs about 24 h after the LH peak.

The behavioural symptoms displayed by the ewe during oestrus have been described in several reports (Hulet et al., 1975); in effect, signs are very few and consist of the ewe remaining close to the ram and standing to be mounted. It should be noted that ewes display ram seeking-activity when they are in oestrus (Inkster, 1957; Lindsay and Fletcher, 1972) so that contact between the sexes is not necessarily dependent wholly on the ram's activity. The absence of any clear symptoms make detection of oestrus, other than in the presence of a ram, extremely difficult; occasionally, the oestrous ewe will move its tail vigorously as part of a display pattern when it is with the ram.

Oestrus is the behavioural response of the ewe

to the action of follicular oestrogen on specific centres in the hypothalamus; the plasma concentration of oestradiol reaches its peak at about the start of oestrus (Smith and Robinson, 1970; Cox et al., 1971; Scaramuzzi and Land, 1978); after which it rapidly disappears. This means that the ewe spends much of oestrus in the absence of ovarian oestrogen and progesterone in the circulation. Progesterone concentration in the plasma is lowest during oestrus but begins to rise immediately after formation of the corpus luteum and reaches a maximum later in the cycle.

11.2.1 Oestrus in pregnancy

Although no evidence has been recorded in Irish studies of oestrus occurring in the pregnant ewe, this phenomenon has been noted in several reports (Williams et al., 1956; Bichard et al., 1974; Younis and Afifi, 1979); some have gone so far as to suggest that oestrus in the pregnant ewe occurs so frequently as to make the practice of putting rams with ewes to detect non-pregnant sheep questionable. This would seem to be very much against the evidence of the literature as a whole.

11.3 PROGESTERONE EVENTS DURING THE OESTROUS CYCLE

The nature of the hormonal mechanisms involved in regulating the ewe's oestrous cycle has been the subject of many investigations, particularly during the most recent decade, when RIA procedures have been available.

11.3.1 Progesterone and the corpus luteum

Edgar and Ronaldson (1958) were among the first to show that the sheep's corpus luteum attains full secretory activity by about the sixth to eighth day of the oestrous cycle and continues secreting progesterone at a fairly constant level until about day-15. The use of RIA procedures have shown that progesterone levels in the blood during the cycle follow the growth and development of the corpus luteum, the maximum concentrations being reached at about day-8 and then beginning to fall a day or two before the next oestrus (Cunningham et al., 1975; Quirke et al., 1979). In some of the early reports, the maximum concentration of progesterone during the luteal phase was given as 2–ng mL$_1$ (Stabenfeldt et al., 1969; Thorburn et al., 1969); it is known that season and nutrition (Lamond et al., 1972) as well as breed and ovulation rate (Thorburn et al., 1979; Bindon et al., 1975; Quirke and Gosling, 1976) can have an influence on the maximum concentration of the steroid. There is only a marginal increase in the progesterone level with two corpora lutea rather than one, so detection of double ovulations in sheep is not possible by measuring the steroid.

The data of Short (1964) and Thorburn et al. (1969) suggested that there was some decline in progesterone levels between the 10th and 15th days of the cycle; electron microscopy studies also provided some evidence of incipient regression commencing as early as day-12–13 (Deane et al., 1966).

This agrees with earlier observations on the morphology of the corpus luteum in the latter part of the oestrous cycle (Warbritton, 1934; Restall, 1964; Hutchinson and Robertson, 1966). There is unanimity among reports in showing that there is a precipitous decline in the plasma concentration of progesterone at about day-15.

There is evidence that both LH and prolactin contribute to the maintenance of the functional activity of the sheep's corpus luteum during the oestrous cycle, according to reports reviewed by Robertson (1977). It is also recognized that the normal growth and development of the ovine corpus luteum can be markedly affected if exogenous progesterone is administered in the early days of the oestrous cycle; this results in a much reduced span of activity (Ginther, 1969; Thwaites, 1971); presumably, progesterone interferes with the hormonal mechanisms responsible for the normal establishment of luteal tissue.

11.4 PROSTAGLANDINS AND LUTEOLYSIS

As already mentioned, the functional activity of the corpus luteum is abruptly terminated at the end of the oestrous cycle; evidence favours the view that its activity is self-regulating. Progesterone secreted by the corpus luteum stimulates the endometrium to synthesize and store the luteolytic agent (Wilson et al., 1972). The belief is that PGF$_{2\alpha}$ is released from the uterus to cause regression (McCracken et al., 1970; Goding, 1973, 1974). Increased levels of PGF$_{2\alpha}$ have been found in the uterine venous blood of sheep on day-15 of the cycle (Bland et al., 1971), although the mode of transfer of the luteolytic agent has been the subject of several reports; there is also the question of what signals the rapid release of PGF$_{2\alpha}$ from the uterus at the end of the cycle. There is evidence (Alwachi et al., 1979) that the ovary exerts a local control over endometrial PGF$_{2\alpha}$ synthesis in the adjacent uterine horn, possibly via the involvement of oestrogen; exogenous oestradiol given in appropriate doses will induce luteolysis when given near the end of the cycle and endogenous production of oestradiol starts about 48 h before the onset of oestrus (Goding et al., 1970; Obst et al., 1971; Bjersing et al., 1972). There is also evidence that X-irradiation of the ovaries destroys follicles and presents luteal regression (Hansel, 1975).

Whatever the precise cause of corpus regression at the end of the normal cycle, it is known that the plasma concentration of progesterone sinks rapidly to a negligible value and that this remains true during oestrus and until the fresh corpus luteum forms at ovulation; the extremely low basal concentration of 0.2 ng mL$_1$ progesterone is believed to be of adrenal origin (Robertson, 1977). There seems to be no evidence in sheep that progesterone is secreted by the preovulatory follicle as this occurs in some mammalian species.

11.5 GONADOTROPHINS AND OESTROGENS

The concentration of LH in the plasma of the ewe is determined by the operation of two distinct systems; preovulatory LH in the female is controlled by one group of neurons whereas a basal (tonic) secretion of LH is regulated in both sexes by neurons in another part of the hypothalamus. In the sheep, the tonic level of LH is apparently maintained in the face of luteal activity whereas the preovulatory surge is blocked by progesterone but released in response to oestrogen at the time of oestrus (Goding et al., 1970).

As plasma progesterone concentration decreases at the end of the cycle, tonic LH level rises to reach values at least five-fold greater than base-line by the time of the onset of the preovulatory LH surge. The rise in LH reflects an increase in the frequency of pulsatile LH discharges (Foster et al., 1975; Baird, 1978) and constitutes an increase in tonic LH secretion separate from the LH surge (Legan and Karsh, 1979). The sustained increase in tonic LH concentration, covering a period of about 48 h, is accompanied by a five-fold increase in oestradiol secreted by the rapidly expanding Graafian follicles in the ovary. It is this sudden increase in oestradiol which triggers the massive preovulatory LH surge (Goding et al., 1969; Scaramuzzi et al., 1971; Karsh and Foster, 1975) and some hours earlier resulted in the onset of oestrus.

The preovulatory LH surge, which occurs in the early hours of the heat period, triggers events in those Graafian follicles (previously sensitized by FSH?) destined for ovulation at that oestrus; among these events is the nuclear and cytoplasmic maturation of the oocyte and rupture of the follicle. Ovulation occurs about 24 h after LH release (Cumming et al., 1971, 1973), which would agree with observations that this event generally coincides with the end of heat (Robinson, 1959; Parsons et al., 1967; Holst and Braden, 1972; Cumming et al., 1973). This timing agrees with data on the occurrence of ovulation after administering hCG in early oestrus (Dziuk, 1965) and with the times recorded for the completion of nuclear maturation in the sheep oocyte cultured in vitro (Crosby and Gordon, 1971).

11.5.1 Control of tonic LH levels

It appears that the oestrous cycle of the ewe is characterized by genuine day-to-day variations in the concentration of LH; levels are relatively high (2-3 ng mL_1) during the first few days after the preovulatory LH surge, decrease to a low point (0.4-1.0 ng mL_1) during the mid-luteal phase and then rise progressively to a high concentration (3-4 ng mL_1) during the last day or

two of the cycle (Hauger et al., 1977). According to evidence reported by Goodman et al. (1980), it would seem that oestradiol contributes to the determination of LH levels in two ways; by acting alone in the late cycle (follicular phase) in partially suppressing tonic LH and in the luteal phase by acting in concert with progesterone in controlling LH. These two effects of oestradiol, together with the known inhibitory effects of progesterone on LH levels (Baird and Scaramuzzi, 1976; Karsh et al., 1977) would seem to account for the way in which tonic LH is secreted during the sheep's cycle (Karsh et al., 1980); it is believed that ovarian secretions other than oestradiol and progesterone play little, if any, physiologically important role in controlling tonic LH in the ewe.

11.5.2 Oestrogen levels

In addition to the preovulatory secretion of oestradiol, already mentioned, there is evidence of fluctuations in oestrogen concentration during the oestrous cycle, the steroid being produced in the ovarian follicles, several waves of which develop and undergo atresia during the course of the 16–17 day period (Scaramuzzi et al., 1970; Smeaton and Robertson, 1971; Baird and Scaramuzzi, 1976); it is believed that ovulation of all but one or two Graafian follicles in the fourth and final wave of the cycle is inhibited by the presence of a functional corpus luteum (Robertson, 1977).

11.5.3 FSH levels

As to the role of FSH in events during the cycle, that is by no means clearly defined at this stage (Goodman et al., 1981). Higher plasma levels of FSH around day-13 of the cycle have been reported by Brien et al. (1976) and have been related to the occurrence of twin rather than single ovulations in the sheep examined. The factors controlling release of FSH have been the subject of some debate in the literature. A highly specific ovine FSH RIA procedure reported by Bolt (1980) has provided evidence of two different control mechanisms for FSH and LH operating during the oestrous cycle; one control system, presumably acting via a hypothalamic releasing hormone, appears to regulate large sudden changes, that affect LH secretion more than FSH; the second control, presumably acting by way of ovarian oestrogen, regulates the gradual changes that occur in FSH and LH levels in a similar way.

11.6 HORMONAL EVENTS IN THE EWE ANOESTRUS

As already mentioned, a major restriction to intensifying lamb production is imposed by the seasonal anoestrus in ewes. For that reason, in the various attempts made to increase the productivity of sheep, studies have been conducted to determine how environmental and other factors modify ovarian activity as assessed by different criteria. The general view is that daylength is the predominant environmental factor regulating breeding activity. There have been experiments reported by several workers showing that decreasing daylengths promote the onset of the sexual season whereas increasing daylengths hasten the start of anoestrus. The hormonal basis for the way in which the breeding activity of the ewe begins and ends is still not clear, although information is accumulating rapidly.

11.6.1 LH levels in anoestrus

During the ewe anoestrus, is is known that ovarian follicles develop, produce steroids and are capable of ovulating; many of the positive and negative feedback effects of ovarian steroids on secretion of LH continue as in the autumn breeding season (Cole and Miller, 1935; Hutchinson and Robertson, 1966; Goding et al., 1969; Karsh and Foster, 1975; Scaramuzzi and Baird, 1977). Nevertheless, despite many similarities in the way the ovarian steroids and pituitary gonadotrophins interact, cyclical breeding activity ceases in the anoestrus.

Evidence reviewed by Legan and Karsh (1979) suggests that anoestrus is not primarily a result of a deficiency in the LH surge mechanism; it is not a result of a change in the behavioural patterns exhibited at oestrus nor due to an absence of oestradiol production. The essential difference appears to be in the lack of a sustained increase in

tonic LH secretion which normally follows the decrease of progesterone in the cyclic ewe. It has been suggested that seasonal anoestrus is a result of light-induced changes in the sensitivity of the hypothalamic–pituitary axis to the negative feedback action of ovarian steroids and workers at Michigan in the U.S.A. suggest that the main change is an increased response to the negative feedback action of oestradiol on tonic LH (Legan et al., 1977; Legan and Karsh, 1979).

According to this explanation, once the last corpus luteum of the breeding season starts to regress, tonic LH secretion would rise, leading to an increase in follicular oestradiol; unlike in the cyclic ewe, however, this elevated oestradiol level would inhibit secretion by its negative feedback action, thereby preventing the normal occurrence of the sustained, 48 h rise in tonic LH secretion. Michigan workers have presented evidence showing that changes in the response of the hypothalamic–pituitary axis to this negative feedback action of oestradiol is governed with considerable precision by the environmental photoperiod (Legan and Karsh, 1979); short days were associated with the breeding season and high tonic LH levels, long days with anoestrus and low LH levels, even when artificial light regimes were completely out-of-phase with the natural environmental photoperiod.

11.6.2 Changes in frequency of LH pulses

The tonic secretion of LH in the sheep is pulsatile and it is known that pulses are more frequent in the breeding season than they are during anoestrus ; these LH pulses are followed by corresponding pulses of ovarian oestrogen (Scaramuzzi and Baird, 1976) and seasonal changes in the sensitivity of the hypothalamus to negative feedback presumably limit the frequency of the LH pulses. Thus, as noted by Brinkley (1981) for a ewe to pass from the anoestrous to the cyclic condition, the longer intervals between LH pulses have to shorten to increase the growth of follicles and to aid in the production of oestradiol; the oestrogen eventually triggers the release of the preovulatory LH surge and ovulation occurs. Subsequently, the sequence of events necessary for a succession of oestrous cycles is continued until events once more alter the frequency of the LH pulses and bring the breeding season to an end.

Although the seasonal changes in the feedback effects of oestradiol observed by Legan and Karsh (1979) may well occur, the precise relationship of such changes to variations in the photoperiodic environment may be questioned on the basis of evidence obtained elsewhere with the intact ewe. Work at Cambridge (Latitude 52°N) by Speedy (1973) showed that sheep maintained on a constant 8-h daylength from the natural shortest day (21 December) onwards ceased breeding activity no later than ewes exposed to the normal increase in daylength; the same author also showed that no light treatment, even a pattern completely the reverse of the natural for the latitude, would induce oestrous cycles earlier than the end of May. If the light environment usually influences the hypothalamic–pituitary axis as precisely as occurred in the ewes dealt with by Legan and Karsh (1979) it might have been expected that the Cambridge results would be different.

Elsewhere, studies with ewes born and reared under a 24 h continuous light regimen have shown, in the presence of a ram, fairly regular periods of sexual activity interspersed with periods of anoestrus (Robertson, 1977). As observed by Owen (1976), it appears likely that there is an inherent physiological mechanism in the ewe which creates a rhythmical pattern and that no one external factor, such as photoperiodism, can completely control breeding activity without there being some alternation between a sexual and non-sexual season.

11.6.3 Prolactin levels

There are several reports showing that anoestrus is associated with elevated levels of prolactin (Walton et al., 1977; Rhind et al., 1978; McNeilly and Land, 1979; McNeilly et al., 1980; Schanbacher, 1980). The possibility that increased prolactin concentrations in the ewe anoestrus may directly affect the function of the sheep's corpus luteum was examined by McNeilly and Land (1979) who were unable to confirm an earlier observation by Rhind et al.

(1978) that high levels of prolactin directly inhibit progesterone secretion by that organ. Schanbacher (1980) reported that exposure of anoestrous ewes to artificially shortened daylengths or treatment with the drug ergocryptine reduced the high prolactin concentrations found in the sheep; McNeilly et al. (1980) concluded that the problem of anoestrus was basically a failure in the normal preovulatory development of ovarian follicles due to an inadequate frequency of LH pulses rather than to difficulties arising from prolactin.

11.6.4 FSH levels

Although it is true that ovarian follicular development is arrested during the ewe anoestrus, the results of several studies would indicate that FSH levels are not significantly different in anoestrous sheep from those in the cyclic animal (Walton et al., 1977; McNeilly et al., 1980).

11.6.5 First cycle of season

It should be mentioned that at the start of the breeding season in sheep, it is only after the end of the first ovarian cycle that behavioural oestrus is exhibited by the animal. The initial ovulations of the season, and the establishment of corpora lutea occur at a "silent" heat (Grant, 1933; Cole and Miller, 1935; Roux, 1936). It is now well accepted that progesterone produced by these first corpora lutea, plays an essential role in sensitizing hypothalamic receptors so that the ewe becomes capable of responding subsequently to minute quantities of ovarian oestrogen and exhibiting the behavioural symptoms of oestrus (Robinson, 1959).

11.7 ENDOCRINE EVENTS IN THE RAM

Although, as previously mentioned, Suffolk rams in Ireland and the U.K. do not apparently show a lack of libido nor any serious reduction in fertility during the ewe anoestrus (Gordon, 1958, 1963), distinct seasonal changes in reproductive ability and behaviour have been recorded in the primitive Soay breed Lincoln, 1976a-c; Lincoln and Davidson, 1977). These changes in the Soay can be related to specific hormonal events which can be controlled by way of the photoperiodic environment (Lincoln, 1976a-c).

Fig. 11.2. Suffolk ram at work during the summer months. Studies conducted in the U.K. and Ireland over a period of years have failed to provide evidence of seriously reduced breeding performance in Suffolk rams during the summer months although some semen characteristics may vary from the values recorded in the autumn season.

11.7.1 Pulsatile release of LH

In the mature ram, LH is released from the pituitary in pulses which occur every few hours at random throughout the day; in the peripheral plasma, this is reflected in the form of transitory surges in LH concentration (Katongole et al., 1974; Sandford et al., 1974). This episodic secretory pattern of LH develops at puberty (Foster, 1974) and in Soay rams has been shown to change in relation to the breeding season (Lincoln, 1976a) and to be capable of alteration by manipulation of the photoperiod (Lincoln, 1976b). Each pulse of LH is known to be related to a corresponding episodic release of Gn-RH, which is presumed to be the result of the agent being released from the Gn-RH secretory neurones.

As mentioned earlier, Soay rams show much more pronounced seasonal changes in reproductive ability compared with the normal commercial breeds, such as the Suffolk; this is reflected in the fact that the Soay's testes regress

under long daylengths to about 20% of their maximum size (Lincoln et al., 1977). Even in the Soay ram, as already noted for the female sheep, there is evidence that an inherent reproductive cycle operates; Lincoln and Davidson (1977) found it necessary to envisage the role of the photoperiod in sheep as being to control the time of the sexual season rather than the cause of it. Under normal circumstances, the stimulatory (autumn) and inhibitory (spring) effects of daylength would serve to align the breeding season to these changes in the environment. Results in work at Nottingham by Howles et al. (1980) have shown that testicular growth and regression occurred under conditions of a constant photoperiod.

11.7.2 Prolactin concentrations

In the ram, as in the ewe, conspicuous changes in the blood levels of prolactin are known to occur during the year, the highest levels occurring during the summer months and the lowest concentrations in the winter (Ravault, 1976). The timings of these seasonal changes can be readily modified by alteration of the photoperiod. There is some evidence that daylength regimes which favour prolactin secretion (long days) have the reverse effect on gonadotrophin secretion (Pelletier and Ortavant, 1975; Lincoln et al., 1977) and under natural daylight conditions, therefore, the implication is that there is an inverse relationship between prolactin levels and the release of gonadotrophins. In all this, it is necessary to keep in mind that the findings obtained in primitive breeds such as the Soay may not operate to the same degree in the improved commercial breeds. However, those reading the literature, may not see this distinction to be as obvious as, in practice, it probably is.

11.7.3 Seasonal changes in semen production

McKenzie and Berliner (1937) in the U.S.A. were among the first to report seasonal variations in both the production and quality of ram semen.

The number of sperm ejaculated and the percentage of abnormal cells was found to vary according to a definite seasonal pattern. The incidence of abnormal sperm was highest and sperm density lowest during the warm summer months; similar results were reported by other American authors (Green, 1940; Comstock *et al.*, 1945; Cupps *et al.*, 1960), but it should be remembered that the temperature component of the environment may have been an important factor in determining semen quality. Smyth and Gordon (1967) in an examination of semen production in rams throughout the year, did find evidence of seasonal fluctuations, but as already mentioned, not to the extent that these would render the ram incapable of an acceptable breeding performance in the spring and summer period.

Table 11.1 *Seasonal variation in the total sperm per ejaculate. From Smyth and Gordon (1967).*

Breed	Total sperm ejaculated ($\times 10^9$ per collection)			
	Autumn	Winter	Spring	Summer
Galway	3.78	3.65	3.01	2.49
Suffolk	3.84	3.47	2.51	1.69
Wicklow	3.58	3.32	1.62	1.99
Dorset Horn	4.10	3.91	3.22	3.01

In France, using tracer techniques, Ortavant (1954) reported that in the ram testes, the rate of division of primary spermatocytes and time of subsequent maturation are relatively unaffected by the photoperiod but that the number of spermatids which survive the complete maturation is affected; under conditions of increasing daylength, the failure rate in spermatids was found to be high. Later studies by the same author (Ortavant, 1977) reported that a 12 h photoperiod provided the optimal short-term light stimulus for spermatogenesis in the ram; it was evident, however, that the maintenance of constant daylengths for periods up to 40 days resulted in a decline in sperm production.

11.7.4 Ewe and Ram breeding seasons

The ewe of normal commercial sheep breeds shows a clear non-breeding season, whereas the ram remains capable of reproduction throughout the year, although many aspects of reproductive activity in rams and ewes are controlled at least in part by the same underlying variables; the same gonadotrophins which control the development of follicles and ovulation in the ewe are responsible for sperm production and libido in the ram, in fact, apart from the one sex chromosome, the genotype of a sheep is independent of its sex and all autosomal genes controlling gonadotrophin production are common to both sexes. Much more needs to be examined in both ewes and rams in order to explain why reproduction halts in the ewe but not in the ram at certain times.

11.8 REFERENCES

Alwachi, S. N., Bland, K. P. and Poyser, N. L. (1979) Uterine prostaglandin $F_{2\alpha}$ and E_2 production and content during the second half of the oestrous cycle of the sheep — possible local control of the uterus by the ovary. *Prostaglandins Med.* **3,** 23–32.

Asdell, S. A. (1964) Patterns of Mammalian Reproduction. *Cornell Univ. Press,* Ithaca, N.Y.

Baird, D. T. (1978) Pulsatile secretion of LH and ovarian estradiol during the follicular phase of the sheep estrous cycle. *Biol. Reprod.* **18,** 359–364.

Baird, D. T. and Scaramuzzi, R. J. (1976) Changes in the secretion of ovarian steroids and pituitary luteinizing hormone in the peri-ovulatory period in the ewe: The effect of progesterone. *J. Endocr.* **70,** 237–245.

Bichard, N., Younis, A. A., Forrest, P. A. and Cumberland, P. H. (1974) Analysis of production research from a lowland flock. *Anim. Prod.* **19,** 177–191.

Bindon, B. M., Blanc, M. R., Pelletier, J., Terqui, M. and Thimonier J. (1975) Preovulatory gonadotrophin and ovarian steroid changes in French Sheep breeds different infecundity. Does FSH stimulate follicles? *Proc. Endocr. Soc. Aust. 18th Ann. Meet.* **18,** 64.

Bjersing, L., Hay, M. F., Kann, G., Moor, R. M., Naftolin, F., Scaramuzzi, R. J. Short, R. V. and Younglai, E. V. (1972). Changes in gonadotrophins, ovarian steroids and follicular morphology in sheep at oestrus. *J. Endocr.* **53**(3), 465–479.

Bland, K. P., Horton, E. W. and Ooyser, N. L. (1971) Levels of prostaglandin $F_{2\alpha}$ in the uterine venous blood of sheep during oestrous cycle. *Life Sci.* **10,** 509.

Bolt, D. J. (1980) Homologous radioimmunoassay for ovine FSH. *J. Anim. Sci.* **51** (Suppl. 1), 261–262.

Brien, R. D., Baxter, R. W., Findlay, J. K. and Cumming, I. A. (1976) Effect of Lupin Grain Supplementation on ovulation rate and plasma follicle stimulation hormone (FSH) concentration in maiden and mature Merino ewes. *Proc. Aust. Soc. Anim. Prod.* **11,** 237–244.

Brinkley, H. J. (1981) Endocrine signaling and female reproduction. *Biol. Reprod.* **24,** 22–43.

Cole, H. H., Miller, R. F. (1935) Changes in the reproductive organs of the ewe with some data bearing on their control. *Am. J. Anat.* **57,** 39.

Comtock, R. D., Green, W. W., Winters, L. M. and Nordskog, A. W. (1945) Studies of semen and semen production. *Tech. Bull. Minn. Agr. Exp. Sta.* No. 162.

Cox, R. A., Mattner, P. E., Shutt, D. A. and Thorburn, G. D. (1971) Ovarian secretion of oestradiol during the oestrous cycle in the ewe. *J. Reprod. Fert.* **24,** 133–134.

Crosby, T. F. and Gordon, I. (1971) II. Timing of nuclear maturation in oocytes cultured in growth medium. *J. Agric. Sci., Camb.* **76,** 373–374.

Cumming, I. A., Brown, J. M., Blockey, M. A. and Goding, J. R. (1971) Regulation of the oestrous cycle in the ewe. *J. Reprod. Fert.* **24,** 148–149.

Cumming, I. A., Brown, J. M., Cerini, J. G., Cerini, M. E., Chamley, W. A., Findaly, J. K. and Goding, J. R. (1973) Ovine luteinizing hormone release induced by a synthetic gonadotrohpin-releasing factor. *J. Reprod. Fert.* **32,** 340.

Cunningham, N. F., Symons, A. M. and Saba, N. (1975) Levels progesterone, LH and FSH in the plasma of sheep during the oestrous cycle. *J. Reprod. Fert.* **45,** 177–180.

Cupps, P. T., McGowran, D. F., Rahlman, A. R., Reddon, A. and Weir, W. C. (1960) Seasonal changes in the semen of rams. *J. Anim. Sci.* **16,** 328.

Deane, H. W., Hay, M. F., Moor, R. N., Rowson, L. E. A. and Short, R. V. (1966) The corpus luteum of sheep; the relationships between morphology and function during the oestrous cycle. *Acta Endocrin. Copenh.* **51,** 245–000.

Dziuk, P. J. (1965(Response of sheep and swine to treatments for control of ovulation. *Prof. Conf. Oestrous Cycle to Control in Domestic Animals, Nebraska, 1904, USDA Misc. Publ.* **1005,** 28–38.

Edgar, D. G. and Ronaldson, J. W. (1958) Blood levels of progesterone in the ewe. *J. Endocr.* **16,** 378.

Fletcher, I. C. and Lindsay, D. R. (1971) Effect of rams on duration of oestrous behaviour in ewes. *J. Reprod. Fert.* **25,** 253–259

Foster, D. L. (1974) Regulation of gonadotrophins during foetal and early postnatal development in the sheep. *INSERM,* **32,** 143–156.

Foster, D. L. and Karsch, F. J. (1975) Development of the mechanism regulating the preovulatory surge of luteinizing hormone in sheep. *Endocrin.* **97,** 1205–1209.

Ginther, O. J. (1969) Length of estrus cycle and size of corpus luteum in guinea pigs and sheep treated with progesterone at different days of estrous cycle. *Am. J. Vet. Res.* **30,** 1975–1978.

Goding, J. R. (1973) The demonstration that PGF$_{2\alpha}$ is the uterine luteolysin in the ewe. In, *Le Corps jaune, Denamur, R., Netler, A. (Ed.)* pp. 311–323.

Goding, J. R. (1974) The demonstration that PDG$_{2\alpha}$ is the uterine leteolysin in the ewe. *J. Reprod. Fert.* **38,** 261–271.

Goding, J. R., Catt, K. J., Brown, J. N., Kaltenbach, C. C., Cumming, I. A. and Mole, B. J. (1969) RIA for ovine LH Secretion of LH during oestrus and following oestrogen administration in the sheep. *Endocrin.* **85,** 133–142.

Goding, J. R., Blockey, M. A., Brown, J. M., Catt, K. J. and Cumming, I. A. (1970) The role or oestrogen in the control of the oestrous cycle in the ewe. *J. Reprod. Fert.* **21,** 368–369.

Goodman, R. L., Legan, S. J., Ryan, K. D., Foster, D. L. and Karsch, F. J. (1980) Two effects of estradiol that normally contribute to the control of tonic LH secretion in the ewe. *Biol. Reprod.,* **23,** 415–422.

Goodman, R. L., Pickover, S. M. and Karsch, F. J. (1981),

Ovarian feedback control of FSH in the ewe: evidence for selective suppression. *Endocrin.,* **108,** 772–777.

Gordon, I. (1958) Studies in the extra-seasonal production of lambs. *J. Agric. Sci., Camb.* **50,** 152.

Gordon, I. (1963) II. Progesterone-PMS applications in anoestrus. *J. Agric. Sci., Camb.* **60,** 43.

Grant, R. (1933) Occurrence at ovulation without heat in the ewe. *Nature, Lond.* **131,** 802.

Grant, R. (1934) Studies on the physiology of reproduction in the ewe. *Trans. R. Soc. Edinb.* **50,** 1.

Green, W. W. (1940) Seasonal trends of sperm cell bypes in sheep. *Proc. Am. Soc. Anim. Prod.* **207.**

Hafez, E. S. E. (1952) Studies on the breeding season and reproduction of the ewe. *J. Agric. Sci., Camb.* **42,** 189.

Hammond, J., Jr. (1944) On the breeding season in the sheep. *J. Agric. Sci., Camb.* **34,** 97–105.

Hansel, W. (1975) Luteal regression in domestic animals. *Ann. Biol. Anim. Bioch. Biophys.* **15,** 147–160.

Haugher, R. L., Karsh, F. J. and Foster, D. L. (1977) A new concept for control of the estrous cycle of the ewe vased on the temporal relationships between luteinizing hormone, estradiol and progesterone in peripheral serum. *Endocr.* **101,** 807.

Holst, P. J. and Braden, A. W. H. (1972) Ovum transport in the ewe. *Aust. J. Biol. Sci.* **25,** 167–173.

Howles, C. M., Webster, G. M. and Haynes, N. B. (1980) The effect of rearing under a long or short photoperiod on testis growth, plasma testosterone and prolactin concentrations, and the development of sexual behaviour in rams. *J. Reprod. Fert.* **60,** 437–447.

Hulet, C. V., Alexander, G. and Hafez, E. S. E. (1975) The behaviour of sheep, In, *The Behaviour of Domestic Animals.* (3rd ed.) Hafez, E. S. E., (Ed.) Bailliere, Tindall, London, 246–294.

Hutchinson, J. S. M. and Robertson, H. A. (1966) The corpus luteum in sheep. *Res. Vet. Sci.* **7,** 17.

Inkster, I. J. (1957) The mating behaviour of sheep. In, *Sheep Farming Annual, Massey College, N.Z.* 163.

Karsch, F. J. and Foster, D. L. (1975) Sexual differentiation of the mechanism controlling the preovulatory discharge of luteinizing hormone in sheep. *Endocrin.* **97,** 373–379.

Karsch, F. J., Legan, S. J., Haugher, R. L. and Foster, D. L. (1977) Negative feedback action of progesterone on tonic LH secretion in the ewe: dependence on the ovaries. *Endocrin.* **101,** 800–806.

Katongole, C. B., Naftolin, F. and Short, R. V. (1974) Seasonal variations in blood LH and testosterone levels in rams. *J. Endocrin.* **60,** 101–106.

Lamond, D. R., Gaddy, R. G. and Kennedy, S. W. (1972) Influence of season and nutrition on luteal plasma progesterone in rambouillet ewes. *J. Anim. Sci.* **34,** 626–629.

Land, R. B., Pelletier, J., Thimonier, J. and Mauleon, P. (1973) A quantitative study of genetic differences in the incidence of oestrus, ovulation and plasma LH concentration in the sheep. *J. Endocrin.* **58,** 305–317.

Legan, S. J. and Karsch F. J. (1979) Neuroendocrine regulation of the estrous cycle and seasonal breeding in the ewe. *Biol. Reprod.* **20,** 74–85.

Legan, S. K., Karsch, F. J. and Foster, D. L. (1977) The endocrine control of seasonal reproductive function in the ewe: a marked changed in response to the negative feedback action of estradiol on LH secretion. *Endocrin.* **101,** 818–824.

Lincoln, G. A. (1976a) Secretion of LH in rams exposed to two different photoperiods. *J. Reprod. Fert.* **47,** 351–353.

Lincoln, G. A. (1976b) Seasonal variation in the episodic

secretion of luteinizing hormone and testosterone in the ram. *J. Endocrin.* **69,** 213–226.

Lincoln, G. A. (1976c) Photoperiodic control of reproduction in the ram: Time-lags from stimulus to response. *Ann. Biol. Anim. Biochim. Biophys.* **16**(2), 170.

Lincoln, G. A. and Davidson, W. (1977) The relationship between sexual and aggressive behaviour, and pituitary and testicular activity during the seasonal sexual cycle of rams, and the influence of photoperiod. *J. Reprod. Fert.* **49,** 267.

Lincoln, G. A., Peet, M. J. and Cunningham, R. A. (1977) Seasonal and circadian changes in the the episodic release of follicular-stimulating hormone, luteinizing hormone and tesosterone in rams exposed to artificial photoperiods. *J. Endocrin.* **72,** 337–349.

Lindsay, D. R. and Fletcher, I. C. (1972) Ram-seeking activity associated with oestrous behaviour in ewes. *Anim. Behav.* **20,** 452–456.

Lindsay, D. R., Cognie, Y., Pelletier, J. and Signoret, J. P. (1975) Influence of the presence of rams on the timing of ovulation and discharge of LH in ewes. *Physiol. Behav.* **15,** 423–426.

McCracken, J. A., Glen M. E. and Scaramuzzi, R. J. (1970) Corpus luteum regression induced by protaglandin $F_{2\alpha}$ *J. Clin. Endocr. Metab.* **30,** 544.

McKenzie, F. F. and Berliner, V. (1937) The reproductive capacity of rams. *Res. Bull. Mo. Agric. Exp. Sta.* No. 265.

McKenzie, F. F. and Terrill, C. E. (1937) Estrus, ovulation and related phenomena in the ewe. *Res. Bull. Mo. Agric. Exp. Sta.* No. 264.

McNeilly, A. S. and Land, R. B. (1979) Effect of suppression of plasma prolactin on ovulation, plasma gonadotrophins and corpus luteum function in LH-RH-treated anoestrous ewes. *J. Reprod. Fert.* **56,** 601–609.

McNeilly, A. S., O'Connell, M. and Baird, D. T. (1980) Induction of ovulation by pulsatile injection of LH in anoestrus ewes. *Biol. Reprod.* **22,** (Suppl. 1) 48a.

Obst, J.M., Seamark, F. R. and Brown, J. M. (1971) Application of a competitive protein binding assay for oestrogens to the study of ovarian function in sheep. *J. Reprod. Fert.* **24,** 140.

Ortavant, R. (1954) Contribution a l'etade de la dvice de processus sperm-atogenetique de believ a laide de P.$_{32}$ C.R. Soc. Biol. Paris, **148,** 866.

Ortavant, R. (1977) Photoperiodic regulation of reproduction in the sheep. *Proc. Symp. Manage. of Reprod. in Sheep and Goats, Univ. Wisconsin. Madison.* pp. 58–71.

Owen, J. B. (1976) *Sheep Production.* Bailliere Tindall, London.

Parsons, S. D. and Hunter, G. L. (1967) Effect of the ram on duration of oestrus in the ewe. *J. Reprod. Fert.* **14,** 61.

Parsons, S. D., Hunter, G. L. and Ravner, A. A. (1967) Use of probit analysis in a study of the effect of the ram on time of ovulation in the ewe. *J. Reprod. Fert.* **14,** 71–80.

Pelletier, J. and Ortavant, R. (1975) Photoperiodic control of LH release in the ram. *Acta. Endocr.* **78,** 442–450.

Quirke, J. F. and Gosling, J. (1976) Progesterone levels throughout the oestrous cycle in three ewe breeds with different ovulation rates. Proc. 8th Int. Congr. Anim. Reprod. AI (Kracow) **3,** 180–183.

Quirke, J. F., Hanrahan, J. P. and Gosling, J. P. (1979) Plasma progesterone levels throughout the oestrous cycle and release of LH at oestrus in sheep with different ovulation rates. *J. Reprod. Fert.* **55,** 37–44.

Ravault, J. P. (1976) Prolactin in the ram: seasonal variations in the concentration of blood plasma from birth until three years old. *Acta. Endocr.* **83,** 720–725.

Restall, B. J. (1964) The growth retrogression of the corpus luteum in the ewe. *Aust. J. Exp. Agric. Anim. Husb.* **4,** 274.

Rhind, S. M., Chesworth, J. M. and Robinson, J. J. (1978) A seasonal difference in ovine peripheral plasma prolactin and progesterone concentrations in early pregnancy and in the relationship between the ewe hormones. *J. Reprod. Fert.* **52,** 79–81.

Robertson, H. A. (1977) Reproduction in the ewe and the goat. In, *Reproduction in Domestic Animals.* 3rd Ed. Cole and Cupps, Ed., Academic Press, NY, pp. 475–498.

Robinson, T. J. (1959) Estrous cycle of the ewe and doe. In, *Reproduction in Domestic Animals,* Cole and Cupps, Ed, Acad. press, New York.

Roux, L. L. (1936) Sex physiology of sheep. *Onderstepoort J. Vet. Sci. Anim. Ind.* **6,** 465.

Sandford, L. M., Winter, J. S. D., Palmer, W. M. and Howland, B. E. (1974) The profile of LH and testosterone secretion in the ram. *Endocrin.* **95,** 627–631.

Scaramuzzi, R. J. and Baird, D. T. (1976) The oestrous cycle of the ewe after active immunization against prostaglandin $F_{2\alpha}$. *J. Reprod. Fert.* **46,** 39–47.

Scaramuzzi, R. J. and Baird, D. T. (1977) Pulsatile release of LH and the secretion of ovarian steriods in sheep anoestrus. *Endocrin.* **101,** 1801–1806.

Scaramuzzi, R. J. and Land, R. B. (1978) Oestradiol levels in sheep plasma during the oestrous cycle. *J. Reprod. Fert.* **53,** 167–171.

Scaramuzzi, R. J., Caldwell, V. B. and Moor, R. M. (1970) RIA of LH and estrogen during the estrous cycle of the ewe. *Biol. Reprod.* **3,** 110–119.

Scaramuzzi, R. J., Tillson, S. A., Thorneycroft, I. H. and Caldwell, B. V. (1971) Action of exogenous progesterone and estrogen on the behavioural estrous and LH levels in the ovariectomized ewe. *Endocrin.* **88,** 1184–1189.

Schanbacher, B. (1980) Relationship of daylength and prolactin to resumption of reproductive activity in anestrous ewes. *J. Anim. Sci.* **50,** 293–297.

Short, R. V. (1964) *Rec. Prog. Hormone Res.* **20,** 303.

Signoret, J. P. (1975) Influence of the presence of rams on the luteinizing hormone surge after oestradiol benzoate injection in ovariectomized ewes. *J. Endocrin.* **64,** 589–590.

Smeaton, T. C. and Robertson H. A. (1971) Studies on the growth and atresia of graafian follicles in the ovary of the sheep. *J. Reprod. Fert.* **25,** 243–252.

Smith, J. F. and Robinson, T. J. (1970) *J. Endocrin.* **48,** 485–496.

Smyth, P. and Gordon, I. (1967) Seasonal and breed variations in the semen characteristics of rams in Ireland. *Ir. vet. J.* **21,** 222–233.

Speedy, A. W. (1973) Increasing the frequency of lambing in sheep. *Ph.D. Thesis, Univ. of Cambridge.*

Stabenfeldt, G. H., Ewing, L. L. and McDonald, L. E. (1969) Peripheral plasma progesterone levels during the bovine oestrous cycle. *J. Reprod. Fert.* **19,** 433–442.

Thimonier, J. and Pelletier, J. (1971) Differences genetique dons la decharge ovulante (LH) chez les brebis de race Ile-de-France: relations avec le nombre d'ovulations. *Ann. Biol. Anim. Biochim. Biophys.* **11,** 559–567.

Thorburn, G. D., Bassett, J. M. and Smith, I. D. (1969) Progesterone concentration in the peripheral plasma of sheep during the oestrus cycle. *J. Endocrin.* **45,** 459–469.

Thwaites, C. J. (1971) Exogenous progesterone and oestrous cycle length in the ewe. *J. Agric. Sci., Camb.* **77,** 147–149.

Van der Westhuysen, J. M., Van Niekerk, C. H. and Hunter, G. L. (1970) Duration of oestrus and time of ovulation in sheep. Effect of synchronization season and ram. *Agroanimalia* **2,** 131–137.

Walton, J. S., McNeilly, J. R., McNeilly, A. S. and Cunningham, F. J. (1977) Changes in concentrations of FSH, LH, prolactin and progesterone in the plasma of ewes during the transition from anoestrus to breeding activity. *J. Endocr.* **75,** 127–136.

Warbritton, V. (1934) The cytology of the corpora lutea of the ewe. *J. Morphol.* **56,** 181–202.

Williams, S. M., Garrigus, U. S., Norton, H. W. and Nalbandov, A. V. (1956) The occurrence of oestrus in pregnant ewes. *J. Anim. Sci.* **15,** 978–983.

Wilson, L. Jr., Cenedella, R. J., Butcher, R. L. and Inskeep, E. K. (1972) Levels of prostaglandins in the uterine endometrium during the ovine estrous cycle. *J. Anim. Sci.* **34,** 93–99.

Younis, A. A. and Afifi, E. A. (1979) On the occurrence of oestrus in pregnant Barki and Merino ewes. *J. Agric. Sci., Camb.* **92,** 505–506.

CHAPTER 12

Artificial Control of Oestrus and Ovulation

12.1 INTRODUCTION

Attempts to control oestrus and ovulation in sheep, whether in the full breeding season or in the ewe's anoestrus, are usually based on trying to simulate the activity of the cyclic sheep's corpus luteum, especially its action in producing progesterone in quantity for about 2 weeks and in shutting off production sharply and completely at the end of the oestrous cycle. In most out-of-season applications, it is also considered essential to augment the supply of endogenous gonado-trophin by administering a follicle-stimulating agent on completion of the progestagen treatment. The cheapest, most readily available and consistently effective gonadotrophin for this purpose is PMSG.

Up until 1964, most attempts at controlled breeding in sheep involved repeated doses of progesterone or oral administrations of potent progestagens; the time and labour involved in giving these agents constituted a serious obstacle to any general acceptance of the techniques. Some discussion of the limitations of injection and oral methods of administration is attempted elsewhere (Gordon, 1971a); in brief, it is difficult to achieve a smooth steady input of progestagen or to get a sharp predictable end-point by such procedures.

Progestagen administration was eventually made commercially feasible by the work of Robinson and his associates at Sydney (Robinson, 1964) using the progestagen impregnated sponge inserted intravaginally. The subsequent monograph by Robinson and colleagues contained an impressive analysis of factors involved in oestrus control by progestagens (Robinson, 1967). Although initial laboratory trials established that a high level of fertility was possible in cyclic Merino ewes after intravaginal treatment, the subsequent outcome of widespread field testing in Australia was far from satisfactory. In retrospect, it now appears that much of the low fertility observed was a result of the testing being carried out in severe drought years, which markedly influenced the nutritional environment, sponges with less than adequate doses of progestagen were used in many instances and semen for the AI was often extended to the limit (Robinson, 1974, 1976).

This Australian experience serves to illustrate the important principle that controlled breeding techniques should only be applied in the appropriate feeding, breeding and management setting. Certainly in Ireland, and probably elsewhere, because of these unforeseen problems associated with the intravaginal sponge technique, there was some tendency to dismiss the method as being of little commercial value. As subsequent events proved, this assessment was premature, and the progestagen impregnated sponge is the cornerstone in almost all controlled breeding applications in France, Ireland, the U.K. and many other countries.

12.2 PROSTAGLANDINS AND ANALOGUES

As already mentioned, there is good evidence that during the ovulatory cycle of the ewe, prostaglandin $F_{2\alpha}$ synthesized in and released from the uterus, causes regression of the corpus luteum (McCracken et al., 1970; Goding, 1974). The literature that is available on the use of prostaglandins in cyclic sheep however, in comparison to that in cattle, is as yet limited. Early reports included those of Douglas and Ginther (1973) and Hawk (1973) who observed that doses of 10–15 mg $PGF_{2\alpha}$ in a single intramuscular injection could induce regression of the corpus luteum and result in oestrus control in cyclic sheep. Workers elsewhere have also shown that a dose of 100 μg (Trounson et al., 1976) or 125 μg (Fairnie et al., 1976) of the analogue Cloprostenol was effective in inducing luteal regression in the sheep.

12.2.1 Natural vs induced regression of corpus luteum

From the several reports which have already appeared on the ultrastructure and function of

sheep corpora lutea in the normal cycle and after prostaglandin treatment (Umo, 1974; Corteel, 1975; Gemmell et al., 1976; McClellan et al., 1976; Stacy et al., 1976) there are indications that $PGF_{2\alpha}$ treatment can have a very rapid and dramatic effect on steroid synthesis in the lutein cells, whereas normal luteolysis would seem to involve more gradual degenerative changes. A single injection of 100 μg of the analogue Cloprostenol has been shown to result in a fall in plasma progesterone concentrations from 3.1 ng/ml to 0.9 ng/ml within a period of a few hours (Acritopoulou et al., 1977). Such considerations may have relevance in explaining the oestrous response and fertility of sheep after this form of treatment; there is evidence that fertility can be quite variable when ewes are bred after oestrus synchronization (Hawk and Conley, 1975; Jennings, 1975; Fairnie et al., 1976; Haresign, 1976; Lightfoot et al., 1976; Trounson et al., 1976; Boland et al., 1978).

12.2.2 Responsive period

The corpus luteum of the ewe is only responsive to prostaglandin between about day 4 and 14 of the oestrous cycle (Chamley et al., 1972; Douglas and Ginther, 1973; Acritopoulou et al., 1977); to ensure that all sheep in the flock are at an appropriate stage of the oestrous cycle to respond, the usual recommendation is that two PG doses should be given 9 or 10 days apart (Haresign, 1978, 1980). Reports show that oestrus occurs about 40 h after PG with ovulation taking place about 70 h from the time of administering the agent (Acritopoulou et al., 1977, 1978; Acritopoulou and Haresign, 1980).

12.2.3 Interval between PG doses

Australian investigators have found evidence that the time interval between the two PG doses may influence fertility. In studies reported by Fairnie et al. (1978), fertility in sheep treated with two doses of 125 μg Cloprostenol at 12 day intervals was much lower than in other groups treated at 14–15 day intervals; there was also an earlier report showing that very poor fertility resulted from ewes treated with two PG doses spaced 8 days apart compared to a 14-day interval (Fairnie et al., 1977). These Australian workers conclude that the time interval between the two PG doses is critical and should not be reduced to less than 13–14 days, otherwise acceptable fertility to breeding by AI may not be achieved; this limitation markedly reduces the way in which prostaglandin or its analogues can be employed in AI programmes as currently practised in West Australia. If a 14-day interval is used, then the problem is that the two-dose PG application may not find all ewes responsive to the second injection.

12.2.4 Dose levels of PG

In comparison with the oestrous response after progestagen treatment in ewes, that which follows PG may be much lower (Boland et al., 1978) regardless of whether PG was administered at 9 or 14 day intervals. There has been some evidence that the oestrous response may be influenced by PG dose level. In Canada, studies reported by Hackett and Robertson (1980) have shown that a dose of 20 mg $PGF_{2\alpha}$ induced oestrus in all sheep treated between day 4 and 15, as compared to only 70% when 15 mg was employed; the same workers report that 67% of ewes lambed to natural service at the synchronized oestrus, which was comparable to the normal level of fertility in their ewes. In South Africa, Greyling and Van der Westhuysen (1979) reported that oestrus could be effectively synchronized by two doses of $250\mu g$ Cloprostenol given at a 10-day interval; lower doses of the analogues ($125 \mu g$) were often insufficient to induce complete luteolysis, as indicated by an initial decline in plasma progesterone followed by a gradual rise in the steroid, suggesting a recovery in luteal function. This ability of the corpus luteum to "recover" after PG had previously been recorded by Thorburn and Nichol (1971). The South Africans found that even with 125 μg doses of Cloprostenol, only 80% of their ewes were in oestrus, as compared with 100% at the 250 μg dose level.

12.2.5 Fertility and ovulation rate

As already mentioned, variable fertility has been reported after the use of prostaglandin or its analogues for the synchronization of oestrus;

however, the treatment does not appear to influence ovulation rate (Bindon et al., 1975). Although some reports show little or no evidence of subfertility in ewes bred by natural service (Hearnshaw et al., 1973; Haresign, 1976; Hughes et al., 1976; Haresign and Acritopoulou, 1978; Fraser et al., 1980) and Trounson et al. (1976) record an acceptable rate of fertilization (55%) in similarly bred PG–PMSG superovulated ewes, the findings of other investigations, as already mentioned, have not always been reassuring; Australian results indicate fertilization and lambing rates to be depressed in ewes bred by AI at the PG controlled oestrus (Fairnie et al., 1976; Lightfoot et al., 1976).

In Ireland, comparisons between prostaglandin and progestagen treated ewes have shown a marked decrease in oestrous response after PG and poor fertility both when natural or artificial insemination has been the method of breeding (Jennings, 1975; Boland et al., 1978). Unlike Australian experiences (Fukui and Roberts, 1977a, b; Fairnie et al., 1978), the work in Ireland has shown little advantage in employing a longer time interval (14 vs 9 days) between $PGF_{2\alpha}$ doses. The indications are that PG treatment interferes in some way with the efficiency of sperm transport; studies by Hawk and Conley (1975) have shown some evidence of partial inhibition of sperm transport in the cervix and disturbed transport of sperm into the oviducts. On the other hand, there are those who maintain that a normal sequence of hormonal events follow the use of PG in the sheep and that there is no reason why fertility should be depressed (Haresign, 1978).

12.2.6 Practical prostaglandin treatments

Although treatment with $PGF_{2\alpha}$ and several of its analogues is now available commercially in a number of countries for cattle oestrus synchronization and the induction of farrowing in pigs, it should be kept in mind that use of this agent in sheep raises certain questions, including the cost of treatment. Although it could be argued that it is simpler to inject ewes on two occasions with $PGF_{2\alpha}$ than employ sponges, the cost in Ireland and perhaps other countries would currently be considerably in excess of that of the progestagen-impregnated sponge, and there is the additional requirement of veterinary control in dealing with the agent. If the natural $PGF_{2\alpha}$ agent is employed, the accepted luteolytic dose of 15 mg is about 60% that required in the bovine; using the Cloprostenol analogue, 100 μg has been employed as a luteolytic dose, which is only 20% that employed in the cow. There is also the point that luteolytic agents can only be employed in ewes that are cyclic, and it is possible that in flocks to be bred in the early part of the breeding season, this may not always be the case.

12.2.7 Progestagen-PG treatments

One way of overcoming the need for two PG doses would be in using short-term progestagen treatment prior to prostaglandin; the use of 7–9-day progestagen intravaginal treatments with 15 mg $PGF_{2\alpha}$ at the end (Fukui and Roberts, 1979) or 31 μg Cloprostenol (Greyling et al., 1979) has been reported. In Ireland, it has been possible to use progestagen treatments as short as 4 days (Gordon, unpublished); although a high oestrous response is shown after the combined progestagen-PG treatment, fertility results have been variable.

In view of the extensive data available from studies and field applications of progestagen treatments in France and elsewhere, the use of prostaglandin either alone or in combination with progestagen would seem to require further investigation before any firm recommendations are made about applications in commercial farm practice.

12.3 PROGESTAGENS AND A STANDARD BREEDING PROCEDURE

The highly potent progestagen, MAP, has been used in sheep by several workers, the compound being employed in daily oral doses. Lindsay et al. (1967) used either 40 or 80 mg MAP per sheep daily over a 16-day period and recorded oestrus in only 58.3% of ewes after the treatment. Other investigators, who have reported using 50–60 mg doses over periods of 14–20 days, record from 87 to 100% of treated sheep coming in oestrus within a week of MAP withdrawal (Evans et al., 1962;

Hogue et al., 1962; Southcott et al., 1962; Baker et al., 1964; Hinds et al., 1964). In more recent times, Norwegian workers have used MAP in daily doses of 50 mg over a 10-day period and recorded 89% coming in oestrus within 6 days and 74.4% of these becoming pregnant at the controlled heat period (Velle and Helle, 1979); although the authors maintain that these results are better than most after controlled breeding, including those following the use of intravaginal sponges, this statement may not be altogether justified. Certainly, work in Ireland has shown that an oestrous response in excess of 95% can be achieved and that conception rates of 75% or more are common after sponge treatment (Gordon, 1975).

Fig. 12.1. Insertion of the intravaginal sponge. With a little experience, insertion of sponges into sheep can be carried out at a very fast rate if the sheep handling facilities on the farm are good. When properly done, no more than four sponges for every 1000 inserted have been lost during the treatment period. Of all the advances in controlled breeding in sheep, that achieved by Professor Robinson and his associates at Sydney in 1964 in developing the sponge was by far the most important. The French in particular, have taken up the sponge method on a very considerable scale.

12.3.1 Implant treatments

An alternative approach to the intravaginal sponge for the sustained administration of progestagen in sheep is the subcutaneous implant, the earliest form being the silicone rubber progestagen impregnated device (Dziuk and Cook, 1966). Reports have appeared on the use of the implant (impregnated with 375 mg progesterone) in the U.S.A. (Leman et al., 1970; Doane, 1971) and elsewhere, especially in Greece

(Zenoulis et al., 1972; Tsamis et al., 1974; Tsakalof et al., 1977). However, in working with these progesterone implants in Ireland, it has not been possible to match the speed and simplicity of the intravaginal sponge technique (O'Reilly, 1972; Keane, 1974; Gordon, 1975a).

Another approach is the much smaller implant designed for use in the ear and impregnated with a highly potent progestagen (SC-21009; Norgestamet). Results for the Norgestamet implant in Irish studies have not been such as to make the device a feasible alternative to the intravaginal sponge (Boland et al., 1979). Elsewhere, the 3 mg Norgestamet implant has been employed for a 10-day period, with an initial oestrogen/progestagen injection (0.5 mg oestradiol valerate + 1.5 mg SC-21009) at time of implantation (Spitzer and Carpenter, 1979); 95% of sheep were in oestrus within 5 days and 62% of all ewes treated became pregnant at the controlled heat. There would seem to be no clear reason for using the initial dose of oestrogen/progestagen.

12.3.2 Standard controlled breeding treatment

In considering the most appropriate hormonal technique for sheep fertility control, it should be emphasized that this is but one of several elements necessary for a successful response and lambing outcome. The basic technique, as employed currently in Ireland, involves intravaginal treatment for 12–14 days with a suitable progestagen, dusting the sponges with an antibiotic powder (such as oxytetracycline) at insertion, involves an intramuscular injection of 400–500 i.u. PMSG at sponge withdrawal, the introduction of sexually experienced rams (1:10 ratio) 48 h after terminating treatment and running the sheep at pasture in groups not exceeding 50 ewes and their five accompanying rams. Such a technique has been employed in Ireland in all months of the year, and among ewes in all the different physiological states in which they are to be found in normal farm practice (prepubertal; anoestrous "dry" and suckler ewes; cyclic "dry" and suckler ewes). This is not to say that the controlled breeding technique as described is equally successful in all conditions, but simply that data are available on the level of

Table 12.1. Lambing outcome in response to standard progestagen-PMSG treatment applied (1968–1975) from U.C.D.

	SEASON		
	Spring	Summer	Autumn
Groups	83	594	41
Ewes treated	2508	21 545	1600
In oestrus (%)	93.0	97.0	97.2
Ewes lambing	871	13 795	1206
Conceptions (%)	37.0	66.0	77.6
Lambs born	1375	22 396	2088
Lambs/conception	1.58	1.62	1.73
% Ewes pregnant (first oestrus)	34.7	64.0	75.4
% Ewes pregnant (first and second oestrus)	35.0	79.6	90.5

response which might be expected. Apart from the application of the technique in commercial sheep farming, there are those who employ the ewe as an experimental animal in research programmes (e.g. in foetal physiology) who are interested in producing lambs in all seasons (Love, 1978; Grant and Warren, 1980).

12.3.3 Progestagens employed

Studies in Australia (Robinson et al., 1968), Ireland (Gordon, 1971b) and France (Colas, 1975) are agreed that a high level of progestagen, followed by its rapid withdrawal and adequate ovarian stimulation, is a necessary prerequisite for acceptable fertility in sheep. It is now well accepted that only compounds with characteristics identical to progesterone, especially in having a short duration of activity, are suitable (Robinson, 1976). The Sydney group concentrated their efforts on one such compound (fluorogestone acetate; FGA) and current large-scale French activities in controlled breeding are based on this progestagen. In Ireland, as a result of many comparative studies, it became clear that medroxyprogesterone acetate (MAP) at the 60 mg dose level can give equally good results when natural service is the method of breeding (Gordon, 1974); when FGA (30 mg) and MAP (60 mg) have been compared in ewes bred by artificial insemination rather than natural service, a small but significant advantage in favour of FGA was found (Smith et al., 1981); such data, based on the lower sperm doses employed in AI, may be taken as a more sensitive indicator of the progestagen's effect on fertility.

12.3.4 Dose level and impregnation method

As well as the question of the particular progestagens which are regarded as acceptable for intravaginal applications (FGA; MAP), there are two other important considerations; dose level of compound and method of impregnation employed in the preparation of sponges. These questions are important because of the need to maintain an appropriate concentration of progestagen in the circulation to mimic the action of the corpus luteum.

Robinson (1968) suggested that many of the progestagen dosages employed to control oestrus in sheep prior to that time had probably been too low to duplicate the action of the natural corpus luteum. He drew attention to evidence that a progestagen dose which will inhibit ovulation in the cyclic ewe is lower than that required to condition for oestrus and that the dose required for such conditioning is lower than that required for full fertility. This was a view different to that previously expressed by Lamond (1964) who tended to the view that optimal fertility in synchronized sheep was likely to be associated with minimal doses of progesterone.

Robinson et al. (1968) reported that the rate of FGA absorption from intravaginal sponges can be significantly affected by the impregnation procedure and by the initial dose of compound; absorption rate significantly affected the percentage of ewes in oestrus and the number of sheep lambing to service at the controlled heats. In Ireland, Gordon (1971b) reported that a significantly higher mating response and lambing outcome resulted from thorough dispersion of a 30 mg dose of FGA in the sponge matrix; such dispersion of FGA in fine crystals presumably ensured a higher uptake of the agent. The amount of FGA released from a sponge can be determined by impregnation procedure more than by the actual dose employed; it has been shown, for instance, that sponges impregnated with a 15 mg dose of FGA in a well-dispersed form can result in a significantly higher conception rate than do sponges carrying double that

progestagen dose (30 mg) but with the compound poorly dispersed (Robinson et al., 1968).

As to the dose of FGA which can be regarded as optimal, the reports available would suggest that it lies in the range of 20–40 mg. Early work by Robinson et al. (1967) showed a significant effect of FGA dose level on fertility over a dose range of 5–20 mg but little effect between a 20 mg and 40 mg dose. French workers using AI as the breeding method in "dry" ewes recommended FGA doses of 30 mg in the seasonal anoestrus and 40 mg in the breeding season (Thimonier and Cognie, 1971; Colas et al., 1973); the experimental basis for such a recommendation is not apparent. In Ireland, Smith et al. (1981) were unable to establish a difference between 30 mg and 45 mg doses of FGA when employed in cyclic ewes prior to breeding by AI. Work with FGA in synchronizing oestrus in ewes in the U.K. has usually been on the basis of 30 mg doses (Robinson, 1974; Vipond and King, 1979); in Canada, 40 mg FGA doses have been reported in studies by Ainsworth et al. (1977) and Heaney et al. (1980). In the U.S.A., apparently as a requirement of regulatory agencies, the permissible FGA dose has been held at 20 mg. With the alternative MAP compound, work in the 1960s did employ sponges impregnated with either 40 mg or 60 mg doses; the 60 mg dose appears to be the standard currently.

12.3.5 Progesterone sponges

Much work was conducted in Ireland at one time using the natural steroid in sponges, usually at dose levels of 500 mg or 1000 mg (Gordon, 1975a). It was found, in extensive field trials, that the 500 mg dose sponge could be successfully employed in the induction of oestrus in the late stages of the non-breeding-season (for early breeding). At other times and in other seasons, however, the progesterone impregnated device may need further testing.

12.3.6 Progestagen without PMSG

Results achieved in the U.K. (Vipond and King, 1979) and in Ireland (Gordon, 1975b; Quirke, 1979) show that a very high degree of control can be achieved over both mating and lambing times merely by the use of the progestagen sponges

Table 12.2. *Relative effectiveness of six progestagen treatments on reproductive performance (U.C.D. data)*

	60 mg Medroxy progesterone acetate	30 mg Cronolone®	500 mg Progesterone	30 mg Cronolone® + 250 mg progesterone	1000 mg Progesterone	30 mg Cronolone® dispersed
Sheep	181	176	175	184	184	180
Pessary loss (No.)	—	1	—	1	11	180
(%)	nil	0.56	nil	0.54	5.9	nil
Sheep bred (No.)	171	172	161	180	158	170
(%)	94.5	98.3	92.0	98.4	91.3	94.4
Ewes lambing (No.)	129	125	109	135	113	130
Conception rate	75.4	72.3	67.7	75.0	71.5	76.4
Lambs born	210	197	175	218	161	217
Lambs/conception	1.63	1.58	1.60	1.60	1.42	1.67

Field trials carried out with sponges impregnated with progesterone — at the 500 or 1000 mg dose level — showed that these were as effective as when the regular FGA or MAP progestagens were employed in advancing the breeding season in sheep during the summer months.

alone during the breeding season. However, it is essential to ensure that progestagen treatment is not applied until it is certain that the sheep in question are showing spontaneous reproductive activity; this will vary with the breed or cross of ewe and other factors, such as age. In Ireland, it means for Suffolk-cross ewes, not starting intravaginal treatment until at least the end of the first week of August, for Galways and Half-Bred/Greyfaces, no earlier than mid-September and for Cheviots, no earlier than October.

12.3.7 Other considerations

The placement of the intravaginal sponge in the sheep may affect the incidence of sponge loss which, in normal circumstances, should not exceed 0.5%; it is important that the device is placed up against the cervix as deep in the vagina as possible. At withdrawal, there will be a small amount of fluid; this is an accumulation of vaginal fluid which does not interfere with the ewe's welfare, nor does it affect fertility.

The outcome of controlled breeding using the intravaginal sponge and PMSG can be markedly influenced by the body condition and age of sheep, and by the degree of stress (social or physical) to which animals are exposed around mating. These same factors are well enough recognised in sheep fertility under any circumstances, they apply to rams as well as ewes, and are embraced by the term "stockmanship". Ewes in

Fig. 12.2. Withdrawing the intravaginal sponge after 12 days treatment. A small quantity of fluid is released when the sponge is withdrawn from the sheep's vagina. Ewes can be expected to come into oestrus some 36 h or so after sponge withdrawal and the heat period can be expected to last for a further 36 h. It is remarkable how consistent results can be when using the progestagen-PMSG treatment to control or induce oestrus in sheep. Two types of sponge are currently available in the Irish Republic, the Chronogest (30 mg FGA) and the Veramix (60 mg MAP) and both work very well.

the early months after parturition and those suckling lambs are clearly in a category of their own and require separate consideration.

12.4 PMSG DOSE LEVELS AND ONSET OF OESTRUS

As already mentioned, the intravaginal progestagen treatment alone (FGA; MAP) is adequate in controlling oestrus among cyclic ewes in the full breeding season (Robinson, 1968). After progestagen withdrawal in such sheep, there presumably is a surge of endogenous gonadotrophin from the anterior pituitary sufficient to initiate the sequence of hormonal events resulting in oestrus and ovulation. However, for progestagen treatment to be effective in the induction of oestrus in the non-breeding season, there does need to be sufficient gonadotrophin available to initiate these preovulatory events and this necessitates the augmentation of endogenous gonadotrophin with some amount of exogenous FSH; the usual preparation employed for this purpose is PMSG.

12.4.1 PMSG doses

Several considerations may influence the decision as to whether an FSH-type preparation such as PMSG should be used and, if employed, the dose level and timing of its administration. Although, as already mentioned, cyclic ewes can be expected to come in oestrus shortly after progestagen withdrawal in the absence of exogenous gonadotrophin, a low dose of PMSG (375 i.u.) does result in a more predictable and precise synchronization of oestrus/ovulation, which can have a favourable effect on the outcome of set-time AI applications (Colas et al., 1973; Jennings and Quirke, 1976). In certain breeds of sheep, PMSG can also have the additional merit of inducing a mild superovulatory response; there is evidence that PMSG can bring the twinning percentage of breeds characterized by low litter-size up to a more acceptable level (Gordon, 1975b). As to the choice of dose-level of gonadotrophin, this would appear to lie within the range 375–750 i.u. PMSG; it is possible to depress rather than enhance conception rate after progestagen–PMSG treatment in sheep by increasing the dose beyond a certain point (Larson et al., 1970; Gordon, 1971b; Botha et al., 1975).

Although there is evidence in cyclic sheep that superovulatory response may be substantially increased when PMSG is given several days prior to withdrawal of intravaginally administered progestagen (Roche, 1968), this does not

necessarily apply for anoestrous ewes; Gordon (1969) reported a reduced ovulatory and oestrous response in sheep receiving 500 i.u. PMSG several days prior to progestagen withdrawal in the ewe anoestrus. On the question of administering the gonadotrophin, South African evidence has shown that an intramuscular injection of PMSG resulted in a superovulatory response more than double that observed after a subcutaneous dose (Boshoff and Burger, 1973).

12.4.2 Refractoriness to PMSG

Over the years, several workers have examined the question of possible refractoriness in sheep to repeated doses of PMSG. In recent times, it has been shown that even after 17 consecutive doses of PMSG, 17 days apart, ewes did not show evidence of refractoriness or anti-PMSG activity (Gherardi and Martin, 1978; Gherardi and Lindsay, 1980).

12.4.3 Onset of oestrus after progestagen-PMSG

Several factors may influence the extent of the interval between the end of progestagen treatment and the start of the controlled heat period; generally, it is an interval of about 36 h, although some ewes may be in oestrus as early as 24 h or as late as 48 h (Gordon, 1975a). The use of PMSG at progestagen withdrawal will certainly shorten the interval to oestrus, as shown in South African studies (Botha et al., 1975).

There is even some suggestion that the time of day (morning or evening) at which intravaginal sponges are removed may influence the interval to oestrus: Robinson (1980) notes that a diurnal pattern of mating has been observed in normal cyclic sheep (Fraser, 1968) and suggests that oestrus may be affected in some similar way by the time of day when progestagen treatment ceases. Elsewhere, and this time with progesterone implants, it has been reported that the time of day of removing the device in anoestrous ewes had an effect on the interval from removal to the preovulatory LH surge (Cunningham et al., 1977). In other work, Cunningham et al. (1980) has noted that although implants were removed from ewes at a 12 h difference (17.30 vs 05.30 h) the times of matings differed only by 2 h; the authors suggest that there may be diurnal variations in the effectiveness of the hypo-thalamic centres responsible for oestrus. For those considering the use of sheep AI on a fixed-time basis, clearly it is important to have information about all factors that may influence the time interval between progestagen-PMSG and oestrus/ovulation.

12.5 USE OF ADDITIONAL AGENTS

According to a report by Hawk and Cooper (1976), a dose of 30 μg oestradiol given to ewes at time of mating (natural service) was found to improve sperm transport; Inskeep et al. (1979) also employed oestradiol in ewes bred by natural service or fresh semen AI. However, efforts to use this agent at oestrus among ewes inseminated after progestagen-PMSG treatment have been less successful (Boland and Gordon, 1978; Langford et al., 1980); the fact has already been mentioned that exogenous oestrogen, even in minute quantities, can adversely affect sheep fertility at oestrus and these latter results would seem to be in accord with that general principle.

12.6 RAM AND MATING MANAGEMENT

In commercial sheep farming in Ireland, ewes are bred by natural service; the same is true in many other countries. As already mentioned, the success or otherwise of controlled breeding in sheep is not alone a question of influencing the reproductive processes in the ewe. The outcome does also depend on the capability of the ram (activity and semen quality). Part of the difficulty is, in fact, created in keeping treatment procedure in ewes as simple as possible; to ensure this, the standard practice is to insert and withdraw intravaginal sponges simultaneously in all the selected sheep. This results in oestrus occurring at the same time in ewes, about 36 h after progestagen withdrawal. Such a synchron-ization of heat periods can result in the ram being confronted with a situation radically different from any that faces him in the normal course of events.

Fig. 12.3. Ewes in oestrus after the end of the progestagen-PMSG treatment pose new problems for the ram. Rams that are to be used in controlled breeding should always be males that have previously worked well among sheep. Providing the testes and genitalia are normal without evidence of problems, there is nothing to be gained by semen examinations unless this is carried out by someone well experienced in this area. As a means of making rams available to Irish farmers for breeding bunches of synchronized ewes, ram "pools" have been operated in various counties — and a similar approach has been used in the North-East of Scotland by workers at Aberdeen University.

12.6.1 Ram management

Several factors are known to be important for successful controlled breeding by natural service; first and foremost, the ram should be in good health, sexually experienced and have a known record of achievement in producing pregnancies in the natural breeding season. Ram management procedures previously described (Gordon, 1963, 1969) suggested that pro-gestagen-PMSG synchronized ewes should be joined with rams at the end of the treatment, that sheep should be confined to small fields or paddocks in the first few days after treatment, that a ram to ewe ratio of 1:10 should be employed and that the size of the sheep groups should not exceed 50 ewes and their accompanying five rams.

Towards the end of the 1960s, comparisons were made between the standard practice of introducing rams at progestagen withdrawal and an alternative system in which ram introduction was delayed until 48 h later; it appeared that conception rate could be improved at the controlled oestrus by this relatively simple ad-justment (Gordon, 1971a). Subsequent reports in Ireland by Joyce (1972) and Boland and Gordon (1979) provided further evidence in support of that finding. Elsewhere, Bryant and Tomkins (1976) in the U.K. recorded observations which were not at variance with the Irish data.

It should be noted that a substantial body of data has been accumulated by investigators on the timing of oestrus (onset and cessation) in progestagen-PMSG treated sheep; in introducing rams at 48 h, it is known that they are joining a group of ewes, most of which would be several hours into oestrus (Gordon, 1971a, b). On the basis of well-established sheep behavioural patterns, as reported by authors such as Hulet (1966), in studies in which rams were found to prefer breeding ewes fresh in oestrus and not recently mated, it is to be expected that the initial ejaculates (with the highest sperm doses) might be distributed more uniformly than in the usual ram joining system, in which males may use up their sperm reserves unduly dealing with the first few ewes in oestrus in the group.

When ewes are perhaps 12 and more hours into the controlled oestrus before mating takes place, conditions in the reproductive tract of the ewe may also be more favourable to sperm transport/survival after the delayed introduction of the ram. It is known, for instance, that the flow of cervical mucus can be markedly influenced by progestagen treatment, and that this is probably a consequence of changes in the way in which oestrogen is being produced (Smith and Allison, 1971); it may be that a heavy flow of cervical mucus in the early hours of oestrus may serve to dilute ram semen to the point at which it is more difficult for a good cervical population of sperm to become established. It is well-established that the cervix acts as a sperm reservoir in the ewe (Quinlan et al., 1933; Mattner, 1966) and it seems likely that factors which affect the retention and survival of sperm in this site can influence fertility.

It should be noted, however, that mating in the late stages of oestrus may have its own share of problems; Mattner and Braden (1969) and Killeen and Moore (1970) have shown that the efficiency of sperm transport is diminished in the late stages of the natural oestrus. This may be one of the sheep's protective mechanisms aimed at preventing the fertilization of aged eggs.

12.6.2 Ewe to ram ratio

In regard to the ram to ewe ratio, this has been held at 1:10 in most of the controlled breeding applications in Ireland (Gordon, 1975a, b). It is not considered commercially feasible to employ a ratio less than this, although French workers have recommended one ram for every five ewes under certain conditions (Colas et al., 1974) and Bryant and Tomkins (1975) have suggested that an individual ram should not be allowed to serve more than six progestagen-treated ewes if high levels of fertility are sought. On the other hand, the possibility of employing a normal ram to ewe ratio of 1:50 among synchronized sheep has been demonstrated by Galindez et al. (1977); the fact that such a ratio involves "staggering" both the start and the termination of intravaginal treatments would not favour this practice in Ireland, in which the farmer is keen on the compactness of the lambing period and a technician service to treat sheep with progestagen-PMSG is in operation, making it necessary to restrict travel to and from farms to a minimum if costs are to remain acceptable.

One problem which the 1:10 ram to ewe ratio raises is that of the farmer finding enough rams to meet his needs. In Ireland and the U.K., ram sharing schemes have been set up to overcome this difficulty in certain instances. Rams are moved to a farm a day or two before the ewes are

Table 12.3. *Effect of timing of ram introduction on the conception rate of FGA-PMSG treated ewes in late anoestrus. From Boland and Gordon (1979)*

	Ram in at pessary withdrawal	Ram in at 48 h after pessary withdrawal
Sheep	79	80
Bred at induced oestrus	76 (96.2%)	77 (96.3%)
Conceptions at induced oestrus	30 (39.5%)	52 (67.5%)
Lambs born	43 (1.43)	80 (1.54)

Trials with 16 pens of sheep — 10 ewes and Suffolk ram per paddock. (P <0.01).

due to be bred and work away in the flock on the day of mating; with such systems, the males can be employed once weekly for a period of several weeks.

12.6.3 Hand-mating techniques

Workers in the State research organisation (Agricultural Institute) in Ireland concentrated time and attention on ram management routines to be used in association with controlled breeding (Jennings and Crowley, 1970; 1972; Jennings, 1976, 1977); the suggestion in several reports was that near-normal conception rates in progestagen-PMSG treated ewes may be achieved by "hand-mating" each ewe on one or two occasions during the controlled oestrus. The Irish workers produced evidence indicating that substantial discrepancies exist between the number of synchronized ewes "marked" by rams and the number actually served; it was suggested that much of the subfertility recorded previously for progestagen-treated sheep was a reflection of inadequacies among the rams, either in libido or fertility, in coping with a situation in which a group of ewes are in oestrus simultaneously.

Undoubtedly, there is much truth in this, but it may not always be clear what "hand-mating" can mean in terms of ram supply and in the time and labour involved in its application. Australian stud farmers accustomed to breeding Merinos by hand-service regard the practice as expensive, time-consuming and generally less effective in getting ewes pregnant than paddock mating (Belschner, 1965). Used with synchronized sheep which are housed and accustomed to handling and with plenty of rams to choose from, the hand-mating system can be the means of introducing larger than usual sperm doses into the ewe at stated intervals during oestrus; Robinson (1974) in his intensive lamb production unit at the Rowett in Scotland, has achieved excellent conception rates in Finn x Dorset crossbreds after two "hand-matings" during the synchronized oestrus with an interval of about 12 h separating services.

With ewes and rams accustomed to pastoral conditions, it becomes a matter of establishing clearly just how far the lambing outcome can be improved beyond that found in unsupervised

mating systems and whether this justified the time and labour involved in its application. In fact, evidence reported by Joyce (1972) showed that, provided rams are kept away from ewes until 48 h after synchronizing treatments, paddock matings can give conception rates equal to those achieved by a "hand-mating" routine (one hand-service at 48 h and ewes thereafter exposed to rams in the field).

12.6.4 Rams and fertilization rates

There is ample evidence to show that any subfertility associated with progestagen treatment in sheep is probably the result of a failure in the fertilization process rather than anything else; this failure stems from an impairment of normal transport and survival of sperm in the cranial part of the cervix (Robinson, 1973). For such reasons, fertilization failure can possibly be avoided in certain categories ("dry" anoestrous and "dry" cyclic sheep) by employing a much larger than usual number of sperm, whether by delaying ram introduction until 48 h, using a "hand-mating" routine or an appropriate AI procedure. In considering ram management routines, it may be relevant to question whether "hand-mating" under certain conditions may constitute an additional "stress-factor" which may reduce rather than enhance conception at the synchronized oestrus; it is possible that with certain farm conditions or perhaps with some sheep and rams, the application of the "hand-mating" technique may be counter-productive.

12.6.5 Irish rams in controlled breeding

It should be noted that the Irish results for ram performance in synchronized flocks relate almost exclusively to males of the Suffolk breed, the predominant fat-lamb sires in the country. They also relate to those rams that are known to have previously "worked" satisfactorily in flocks. As mentioned at several points previously, it would appear that Suffolks and rams of other breeds in Ireland produce semen, apparently of good quality, and maintain sex drive at a high level throughout the year. This is not to say that the most intense sexual activity and highest quality semen is not to be found in the autumn season, but there is no evidence that serious ram

Table 12.4. *Effect of season on the incidence of sperm abnormalities in Texel rams (U.C.D. data)*

Season	No. of collections	Morphologically abnormal sperm			
		Primary (%)	Secondary %		
			Free heads	Bent tails	Total
Winter	43	0.18	2.24	0.30	2.54
Spring	41	0.21	2.96	0.46	3.42
Summer	42	Nil	2.29	0.20	2.49
Autumn	44	Nil	1.57	0.14	1.71
Totals	170	0.10	2.26	0.29	2.55

French workers have reported a significantly higher proportion of secondary sperm abnormalities (especially sperm showing the cytoplastic droplet in the distal position) among Ile-de-France rams when daylight increased than when it decreased (22 vs 10%).

inadequacies occur in the ewe anoestrus as has been recorded elsewhere (Colas *et al.*, 1974; Colas, 1979).

12.7 COMPACTNESS OF LAMBINGS

The application of controlled breeding, when ewes in the flock are bred on the one day, can mean that up to 80% of lambs born in the flock are produced within a period of little more than a week, thus giving an extremely compact lambing. As mentioned previously, the sheep which can be expected to give the most compact lambings, on a flock basis, are likely to be the highly prolific breeds or crossbreds (Finn x Dorset, would be an example) that usually have a high conception rate to first service.

Compact lambings can have several advantages, particularly in flocks of less than 100 ewes where the hours spent attending ewes can be literally halved and the potential for saving lambs around the time of birth can be increased. A compact rather than a protracted lambing also ensures that supplementary meal feeding can be more accurately timed according to the stage of pregnancy, producing at time of birth, a more even-sized batch of lambs. The cross-fostering of lambs at birth is made much easier than usual and management of lambs for clostridial disease control and docking can be carried out at optimum times. Advantages carry on through until marketing, when the lambs for sale are likely to be ready at much the same time.

12.8 OTHER ADVANTAGES OF COMPACTNESS

Sheep farmers in Ireland traditionally join rams with the ewe flock for a 6–8 week period during the autumn breeding season, a practice which may often result in a very protracted lambing season. For that reason, the concentration of both mating and lambing into a short and predictable period has several advantages, over and above those already mentioned. A foreknowledge of the mating and lambing dates can permit economies in feed requirements, both at "flushing" in the autumn mating period and during the supplementary period prior to lambing; parturition in ewes can be supervised more closely and better use made of overnight housing and shelter, thereby reducing lamb losses.

12.9 FUTURE DEVELOPMENTS

Of the several practical methods now commercially available for the control of the ewe's oestrous cycle, the intravaginal sponge, impregnated with FGA or MAP, is probably the simplest to apply; indeed, it is the type of treatment that can be handled by the farmer himself after a minimum of training. An implantation method, which calls for the subsequent removal of the implant, as in the case of the progesterone impregnated Sil-Estrus® device or the Norgestamet® miniature ear-implant, may not have this same advantage. Other agents for controlling oestrus, such as prostaglandin $F_{2\alpha}$ or its analogues, even if it were demonstrated that their efficiency matched that of intravaginal sponges, would inevitably remain a prescribed drug and at current costs would probably be more costly to employ than progestagen sponges.

12.10 REFERENCES

Acritipoulou, S., Haresign, W., Foster, J. P. and Lamming, G. E. (1977) Plasma progesterone and LH concentrations in ewes after injection of an analogue of prostaglandin $F_{2\alpha}$. *J. Reprod. Fert.* **49**, 337–340.

Acritopoulou, S., Haresign, W. and Lamming, G. E. (1978) Time of ovulation in ewes after treatment with a prostaglandin $F_{2\alpha}$ analogue. *J. Reprod. Fert.* **54**, 189–191.

Acritopoulou, S. and Haresign, W. (1980) Response of ewes to a single injection of an analogue of $PGF_{2\alpha}$ given at different stages of the oestrous cycle. *J. Reprod. Fert.* **58**, 219–223.

Ainsworth, L., Hackett, A. J., Heaney, D. P., Langford, G. A. and Peters, H. F. (1977) A multidisciplinary approach to the development of controlled breeding and intensive production systems for sheep. In, *Management of Reprod. in Sheep and Goats*, pp. 101–108. Madison, Wisc. SID Publn.

Baker, B., Edgar, R. A. and Christians, C. J. (1964) use of oral progesterone for the synchronization of estrus in the ewe. *J. Anim. Sci.* **23**, 295.

Belschner, H. G. (1965) *Sheep Management and Diseases.* Sydney, Angus & Robertson.

Bindon, B. M., Blanc, M. R., Pelletier, J., Terqui, M. and Thimonier, J. (1975) *18 Ann. Meet. Endocr. Soc. Aust.* **18**, 64 (Abs.).

Boland, M. P. and Gordon, I. (1978) Faculty of Agriculture, UCD, Dublin. Research Rpt.

Boland, M. P. and Gordon, I. (1979) Effect of timing or ram introduction on fertility in progestagen-PMSG treated anoestrous ewes. *J. Agric. Sci., Camb.* **92**, 247–249.

Boland, M. P., Lemainque, F. and Gordon, I. (1978) Comparison of lambing outcome in ewes after synchronization of oestrus by progestagen or prostaglandin treatment. *J. Agric. Sci., Camb.* **91**, 765–766.

Boland, M. P., Kelleher, D. and Gordon, I. (1979) Comparison of control of oestrus and ovulation in sheep by an ear implant (SC.21009) or by intravaginal sponge. *Anim. Reprod. Sci.* **1**, 275–283.

Boshoff, D. A. and Burger, F. J. L. (1973) Limitation of multiple-ovulations in Karakul ewes after the use of PMSG. *S. Afr. J. Anim. Sci.* **3**, 79–81.

Botha, H. K., Van Niekerk, C. H. and Pagel, R. F. E. (1975) Influence of synchronization of the oestrous period, PMSG administration and flushing on oestrus and conception of S. African mutton Merino ewes. *S. Afr. J. Anim. Sci.* **5**, 231–233.

Bryant, M. J. and Tomkins, T. (1975) The flock-mating of progestagen-synchronized ewes. 1. The influence of ram-to-ewe ratio upon mating behaviour and lambing performance. *Anim. Prod.* **20**, 381–390.

Bryant, M. J. and Tomkins, T. (1976) The flock mating of progestagen-synchronized ewes. 2. The influence of time

of ram introduction upon mating behaviour and lambing performance. *Anim. Prod.* **22**, 379–384.

Chamley, W. A., Buckmaster, J. M., Cain, M. D., Cerini, J., Cerini, M. E., Cunningham, I. A. and Goding, J. R. (1972) The effect of $PGF_{2\alpha}$ on progesterone oestradiol and LH secretion in sheep with ovarian transplants. *J. Endocr.* **55**, 253–263.

Colas, G. (1975) The use of the progestagen SC 9880 as an aid for AI in ewes. *Ann. Biol. Anim. Bioch. Biophys.* **15**(2), 353–363.

Colas, G. (1979) Fertility in the ewe after AI with fresh and frozen semen at the induced oestrus, and influence of the photoperiod on the semen quality of the ram. *Livest. Prod. Sci.* **6**, 153–166.

Colas, G. Brice, G. and Guerin, Y. (1974) Acquisitions recentes en matier d'insemination artificielle ovine. *Bull. Tech. Inform. Minist. Agric.* **294**, 795–800.

Colas, G., Thimonier, J., Courot, M. and Ortavant, R. (1973) Fertility, prolificacy and fecundity during the breeding season of ewes artificially inseminated after treatment with fluorogestone acetate. *Annls. Zootech.* **22**, 441–451.

Corteel, M. (1975) Luteolysis induced by $PGF_{2\alpha}$ compared with natural luteolysis in the ewe. *Ann. Biol. Anim. Bioch. Biophys.* **15**(2), 175–180.

Cunningham, N. F., Saba, N. and Millar, P. G. (1977) The effects of progesterone and oestradiol-15$_B$ treatment on plasma hormone levels and on the reproductive behaviour of ewes in late anoestrus and early in the breeding season. *Res. Vet. Sci.* **22**, 324–329.

Cunningham, N. F., Saba, N., Boarer, C. D. H. and Hattersley, J. J. P. (1980) Plasma hormone levels and reproductive behaviour in anoestrous ewes after treatment with progesterone and PMSG. *J. Reprod. Fert.* **60**, 177–185.

Doane, B. B. (1971) Practical husbandry methods for increasing sheep prolificacy. In, *Lamb Production.* pp. 5–10. U.S. Feed Grains Council.

Douglas, R. H. and Ginther, O. J. (1973) Luteolysis following a single injection of $PGF_{2\alpha}$ in sheep. *J. Anim. Sci.* **37**, 990–993.

Dziuk, P. J. and Cook, B. (1966) Passage of steroids through silicone rubber. *Endocrin.* **78**, 208–211.

Evans, J. S., Cutt, R. H. and Simpson, E. C. (1962) Breeding performance in ewes after synchronizing estrus by feeding MAP. *J. Anim. Sci.* **21**, 804.

Fairnie, I. J., Cumming, I. A. and Martin, E. R. (1976) Use of the prostaglandin analogue ICI 80996 to synchronize ovulation in sheep in an AI programme. *Prod. Aust. Soc. Anim. Prod.* **11**, 133–136.

Fairnie, I. J., Wales, R. G. and Gherardi, P. B. (1977) Time of ovulation, fertilization rate and blastocyst formation in ewes following treatment with prostaglandin analogue (ICI 80996). *Theriogen.* **8**(4), 183.

Fairnie, I. J., Martin, E. R. and Rogers, S. C. (1978) The lambing performance of Merino ewes following synchronization of ovulation with cloprostenol, a prostaglandin analogue (ICI 80996). *Proc. Aust. Soc. Anim. Prod.* **12**, 256.

Frazer, A. F. (1968) *Reprod. Behav. Ungulates.* Academic Press, London.

Fukui, Y. and Roberts, E. M. (1977a) Fertility of ewes treated with $PGF_{2\alpha}$ and artificially inseminated at predetermined intervals thereafter. *Aust. J. Agric. Res.* **28**, 891–897.

Fukui, Y. and Roberts, E. M. (1977b) Observation of uterine contractions in ewes treated with $PGF_{2\alpha}$. *Jap. J. Anim. Reprod.* **24**, 165–170.

Fukui, Y. and Roberts, E. M. (1979) Comparison of methods for estrous synchronization in sheep. *Jap. J. Anim. Reprod.* **25,** 131–135.

Galindez, F. J., Prud'Hon, M. and Reboul, G. (1977) Reproductive performance of group-synchronized Merino d'arles and Romanov crossbredd ewes. *Anim. Prod.* **24,** 113–116.

Gemmell, R. T., Stacy, B. D. and Thorburn, G. D. (1976) Morphology of the regressing corpus luteum in the ewe. *Biol. Reprod.* **14,** 270–279.

Gherardi, P. B. and Lindsay, D. R. (1980) The effect of season on the ovulatory response of Merino ewes to serum from pregnant mares. *J. Reprod. Fert.* **60,** 425–429.

Gherardi, P. G. and Martin, G. B. (1978) The effect of multiple injections of pregnant mare serum gonadotrophin on the ovarian activity of Merino ewes. *Proc. Aust. Soc. Anim. Prod.* **12,** 260.

Goding, J. R. (1974) The demonstration that PGF$_{2\alpha}$ is the uterine luteolysin in the ewe. *J. Reprod. Fert.* **38,** 261–271.

Gordon, I. (1963) The induction of pregnancy in the anoestrous ewe by hormonal therapy. I. Progesterone-PMS therapy during the breeding season. *J. Agric. Sci., Camb.* **60,** 31.

Gordon, I. (1969) Factors affecting response of anoestrous sheep to progestagen treatment. *J. Ir. Dept. Agric., Dublin* **66,** 232.

Gordon, I. (1971a) Control of reproduction in sheep; towards programmed lamb production. *Jr. Ir. Dept. Agric, Dublin* **68,** 3.

Gordon, I. (1971a) Induction of early breeding in sheep by standard and modified progestagen-PMS treatments. *J. Agric. Sci., Camb.* **76,** 337.

Gordon, I. (1974) Controlled breeding in sheep. *Ir. Vet. J.* **28**(6), 118–126.

Gordon, I. (1975a) The use of progestagens in sheep bred by natural and artificial insemination. *Ann. Biol. Anim. Bioch. Biophys.* **15**(2), 303–315.

Gordon, I. (1975b) Hormonal control of reproduction in sheep. *Proc. Br. Soc. Anim. Prod.* **4,** 79–93.

Grant, C. G. and Warren, R. A. (1980) Sheep breeding program for the year-round production of timed pregnancies for experimental foetal surgery. *Lab. Anim.* **14,** 317–321.

Greyling, J. P. S. and van der Westhuysen, J. M. (1979) The synthronization of oestrus in sheep. II. Dose effect of prostaglandin in the double injection regime. *S. Afr. J. Anim. Sci.* **9,** 193–195.

Greyling, J. P. C., van der Westhuysen, J. M. and van Niekerk, C. H. (1979) The synchronization of oestrus in sheep. I. Dosage and time of prostaglandin administration following progestagen pre-treatment. *S. Afr. J. Anim. Sci.* **9,** 185–187.

Hackett, A. J. and Robertson, H. A. (1980) Effect of dose and time of injection of prostaglandin F$_{2\alpha}$ in cycling ewes. *Theriogen.* **13,** 347–351.

Haresign, W. (1976) Controlled breeding in sheep using the prostaglandin analogue ICI 80886. *Anim. Prod.* **22,** 137 (Abs.).

Haresign, W. (1978) Ovulation control in the sheep. In, *Control of Ovulation.* Crighton et al., Eds. pp. 435–451. Butterworths, London.

Haresign, W. (1980) Controlling reproduction in sheep. *Span,* **23**(2), 88–91.

Haresign, W. and Acritopoulou, S. (1978) Controlled breeding in sheep using the prostaglandin analogue ICI-80996. *Livest. Prod. Sci.* **5,** 313–319.

Hawk, H. W. (1973) Uterine motility and sperm transport in the

estrous ewe after prostaglandin induced regression of corpora lutea. *J. Anim. Sci.* **37,** 1380–1385.

Hawk, H. W. and Conley, H. H. (1975) Involvement of the cervix in sperm transport failures in the reproductive tract of the ewe. *Biol. Reprod.* **13,** 322–328.

Hawk, H. W. and Cooper, B. S. (1976) Ovum fertilization and embryo survival in ewes treated with estradiol immediately prior to mating. *J. Anim. Sci.* **42,** 677–680.

Heaney, D. P., Ainsworth, L., Batra, T. R., Fiser, P. S., Langford, G. A., Lee, A. J. and Hackett, A. J. (1980) Research for an intensive total confinement sheep production system. *Anim. Res. Inst. Tech. Bull. No. 2;* Agriculture Canada Publication.

Hearnshaw, H., Restall, B. J. and Gleeson, A. R. (1973) Observations on the luteolytic effects of PGF$_{2\alpha}$ during the oestrous cycle and early pregnancy in the ewe. *J. Reprod. Fert.* **32,** 322–323.

Hinds, F. C., Dziuk, P. J. and Lewis, J. M. (1964) Control of estrus and lambing performance in cycling ewes fed MAP. *J. Anim. Sci.* **23,** 782.

Hogue, D. E., Hansel, W. and Bratton, R. W. (1962) Fertility of ewes bred naturally and artificially after estrus cycle synchronization with an oral progestational agent. *J. Anim. Sci.* **21,** 625.

Hughes, F., Lucan, J. M. S. and Notman, A. B. (1976) The synchronization of oestrus and subsequent fertility in ewes following treatment with a synthetic PG analogue (ONO453). *Prostaglandins* **11,** 1033–1038.

Hulet, C. F. (1966) Behavioural, social and psychological factors affecting mating time and breeding efficiency in sheep. *J. Anim. Sci.* **25,** (Suppl.), 5.

Inskeep, E. K., Stevens, L. P. and Rudy, C. R. (1979) Fertility in ewes receiving low doses of estradiol during synchronized estrus. *J. Anim. Sci.* **48,** 52–53.

Jennings, J. J. (1975) Effect of ICI 80996 on conception rate in ewes. *Anim. Prod. Res. Rept. (An Foras Taluntais,* 34–35.

Jennings, J. J. (1976) Mating behaviour of rams in late anoestrus. *Ir. J. Agric. Res.* **15,** 301–307.

Jennings, J. J. (1977) Influence of mating behaviour of rams on fertility in progestagen-PMS-treated anoestrous ewes. *Ir. J. Agric. Res.* **16,** 155–162.

Jennings, J. J. and Crowley, J. P. (1970) The mating of hormone-treated sheep. *Proc. Br. Soc. Anim. Prod. 51st Mt. Anim. Prod.* **12,** 357.

Jennings, J. J. and Crowley, J. P. (1972) The influence of mating management on fertility in ewes following progesterone-PMS treatment. *Vet. Rec.* **90,** 495–498.

Jennings, J. J. and Quirke, J. F. (1976) Artificial insemination in sheep. *Ann. Rpt. Anim. Prod. Div. An Foras Taluntais,* Dublin, 35–36.

Joyce, M. J. B. (1972) A comparison of three different mating systems. *Proc. 7th Int. Congr. Anim. Reprod. AI (Munich),* **2,** 935–938.

Keane, M. G. (1974) Effect of progestagen-PMS hormone treatment on reproduction in ewe-lambs. *Ir. J. Agric. Res.* **13,** 39–48.

Killeen, I. D. and Moore, N. W. (1970) Transport of spermatozoa and fertilization in the ewe following cervical and uterine insemination early and late in oestrus. *Aust. J. Biol. Sci.* **23,** 1271–1277.

Lamond, D. R. (1964) Synchronization of ovarian cycles in sheep and cattle. *Anim. Breed, Abstr.* **32,** 269–285.

Langford, G. A., Marcus, G. J., Hackett, A. J. and Ainsworth, L. (1980) Embryonic mortality in ewes given estradiol and bred with frozen semen. *Can. J. Anim. Sci.* **60,** 1062 (Abs.).

Larson, W. M., Banbury, E. D. and Spaeth, C. W. (1970) Effect of previous lambing rate on response to PMS. *J. Anim. Sci.* **31,** 225.

Leman, A. A., Dziuk, P. J. and Doane, B. B. (1970) Synchronization of estrus and shortening of the interval between lambing by induction of estrus and ovulation during anestrus. *J. Am. Vet. Med. Ass.* **157,** 1574-76.

Lightfoot, R. J., Croker, K. P. and Marshall, R. (1976) Use of a prostaglandin analogue (ICI 80996) for the synchronization of estrus and lambing in Merino ewes. *Proc. Int. Sheep Bred. Congr. Muresk and Perth,* (ed Tomes et al), 449-454.

Lindsay, D. R., Moore, N. W., Robinson, T. J., Salamon, S. and Shelton, J. N. (1967) The evaluation of an oral progestagen (Provera:MAP) for the synchronization of oestrus in the entire cyclic Merino ewe. In, *Control of the Ovarian Cycle in the Sheep.* T. J. Robinson, Ed. pp. 155-165. Univ. Press, Sydney.

Love, J. A. (1978) Controlled breeding in sheep for studies in foetal physiology. *Lab. Anim. Sci.* **28,** 611-614.

Mattner, P. E. (1966) Formation and retention of the spermatozoan reservoir in the cervix of the ruminant. *Nature, Lond.* **212,** 1479.

Mattner, P. E. and Braden, A. W. H. (1969) Comparison of the distribution of the motile and immotile spermatozoa in the ovine cervix. *Aust. J. Biol. Sci.* **22,** 1069-1070.

McClellan, M. C., Abel, J. H. Jr. and Niswender, G. D. (1976) Cyclic and induced regression of ovine corpora lutea. *Anat. Rec.* **184,** 473-474.

McCracken, J. A., Glen, m. E. and Scaramuzzi, R. J. (1970) Corpus luteum regression induced by $PGF_{2\alpha}$. *J. Clin. endocr. metab.* **30,** 544-546.

O'Reilly, P. J. (1972) Fertility resulting from AI or natural mating using pessaries or implants to synchronize oestrus in ewes. *Proc. 7th Congr. Reprod. A.I. (Munich),* **2,** 941-944.

Quinlan, J., Mare, G. S. and Roux, L. L. (1933) A study of the duration of motility of spermatozoa in the different divisions of the reproductive tract of the Merino ewe. *Onderstepoort J. Vet. Sci.* **1,** 135.

Quirke, J. F. (1979) Control of reproduction in adult ewes and ewe lambs and estimation of reproductive wastage in ewe lambs following treatment with progestagen impregnated sponges and PMSG. *Livest. Prod. Sci.* **6,** 295-305.

Robinson, J. J. (1974) Intensifying ewe productivity. *Proc. Br. Soc. Anim. Prod.* **3,** 31-40.

Robinson, T. J. (1964). Synchronization of oestrus in sheep by intravaginal and subcutaneous application of progestin impregnated sponges. *Proc. Aust. Soc. Anim. Prod.,* **8,** 47-49.

Robinson, T. J. (1967) Conclusions. In, *Control of the Ovarian Cycle in the Sheep.* T. J. Robinson, Ed. University Press, Sydney.

Robinson, T. J. (1968) The synchronization of the oestrous cycle and fertility. *Proc. 6th Int. Congr. Anim. Reprod. A.I. (Paris),* **2,** 1347-1383.

Robinson, T. J. (1973) Contraception and sperm transport in domestic animals. *INSERM.* **26,** 453-478.

Robinson, T. J. (1974) The present status of applied reproductive physiology in animal production. *Proc. N.Z. Soc. Anim. Prod.* **34,** 37-44.

Robinson, T. J. (1976) Controlled breeding of sheep and goats. *Proc. Int. Sheep Breeding Congr. (Muresk),* 1976.

Robinson, T. J. (1980) Programmed year-round sheep breeding. *Aust. J. Exp. Agric. Anim. Husb.* **20,** 667-673.

Robinson, T. J., Quinlivan, T. D. and Baxter, C. (1968) The relationship between dose of progestagen and method of preparation of intravaginal sponges on their effectiveness for the control of ovulation in the ewe. *J. Reprod. Fert.* **17,** 471.

Robinson, T. J., Salamon, S., Moore, N. W. and Smith, J. F. (1967) The evaluation of SC9880-impregnated intravaginal sponges for the synchronization of oestrus for large scale AI of Merino ewes in summer and autumn. In, *The Control of the Ovarian Cycle of the Sheep.* T. J. Robinson, Ed. pp. 208-236. University Press, Sydney.

Roche, J. F. (1968) Effect of the interval between withdrawal of progestagen pessaries and time of PMS administration on oestrus and ovulation in cyclic ewes. *Ir. J. Agric. Res.* **7,** 1.

Smith, J. F. and Allison, A. J. (1971) The effect of exogenous progestagen on the production of cervical mucus in the ewe. *J. Reprod. Fert.* **24,** 279-282.

Smith, P. A., Boland, M. P. and Gordon, I. (1981a) Effect of type of intravaginal progestagen on the outcome of fixed-time A.I. *J. Agric. Sci., Camb.* **96,** 243-245.

Smith, P. A., Boland, M. P. and Gordon, I. (1981b) Effect of dose of Cronolone in intravaginal sponges on lambing outcome to fixed-time A.I. *J. Agric. Sci., Camb.* **96,** 253-254.

Southcott, W. H., Braden, A. W. H. and Moule, G. R. (1962) Synchronization of estrus in sheep by an orally active progesterone derivative. *Aust. J. Agric. Res.* **13,** 901.

Spitzer, J. C. and Carpenter, R. H. (1979) Synchronized breeding of cycling ewes to produce fetuses of known gestational age. *Lab. Anim. Sci.* **29,** 755-758.

Stacy, B. D., Gemmell, R. T. and Thorburn, G. D. (1976) Morphology of the corpus luteum in the sheep during regression induced by prostaglandin $F_{2\alpha}$. *Biol. Reprod.* **14,** 280-291.

Thimonier, J. and Cognie, Y. (1971) Acceleration des mises bas et conduite d'elevage chez les ovins. *Bull. Tech. Inform. Minist. Agric.* **257,** 187-196.

Thorburn, G. D. and Nicol, D. H. (1971) Regression of ovine corpus luteum after infusion of $PGF_{2\alpha}$ into ovarian artery and vein. *J. endocr.* **51,** 751-752.

Trounson, A. O., Willadsen, S. M. and Moor, R. M. (1976) Effect of prostaglandin analogue Cloprostenol on oestrus, ovulation and embryonic viability in sheep. *J. Agric. Sci., Camb.* **86,** 609-611.

Tsamis, C., Poilas, S., Coutras, A., Hanjithomas, V. and Liossis, G. (1974) Fertility of oestrus by intravaginal sponges and implants on anoestrous ewes. *Thessaloniki* 88-93.

Tsakalof, P., Vlanchos, N. and Iatomsakis, D. (1977) Observations on the reproductive performance of ewe lambs synchronized for oestrus. *Vet. Rec.* **100,** 380-382.

Umo, I. (1974) Effect of prostaglandin $F_{2\alpha}$ on the ultrastructure and function of sheep corpora lutea. *J. Reprod. Fert.* **43,** 287-292.

Velle, W. and Helle, Oddvar (1979) Experience with estrus synchronization in sheep over a twelve-year period. *J. Anim. Sci.* **48,** 1015-1019.

Vipond, J. E. and King, M. E. (1979) Synchronization of oestrus as an aid to management in small flocks. *Anim. Prod.* **28,** 447.

Xenoulis, P. C., Minotakis, C. S. and Tsamis, C. (1972) The evaluation of progesterone implants and MPA-impregnated sponges for the advancement of the breeding season in ewes. *Proc. 7th Int. Congr. Anim. Reprod. & A.I. (Munich),* **2,** 990-994.

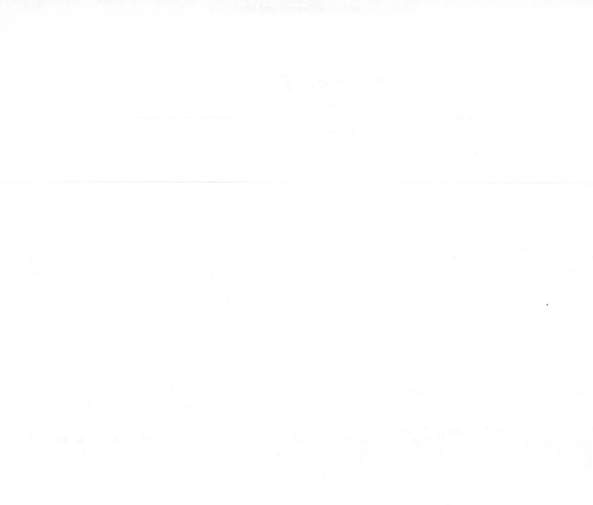

CHAPTER 13

Fixed-Time Sheep Artificial Insemination

13.1 INTRODUCTION

Artificial insemination of sheep has been applied most extensively in the Soviet Union and in countries of Eastern Europe where most of the breeding ewes on collective farms are bred by this method (Ozin, 1966, 1968; Jheltobruch, 1979). However, the sheep AI technique as practised in Russia involves the use of teaser rams to detect those sheep in oestrus and inseminating each ewe as she comes into her natural heat period; most ewes are bred using 0.05 ml of undiluted semen within 20 min of taking the collection from the ram (Jheltobruch, 1979). The system would not be practicable but for the large-flock conditions in the Soviet Union which permit an acceptable number of ewes to be available for insemination on a daily basis. For this reason, the application of sheep AI in Ireland and various other Western European countries has, until recently, been confined to experimental work. For any serious thought of applying AI under the small flock conditions of Ireland, it is essential that any need for oestrus detection be eliminated and that all members of the flock or selected group be inseminated at a pre-determined hour.

13.1.1 Possible advantages of sheep AI

Artificial insemination could offer the sheep farmer three possible advantages over natural service in controlled breeding applications; it could be used to overcome the present need to gather a bunch of rams to meet the 1:10 ram/ewe ratio, to avoid instances of poor conception rate in sheep arising from ram subfertility and it could have merit in making rams of particular genetic value freely available to farmers. There is also the important possibility of employing sheep AI in breeding improvement programmes in order to identify the genetically superior sires.

In Ireland, as in many other countries, breed improvement is effected by what is done in pedigree flocks where the pure-bred sires are produced for sale subsequently to the commercial farmers. Any improvement that is achieved in the pedigree flocks will be reflected eventually in the quality of the commercial sheep population. There are many ways in which AI can play a valuable role in the progeny testing of rams.

197

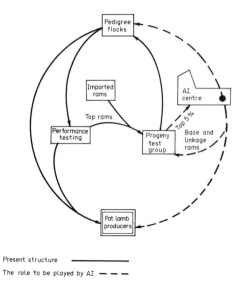

Present structure   ——————————

The role to be played by AI — — —

Fig. 13.1. Diagrammatic representation of a proposed breeding and testing system for using AI in Suffolk ram breeding. (From Smith, 1977)

In France, where it is estimated that more than 200 000 ewes are currently bred each year by AI, the technique is employed among milking sheep very much with a view to improving genetic quality by the use of superior sires. In North America, according to Langford et al. (1979), the desirability of adopting AI in the sheep industry is becoming increasingly important with the greater recognition of the need for breeding programmes to maximize genetic progress for economic traits.

13.1.2 AI and conception
As well as making genetically desirable rams available, sheep AI should also be capable of getting ewes pregnant as readily as when rams are employed in breeding by natural service; if the technique is to be usefully employed in commercial practice, the cost and labour involved in its application can only be justified if there is a consistent and acceptably high conception rate to the AI service. However, AI is certainly not a magic wand that can be waved over the flock; it does have technical problems of its own (storage and dilution of semen) and there is the important question of cost. Until about 1970, conception rates with AI in sheep after

controlled breeding were quite unacceptable in the great majority of reports.

13.2 PROGESTAGEN-PMSG TECHNIQUES

French investigators were the first to develop satisfactory semen handling procedures and to show that it was possible to obtain acceptable conception rates using the intravaginal sponge and PMSG to control ovulation and a two dose insemination technique (Colas et al., 1968; Colas and Brice, 1970; Brice, 1972; Colas et al., 1973, 1974; Colas, 1975b; 1979). In their work, there was no attempt to detect oestrus and the timing of the two inseminations was based on the time of progestagen withdrawal rather than on the time of oestrus onset; the times chosen were 50 and 60 h after terminating treatment. In using AI after the progestagen-PMSG technique, it was known that the oestrus control measure could be applied without reducing the ewe's fertility to any great extent. Although the studies of the sixties had shown that pre-treatment of ewes with progestagens could result in an impairment of sperm transport (Quinlivan and Robinson, 1969) with a consequent reduction in fertility, later studies showed that this need not always be so (Allison and Robinson, 1970). If it was a matter of applying an optimal controlled breeding technique to sheep in the autumn breeding season, then the ewes could exhibit a degree of fertility much the same as in the untreated sheep.

13.2.1 Irish efforts in AI
In Ireland, farm applications of AI were first attempted in the early 1970s, using the semen processing techniques described by Colas et al. (1968) as the basis of the work. The sheep AI application involved two inseminations, each of 200×10^6 sperm in 0.2 ml volume, with an interval of 10–14 h separating the two sperm doses. Smith et al. (1977) used FGA-PMSG to control oestrus in 853 cyclic sheep, the ewes being either naturally mated or artificially inseminated. There was no significant difference between the two breeding methods in the number of sheep conceiving to

Table 13.1 *Effect of PMSG dose level on lambing outcome in ewes conceiving at the synchronized oestrus. From Smith et al. (1977)*

Breeding Method	PMSG i.u.	No ewes	Litter size				Ewes lambing	(%)	Lambs born	Lambs ewe
			1	2	3	4+				
Artificial	375	214	70	65	10	1	146	(68.2)	234	1.60
Insemination	750	210	48	77	20	6	151	(71.9)	287	1.89
Natural	375	214	15	80	17	2	156	(72.9)	277	1.77
Service	750	215	45	83	30	10	168	(78.1)	343	2.04

first service (AI, 70%; Natural service, 75.5%); these results were comparable to those reported elsewhere for two insemination procedures. Thus, French studies reported average conception rates ranging from 60.5 to 75% Colas et al., 1968, 1973; Colas, 1975); in the U.K., the Meat and Livestock Commission in their field trials, involving 1000 sheep treated with MAP-PMSG, reported conception rates ranging from 52 to 78% with an overall average of 59%.

13.2.2 Progestagen and PMSG doses

In Ireland, several trials have been conducted to look specifically at the effect of PMSG dose level and at the particular progestagen employed in the intravaginal sponge; as already mentioned, these studies have shown a small but significant difference in conception rate to the AI in favour of FGA (30 mg dose level) when compared with MAP (60 mg dose level) and no effective improvement in conception rate when 750 i.u. rather than 375 i.u., was the gonadotrophin dose level chosen (Smith et al., 1981), Such data are of general interest, in view of the fact that current French efforts in sheep AI are apparently based on the use of sponge pessaries impregnated with 30–40 mg FGA (Colas, 1975, 1979), whereas efforts in the U.K. by the M.L.C. and in sheep AI work in Iceland have been based on the 60 mg MAP intravaginal sponge (Barlow et al., 1974; Dyrmundsson, 1977). The importance of using PMSG in association with intravaginal FGA in improving the precision of ovulation has been mentioned by Canadian workers who have also shown that low doses of PMSG (150–300 i.u.) were effective with their particular sheep breeds (Langford and Hackett, 1980).

13.3 COLLECTING SEMEN FOR AI PURPOSES

Rams should be carefully trained for semen collection by artificial vagina and frequent semen collections should be maintained at regular intervals throughout the year. Most rams can be readily trained, using teaser ewes that are artificially induced in oestrus (spayed ewes treated with intravaginal progestagen and a dose of 25–50 μg oestradiol at sponge withdrawal). Various methods may be employed to increase sperm output, such as exposing the ram to ewes in oestrus and to witnessing other males being collected from McGrath et al., 1979). Work elsewhere has shown that testicular function may be enhanced under certain conditions if rams are constantly kept in close proximity to oestrous ewes (Sanford and Yarney, 1980). There is ample evidence to show that the artificial vagina, rather than electro-ejaculation, is the preferred method of semen collection (Memon and Ott, 1981).

13.3.1 Semen doses

In work in Ireland, the usual procedure is to take one or two collections per day from each ram during the working week (Monday–Friday) and to provide the males with a 2-day period over the weekend to rest; at this rate of semen collection, it is possible to plan on each ram providing 50 semen doses per week (400–500 million sperm per dose) for just as long as the AI season lasts. Elsewhere, semen collection studies in the U.K., carried out with Suffolk rams by the M.L.C., have shown them to be capable of producing some 220 semen doses weekly during the breeding season as compared with only about 50 doses in the ewe anoestrus (Anon, 1978); this would be a measure of semen production as between autumn and

Table 13.2 *Effect of oestrous teaser on total sperm output (sperm/ejaculate $\times 10^9$)*

Rams		Oestrus teaser	Non-oestrous teaser
Breed	No.	Total sperm output sperm/ejaculate $\times 10^9$	Total sperm output sperm/ejaculate $\times 10^9$
Suffolk	(5)	2.10	1.85
Texel	(5)	1.63	1.23
Dorset Horn	(5)	2.29	2.02
Total	(15)	2.01	1.70

McGrath *et al.* (1979)

spring. As mentioned earlier, French workers have reported that ram semen collected in the spring contains a much higher incidence of morphologically abnormal sperm than that collected in the autumn and have suggested that this can influence fertility of the males markedly (Colas, 1979, 1980, 1981); these studies were with Ile-de-France rams and it is not yet clear how far these findings apply to other breeds. Certainly, in Ireland, there has been no evident increase in morphological abnormalities in the semen produced by Suffolks in the spring.

13.4 PREPARATION AND PROCESSING OF SEMEN

In current AI work in Ireland (Gordon and Crosby, 1980), semen is collected from rams and used in inseminations within 6 h; only those rams yielding ejaculates of high quality are allowed to contribute to the day's AI programme. The quality of semen is assessed on the basis of motility, concentration and morphology of the sperm. Motility of sperm, or wave motion as it occurs in undiluted semen under low power microscopy, is described by a grade (0, no wave motion; 5, very fast moving waves). Smith *et al.* (1979) used semen samples with a wave-motion grading of 3.0 or above in their AI work; this involved rejection of about 20% of samples collected from Suffolk, Texel and Dorset Horn rams in their programme.

13.4.1 Pooled semen and milk diluent
Pooled semen (at least three rams contributing) is extended in a skim-milk diluent, the

Fig. 13.2. Evaluation and processing of ram semen. Semen of high quality is essential to maintain acceptable conception rates when operating a Sheep AI Service. Grading of semen samples is on the basis of wave-motion, using a 0–5 scale. No semen sample is accepted unless it shows a grading of 3.5 or higher. Rams that are employed in the AI are monitored at regular intervals to get a complete evaluation of their fertility status. After a great deal of testing in the 1960s, the standard diluent adopted was skim milk. This had been shown by French workers to be excellent medium for diluting ram semen and all the experience at Lyons has gone towards confirming that fact.

formulation being based on that given in the report of Colas *et al.* (1978). Most diluents for ram semen have either egg yolk or milk or a combination of the two as a basic ingredient; in the present instance, the diluent is reconstituted skim-milk, heated (92–90°C for 10 min) to inactivate a factor harmful to ram sperm and containing trace amounts of antibiotics and other ingredients (penicillin, streptomycin, sulphanilamide, catalase). In present work, semen is diluted to provide a standard sperm density of 2000 million per ml. Diluted semen is cooled to 15°C over a period of 30 min before being loaded into 0.25 ml capacity Cassou straws and packed into vacuum containers before transport to the farm; a storage temperature of 15°C is maintained up to the time of using the semen in AI.

Elsewhere, Canadian workers report using skim-milk and adjusting the sperm density to a value of 900 million sperm/ml, a 0.5 ml volume of diluted semen is employed to provide a sperm dose of 450 million in an insemination (Langford and Hackett, 1980). The influence of storage time and temperature on the fertility of ram has been reported, in a preliminary study, by Langford and Fisher (1980); at sperm doses of 450 million in 0.5 ml, storage at 4°C allowed semen to be kept for 24 h without reducing fertility whereas at 15°C, fertility decreased markedly when storage time exceeded 6 h.

13.4.2 One vs two inseminations

An important advance in the development of a commercially acceptable AI technique came by way of reducing from two inseminations to a single one in suitable categories of sheep (Colas, 1975, 1979; Smith et al., 1978). In adopting this simplification, it seems necessary for ewes to be inseminated with the same total sperm dose (400–500 million) as that employed with two insemination procedures (2×200 million or more); in regard to timing, it has usually been a question of using the figure mid-way between the two times previously employed (making it 55–57 h after progestagen-PMSG for most single dose AI techniques). In Ireland, experimental results have been borne out in subsequent farm applications in which conception rates in excess of 70% have been achieved after breeding cyclic

ewes at 56 h after progestagen withdrawal (Gordon and Crosby, 1980).

Simplification of the AI technique to a single insemination eases considerably the cost and labour involved in farm applications and opens the way to much greater use of the procedure in sheep breeding programmes. In the Irish experience, the denser semen (2000 million per ml) employed in single insemination has a shorter storage life in the 0.25 ml Cassou straw than the semen previously employed in double inseminations (1000 million/ml); a 6-h rather than a 12-h storage period is currently employed to meet that difficulty.

The timing, when two inseminations are carried out after progestagen-PMSG treatment, differs in a minor way from country to country. French workers have inseminated ewes at 50 and 60 h after sponge withdrawal (Colas et al., 1973) whereas M.L.C. researchers have inseminated at 48 and 64 h (Barlow et al., 1974). In Canada, the timings have been 54 and 60 h (Langford and Hackett, 1980); earlier work in the U.K. employed inseminations at 48 and 58 h (McClelland and Quirke, 1971). In Ireland, two main systems have been employed in timing double inseminations (Smith et al., 1977b). In one system, the first insemination was timed for 09.00 h and the second for 19.00 h; this was on the second day after progestagen (i.e. at 48 and 58 h). The alternative to this system was where the first insemination was at 19.00 h on the second day and the final one at 09.00 h on the third day (48+62 h). The percentage of ewes conceiving after AI was much the same in the two systems (Smith et al., 1977b).

Table 13.3 *Effect of sperm doses on outcome of sheep AI (1973 to 1976) (U.C.D. data)*

Season	Ewes to AI	Lambed	Lambs born	Conception rate (%)	Litter-size	Sperm doses
		First services only				
	5072	3461	6171	68.2%	1.78	2×200 million
Autumn breeding season	396	250	456	63.2%	1.82	1×200–300 million
	478	354	601	74.0%	1.70	1×400 million
Totals	5946	4065	7228	68.5%	1.78	1–2 doses

13.4.3 Insemination and ovulation

As already mentioned, much is known about the timing of oestrus and ovulation after progestagen-PMSG in sheep; it is usual for oestrus to commence about 36 h after sponge withdrawal, for the heat period to be about 36 h in length and for ovulation to occur about 70 h or so after progestagen withdrawal (Boland et al., 1978). Thus, a single insemination at 56 h should permit sperm to be available in the reproductive tract for some hours before ovulation.

For ease of applying the AI technique on the farm, there would be much in favour of carrying out insemination at 48 rather than 56 h; present timing involves withdrawal of progestagen at 08.00 h to permit a 16.00 h insemination 2 days later. In view of the evidence showing that ovulation in FGA/MAP-treated ewes occurs about 70 h after sponge removal (Boland et al., 1978) conducting the AI at 48 h would not be appropriate, although such timing would greatly facilitate the planning of on-farm operations. Greater knowledge of factors influencing the timing of ovulation may permit it to be done in some circumstances.

13.5 INSEMINATION PROCEDURES

One major difficulty with these fixed-time AI procedures is the fact that very large sperm doses are required (400–500 million total sperm in one or two inseminations). In normal AI, as employed, for instance in Soviet Russia, the sperm dose is of the order of 120–150 million; in Australia, Salamon (1962, 1977) and Allison and Robinson (1971) showed in their AI studies that something of the order of 120 million sperm could be regarded as the minimal sperm dose for normal conception rates in untreated cyclic sheep.

Present AI applications in France and Ireland among synchronized sheep involve using the Cassou sheep inseminating gun to deposit semen in the first fold of the cervix (Colas, 1975; Gordon, 1975; Smith et al., 1978); attempts have been made in Ireland, using a specially designed inseminating instrument, to deposit semen deeper than usual in the cervical folds but this depressed rather than enhanced the conception rate (Smith et al., 1978).

13.5.1 Intrauterine AI

Although at one time it was held that nonsurgical insemination into the uterus of the ewe could not be achieved (Grant, 1934; Gunn, 1936), it has been shown to be a possibility by others in more recent times (Andersen et al., 1973; Fukui and Roberts, 1976). Nevertheless, it remains too tedious and difficult a procedure to be considered as a viable alternative to the usual cervical technique. Intrauterine deposition of semen performed by surgery can be employed in certain situations, such as in embryo transfer operations in sheep (Boland and Gordon, 1978), but is obviously not applicable in normal AI programmes on farms.

13.5.2 Inseminator effects

As in cattle, the ability of the inseminator can have a marked effect on the outcome of sheep AI; this has been noted in France (Aguer and Le Provost, 1976) and elsewhere (Gordon and Crosby, 1980). In the U.K. trials have been conducted to examine the possibility of suitably trained farm staff carrying out inseminations with semen supplied from a central ram stud (Anon, 1978); working with 444 MAP-PMSG-treated ewes and using semen stored for up to 8 h, the average conception rate achieved with farm staff as inseminators was 53% compared with 66% with M.L.C. inseminators. This work did show, however, that in certain instances, farm staff achieved results comparable with trained inseminators.

13.5.3 Restraining ewes

Work in Ireland shows that sheep handling facilities on the farm need not be elaborate; the usual method employed for restraining is to hold the ewe over a bale of straw. The actual insemination, although requiring some degree of skill and experience on the part of the operator, can occupy less than 1 min per ewe; efficiency in locating the mouth of the cervix can vary with the age of the ewe and the equipment used. In the Irish experience, it is regarded as essential that ewes for AI are handled as gently as

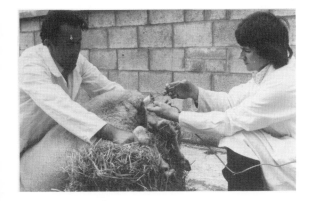

Fig. 13.3. Standard method of restraining ewe for AI over a straw bale. Among the different considerations in developing a commercially viable Sheep AI Service for Irish conditions is the amount of time and labour involved in carrying out the actual insemination. What is needed is a simple straight-forward method of restraint, which involves a minimum of discomfort to the ewe — and which is capable of permitting a rapid throughput of sheep. The standard method involves holding the ewe over a bale of straw — to afford ready access to the inseminator to place the 0.2 ml semen dose in the first fold of the sheep's cervix. Every effort is made to prevent undue agitation of the ewe around the time of AI — on the understanding that this will assist the fertilization process.

possible at the time of insemination and that the flock as a whole is not subjected to any unnecessary agitation. French experience appears to agree with this and workers in that country have suggested that the group awaiting insemination should not exceed 40–50, no matter how many sheep are to be dealt with (Aguer and Le Provost, 1976). This group size phenomenon is presumably a measure of the agitation which can arise among sheep if they are being constantly disturbed as members of a large flock.

13.5.4 Stress and sheep AI

There is evidence that ewes subjected to relatively short-term nutritional or management stress around the time of mating can show markedly reduced fertility, whether this stems from problems that interfere with fertilization or from a higher than usual loss of embryos after conception (Gunn and Doney, 1975; Doney et al., 1976). It has always been a rule, with controlled breeding techniques as applied in Ireland, that farmers should handle the ewes (and rams) with the minimum of disturbance around the time of oestrus; the observance of this principle

probably becomes all the more important when breeding sheep by AI rather than natural service.

Robinson (1973) is one worker who has noted that the passage of sperm through the ewe's cervix may be impaired in stressed sheep; such stress could arise from having ewes in unfamiliar surroundings, the presence of dogs and even the act of insemination itself. Manipulations of the cervix to collect mucus in progestagen-PMSG-treated sheep bred by AI apparently decreased conception rate in a study reported by Le Roux (1976). It should also be mentioned that, other things being equal, it would seem preferable to operate sheep AI on the basis of a single insemination technique rather than one involving several inseminations, for reason of minimizing stress effects; this type of consideration could be especially relevant in dealing with sheep unaccustomed to regular handling.

13.6 SHEEP AI AND PROSTAGLANDINS

The results from some studies in Ireland did indicate that a single set-time insemination at 56 h (after treatment) was much less effective in

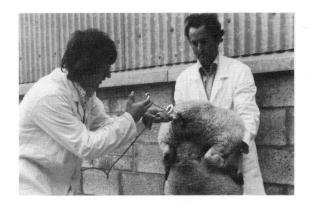

Fig. 13.4. Alternative method of holding sheep for insemination. This method is not for use on the large Galway (73 kg bodyweight) type of sheep — but it can be employed in light breeds of ewe. An important aspect of sheep AI is the skill and experience of the inseminator. In field work in sheep AI conducted from the University farm, the ability of inseminators has been shown to be one source of variation in conception rates, even though a standard training method has been employed. It is certainly possible to think in terms of farm staff being able to inseminate ewes after a training period.

achieving fertilization in Cloprostenol-treated ewes than in FGA-treated sheep (Boland et al., 1978); It was felt that there was need for further investigations before it could be concluded that prostaglandins are an alternative to progestagens for oestrus control, when breeding is by AI. Elsewhere, one study was reported by the M.L.C. in the U.K. which gave results of a comparison between MAP-progestagen treated ewes and sheep receiving a two dose prostaglandin analogue treatment (9-day interval); the work involved 300 ewes, and conception rates were 26% for prostaglandin and 61% for progestagen-treated ewes, respectively. In Canada, Hackett et al. (1980) also presented evidence of variable fertility when prostaglandin treatment was followed by timed AI in different breeds of sheep; it appeared that breed type influenced the timing of ovulation in the sheep. The present conclusion to be drawn from prostaglandin work is that it does not currently offer a viable alternative to progestagens if fixed-time AI is to be the method of breeding; it remains to be seen whether further work will change this view.

13.6.1 Prostaglandins in semen

Apart from the possible use of prostaglandins in controlling oestrus and ovulation in the ewe, there is a further consideration; the use of PG's as semen additives to improve fertility after sheep AI. The seminal plasma of the ram is one of the richest natural sources of prostaglandins, which are synthesized in the seminal vesicles and secreted into the plasma; several prostaglandins have been identified, including PGE_2 and $PGF_{2\alpha}$. There is evidence in some mammals that sperm motility can be influenced by the presence of certain levels of PG (Schleger et al., 1981); the indications are that PG's exert a protective influence on sperm motility. As mentioned earlier, the addition of PGs to ram semen has been shown to result in an increased conception rate in some studies (Dimov and Georgiev, 1977; Gustafsson et al., 1975); it is not clear whether the effect arose from improvements in sperm transport or in the survival rate of the cells. In Ireland, the use of PGE_2 and $PGF_{2\alpha}$ in sheep AI work was not found to improve fertility but

effects were evident in vitro on sperm motility (Boland, unpublished data; other workers have also reported that PGs at certain concentrations can reduce sperm motility (Cohen et al., 1976; Schleger et al., 1981). The eventual hope in this type of research, is that semen additives such as prostaglandins may increase the effectiveness of a single insemination procedure.

13.7 ADDITIONAL AGENTS TO CONTROL OVULATION

As already mentioned, there is plenty of evidence to show that conception rates in sheep inseminated after intravaginal progestagen treatment are significantly and often substantially greater among those receiving PMSG than those that do not (Colas and Brice, 1970; Colas, 1972); the explanation of the PMSG effect is presumably that of confining the time of ovulations within more precise limits. There have been some attempts to confine the occurrence of ovulation within narrow time-limits more directly; this has involved administering an ovulating hormone preparation (hCG) at a certain time (e.g. 28–32 h) after progestagen withdrawal on the assumption that ovulation would occur about 24 h later (Dziuk et al., 1970; Roche and Crowley, 1971). In such studies, ewes have been bred either by AI or natural service at a predetermined hour some time before the expected ovulations; according to Dziuk (1970), the optimum time for breeding is about 12 h prior to ovulation.

In practical terms, the cost and labour involved in administering an ovulating hormone, even if it were shown to be effective in gaining closer control of the ovulatory process, would be a serious obstacle at farm level. As it is, several other investigators who have employed hCG after a progestagen-PMSG regimen have found no effect on the timing of ovulation (Killeen and Moore, 1970; Smith, 1977).

13.7.1 Oestradiol and sheep AI

The results of some studies in the U.S.A. have suggested that the administration of oestradiol to oestrous ewes near the time of natural service may improve sperm transport through the cervix,

Fig. 13.5. ⌐Establishing a sheep AI service in the Irish Republic. In Ireland, sheep AI has been seen as a method of making Texel and other rams available to farmers who would otherwise not have an opportunity of using them. It is also seen as a possible contributor to the progeny testing of the main fat-lamb sire breed — the Suffolk. Dr. Tony Smith, seen here, was responsible for developing the Sheep AI Service in the early 1970s and for demonstrating that it was possible to achieve a 70% conception rate to a single AI under Irish conditions of breed and management. In the 9 years, 1973–1981, 13 541 ewes in 436 different farm flocks around the country have been inseminated by a Sheep AI Service operated from the University Farm at Lyons Estate. The aim has been to refine techniques to the point that they could be taken over by one or other of the Cattle AI Stations in the Republic.

ported lambing rates of 6, 25 and 69% for sheep injected with oestradiol and bred with frozen–thawed semen, ewes inseminated with frozen semen without oestradiol and ewes bred with fresh semen without oestradiol, respectively; the authors considered that the oestrogen dose probably led to an increase in embryonic mortality.

13.8 FROZEN SEMEN POSSIBILITIES

There is ample evidence in the literature showing that AI in sheep permits a reproductive performance in the ewe comparable to that obtained by natural mating (Colas, 1975, 1979; Gordon, 1975a) but results also show that the performance obtainable with fresh semen cannot yet be achieved with frozen semen (Colas, 1979; Langford et al., 1979). The general view is that the use of frozen ram semen fails primarily because of the reduced viability of the cells and the impairment of sperm transport through the cervix; this results in a reduction in the number of sperm reaching the site of fertilization (Mattner et al., 1969; Lightfoot and Salamon, 1970). Avoiding the cervix by way of uterine insemination, whether via laparotomy (Lightfoot and Salmon, 1970) or by non-surgical intrauterine insemination (Fukui and Roberts, 1976) has apparently given similar fertilization rates for both fresh and frozen semen. Whether this is the whole story, remains to be seen. Langford et al.(1979) did find evidence of increased embryonic mortality when they used frozen rather than fresh ram semen (33% wastage vs 6% in the period between day-18 and term); differences between frozen and fresh were also noted at an earlier stage by Lightfoot and Salamon (1970).

13.9 FUTURE DEVELOPMENTS

Considerable effort has been made in recent times to bring the reproductive processes of the ewe under close and effective control; having gone to the trouble and cost of doing this, then it may seem unwise that the question of conception should be left very much to the behaviour and

counteract the inhibitory effect of a progestagen-regulated oestrus on sperm transport and increase the proportion of uterine contractions moving towards the oviduct (Hawk, 1975a, b; Hawk and Cooper, 1975, Hawk et al. (1978). However, in Canada, Langford et al. (1980) examined the effect of oestradiol on fertility in ewes inseminated with frozen semen at a progestagen-PMSG controlled oestrus and re-

Table 13.4 *Lambing outcome in 1980 and 1981 to AI in the counties of Roscommon and Wexford (Texel rams)*

County	Year	Sheep to AI	Ewes lambing to artificial insemination			
			Lambed	Lambs born	Conceptions to AI	Litter size
Roscommon	1980	759	561	1023	73.9%	1.82
	1981	639	465	809	72.8%	1.74
Wexford	1980	428	329	650	70.3%	1.91
	1981	265	183	356	69.1%	1.94
Totals	—	2145	1538	2838	71.7%	1.85

Table 13.4 sets out results that were achieved by a single AI (at 56 h after progestagen–PMSG) in the recent two breeding seasons. There is every indication that it is possible to maintain a 70% conception rate to a single service–based on the use of fresh semen and a sperm dose of 400 × million.

fertility of rams under a system of natural mating. The fixed-time AI technique, as currently available for use in the autumn breeding season, is the simplest type of AI now possible in any of the farm species. There is the problem that insemination at 56 h after progestagen–PMSG makes careful planning on the farm necessary, both in terms of terminating treatment and in conducting the AI subsequently. However, the insemination procedure itself is technically less difficult than either in cattle or pig AI, so that farmers or shepherds could be expected to carry out the procedure themselves, where necessary. There is no reason why further improvements in the AI technique cannot be achieved, either as a result of adjustments to the oestrus control procedure or to certain aspects of semen quality.

13.10 REFERENCES

Aguer, D. and Le Prevost L (1976) *L'Insemination artificielle ovine.* Searle Lab. Publn. 123 pp.

Allison, A. J. and Robinson, T. J. (1970) The effect of dose level of intravaginal progestagen on sperm transport, fertilisation and lambing in the cyclic Merino ewes. *J. Reprod. Fert.* **22,** 515–521.

Allison, A. J. and Robinson, T. J. (1971) Fertility of prostagen-treated ewes in relation to the numbers and concentration of spermatozoa in the inseminate. *Aust. J. Biol. Sci.* **24,** 1001–1008.

Anderson, K., Amadal, J. and Fougner, J. A. (1973) Intrauterine and deep cervical insemination with frozen semen in sheep. *Zuchthygiene* **8,** 113–118.

Anon (1978) Artificial insemination and reproduction. *M.L.C. 11th Ann. Rept.* 25.

Barlow, M., Pryce-Jones, D. and Reed, H. C. B. (1974) MCL

Sheep AI field trials: A comparison of milk and egg-yolk diluents. *Vet. Rec.* **94,** 159–160 (Abs).

Boland, M. P. and Gordon, I. (1978) Recovery and fertilization of eggs following natural service and uterine insemination in the Galway ewe. *Ir. Vet. J.* **32**(7), 123–125.

Boland, M. P., Gordon, I. and Kelleher, D. L. (1978) The effect of treatment by prostaglandin analogue (ICI 80996) or progestagen (SC 9880) on ovulation and fertilization in cyclic ewes. *J. Agric. Sci., Camb.* **91,** 765–766

Brice, G. (1972) Artificial insemination of sheep in France. *Patre* **190,** 18–21.

Cohen, M. S., Colm, M. J., Golimbu, M. and Hotchkiss, R. S. (1976) The effects of prostaglandins on sperm motility. *Fert. Steril.* **28,** 78.

Colas, G. (1972) Ewe fertility following insemination with liquid or deep frozen semen in the course of oestruses induced by progestins during the breeding season. *Proc. 7th Int. Congr. Anim. Reprod. A.I. (Munich),* **3,** 924–930.

Colas, G. (1975a) Effect of initial freezing temperature, addition of glycerol and dilution on the survival and fertilizing ability of deep-frozen ram semen. *J. Reprod. Fert.* **42,** 277–285.

Colas, G. (1975b) The use of progestagen SC 9880 as an aid for A.I. in ewes. *Ann. Biol. Anim. Bioch. Biophys.* **15**(2), 317–327.

Colas, G. (1979) Fertility in the ewe after A.I. with fresh and frozen semen at the induced oestrus, and influence of the photoperiod on the semen quality of the ram. *Livest. Prod. Sci.* **6,** 153–166.

Colas, G. (1980) Suggested international standards for ram semen exchange. *Proc. 9th Int. Congr. Anim. Reprod. A.I. (Madrid)* **2,** 287–296.

Colas, G. and Brice, G. (1970) Fertility of ewes treated with FGA and inseminated artificially with frozen semen; preliminary results Annls. Zootech. 353–357.

Colas, G. and Cognie, Y. (1968) A.I. with or without estrus detection following a progestational treatment in the ewe. *Proc. 6th Int. Congr. Reprod. A.I. (Paris)* 264.

Colas, G., Dauzier, L., Courot, M., Ortanvant, R. and Signoret, J. P. (1968) Results obtained while investigating some important factors in A.I. in Sheep. *Ann. Zootech.* **17,** 47–57.

Colas, G., Thimonier, J., Courot, M. and Ortavant, P. (1973) Fertility prolificacy and fecundity during the breeding season of ewes artificially inseminated after treatment with fluorogestrone acetate. Ann. Zootech. 22(4), 441–451.

Colas, G., Brice, G. and Guerin, Y. (1974) Acquisitions recentes en Matiere d'insemination artificielle ovine. Bull. Tech. Inform. Minist. Agric. 294, 795–800.

Dimov, V. and Georgiev, G. (1977) Ram semen prostaglandin concentration and its effect on fertility. J. Anim. Sci. 44, 1050–1054.

Doney, J. M., Smith, W. F. and Gunn, R. G. (1976) Effects of post-mating environmental stress or administration of ACTH on early embryonic loss in sheep. J. Agric. Sci., Camb. 87, 133–136.

Dyrmundsson, O. R. (1977) Synchronization of oestrus in Iceland ewes with special reference to fixed-time artificial insemination. Acta. Agric. Scand. 27, 250–252.

Dziuk, P. J. (1970) Estimation of optimum time for insemination of gilts and ewes by Double mating at certain times relative to ovulation. J. Reprod. Fert. 22, 277–282.

Dziuk, P. J., Ellicott, A. R., Webel, S. K. and O'Reilly, P. D. (1970) Appointment of the hour of mating in the ewe. J. Anim. Sci. 31, 221.

Fukui, Y. and Roberts, E. M. (1976) Fertility of non-surgical intra-uterine insemination with frozen-pelleted semen in ewes treated with prostaglandin $F_{2\alpha}$. Proc. Int. Congr. Sheep Breed, Muresk, 482–494.

Gordon, I. (1975a) The use of progestagens in sheep bred by natural and A.I. Ann. Biol. Anim. Biochim. Biophys. 15(2), 303–316.

Gordon, I. (1975b) Hormonal control of reproduction in sheep. Proc. Br. Soc. Anim. Prod. 4, 79–93.

Gordon, I. and Crosby, T. F. (1980) A.I. in sheep promises well. Ir. Farmers J. 32(25), 12–13.

Grant, R. (1934) Studies on the physiology of reproduction in the ewe. Trans. R. Soc. Edin. 58, 1.

Grant, R. (1934) Studies on the physiology of reproduction in the ewe. Trans. R. Soc. Edin. 58, 1.

Gunn, R. M. C. (1936) Bull. C.S.I.R.O. 94, 125.

Gunn, R. G. and Doney, J. M. (1975) The interaction of nutrition and body condition at mating on ovulation rate and early embryo mortality in Scottish Blackface ewes. J. Agric. Sci. Camb. 85, 465–470.

Gustafsson, B., Edqvist, S., Einarsson, S. and Linge, F. (1975) The fertility of deep frozen ram semen supplemented with $PGF_{2\alpha}$. Acta Vet. Scand. 16, 468–470.

Hackett, A. J., Langford, G. A. and Robertson, H. A. (1980) Fertility and prolificacy of confined ewes treated with $PGF_{2\alpha}$ and bred by A.I. J. Anim. Sci. 51(Suppl. 1), 282 (abs).

Hawk, H. W. (1975a) Enhancement by exogenous estradiol of uterine motility in estrous ewes. J. Anim. Sci. 41, 572–577.

Hawk, H. W. (1975b) Hormonal control of changes in the direction of uterine contractions in the estrous ewe. Biol. Reprod. 12, 423–430.

Hawk, H. W. and Cooper, B. S. (1975) Improvement of sperm by the administration of estradiol to estrous ewes. J. Anim. Sci. 41, 1400–1406.

Hawk, H. W., Conley, H. H. and Cooper, B. S. (1978) Number of sperm in the oviducts uterus and cervix of the mated ewe as affected by exogenous estradiol. J. Anim. Sci. 46, 1300–1308.

Jheltobruch, N. A. (1979) AI of sheep in the Soviet Union. In, Sheep Breeding, 2nd Ed. Tomes, et al., revised Haresign, W. Butterworths, London.

Killeen, I. D. and Moore, N. W. (1970) Fertilization and survival of fertilized eggs in the ewes following surgical insemination at various times after the onset of oestrus. Aust. J. Biol. Sci. 23, 1279–1287.

Langford, G. A. and Fisher, P. S. (1980) Influence of storage temperature and duration of storage on the fertilizing capacity of extended ram semen. J. Anim. Sci 51(Suppl. 1), 295 (abs).

Langford, G. A. and Hackett, A. J. (1980) Dose-related effects of PMSG in breeding confined sheep by artificial insemination. Can. J. Anim. Sci. 60, 562–563.

Langford, G. A., Ainsworth, L., Hackett, A. J., Heaney, D. P. and Peters, H. F. (1979) A.I. of sheep with fresh and frozen spermatozoa. Can. J. Anim. Sci. 59, 835.

Langford, G. A., Marcus, G. J., Hackett, A. J., Ainsworth, L., Wolynetz, M. S. and Peters, H. F. (1979) A comparison of fresh and frozen semen in the insemination of confined sheep. Can. J. Anim. Sci. 59, 685–691.

Langford, G. A., Marcus, G. J., Hackett, A. J., Ainsworth, L. and Wolynetz, M. S. (1980) Influence of estradiol-17B on fertility in confined sheep inseminated with frozen semen. J. Anim. Sci. 51, 911–916.

Le Roux, P. J. (1976) The conception rate of MAP and MAP-PMSG-treated Karakul ewes inseminated with diluted semen. S. Afr. J. Anim. Sci. 6, 1–5.

Lightfoot, R. H. and Salamon, S. (1970) Fertility of ram spermatoza frozen by the pellet method. I. Transport and viability of spermatozoa within the genital tract of the ewe. J. Reprod. Fert. 22, 385–398.

McClelland, T. H. and Quirke, J. F. (1971) Artificial insemination and natural service at a pre-determined time in cyclic sheep treated with SC 9880 — Progesterone sponges. Anim. Prod. 13, 323–328.

McGrath, P. E., Boland, M. P. and Gordon, I. (1979) Effect of sexual preparation procedures on semen characteristics in the ram. J. Agric. Sci., Camb. 93, 761–763.

Mattner, P. E., Entwhistle, K. W. and Martin, I. C. A. (1969) Passage, survival and fertility of deep frozen ram semen in the genital tract of the ewe. Aust. J. Biol. Sci. 22, 181–187.

Memon, M. A. and Ott, R. S. (1981) Methods of semen preservation and artificial insemination in sheep and goats. Wld Rev. Anim. Prod. 17(1), 19–24.

Ozin, F. V. (1966) A.I. in sheep — an outstanding achievement of scientists in the U.S.S.R. Zhivotnovodstvo 28(3), 27–31.

Ozin, F. V. (1968) The role of artificial insemination in the re-organisation of sheep breeding in the U.S.S.R. Zhivotnovodstvo 30(7), 64–69.

Quinlivan, T. D. and Robinson, T. J. (1969) Numbers of spermatozoa in the genital tract after artificial insemination of progestagen-treated ewes. J. Reprod. Fert. 19, 73–96.

Roche, J. F. and Crowley, J. P. (1971) The effect of controlling the interval from mating to ovulation on pregnancy rate in ewes treated with progesterone. J. Reprod. Fert. 24, 307–309.

Sanford, L. M. and Yarney, T. A. (1980). Social environment and seasonality in reproductive processes of rams. Can. J. Anim. Sci., 60, 1040.

Salamon, S. (1962) Studies on the artificial insemination of merino sheep. Aust. J. Agric. Res. 13, 1137.

Salamon; S. (1977) Artificial Insemination of Sheep. Chippendale, N.S.W. Publicity Press Ltd.

Schleger, W., Rotermundis, S., Farber, G and Nieschlag, E. (1981) The influence of prostaglandins on sperm motility. Prostaglandins 21, 87–99.

Smith, J. F. (1977) Estrus, ovulation and conception following times insemination in Romney ewes treated with progestagen and gonadotrophins. *Theriogen.* **7**(2), 63–72.

Smith, P. A. (1977). Studies in the artificial insemination of sheep. Ph.D. thesis, National University of Ireland, Dublin.

Smith, P. A., Boland, M. P. and Gordon, I. (1977a) Lambing outcome in farm flocks following set-time A.I. and natural service. *J. Dept. Agric. (Dublin)* **74**, 44–49.

Smith, P. A., Boland, M. P. and Gordon, I. (1977b) Effect of timing of inseminations on lambing to a double A.I. *Jr. Ir. Dept. Agric. (Dublin)* **74**, 50–55.

Smith, P. A., Boland, M. P. and Gordon, I. (1978) Conception rate in ewes: effect of method of breeding and number of inseminations. *J. Agric. Sci., Camb.* **91**, 511–512.

Smith, P. A., Boland, M. P. and Gordon, I. (1979) Studies in ram semen collection for use in A.I. during the breeding season. *J. Ir. Dept. Agric. (Dublin)* **74**, 56–65.

Smith, P. A., Boland, M. P. and Gordon, I. (1981) Effect of type of intravaginal progestagen on the outcome of fixed-time A.I. *J. Agric. Sci., Camb.* **96**, 243–245.

CHAPTER 14

Advancing the Sheep Breeding Season

14.1 INTRODUCTION

Although it is generally held that the beginning and end of the sheep's breeding season is controlled by natural daylength changes, the precise onset of the season in any one year is probably the result of many modifying factors. The breed, age and previous reproductive history of ewes, changes in the environmental temperature and the sudden introduction of the ram to ewes can all have a modifying effect on the occurrence of oestrus. It has been suggested that the onset of breeding is probably unaffected by the nutritional status of the ewe unless it is very low (Hafez, 1952; Radford, 1959; Ducker and Boyd, 1974).

As already mentioned, the relationship between photoperiodicity and ovarian activity in the ewe is probably more complex than some reports and reviews may indicate. Certainly, as noted by Robertson (1977), the fact remains that no continuously successful system of breeding ewes on a production basis at 6–8 month intervals by the use of controlled lighting alone, has as yet been reported. In the various studies which have been made with a view to advancing the breeding season, it has been a matter of looking at possible light manipulations, at hormonal treatments and

at producing breeds or crosses of sheep which start showing oestrous cycles earlier than usual.

14.2 LIGHT MANIPULATIONS

There are two main types of artificial daylength control which are capable of influencing reproductive activity in ewes; it can be a matter of providing a gradual decrease or increase in artificial daylength, similar to what occurs under natural daylength conditions (Yeates, 1949) or it may be done by subjecting the ewes to an abrupt decrease on one day and thereafter maintaining them at that daylength until a response is shown (Hafez, 1952; Fraser and Laing, 1969).

Inevitably, the response of ewes to any light manipulation is not immediate and may often be a matter of months rather than weeks. However, the time of year at which light treatment is applied is known to have a marked effect on the speed of response (Ducker and Bowman, 1970b) and the greater the decrease or increase in daylength applied, the quicker the ewes respond (Ducker et al., 1970; Ducker and Bowman, 1970a). Inducing ewes in the U.K. to breed by light control soon after the longest day in June was reported by Ducker and Bowman (1970b) to be much more effective than if attempts were being made when natural daylength is increasing and ewes have just entered anoestrus (in the March to May period). One practical disadvantage of using light control is the fact that individual ewes show oestrus after varying intervals; several weeks may elapse between the time the first and the last sheep in the flock comes in heat.

14.2.1 Lighting systems employed

As to the lighting regimens employed by different investigators, Ducker and Bowman (1972) used one involving the abrupt extension of daylength to 22 h either in late pregnancy or at parturition followed by a reduction to that of natural daylength; this system had the merit of dispensing with the need for a light-proof building, which it would be difficult to justify on the basis of the high costs involved (requirement for forced ventilation, among other things). Newton and Betts (1972), on the other hand, used a regimen involving an abrupt increase in daylength to 18 h for 1 month during late pregnancy followed by an abrupt decrease to a constant level of 8 h; this proved effective in inducing a fertile oestrus within about 3 months after parturition in March-lambing ewes. Despite such experimental work in the U.K. in developing these light control measures, it appears that only one large-scale commercial unit in England has regularly employed this approach towards advancing the breeding season (Murdoch, 1975); the practical aim has been to get ewes breeding in June for very early lamb production.

14.3 RAM EFFECT

Seasonally anoestrous ewes of many breeds, if preconditioned by a period of isolation from rams, respond to the reintroduction of rams (teasing) by exhibiting a relatively well synchronized heat period about one oestrous cycle interval later, as shown in studies with Merinos (Underwood et al., 1944; Schinckel, 1954a, b; Watson and Radford, 1960; Hunter and Lishman, 1967; Oldham et al., 1979; Martin et al., 1980; Fulkerson et al., 1981) with Romneys (Edgar and Bilkey, 1963; Coop and Clark, 1968; Tervit et al.,

1977; Knight et al., 1981) and Merino's d'Arle (Prud'hon and Denoy, 1969). This phenomenon, known as the "ram effect", has been used in commercial sheep farming with varying degrees of success.

Coop and Clark (1968) suggested that an acceptable result for their South Island conditions in New Zealand was 80% of Romney ewes mated in 6 days, 55–66% of ewes lambing within 1 week, 12% of ewes lambing in 1 day at the peak of lambing and this date predictable to 2 days. Results from ram introductions conducted elsewhere in New Zealand, however, particularly in the North Island, have shown that there may be no response among ewes to the ram effect in some seasons yet a satisfactory response in others (McDonald, 1971). There is evidence that some ram breeds (Dorset) can induce a greater response than others (Romney) among Romney ewes (Tervit et al., 1977); an even greater effect, in which Dorset teaser rams initiated cyclic breeding in ewes about 16 days earlier on average than Romney teasers was noted in similar work done later (Meyer, 1979).

Fig. 14.1. Use of the ram to stimulate an earlier start to breeding in the ewe. The introduction of the ram among ewes during the later part of the non-breeding season has been shown to be effective in inducing ovulation and subsequently oestrus. However, the response of the ewe to the ram will certainly vary according to a number of factors, and it is unwise to rely on such an approach under Irish conditions. When used in conjunction with the intravaginal sponge, the presence of the ram from the time of progestagen withdrawal can serve as a stimulus to the occurrence of oestrus among ewes that would otherwise show a "silent-heat". However, should there be any doubt as to whether ewes are cyclical or not, the normal policy is to use PMSG and leave ram introduction until 48 hr later

14.3.1 Ram pheromone effect

It is apparent that rams do not need to be in physical or visual contact with the ewe to produce an effect (Watson and Radford, 1960) and ewes with their sense of smell impaired do not exhibit oestrus after being stimulated by rams (Morgan et al., 1972). Such evidence led to the suggestion that pheromones may be produced by the rams which stimulate breeding activity. It may be that differences between Dorset and Romney rams in their ability to stimulate ewes may arise from differences in the production of pheromones (Tervit and Peterson, 1978). Knight and Lynch (1980) have also reported that pheromones present in the wool and/or wax of entire rams were able to produce a response in ewes, further strong evidence that olfactory cues constitute the main sensory input from the ram at teasing. As a means of alleviating the problem of a slow onset of oestrous activity in New Zealand Romneys early in the autumn season, Knight and Lynch (1980) suggest the isolation and subsequent commercial use of this pheromone in concentrated form to stimulate ewes to exhibit oestrus earlier and to achieve partial synchronization.

14.3.2 Timing of oestrus and ovulation

As already mentioned, the introduction of rams in the latter weeks of the ewe's non-breeding season will often stimulate some proportion of anoestrous ewes to ovulate within 2–3 days (Knight et al., 1978; Oldham et al., 1979) although behavioural oestrus is not shown at this time but usually after about 3 weeks (Schinckel, 1954). In recent years, it has become clear that the response of ewes, in ovarian terms, is rather more complex than was at one time thought. It appears that there are often two peaks of oestrous activity in response to the ram effect, the first at about 18 days after contact with the male and the second at about 22–24 days (Schinckel, 1954a, b; Hunter et al., 1971; Fairnie, 1976; Fulkerson et al., 1981). If ovulation occurs within 3 days of exposure to the ram and the normal life span of the ovine corpus luteum is taken as 14 days, then some other factor must be operating in ewes that show oestrus at 3 weeks or later.

An explanation of the delayed oestrus was suggested in the observations of Tervit et al.

(1977) who reported that many of the Romneys in his study ovulated twice before exhibiting oestrus; it appeared that the first corpus luteum had regressed after 6–8 days. This was in agreement with earlier work elsewhere in which premature regression of corpora lutea by day-10 has been found in Merinos stimulated to ovulate by rams (Oldham and Martin, 1979) and was supported in subsequent studies reported by Knight et al. (1981); in the latter work, a small peak of progesterone indicated that such corpora lutea did secrete some amount of steroid. As noted already, adequate progesterone priming is essential in the ewe if behavioural oestrus is to accompany ovulation (Robinson, 1959). When progestagen was administered to anoestrous ewes prior to teasing, there was no evidence of premature regression of corpora lutea (Hunter et al., 1971); this suggested to Oldham and Martin (1979) that a progestational phase not only facilitates behavioural oestrus but also prevents premature regression of the ram-induced corpora lutea.

14.3.3 Ram effect and LH

According to Michigan workers (Legan and Karsch, 1979) lack of ovulation in sheep during the ewe anoestrus is the result of an increased negative feed-back action of oestrogen upon the tonic secretion of LH. Ram introduction is believed to result in a sustained increase in LH through increased pulse frequency of release of the gonadotrophin. Chesworth and Tait (1974) observed LH levels to increase within 1 h of exposing Greyface ewes to the ram just prior to the breeding season. There is also evidence that the frequency of LH pulses may be greater in Merinos than in Welsh Mountain ewes during anoestrus and this may explain why certain breeds such as the Merino can respond to the ram effect even in mid-anoestrus (Schinckel, 1954a); such stimulated ewes apparently experience a preovulatory surge of LH similar to that of spontaneously ovulating sheep and ovulate on average about 40 h after ram introduction (Oldham et al., 1980). It would seem possible that ram-induced ovulations occur because there is a lowering of the sensitivity of the hypothalamus to the negative feedback action of oestrogen

(Martin et al., 1979); this permits an increased frequency of LH pulses, which may be easier to activate in Merinos than in some other breeds.

14.3.4 Overexposure to rams

Schinckel (1954a, b) did observe that ewes which had been continually exposed to sterile rams during the non-breeding-season resumed their seasonal reproductive activity at a later date than sheep isolated from males during anoestrus; it is evident that individual ewes differ in their sensitivity to oestrogen (Robinson, 1955; Robinson and Moore, 1956) and it is possible that the continuous presence of the ram during the anoestrous season might modify the sensitivity of the nervous mechanisms mediating oestrous behaviour. There are other reports which would indicate that when ewes are subjected to the ram stimulus for several months, adaptation to this stimulus occurs and such sheep apparently become less sensitive to stimuli which induce breeding activity (Radford and Watson, 1957; Lishman, 1975). The practical point here is that farmers should ensure that rams are well and securely separated from the ewes during the spring and summer months if they are to attempt using the ram to induce early breeding.

14.4 POSSIBLE RAM SUBSTITUTES

The introduction of vasectomized "teaser" rams has been employed in New Zealand sheep to induce early breeding (Edgar and Bilkey, 1963). It has been observed that vasectomy is relatively expensive and more care is required to manage rams than wethers or ewes; an alternative system using ewes or wethers as the "teasers" could be of advantage. Lishman et al. (1969) and D'Occhio and Brooks (1976) have been among those to suggest that hormone-treated castrate male sheep (wethers) may provide a reasonable substitute for the vasectomized ram. Marit et al. (1979) reported that treatment with doses of 50 mg testosterone propionate at 2-day intervals for 20 days (induction regimen) and at 10-day intervals afterwards (maintenance regimen) produced male type behaviour in ewes; not only did testosterone-treated ewes exhibit male

behaviour but other ewes treated them as such. Work reported by Fulkerson et al. (1981) has shown that wethers treated with oestrogen or testosterone, but not untreated wethers, could be effective in the initiation of breeding activity in ewes in late anoestrus.

14.5 USE OF PROGESTAGEN-PMSG

In summer 1973, lowland sheep farmers in most counties in the Irish Republic could telephone their local Cattle AI centre and request the services of a technician to treat sheep for early-lamb production with intravaginal sponges (FGA/MAP) and PMSG. The 60 p per sheep service, which was made available at that time, covered two farm visits by the technician; the first to insert sponges, the second, 12–14 days later, to withdraw them and administer the doses of 500 i.u. PMSG. On the basis of considerable experimental evidence, the farmer could expect about 60–70% of ewes treated to conceive to first services and to lamb within about a week in December or early January; between the first and second services, some 80% of the flock would produce early-lambs. The service, based on natural mating, was used by several hundred farmers in that first year of operation and has been made available on a similar basis each year up to the present time; in 1981, the fee per ewe stood at £2.00 but the price for the early-lamb had increased four-fold from £12 to £50 and more (40 lb carcase at Easter).

The introduction of this cheap, effective and simple controlled breeding technique for the advancement of the sexual season in sheep was the result of considerable research and development activity during the 1960s and early seventies by researchers in the Agricultural Institute and by workers in University College Dublin. Due credit should also be given to the State Department of Agriculture, the body that had initially sponsored extensive field-testing of early-breeding techniques and had arranged with the Cattle AI centres to provide countrywide coverage on a fee per ewe basis from 1973.

Fig. 14.2 Start of early breeding service offered by Cattle AI Stations in the Irish Republic since 1973. Controlled breeding has been made available as a service by the Dublin AI Station and others since the summer of 1973. The first flock treated under the scheme is being dealt with here by Mr. Jimmy Edwards. A number of technicians were trained at Lyons Farm in the early 1970s and since then have carried on the service in various parts of the country.

Table 14.1. *Lambing results for Department scheme in 1972 and 1973*

| | | | Birth of "early-lambs" | | | | | |
| | | | Lambed to first service | | | Lambed to 1st and 2nd services | | |
Year	No. Flocks	Sheep	% ewes	Lambs per conception	Lambs per 100 ewes treated	% ewes	Lambs per conception	Lambs per 100 ewes treated
1972	207	8314	61.6	1.6	100	80.2	1.6	126
1973	307	11 159	65.6	1.6	105	79.3	1.6	124

As a result of the encouraging results which were obtained in field trials operated from UCD Lyons Estate in the late 1960s, the State Department of Agriculture agreed to sponsor a 2-year trial on controlled breeding for early lamb production in 1971 and 1972. Table 14.1 summarizes the results that were obtained in the 2 years of the trial. It was on the basis of these findings that the State Department of Agriculture brought in a fee-paying service for controlled breeding which has been operated since 1973 by Cattle AI Stations in the country.

14.5.1 Late anoestrus in Irish sheep

As already mentioned, daylength plays an important role in maintaining seasonal reproductive activity in Irish and British sheep breeds, but other factors, such as temperature, ram effect and possibly nutrition, quite apart from the breed of ewe, may exert an effect on the initiation of the mating season. Irish sheep which lamb at the usual time in February/March and nurse their lambs for 12–16 weeks certainly do not show evidence of spontaneous heats in the month of July; these are the sheep which are generally treated for early-lamb production.

The controlled breeding treatment offers the sheep farmer three possible advantages; the birth of most of the lambs at an agreed time in December/January; a litter-size which is in keeping with the mid-season performance of the sheep breed; and that most of the lambs will be born in a compact period of about 1 week. It should be mentioned here that ewes that breed spontaneously show a much lower litter-size at the start of their season than they do a month or two later (Johansson and Hansson, 1943); the use of the gonadotrophin in the controlled breeding technique can overcome this difficulty. The Irish experience is that the hormonal approach gives an acceptable early-lambing result when applied to adult sheep; whether the sheep farmers gain financially is very much a question of their adopting low-cost lamb rearing systems (Keane, 1975).

14.5.2 Outcome in relation to time of treatment

The usual period of treatment for early-lambs in Ireland extends for 6 weeks, sponges being inserted from about the end of June until mid-August. Within this period, the percentage of ewes becoming pregnant (first and second services) should rise as the summer progresses; to the farmer, the lambing outcome can almost be the same in sheep bred in early July as in those bred a month later in August. The fact that the response of ewes to the progestagen-PMSG treatment is little affected during the last several weeks of anoestrus is of general interest because it agrees with some previous observations (Gordon et al., 1969) in which dry anoestrous ewes, treated in May and June (mid-anoestrus) were often found to exhibit a second (spontaneous) heat period when conception did not occur at the controlled oestrus. Clearly, cyclical release of pituitary gonadotrophins may be initiated some months prior to the normal autumn season, and not only during the last few weeks of the ewe anoestrus.

As already mentioned, the general view is that daylength is the overriding environmental factor controlling reproductive activity in the ewe; the

Table 14.2. *Early-lambing outcome in relation to time of treatment*

Time of treatment	Sheep	Lambing to 1st service		Lambing to 1st + 2nd services	
		No.	%	No.	%
Early — June 30 to July 14	2632	1524	58%	2065	79%
Medium — July 15 to July 28	4278	2719	63%	3487	81%
Late — July 29 to Aug. 11	1085	726	67%	916	84%

results from the early-lamb studies suggest that the hypothalamic centres involved in gonadotrophin release can be activated to maintain cyclical activity, even when a factor such as daylength is not operating favourable. This may suggest that much of the ewe's early anoestrus is really a refractory period in which neural centres become unduly sensitive to the negative feedback effects of ovarian oestrogen; however, this refractoriness may eventually lessen to the extent that certain stimuli may be capable of initiating cyclical ovarian activity some time prior to that usual with decreasing daylength as the main controlling exteroceptive factor.

14.6 USE OF Gn-RH

Attempts have been made to induce resumption of oestrous cycles by administering Gn-RH to ewes during the seasonal anoestrus (Crighton and Foster, 1976, 1977; Haresign et al., 1975; Sharenha et al., 1976; Haresign and Lamming, 1978) but there is evidence of a sub-normal luteal phase in the ewes which have ovulated (Haresign et al., 1975; Shareha et al., 1976). One suggestion is that this sub-normal function is the result of an inadequate release of LH at ovulation (Crighton et al., 1973). However, the fact that PMSG treatment in such sheep has resulted in fully functional corpora lutea may indicate that the difficulty is one of inadequate gonadotrophin priming before the preovulatory LH surge rather than to an inadequacy in the LH surge itself (Haresign and Lamming, 1978). The method of administering the Gn-RH may also be a relevant consideration; Kesler and Vincent (1980) gave the agent subcutaneously in such a way in carboxymethylcellulose or in a gelatin capsule) as to prolong its action and reported evidence of a much more natural (prolonged) LH surge than when Gn-RH was given by injection. At this point in time, natural and synthetic forms Gn-RH have been employed in seasonally anoestrous ewes to induce ovulation but such methods do not yet appear to have practical relevance.

14.7 BREEDING AND FEEDING

Of the various breed-types of sheep entered by Irish farmers for early-lamb production, using the intravaginal progestagen-PMSG treatment, the best results have been achieved with the more prolific ewes (e.g. Half-Breds or Greyfaces); they have shown the highest conception rates and litter-sizes in response to a standard FGA-PMSG regimen (Jennings, 1973; Gordon, 1975). It has also been observed that the prolific Half-Bred/Greyface type of sheep can show a greater readiness than some other breeds to maintain cyclical activity, when conception does not occur at the FGA-PMSG-induced heat; this can result in a high percentage (86%) of the treated ewes becoming pregnant to first and second services. It may be that the greater gonadotrophin levels associated with prolific sheep permits them to maintain cycles in the summer in a way less likely with other breeds.

Table 14.3. *Lambing outcome after summer breeding in relation to breed of ewe*

Breed or Cross of ewe	PMS dose (i.u.)	No. of ewes	% lambed	Litter size	No. of ewes	% lambed	Litter size	% lambing to 1st and 2nd services
Galway	500	991	52.9	1.55	7974	63.8	1.54	77.4
	750	1027	59.2	1.65				
Suffolk-Cross	500	827	58.6	1.67	5964	64.4	1.71	82.5
	750	789	60.7	1.77				
Cheviot	500	316	64.9	1.51	1743	61.7	1.58	76.5
	750	332	65.2	1.75				
Border Leicester x Blackface/ Border Leicester x Cheviot	500	293	65.0	1.72	1234	68.1	1.71	85.8
	750	290	69.0	1.85				
		(Jennings, 1973)				(Gordon, 1974)		

14.8 REFERENCES

Chesworth, J. M. and Tait, A. (1974) A note on the effect of the presence of rams upon the amount of luteinizing hormone in the blood of ewes. *Anim. Prod.* **19,** 107–110.

Coop, I. E. and Clark, V. (1968) *Proc. N.Z. Soc. Anim. Prod.* **28,** 114.

Crighton, D. B. and Foster, J. P. (1976) Effects of duplicate injections of synthetic LH-RH at various intervals on LH release in the anoestrous ewe. *J. Endocr.* **69,** 36–37.

Crighton, D. B. and Foster, J. P. (1977) Luteinizing hormone release after two injections of synthetic luteinizing hormone releasing hormone in the ewe. *J. Endocr.* **72,** 59–67.

Crighton, D. B., Hartley, B. N. and Lamming, G. E. (1973) Changes in the luteinizing hormone releasing activity of the hypothalamus, and in the pituitary gland and plasma luteinizing hormone during the oestrous cycle of the ewe. *J. Endocr.* **58,** 377–385.

D'Occhio, M. J. and Brooks, D. E. (1976) The influence of androgens and oestrogens on mating behaviour in male sheep. *Theriogen.* **6,** 614.

Ducker, M. J. and Bowman, J. C. (1970a) Photoperiodism in the ewe. 3. The effects of various patterns of increasing daylength on the onset of anoestrus in Clun Forest ewes. *Anim. Prod.* **12,** 465–471.

Ducker, M. J. and Bowman, J. C. (1970b) Photoperiodism in the ewe. 4. A note on the effect of onset of oestrus in Clun Forest ewes of applying the same decrease in daylength at two different times of the year. *Anim. Prod.* **12,** 513–516.

Ducker, M. J. and Bowman, J. C. (1972) Photoperiodism in the ewe. 5. An attempt to induce sheep of three breeds to lamb every eight months by artificial daylength changes in a non-light-proofed building. *Anim. Prod.* **14,** 323–334.

Ducker, M. J. and Boyd, J. S. (1974) The effect of daylength and nutrition on the oestrous and ovulatory activity of Greyface ewes. *Anim. Prod.* **18,** 159–167.

Ducker, M. J., Thwaites, C. J. and Bowman, J. C. (1970) Photoperiodism in the ewe. 1. The effects of decreasing daylength on the onset of oestrus in Clun Forest ewes. *Anim. Prod.* **12,** 115–123.

Edgar, D. G. and Bilkey, D. A. (1963) The influence of rams on the onset of the breeding season in ewes. *Proc. N.Z. Soc. Anim. Prod.* **23,** 79–87.

Fairnie, I. J. (1976) Organisation of artificial breeding programmes of sheep in Western Australia. *Proc. Int. Sheep Breed. Congr.* Tomes et al., Eds. pp. 500–508. Waite Press, Perth.

Fraser, A. F. and Laing, A. H. (1969) Oestrus induction in ewes with standard treatments of reduced natural light. *Vet. Rec.* **84,** 427–430.

Fulkerson, W. J., Adams, N. R. and Gherardi, P. B. (1981) Ability of castrate male sheep treated with oestrogen or testosterone to induce and detect oestrus in ewes. *Appl. Anim. Ethol.* **7,** 57–66.

Gordon, I. (1974). Controlled breeding in sheep. *Ir. vet. J.,* **28,** 118–126.

Gordon, I. (1975) Hormonal control of reproduction in sheep. *Proc. Br. Soc. Anim. Prod.* **4,** 79–93.

Gordon, I., Caffrey, W. and Morrin, P. (1969) Induction of early breeding in sheep following treatment with progestagen impregnated pessaries and PMSG. *J. Ir. Dept. Agric. Dublin* **66,** 3–22.

Hafez, E. S. E. (1952) Studies on the breeding season and reproduction of the ewe. *J. Agric. Sci., Camb.* **42,** 189–265.

Haresign, W., Foster, J. P., Hayne, N. B., Crighton, D. B. and Lamming, G. E. (1975) Progesterone levels following treatment of seasonally anoestrous ewes with synthetic LH-releasing hormone. *J. Reprod. Fert.* **43,** 269–279.

Haresign, W. and Lamming, G. E. (1978) Comparison of LH release and luteal function in cyclic and LH-RG-treated anoestrous ewes pretreated with PMSG or oestrogen. *J. Reprod. Fert.* **52,** 349–353.

Hunter, G. L. and Lishman, A. W. (1967) Effect of the ram early in the breeding season on the incidence of ovulation and oestrus in sheep. *Proc. S. Afr. Soc. Anim. Prod.* **6,** 00–00.

Hunter, G. L., Belonje, P. D. and Von Niekerk, C. H. (1971) Synchronized mating and lambing in spring-bred Merino sheep flocks: the use of progestagen-impregnated intravaginal sponges and teaser rams. *Agroanimalia* **3,** 133–140.

Jennings, J. J. (1973) Effect of progestagen treatment, number of matings and the time of mating on fertility in sheep. *Ann. Rpt. Anim. Prod. Div. AFT, Dublin.*

Johansson, I. and Hansson, A. (1943) The sex ratio and multiple births in sheep. *Lantbruk, Hoesk. Ann.* **11,** 145–171.

Keane, M. G. (1975) Use of forage crops in early fat lamb production. *Ir. J. Agric. Res.* **13,** 251–262.

Kesler, D. J. and Vincent, D. L. (1980) Effect of carrier and administration on luteinizing hormone release by gonadotropin releasing hormone. *J. Dairy Sci.* **63,** 2121–2125.

Knight, T. W. and Lynch, P. R. (1980) Source of ram pheromones that stimulate ovulation in the ewe. *Anim. Reprod. Sci.* **3,** 133–136.

Knight, T. W., Peterson, A. J. and Payne, E. (1978) The ovarian and hormonal response of the ewe to stimulation by the ram early in the breeding season. *Theriogen.* **10**(5), 343, 353.

Knight, T. W., Tervit, H. R. and Fairclough, R. J. (1981) Corpus luteum function in ewes stimulated by rams. *Theriogen.* **15**(2), 183–190.

Legan, S. J. and Karsch, F. J. (1979) Neuroendocrine regulation of the estrous cycle and seasonal breeding in the ewe. *Biol. Reprod.* **20,** 74–85.

Lishman, A. W. (1975) Reduced sensitivity to oestrogen in ewes continuously associated with rams. *S. Afr. J. Anim. Sci.* **5,** 235–238.

Lishman, A. W., de Lange, G. M. and Viljoen, J. T. (1969) Ability of masculinized ewes to stimulate onset of the breeding season in maiden Merino ewes. *Proc. S. Afr. Soc. Anim. Proc.* **8,** 141.

McDonald, M. F. (1971) Factors associated with onset of the breeding season in sheep. *Sheepfarming Annual, Massey Univ.,* 23–30.

Marit, G. B., Scheffrahn, N. S., Troxel, T. R. and Kesler, D. J. (1979) Sex behaviour and hormone responses in ewes administered testosterone propionate. *Theriogen.* **12,** 375–381.

Martin, G. B., Oldham, C. M. and Lindsay, D. R. (1980) Increased plasma LH levels in seasonally anovular Merino ewes following the introduction of rams. *Anim. Reprod. Sci.* **3,** 125–132.

Meyer, H. H. (1979) Ewe and teaser breed effects on reproductive behaviour and performance. *Proc. N.A. Soc. Anim. Prod. 39th Ann. Conf.* **39,** 68–76.

Morgan, P. D., Arnold, G. W. and Lindsay, D. R. (1972) A note on the mating behaviour of ewes with various senses impaired. *J. Reprod. Fert.* **30,** 151–152.

Murdoch. D. (1975). Change of season for 1000 ewes. *Farmers' Weekly,* **83,** 62.

Newton, J. E. and Betts, J. E. (1972) A comparison between the effect of various photoperiods on the reproductive performance of Scotch half-bred ewes. *J. Agric. Sci., Camb.* **78,** 425–433.

Oldham, C. M. and Martin, G. B. (1979) Stimulation of seasonally anovular Merino ewes by rams. II. Premature regression of ram-induced corpora lutea. *Anim. Reprod. Sci.* **1,** 291–295.

Oldham, C. M., Martin, G. B. and Knight, T. W. (1979) Stimulation of seasonally anovular Merino ewes by rams. I. time from introduction of the rams to the preovulatory LH surge and ovulation. *Anim. Reprod. Sci.* **1,** 283–290.

Prud'hon, M. and Denoy, I. (1969) The effect of ram introduction on oestrus in Merinos d'Artes sheep, the frequency of errors in the detection of oestrus and the fertility of the ewe. *Ann. Zootech.* **18,** 95–106.

Radford, H. M. (1959) *Aust. J. Agric. Res.* **10,** 377.

Robinson, T. J. (1955) Endocrine relationships in the induction of oestrus and ovulation in the anoestrous ewe. *J. Agric. Sci., Camb.* **46,** 37–43.

Robinson, R. J. (1959) Estrous cycle of the ewe and doe. In, *Reproduction in Domestic Animals.* Cole, H. H. and Cupps, P. T. Eds. Academic Press, New York.

Robinson, T. J. and Moore, N. W. (1956) The interaction of oestrogen and progesterone on the vaginal cycle of the ewe. *J. Endocr.* **14,** 97–109.

Robertson, H. A. (1977) Reproduction in the ewe and the goat. In, *Reproduction in Domestic Animals, 3rd Ed.* Cole, H. H. and Cupps, P. T. Eds. pp. 477–498. Academic Press, New York.

Schinckel, P. G. (1954a) The effect of the presence of the ram on ovarian activity of the ewe. *Aust. J. Agric. Res.* **5,** 465.

Schinckel, P. G. (1954b) The effect of the presence of the ram on the incidence and occurrence of oestrus in ewes. *Aust. Vet. J.* **30,** 189.

Shareha, A. M., Ward, W. R. and Birchall, K. (1976) Effect of continuous infusion of gonadotrophin-releasing hormone in ewes at different times of the year. *J. Reprod. Fert.* **46,** 331–340.

Tervit, H. R. and Peterson, A. J. (1978) Testosterone levels in Dorset and Romney rams and the effectiveness of these breeds in stimulating early onset of estrus in Romney ewes. *Theriogen.* **9**(3), 279–294.

Tervit, H. R., Havik, P. G. and Smith, J. F. (1977) Effect of breed of ram on the onset of the breeding season in Romney ewes. *Proc. N.Z. Soc. Anim. Prod.* **37,** 142–148.

Underwood, E. J., Shier, F. L. and Davenport, N. (1944) Incidence of oestrus in sheep. *J. Dept. Agric. W. Aust.* **21,** 135.

Watson, R. H. and Radford, H. M. (1960) The influence of rams on onset of oestrus in Merino ewes in the spring. *Aust. J. Agric. Res.* **11,** 65–71.

Yeates, N. T. M. (1949) The breeding season of the sheep, with particular reference to its modification by artificial means using light. *J. Agric. Sci., Camb.* **39,** 1–43.

CHAPTER 15

More Frequent Lambings in Sheep

15.1 INTRODUCTION

In most countries, production from sheep is very seasonal, meat and wool products coming available for marketing at regular dates once per year. Such seasonality of output places the sheep at some disadvantage compared with the other farm animals. At the same time, as noted by Wilson (1968), the ewe, with an estimated "biological ceiling" of five lambs per pregnancy and a potential mean lambing interval of 6 months, has much further to go in achieving her full reproductive potential than other farm species.

From the farmer's point of view, the economic return from his sheep will depend primarily on their reproductive efficiency. Increasing the frequency of lambing could increase reproductive efficiency, level out the flow of milk-fat lambs to the market and utilize buildings, capital and labour more efficiently (Hulet, 1979). However, because of the seasonal nature of breeding in sheep, any attempt to breed ewes at a greater frequency than once a year is likely to result in at least one mating during or near the sheep anoestrus in conventional seasonal breeding ewes. Despite a considerable amount of research on the reproductive biology of the ewe, little

practical use has been made of the new techniques designed to permit greater exploitation of the ewe's reproductive potential.

Although ewe productivity may be improved by increasing the frequency of lambing and modern technology now allows the farmer to manipulate breeding of the animal in ways not previously possible, there are still areas in which further research is required. It should also be remembered that the outcome of hormonal methods (progestagen-PMSG) may be markedly affected by factors such as feeding, lactational status, *post-partum* interval, ram effect, stress and the environment in general.

15.2 ENDOCRINE BASIS OF *POST-PARTUM* ANOESTRUS

If a ewe is to be bred twice yearly or three times in 2 years, the interval between lambing and rebreeding will be markedly shorter than usual. Thus, events in the *post-partum* ewe become of great importance in any consideration of frequent lambings. There is also the question of when the sheep is giving birth, for this may be at times in the year other than the normal spring period. With normal flock events, ewes give birth in spring, at the time they would be about to become anoestrous even if no pregnancy had occurred. The spring-lambing ewe, with lambs at foot, represents the most difficult category of ewe to deal with by way of controlled breeding procedures; she has both lactational anoestrous as well as seasonal anoestrus to deal with in the early months after giving birth.

The resumption of ovulation and ovarian activity in *post-partum* ewe can be influenced by season, lactation, nutrition and breed (Mauleon and Dauzier, 1965; Hunter, 1968; Restall, 1971; Mallampati *et al.*, 1971; Shevah *et al.*, 1974; Restall and Starr, 1977) but the endocrine basis of *post-partum* ovarian inactivity is not yet fully understood. During pregnancy in sheep, it is known that the pituitary content of LH may be depleted to less than 20% of that found in anoestrous ewes (Chamley *et al.*, 1974a, b; Jenkin *et al.*, 1977); this can be demonstrated by the fact that the amount of LH released in response to a dose of Gn-RH is markedly decreased. It is also known that this pituitary response to Gn-RH increases with time *post-partum* and that maximum response may be achieved earlier (5–7 weeks) in dry than in lactating (8–10 weeks) ewes (Pelletier and Thimonier, 1975); the suggestion is that the lower response in lactating ewes is due to lower production of ovarian steroids, particularly oestrogen, which plays a part in sensitizing the pituitary to Gn-RH.

There may be breed differences in responsiveness to Gn-RH; in Clun Forest and Finn Landrace ewes lambing in anoestrus, normal responsiveness to Gn-RH had returned within 6–8 weeks of parturition (Jenkin *et al.*, 1977) whereas Romney ewes lambing in anoestrus only exhibited partial restoration of responsiveness to Gn-RH at a similar period (Chamley *et al.*, 1974a). It has not been found, however, that Gn-RH responsiveness is of value in predicting the time at which breeding resumes after parturition in the sheep (Wright *et al.*, 1980).

15.2.1 Tonic LH levels post-partum

The immediate *post-partum* period is characterized by a gradual recovery of ovarian activity

(Van Niekerk, 1976), high prolactin levels which gradually decrease after the first week (Lamming *et al.*, 1974) and a low tonic LH level which increases slowly (Restall and Starr, 1977). Lack of ovarian activity could be due to an alteration in the response of the hypothalamic–pituitary axis to the negative feedback effect of oestrogen, similar to that shown for spayed ewes during anoestrus (Legan *et al.*, 1977). In the results presented by Wright *et al.* (1981a, b) there are indications that in *post-partum* ewes there is an increased inhibitory (negative-feedback) effect of oestradiol on LH release and a lower intrinsic frequency of pulsatile release of LH; the authors suggest that both seasonal anoestrus and the *post-partum* anoestrus may involve suppression of tonic LH due to increased inhibition by oestradiol.

15.2.2 Suckling effects

Among the factors known to influence the duration of the *post-partum* interval is suckling (Hunter, 1968) although there has been some debate in separating the effect of suckling from lactation. There have been those who argue that the early weaning of lambs reduces the interval to resumption of breeding (Mauleon and Dauzier, 1965; Mallampati *et al.*, 1971) and delays uterine involution (Van Niekerk, 1976; Honmode, 1977); others have maintained that lactation itself has little effect (Wagner and Veenhuizen, 1968; Fletcher, 1973) while some say that nutrition and season can modify the effects of suckling and lactation (Hunter and Van Aarde, 1973; Theriez and Molenat, 1975; Restall and Starr, 1977). Certainly, it would be generally accepted that lactational anoestrus is more pronounced at the end of the breeding season than at the beginning and where feeding is poor rather than generous.

Fletcher (1971) showed that the frequency of suckling in the first 2 weeks after lambing was correlated with the duration of the *post-partum* interval and Cognie *et al.* (1975) found that fertility at an induced oestrus in the *post-partum* ewe was reduced when two lambs rather than one were suckled. The stimulus of suckling in sheep can apparently result in elevated levels of prolactin in the blood and this can affect the release of LH in the *post-partum* period (Kann *et*

Fig. 15.1. Ewes nursing lambs in the spring season have been notoriously reluctant to respond effectively to hormonal treatments. It is very difficult to get the normal breed of ewe that lambs in the spring and is nursing lambs pregnant by controlled breeding procedures. Many farm trials, involving thousands of lactating sheep, have shown a conception rate of less than 40% at the induced oestrus. One category of ewe which can respond better is the early-lambing sheep, especially when the birth of lambs is in December and the ewes are treated with progestagen-PMSG in February or so. Response is likely to vary with the body condition of the ewe and is improved if the lambs have been taken away by the time of treatment. In Ireland, a bonus crop of lambs can be taken from some proportion of early-lambing sheep. Lambing in August or early-September means that they are ready to take the ram by October.

al., 1977); Kann and Martinet (1975) also showed that the *post-partum* interval was 30–40 days in milking ewes in contrast to 60–80 days among similar ewes nursing lambs.

As previously mentioned, it is known that the concentration of prolactin in sheep plasma is elevated during the seasonal anoestrus, not only in ewes (Pelletier, 1973; Erb *et al.*, 1977; Walton *et al.*, 1977) but in rams as well (Ravault, 1976). The prolactin concentration is also increased during lactation (Lamming *et al.*, 1974), particularly during and immediately after suckling (McNeilly *et al.*, 1972). Fitzgerald and Cunningham (1981) examined factors influencing prolactin concentrations in sheep and reported evidence suggesting that when plasma levels of prolactin are low, there is a greater likelihood of an earlier resumption of breeding activity in the ewe, although this was by no means always true; the findings did lend support to data presented earlier by Rhind *et al.* (1980) showing reduced fertility to be associated with high concentrations of prolactin.

15.2.3 Corpus luteum function

In the *post-partum* sheep, first ovulations may be characterized by a lower oestrogen peak in lactating than in non-lactating animals (Cognie *et al.*, 1975), a lower preovulatory LH peak (Lewis *et al.*, 1974; Cognie and Pelletier, 1976) and subsequent lower progesterone production by the corpus luteum (Cognie *et al.*, 1975) with a reduced lifespan (Restall, 1971). The occurrence of corpora lutea with a lifespan of only 6–7 days was also observed after parturition in lactating (Walton *et al.*, 1977) and non-lactating sheep (Land, 1971). As already mentioned, sub-normal corpora lutea of limited life-span may occur at the commencement of the normal autumn breeding season in response to the "ram effect".

15.2.4 Response to exogenous hormones

In considering out-of-season breeding in sheep, whether in the early months after parturition or later, it is relevant to mention the way in which season may influence the ewe's ability to respond to exogenous hormones; even in progestagen-PMSG treated ewes, oestrus and ovulation is the result of an interaction between the sensitivity of the appropriate neural centres and the quantity of ovarian oestrogen produced. Studies in the 1970s suggested that compared to the autumn ewe the quantity of oestrogen required to induce oestrus in the spring is increased by 40% and the amount of oestrogen produced per follicle reduced by 40% (Robinson, 1980); to correct for such seasonal differences, which may mean a late onset of heat and one of shorter duration than normal, Evans and Robinson (1980) suggested a 50% increase in the dose level of PMSG. In Ireland, however, the regular PMSG dose level of 500 i.u. has apparently induced oestrus almost as readily in the spring lactating ewe as in the "dry" sheep treated several months later (Gordon, 1975).

15.2.5 Failure of cyclical breeding activity

In the autumn season and in the normal flock situation, ewes which do not become pregnant at a progestagen-controlled oestrus almost invariably repeat an ovarian cycle later and are in a position to accept a second service. In the Irish experience, this results in about 90% of ewes conceiving at the first two heat periods. In the spring, the story is likely to be quite different; in many flocks, none of the sheep may "repeat" (return for a repeat service). Although these spring-mated ewes may have 2-month-old lambs at foot, this is not the principal reason why they fail to "repeat". The fact is that when autumn-lambing ewes are treated at a corresponding interval after parturition, they will "repeat" in much the same way as do "dry" cyclic ewes, and they conceive readily at the "repeat" oestrus, despite the fact that they may find themselves in an increasingly difficult nutritional environment as the autumn months progress. In all of this, the discussion applies to an outdoor commercial farming situation; it may not necessarily be so true when sheep are housed under well-controlled nutritional and environmental condition.

15.3 INVOLUTION OF THE UTERUS
POST-PARTUM

When lambings occur at the usual time in the spring, the sheep's uterus has ample time (7 months) prior to the autumn breeding season, in which to become prepared to sustain the next pregnancy. The question of restoration of uterine condition may be influenced by the season in which lambing occurs. In the spring, Robinson (1959) reported finding in the early *post-partum* uterus what appeared to be blood undergoing autolysis; it appeared that material arising from *post-partum* haemorrhage had been retained through inability to pass the cervix. Robinson (1959) concluded that this could be expected in sheep, a species which has a tightly interlocking cervix and which usually enters anoestrus on lambing in the spring with resultant uterine

Fig. 15.2. Autumn lambing ewes that produce lambs (after controlled breeding) in the autumn months can be expected to return in oestrus even though they may be nursing one or more lambs. Gestation periods for autumn-lambing ewes in the U.K. and Ireland have been shorter by a few days than spring lambings. Autumn lambing ewes can also show a much higher incidence of heats immediately after parturition — although these are anovulatory heats that occur presumably because the oestrogen levels or the sensitivity of the ewe to oestrogen varies with season.

inactivity and cervical closure; this view found further support in the evidence of McDonald and Rowson (1962) who reported the presence of detritus in the sheep's uterus in the early weeks after parturition in the spring.

Discussing some of the limitations to *post-partum* breeding in sheep, Niekerk (1976) notes that although ovulation may occur in some circumstances between 12–25 days after lambing, uterine involution and regrowth of epithelium may not be complete until the 26th day in the breeding season; during anoestrus, involution was delayed until the 30th day in "dry" sheep and the 36th day in nursing ewes. Elsewhere, uterine involution has been estimated to be complete within 24 days (Call *et al.*, 1976) or from 35 days for non-lactating to 60 days for lactating ewes (Honmode, 1977). Clearly, for those striving to achieve a lambing interval of 6 months, the efforts may be counter-productive; although individual ewes may well conceive within 6 months of a previous conception the above observations on involution would suggest that the time taken for the uterus to recover is too long to permit a continuous 6-month lambing interval on a flock basis; a more realistic minimum interval is probably about 7 months.

15.4 ACCELERATED LAMBING SYSTEMS

Hunter (1968) reviewed attempts up to that time to increase the frequency of lambing but concluded that there was no way in which this could be achieved consistently on a flock basis with techniques then available. Since that time, however, it has been clearly demonstrated that, given a suitable blend of animal, feeding and management, highly acceptable results can be obtained; studies at the Rowett in Aberdeen showed it was possible to achieve two lambings every 13 months on a flock basis and for the sheep to produce an average of twins each time, giving the remarkable figure of 3.7 lambs per ewe per year (Robinson, 1974; Robinson *et al.*, 1975a, b; Robinson and Orskov, 1975). The figure of 3.5 lambs may be compared with an average of 1.28 weaned lambs/ewe/year recorded elsewhere in the U.K. (M.L.C., 1973); even in the top flocks

surveyed (1.67 live lambs born/ewe/year) production was far below the Rowett figure.

The particular ingredients of the Rowett success story included the Finn x Dorset ewe, controlled light environment, controlled breeding (intravaginal FGA), adequate and controlled nutrition and the abrupt weaning of lambs at 1 month old. From the results obtained under close control at the Rowett, it was possible to draw up a specification for a frequent breeding system suitable for commercial sheep farming in the U.K. (Scottish Agricultural Colleges, 1977). This specification dealt with a "three lambings in 2 years" programme, using a two-flock system with matings in October, February and July. Lambs from the July mating are weaned at 1 month old and reared on a cereal-based diet and the ewes rebred in February. Sheep are kept at a high stocking rate at pasture in spring and early summer, the stocking density being reduced in preparation for lambing; these lambs stay with the ewes for 2 months before being finished on concentrates in the autumn. In that season, ewes are "flushed" in preparation for remating in October and the subsequent production of normal season lambs.

The commercial programme as described above was feasible because it has been demonstrated experimentally that light control was unnecessary. Initially, it had been felt that regulation of the photoperiod was probably an essential ingredient, but this was later shown not to be so. Reports by Frazer *et al.* (1976) and Robinson (1979) described trials with Finn x Dorsets using similar intravaginal progestagen and ram mating procedures as those previously employed but otherwise with normal outdoor flock management; the authors concluded that it was possible to breed the Finn x Dorset crossbred at intervals of 7–8 months without employing light control if a small dose of PMSG is used with the progestagen. This was obviously a finding of considerable practical importance, for the costs involved in housing sheep for light control could otherwise be quite prohibitive.

15.4.1 Canadian efforts
Heaney *et al.* (1980) has described progress in research and development in intensive lamb

production at the Animal Research Institute at Ottawa in Canada, which started in 1968. The report outlines what it describes as very encouraging results for a system of total confinement; controlled breeding (intravaginal FGA and PMSG) is employed to produce three lamb crops every two years. A group of 1600 ewes is arranged in two flocks that lamb at 8-month intervals, the flocks being out-of-phase so that matings and lambings are taking place every 4 months. The sheep employed in the programme have been bred with more frequent lambings in mind. Whether the Canadian system can be used commercially remains to be seen.

15.4.2 Northern Ireland

Although it is now clear that Finn x Dorset sheep, as used by Robinson (1979) at the Rowett, are capable of maintaining a remarkable reproductive performance under appropriate conditions of feed and management, this particular crossbred is only in limited supply; there is also the question of carcase quality, which is not enhanced by the Finn contribution to the lamb's genetic make-up. In Northern Ireland, work has been conducted with a popular fat-lamb mother, the Greyface (Border Leicester x Blackface Mt) in efforts to achieve three lamb crops every 2 years. In an investigation conducted over a 4-year-period, using controlled breeding techniques and weaning lambs at 4 weeks, the best estimate of production was 1.82 lambs weaned/ewe/year (Foster et al., 1977); this was of the same order as that found in similar work with Greyfaces at Edinburgh (1.66 weaned lambs/ ewe/year; Anon., 1976) and at Aberdeen University (1.76 weaned lambs/ewe/year; Anon., 1975). The work in Northern Ireland showed that Suffolk, Dorset Horn and other rams performed satisfactorily at all times of the year but that conception rates, particularly in the ewe anoestrus were variable and disappointing. With Finn x Dorsets, the expectation is that 90% of the flock become pregnant to first and second services; with Greyfaces, this figure was often much lower. In fact, it was concluded that the relatively small improvement in lamb output was

barely sufficient to justify the expense and expertise necessary in applying the programme.

15.4.3 French efforts

Investigators in France during the last decade have put considerable effort into developing systems of more frequent lambings (Thimonier et al., 1975; Thimonier and Cognie, 1977). Some of these involve control of reproduction to the point at which lambings occur in all months of the year, with work at weekends, at night and on public holidays largely avoided. Intravaginal FGA-PMSG treatment is employed in noncyclic ewes and FGA-impregnated sponges alone in those that are cyclic. The most sophisticated system appears to be that developed by French researchers at the Nouzilly centre (Thimonier et al., 1975); this involves a series of seven flocks, each separated in their reproductive status by 7 weeks; ewes which do not conceive at the controlled breeding in one flock are transferred to the subsequent flock for remating. The output of lambs with this system was found to depend, however, on the particular type of sheep involved; Romanov x Prealpe ewes produced 301 lambs per 100 ewes per year, compared to 223 for Prealpe ewes and only 181 lambs for Ile de France ewes (Thimonier and Cognie, 1977). As already noted in comparing the performance of Finn x Dorset ewes with that of Greyfaces, the Romanov x Prealpe in the French system is a much more suitable candidate for frequent breeding than the others.

15.4.4 Israeli studies

Attempts have been made to increase flock profitability in Israel using more prolific ewes and an accelerated lambing frequency; this has involved crossing Finn rams with the local Awassi ewe in order to increase its prolificacy (Goot et al., 1975) and make it more suitable for a system of more frequent breeding (Amir and Schindler, 1977). The breeding of Finn x Awassi ewes at three periods of the year (June, September, December/ January) is dealt with in a report by Amir et al.(1981), who found changes in litter-size according to season of mating. The Israeli work is another example of using the highly prolific Finn to introduce a capability for a longer breeding season as well as a higher litter-size.

15.4.5 American studies

Use has been made of the Finn in the U.S.A. in developing the Morlam crossbred at the Beltsville centre of the Department of Agriculture (Hulet, 1977) and the Polypay crossbred at the Dubois centre. Elsewhere, in Wisconsin, Lax et al. (1979) examined the incidence of oestrus in different breeds of sheep to determine which breeds and management systems might offer the greatest opportunity for lambing more than once a year; they concluded that lambing every 8-months would not work with their sheep and suggested that twice-yearly systems, using March–September timings, offered more promise. Unfortunately, the study only dealt with cyclic sheep in arriving at these estimates and it would be necessary for post-partum considerations to be given closer attention. Even with the Finn x Dorset crossbred, attempts to lamb at 6-month rather than 8-month intervals have not apparently proved successful (Speedy et al., 1976), although it should be noted that the work was carried out among ewes at pasture rather than under controlled conditions.

15.5 BREEDING, TREATMENT AND MANAGEMENT

As already mentioned, it would appear that certain types of sheep, when provided with suitable feeding and in conjunction with early-weaning, can breed satisfactorily after controlled breeding in all seasons of the year. Reviewing the reproductive performance of sheep in frequent breeding programmes, Robinson (1979), observed that the high annual lamb output of the Finn and Finn-cross ewe is not only a result of the large litter-size but also arises from their reduced lambing interval. There is now clear evidence that the Finn sheep has a relatively long breeding season under a wide range of environmental and management conditions (Maijala and Osterberg, 1976; Wheeler and Land, 1977) a characteristic which is also evident in the Romanov breed

(Veress et al., 1976; Ricordeau et al., 1976). Available evidence suggests that it is probably easier to achieve increased lambing frequency with sheep normally associated with higher than average litter-size (Finn-crosses; Romanov-crosses) than with breeds, such as the Merino and its derivatives, which are associated with a low litter-size, even though that particular breed is thought to have the merit of an extended breeding season. There is perhaps some support for this in the fact that Merino ewes of the high fertility Booroola strain developed in Australia continue to show breeding activity when inhibitory seasonal factors have suppressed such activity in the normal type of Merino (Bindon and Piper, 1976).

15.5.1 Suffolk crossbreds

One of the first reports dealing with successful frequent breeding without the use of exogenous hormones, was that of Copenhaver and Carter (1964) who used Suffolk-crosses; South-Suffolk-crossbred ewes were found to be the best suited, of several types, to twice-yearly breeding in studies reported by Evans and Robinson (1980) in Australia. However, on the basis of litter-size performance, it would not appear that Suffolk blood in itself would contribute any ingredient essential to an accelerated lambing system.

15.5.2 Treatment considerations

Given a suitable breed of sheep to work with, there are various considerations in regard to the controlled breeding techniques employed. According to Hamilton and Lishman (1979), for instance, intravaginal sponges are not likely to be suitable during the early post-partum period as the elimination of debris during uterine involution may be retarded; nonetheless, Robinson (1974) employed such sponges to good effect in Finn x Dorsets within 8 weeks of lambing and the same could be said for French researchers with their Romanov crossbreds (Thimonier et al., 1975).

Work by French investigators among ewes of the more usual breeds that are nursing lambs in the seasonal anoestrus would seem to indicate that it may be necessary to employ a higher dose of PMSG (at the termination of progestagen) for lactating sheep than for those weaned at lambing or for "dry" ewes (Thimonier et al., 1968); it was further suggested that this may result in a greater variation in the number of ovulations and in a greater spread in the time over which ovulation occurs (Signoret and Cognie, 1975). Such abnormalities in the ovulatory process could be a factor implicated in the low level of fertility shown by the spring lactating ewe of the average lowland breed; fertilization rate may be lower as a result of the different times at which eggs are released (Cognie et al., 1975).

According to Mauleon (1976), difficulties in this category of ewe could also continue during embryonic development, with problems arising from delayed development (which may result in a failure of the corpus luteum to be maintained) and embryonic deaths occurring in the period 18–50 days after breeding (Thimonier et al., 1975); a lower pregnancy rate as compared to that in "dry" ewes may also have been implicated in this early mortality (Cognie et al., 1975). Inadequacies in the post-partum restoration of the uterus has already been mentioned as a factor which may militate against conception in sheep involved in frequent breeding; a low survival rate in normal sheep embryos after transfer to lactating ewes has been noted by the French workers (Cognie et al., 1975).

As a means of overcoming the problems associated with the reproductive tract in the lactating ewe in the early months after lambing, French workers use two inseminations and twice the normal sperm dose in breeding the sheep by AI. The application of photoperiodic control (to provide autumn lighting conditions at breeding) in addition to the standard progestagen-PMSG oestrus induction treatment was attempted in lactating ewes bred twice a year; although this did not influence first service fertility (25% conceptions in April; 75% in November), non-pregnant sheep were observed to return in oestrus (Mauleon and Rougeot, 1962), something which did not occur in the absence of light control. It should be noted that the Finn x Dorset type of ewe in a more frequent lambing system will usually return in oestrus after FGA-PMSG treatment, where she fails to conceive at the

induced oestrus, and this is something which breeds of more average performance (e.g. Greyface) will not do during the spring and summer period. Speedy and Fitzsimons (1977) did a comparison which showed conception rates of the order of 73–88% in Finn x Dorsets bred at different times of the year whereas in Greyfaces, conception rates were high at the natural mating time in November (96%) but lower in August (55%) and still lower in February (26%); part of the problem was the fact that Greyfaces did not return for a second service outside their normal season. Evidence in studies conducted in late anoestrus has also suggested a relationship between readiness of the non-pregnant ewe to return in oestrus and breed type (Gordon, 1975); the higher the natural fertility of the breed in question, then the more ready the ewe was to show evidence of cyclical breeding activity.

15.5.3 Pregnancy and lactation

Although Robinson et al. (1975a) showed that a mean annual production of 3.5 lambs per ewe per year could be achieved in his frequent breeding programme, this was with the Finn x Dorsets weaned at 4–6 weeks; one question of interest was whether acceptable conception rates could be maintained if the length of lactation was extended. In studies reported by Rhind et al. (1977), conception rates of 100, 80, 70 and 58% to the FGA-controlled oestrus were found for ewes mated in December (2 months after parturition) and weaned at 30, 50, 70 and 100 days of lactation, respectively; corresponding values for a second flock of sheep mated in March were 92, 83, 36 and 33%. Robinson, et al. (1977), in observing that about 50% of those ewes that did not conceive to the induced oestrus did so at the second heat, considered it possible that extension of the lambing interval from 7 to 8 months would enable lactation to be extended from 1 month in the Finn x Dorsets without impairing fertility. In the system subsequently recommended for commercial use, it was possible to take advantage of that fact; from the practical viewpoint, it is generally desirable that lambs remain on the ewes for as long as they can take advantage of the mother's milk supply.

15.5.4 Lactational effects

The fact that suckling and lactation need not necessarily disturb conception in the ewe is apparent from several reports dealing with autumn lactating ewes; in the autumn, such ewes can return in oestrus (without hormonal intervention) within 2 months of parturition and conceive reasonably well (Gordon, 1958, 1975; Barker and Wiggins, 1964; Lees, 1964; Newton, 1969; Steele-Bodger, 1969; Rankin et al., 1969). Such evidence suggests that seasonal environmental factors, rather than lactation itself, may be responsible for the particular problem of low conception rates in the spring lactating sheep; even with the lactating Finn x Dorset, fertility has been depressed to a greater extent in spring than in winter (Rhind et al., 1980).

In explaining fertility differences between autumn and spring-lambing ewes, one consideration is the fact that autumn-lactating sheep show a silent heat prior to the first full oestrus (Miller and Wiggins, 1964; Mauleon and Dauzier, 1965; Restall, 1971); it is possible that the hormonal events at this silent heat may be important in facilitating proper involution of the uterus, so that the ewe approaches full oestrus with its reproductive tract in a condition adequate for sustaining pregnancy. With the same sheep lambing in spring, it is probable that no such silent heats occurs in the post-partum ewe.

If the ewe is subsequently treated with progestagen-PMSG to induce breeding in the early months post-partum, this may mean that she approaches the controlled heat with the uterus in a relatively unprepared state; on the other hand, should such ewes show a "repeat" oestrus (either spontaneous or induced), then they might be expected to approach that second heat period with their breeding tracts more adequately prepared. It was such reasoning which led to the development of a "double-cycle" treatment in anoestrous sheep (Gordon, 1963), a procedure which unfortunately was too cumbersome and prolonged to be commercially useful. However, it may well be possible to circumvent the need for a double-cycle (progestagen-PMSG + progestagen-PMSG) treatment by simulating events that normally occur at the start of the breeding season, namely, oestrogen build-up, ovulation and formation of the corpus luteum. In artificial control, the usual progestagen-PMSG regimen may perhaps be preceded by a dose of oestrogen on the assumption that the interaction between oestrogen and subsequent progestagen treatment may improve conditions in the uterus; some favourable effect on fertility has been recorded after using a dose of 50 μg oestradiol prior to application of normal FGA-PMSG (Cognie and Pelletier, 1976).

15.5.5 Progestagen and PMSG dose levels

Little has been reported to suggest that the dose levels of progestagen and PMSG required for the post-partum ewe should be materially different from those employed in other categories of sheep. Trials which examined decreasing the dose of progestagen (20 mg vs 40 mg FGA) did not result in any improvement in fertility (Mauleon, 1976); the same author noted, however, some tendency for a short progestagen treatment (6 days vs 12 days) to produce a more favourable response in ewes that showed no evidence of ovarian activity. As already mentioned, there has been a suggestion that higher PMSG dose levels may be required in lactating sheep in French studies (Thimonier et al., 1968); in Australia, Evans and Robinson (1980) also suggest that more than 750 i.u. PMSG may be needed with ewes in the early post-partum period. This was on the basis of evidence showing that normal pituitary function is impaired for some weeks after parturition. Nevertheless, convincing evidence on the need for doses of progestagen and PMSG different from those used on other controlled breeding occasions has yet to be demonstrated.

15.5.6 Light regimens

For those accelerated lambing systems in which sheep are to be indoors at all times, it is possible to control the light regimen; according to Vesely and Bowden (1980), it is important that periods of short and long daylength applied for oestrus control in sheep should be of a rhythmic nature, as they are under natural daylight conditions. If the complete production cycle (lambing to lambing) is 210 days (three lamb crops every 2 years) then light changes should vary within that period as in the normal 365 days yearly pattern.

15.6 INTEGRATION OF TECHNIQUES

The past two decades have witnessed several useful technological advances in sheep breeding and production. These advances include the development of a practical method of administering progestagen for oestrus control in the cyclic sheep and for inducing oestrus in the non-breeding-season, ability to carry out early pregnancy diagnosis at 18 days and reliable methods of inducing parturition. British, French and Australian workers have sought to put these techniques together and to employ them in systems aimed at producing lambs all the year round.

Robinson (1980) has shown that it is feasible to produce lambs in all seasons from crossbred ewes under certain Australian conditions, using existing technology. The system, as reported, suffered from problems in ram matings and the early progesterone pregnancy test proved to be both costly and not readily available in some parts of Australia; there was also a difficulty from the test giving false positives because of embryonic mortality. There was a need for a pregnancy test that could be employed at 45 days so that non-pregnant ewes could be identified and rebred without delay. Whether the system could be employed successfully in commercial farming would be a question of costs in relation to value of the product at marketing; the author estimated

Fig. 15.3. Finn × Dorset ewes and their lambs. It is now possible to bring together a wide range of sheep husbandry practices which have developed over the past decade or more and apply them in the one system of accelerated lamb production. Work in the U.K. pioneered by Dr. John Robinson at the Rowett, has shown that the use of Finn × Dorset ewes and controlled breeding techniques can more than double performance compared with conventional lowland flocks producing the one lamb crop per year. An increased frequency of lambing, such as being practised here on the University Farm, requires a well thought-out programme, with ewes such as Finn × Dorset and weaning not later than 50 days to prevent the detrimental effect of lactation on rebreeding.

that the cost of a viable lamb from the system was the cost of the treatment (Robinson, 1980).

15.7 NUTRITION IN FREQUENT LAMBING SYSTEMS

In studies at the Rowett, little difficulty has been experienced in maintaining the body weight of the highly productive Finn x Dorset ewes in their frequent breeding programme, provided the animals had been weaned at 1 month and well-fed for the 3 weeks before mating to ensure that the tissue loss in late pregnancy and early lactation is replaced before remating (Robinson, 1979). One of the important considerations is the pattern of feed intake; if the high body condition at mating were to be maintained until late pregnancy, then this could result in appetance and hypoglycaemia, particularly in sheep carrying multiples (Robinson, 1979).

In recent times, much progress has been made towards a better understanding of the digestion and utilization of protein by ruminants. The view would seem to be that for low producing sheep such as "dry" ewes, pregnant ewes up to a few weeks before lambing and "store" lambs, microbial protein will usually meet the animal's net requirements for amino-acid nitrogen; however, for young fast growing lambs and ewes in the final weeks of pregnancy and during early lactation, the maximal yield of microbial protein will not necessarily meet their needs and such animals require protein supplements which at least in part escape degradation in the rumen.

In the frequent lambing system described by Robinson et al. (1975a), it would be usual for the sheep rearing lambs to be in negative energy balance during the first month of lactation. Under these conditions, Robinson et al. (1979) have shown that increases in the concentration of dietary crude protein stimulate the utilization of body fat and improve milk production. The response occurs within 3 days and is greatest with protein supplements, such as fish meal, which have a low degradability in the rumen. Using this principle, sheep in moderate condition at lambing can be stimulated to mobilize enough body fat for the provision of energy needed in the daily production of additional milk without any detrimental effects.

Such findings are of particular interest in a frequent lambing system in that a high milk yield is desirable in early lactation to ensure a high initial growth rate in the lambs before they are weaned. Body fat that is deposited at low cost during pregnancy from grass may be utilized after lambing when food energy may be much more expensive. Removing the dietary protein supplement should have the effect of reducing the milk yield and body fat mobilization of the ewe, thus preparing the lamb for early weaning on to solid food and at the same time avoiding the detrimental effects of excessive body fat utilization on the subsequent fertility of the ewe.

15.8 LAMB REARING CONSIDERATIONS

As part of frequent lambing programmes, lambs are often weaned much earlier than usual and reared on all-concentrate diets. Weaning of lambs at birth is not often regarded as an option in view of the very high feed and other costs involved. With weaning at 1 month or so, the growth performance to slaughter can be high (around 350 g/day) and feed conversion rates of about 3 : 1 can be achieved (Robinson and Orskov, 1975; Orskov, 1976). The carcases of indoor-reared lambs have been a source of concern on occasions because of unacceptably soft subcutaneous fat as compared with outdoor lambs (Robinson and Orskov, 1975) but these problems should be overcome by modifying feeding techniques (use of whole barley) and probably by using genotypes which yield leaner carcases (Orskov and Robinson, 1981).

The fact that sheep such as Finn x Dorsets are essential for success in frequent lambing systems does produce some conflict of interest when it comes to the marketing of their progeny, in view of the fact that the Finn is not at all renowned for its carcase characteristics. In most situations, Suffolk rams would be used on the Finn x Dorset, but some attempt has been made to employ the Texel. Studies in several countries have shown that the carcases of Texel-sired lambs contain less fat and more lean than the carcases of lambs sired by many other breeds (ABRO, 1975; More O'Ferrall and Timon, 1977; Latif and Owen, 1979). In one recent report, Texel-cross lambs were compared with Suffolk-crosses and it was found that they had a similar growth rate and feed conversion efficiency (Latif and Owen, 1980); the Texel-sired lambs, however, had significantly higher carcase weights and killing out percentages than the Suffolk-sired animals.

In dealing with sheep such as the Finn x Dorset, which may produce litters of three and four lambs quite commonly, an essential need is to ensure the survival of such lambs. As noted by Robinson (1981), one invaluable technique for boosting the energy supply of the small lamb, thereby preventing its demise from starvation, is the administration of colostrum (up to 30 ml-kg bodyweight of lamb) within a few minutes of birth, directly into its stomach using a catheter and syringe; the procedure is quick, simple and safe and its use in supervized lambings at the Rowett Institute has reduced lamb mortality to less than 2% in the frequent lambing flocks.

15.9 FUTURE DEVELOPMENTS

During the last decade, largely due to work in Scotland by Robinson and associates and in France by Thimonier and colleagues, much valuable information has been built up about more frequent lambing systems. It is clear that all-year-round production of lambs is possible given appropriate sheep (Finn x Dorsets; Romanov x Prealpes) and management. The question is, however, one of determining how the prolific type of sheep is capable of an acceptable reproductive performance in all seasons whereas the normal breeds (Suffolk, Greyface) are not. It is obviously a matter of their greater ovarian activity and the hormonal consequences of that greater activity. It may be worth doing comparative studies in sheep that include animals ranging from the highly prolific Finn x Dorset to the more usual Suffolk or Galway type of animal to gain much more quantitative information about steroid and polypeptide hormone levels in these ewes.

In the meantime, for the sheep farmer who is contemplating inducing pregnancy in spring lactating ewes (in the early *post-partum* period) to produce autumn as well as spring-born lambs, it has to be said that no satisfactory hormonal technique is available. It would seem to be a question of factors affecting the sheep's ovarian response to progestagen-PMSG on the one hand and the resolution of inadequacies in the uterus as they exist at that time on the other. The ultimate object in all frequent lambing programmes is probably to have ewes producing twin lambs twice a year.

15.10 REFERENCES

A.B.R.O. (1975) A note on the A.B.R.O. experiments evaluating six sire breeds for lowland slaughter lamb production. *A.B.R.O. Ann. Rpt. Edinb.*

Amir, D. and Schindler, H. (1977) Induction of oestrus and fertility of ewes at the beginning and the end of the sexual season. *Hassadeh*, **57**, 1663–1667.

Amir, D., Schindler, H. and Genizi, A. (1981) A note on seasonal changes in litter size of Finn x Awassi ewes. *Anim. Prod.* **32**, 121–123.

Anon (1975) *North of Scotland College of Agriculture, Ann. Rpt.* 1974–75, p. 47.

Anon (1976) *Edinburgh School of Agric. Ann. Rpt.* 1975, p. 37.

Barker, H. B. and Wiggins, E. L. (1964). Occurrence of post-partum estrus in Fall-lactating ewes. *J. Anim. Sci.* **23**, 967.

Bindon, B. M. and Piper, L. R. (1976). Assessment of new and traditional techniques of selection for reproduction rate. *Proc. Int. Congr. Sheep Breed. Muresk*, 357–371, Waite Press, Perth.

Call, J. W., Foote, W. C., Eckie, C. D. and Hulet, C. V. (1976) Post-partum uterine and ovarian changes and estrous behaviour from lactation effects in normal and hormone treated ewes. *Theriogen.* **6**, 495–501.

Chamley, W. A., Findlay, J. K., Jonas, H., Cumming, I. A. and Goding, J. R. (1974a) Effect of pregnancy on the FSH response to synthetic gonadotrophin-releasing hormone in ewes. *J. Reprod. Fert.* **37**, 109–112.

Chamley, W. A., Findlay, J. K., Cumming, I. A., Buckmaster, J. M. and Goding, J. R. (1974b) Effect of pregnancy on the LH response to synthetic gonadotrophin releasing hormone in the ewe. *Endocrin.* **94**, 291–293.

Cognie, Y. and Pelletier, J. (1976) Preovulatory LH release and ovulation in dry and in lactating ewes after progestagen and PMSG treatment during the seasonal anoestrum. *Ann. Biol. Anim. Bioch. Biophys.* **16**(4), 529–536.

Cognie, Y., Hernandez-Barreto, M. and Saumande, J. (1975) Low fertility in nursing ewes during the non-breeding season. *Ann. Biol. Anim. Bioch. Biophys.* **15**(2), 329–343.

Copenhaver, J. S. and Carter, R. C. (1964) Maximizing ewe productivity by very early weaning and re-breeding. *J. Anim. Sci.* **23**, 302 (Abs).

Erb, R. E., Sitarz, N. E. and Malven, P. V. (1977) Blood plasma and milk prolactin and effects of sampling technique on composition of milk from suckled ewes. *J. Dairy Sci.* **60**, 197–203.

Evans, G. and Robinson, J. T. (1980) The control of fertility in sheep: Endocrine and ovarian responses to progestagen-PMSG treatment in the breeding season and in anoestrus. *J. Agric. Sci., Camb.* **94**, 69–88.

Fitzgerald, B. P. and Cunningham, F. J. (1981) Effect of removal of lambs or treatment with bromocriptine on plasma concentrations of prolactin and FSH during the post-partum period in ewes lambing at different times during the breeding season. *J. Reprod. Fert.* **61**, 141–148.

Fletcher, I. C. (1971) Relationships between frequency of suckling, lamb growth and post-partum oestrous behaviour in ewes. *Anim. Behav.* **19**, 108–111.

Fletcher, I. C. (1973) Effects of lactation, suckling and oxytocin on post-partum ovulation and oestrus in ewes. *J. Reprod. Fert.* **33**, 293.

Foster, W. H., McCaughey, W. J., Logan, E. F. and Irwin, D. (1977) Controlled breeding of sheep. *50th Ann. Rept. Agric. Res. Inst., Nth. Ir.,* 19–27.

Frazer, C., Robinsin, J. J., McHattie, I. and Gill, J. C. (1976) Field studies on the reproductive performance of Finnish Landrace x Dorset Horn ewes. *Proc. Br. Soc. Anim. Prod.* **5**, 162–163.

Goot, H., Folman, Y., Dori, D. and Eyal, E. (1975) The Finn x Awassi cross of sheep (preliminary results). *Hassadeh* **55**, 1881–1883.

Gordon, I. (1958). Studies in the extra-seasonal production of lambs. *J. Agric. Sci. Camb.* **50**, 125.

Gordon, I. (1963). The induction of pregnancy in the anoestrous ewe by hormonal therapy. *J. Agric. Sci. Camb.* **60**, 77.

Gordon, I. (1975) The use of progestagens in sheep bred by natural and artificial insemination. *Ann. Biol. Anim. Bioch. Biophys.* **15**(2), 303–315.

Hamilton, C. D. and Lishman, A. W. (1979) Reducing the partum-to-mating period in autumn lactating ewes through the use of exogenous hormones. *S. Afr. J. Anim. Sci.* **9**, 59–63.

Heaney, D. P., Ainsworth, L., Batra, T. R., Fiser, P. S., Langford, G. A., Lee, A. J. and Hackett, A. J. (1980) Research for an intensive total confinement sheep production system. *Anim. Res. Inst. Tech., Bull. No. 2.* Agric. Canada pp. 56.

Honmode, D. (1977). *Anim. Breed Abstr.* **45**, 384.

Hulet, C. V. (1977) Management of reproduction in sheep. In, *Management of Reprod. in Sheep and Goats, Symp. Univ. Wisconsin,* pp. 119–133.

Hulet, C. V. (1979) Improving reproductive efficiency in sheep. In, *Anim. Reprod. BARC. Symp. No. 3,* H. Hawk, Ed., pp. 31–40 Allanheld, Osmun, Montclair.

Hunter, G. L. (1968) Increasing the frequency of pregnancy in sheep. *Ann. Breed. Abs.* **36**, 347–378 and 533–553.

Hunter, G. L. and Aarde, I. M. R. van (1973) Influence of season of lambing on part-partum intervals to ovulation and oestrus in lactating and dry ewes at different nutritional levels. *J. Reprod. Fert.* **32**, 1–8.

Jenkin, G., Heap, R. B. and Symons, D. B. A. (1977) Pituitary responsiveness to synthetic LH-RH and Pituitary LH content at various reproductive stages in the sheep. *J. Reprod. Fert.* **49**, 207–214.

Kann, G. and Martinet, J. (1975) Prolactin level and duration of post-partum anoestrus in lactating ewes. *Nature Lond* **257**, 63–64.

Kann, G., Harbert, R., Meusnier, C. and Ryniewicz, H. S. (1977) Prolactin release in response to nursing or milking stimulus in the ewe. It is mediated by thyrotrophin releasing hormone. *Ann. Biol. Admin. Bioch. Biophys.* **17**(3b), 441–452.

Lamming, G. E., Moseley, S. R. and McNeilly, J. R. (1974) Prolactin release in the sheep. *J. Reprod. Fert.* **40**, 151–168.

Land, R. B. (1971) The incidence of oestrus during lactation in Finnish landrace, Dorset horn and Finn x Dorset sheep. *J. Reprod. Fert.* **24**, 345–352.

Larif, M. G. A. and Owen, E. (1979) Comparison of Texel and Suffolk-sired lambs out of Finnish Landrace x Dorset Horn ewes under grazing conditions. *J. Agric. Sci., Camb.* **93**, 235–275.

Larif, M. G. A. and Owen, E. (1980) A note on the growth performance and carcase composition of Texel and Suffolk-sired lambs in an intensive feeding system. *Anim. Prod.* **30**, 311–314.

Lees, J. L. (1964). Inhibitory effect of lactation on the breeding activity of the ewe. *Nature (Lond.),* **203**, 1089.

Legan, S. J., Karsch, F. J. and Foster, D. L. (1977) The endocrine control of seasonal reproductive function in the ewe: A marked change in response to the negative feedback action of estradiol on luteinizing hormone secretion. *Endocrin.* **101**, 818.

Lewis, P. E., Bolt, D. J. and Inskeep, E. K. (1974) Luteinizing hormone release and ovulation in anoestrous ewes. *J. Anim. Sci.* **38**, 1197–1203.

Lox, J., French, L. R., Chapman, A. B., Pope, A. L. and Casida, L. E. (1979) Length of breeding season for eight breed groups of sheep in Wisconsin. *J. Anim. Sci.* **49**, 939–942.

McDonald, M. F. and Rowson, L. E. A. (1962) Ovum transfer to lactating ewes. *J. Reprod. Fert.* **4**, 205.

McNeilly, J. R., Mosely, S. R. and Lamming, G. E. (1972) Observations on the pattern of prolactin release during suckling in the ewe. *J. Reprod. Fert.* **31**, 487–488.

Maijala, K. and Osterbert, S. (1976) Productivity of pure Finn sheep in Finland and abroad. *Proc. 27th Ann. Mt. EAPP (Zurich),* G 20528, 1–33.

Mallampati, Rao, S., Pope, A. L. and Casida, L. E. (1971) Breeding pattern in Targhee ewes and ewe lambs throughout the year. *J. Anim. Sci.* **33**, 1278–1281.

Mauleon, P. (1976) Manipulation of the breeding cycle. *Proc. Int. Congr. Sheep Breed., Muresk,* pp. 310–321 Waite Press, Perth.

Mauleon, P. and Dauzier, L. (1965) Variations in the duration of lactation anoestrus in ewes of the Ile-de-France breed. *Ann. Biol. Anim. Bioch. Biophys.* **5**, 131.

Mauleon, P. and Rougeot, J. (1962) *Anim. Biol. Anim. Biochim. Biophys.* **2**, 209.

Miller, W. W. and Wiggins, E. L. (1964). Ovarian activity and fertility in lactating ewes. *J. Anim. Sci.* **23**, 981.

M.L.C. (1973) *Sheepfacts.* Meat and Livest. Comm. Milton Keynes.

More O'Ferrall, G. D. and Timon, V. M. (1977) A comparison of eight sire breeds for lamb production. 2. Lamb carcase composition. *Ir. J. Agric. Res.* **16**, 277–284.

Orskov, E. R. (1976) The effect of processing of cereals on digestion in ruminants. *A.R.C. Res. Rev.* **2**, 37–41.

Orskov, E. R. and Robinson, J. J. (1981) The application of modern concepts of ruminant protein nutrition to sheep production systems. *Livestock Prod. Sci.* **8**(4), 339–350.

Pelletier, J. (1973) Evidence for photoperiodic control of prolactin release in rams. *J. Reprod. Fert.* **35**, 143–147.

Pelletier, J. and Thimonier, J. (1975) Interactions between

ovarian steroids or progestagens and LH release. *Ann. Biol. Anim. Biochim. Biophys.* **15,** 131–146.

Ravault, J. P. (1976) Prolactin in the Ram: Seasonal variations in the concentration of blood plasma from birth until three years old. *Acta Endocr.* **83,** 720–725.

Restall, B. J. (1971) The effect of lamb removal on reproductive activity in DH x Merino after lambing. *J. Reprod. Fert.* **24,** 145–146.

Restall, B. J. and Starr, B. G. (1977) The influence of season of lambing and lactation on reproductive activity and plasma LH concentrations in Merino ewes. *J. Reprod. Fert.* **49,** 297–303.

Rhind, S. M., Robinson, J. J., Fraser, C. and Phillipo, M. (1977). *Anim. Prod.* **24,** 128.

Rhind, S. M., Robinson, J. J., Chetworth, J. M. and Crofts, R. M. J. (1980) Effects of season, lactation and plane of nutrition on prolactin concentrations in ovine plasma and the role of prolactin in the control of ewe fertility. *J. Reprod. Fert.* **58,** 145–152.

Ricordeau, G., Tchamitchion, L., Thimonier, J., Flamant, J. C. and Theriez, M. (1970) *Proc. 27th Mt. EAAP (Zurich).*

Robinson, J. J. (1974) Intensifying ewe productivity. *Proc. Brit. Soc. Anim. Proc.* **3,** 31–40.

Robinson, J. J. (1979) Intensive systems. In, *Management and Diseases of Sheep.* pp. 431–446 Comm. Agric. Bur. Slough.

Robinson, J. J. (1981) Prenatal growth and development in the sheep and its implications for the viability of the newborn lamb. *Livestock. Prod. Sci.* **8**(3), 273–281.

Robinson, J. J. and Orskov, E. R. (1975) An integrated approach to improving the biological efficiency of sheep meat production. *Wld. Rev. Anim. Prod.* **11**(3), 63–76.

Robinson, J. J., Fraser, C. and McHattie, I. (1975a) The use of progestagens and photoperiodism in improving the reproductive rate of the ewe. *Ann. Biol. Anim. Bioch. Biophys.* **15,** 345–352.

Robinson, J. J., Fraser, C., McHattie, I. and Gill, J. C. (1975b) The long-term reproductive performance of Finnish landrace x Dorset Horn ewes subjected to photostimulation and hormone therapy. *Br. Soc. Anim. Prod.* 115–116.

Robinson, J. J., Fraser, C. C. and McHattie, I. (1977). Development of systems for lambing sheep more frequently than once per year. In, *Sheep Nutrition and Management,* U.S. Feed Grains Council, London, 5–33.

Robinson, J. J., McHattie, I., Calderon, C. J. F. and Thompson, J. L. (1979) Further studies on the response of lactating ewes to dietary protein. *Anim. Prod.* **29,** 257–269.

Robinson, T. J. (1959) The estrous cycle of the ewe and doe. In, *Reproduction in Domestic Animals,* Cole, H. H. and Cupps. P. T., Eds, Acad. Press, New York.

Robinson, T. J. (1980) Programmed year-round sheep breeding. *Aust. J. Exp. Agric. Anim. Husb.* **20,** 667–673.

Scottish Agricultural Colleges (1977) *Technical Notes No. 16.*

Shevah, Y., Black, W. J. M., Carr, W. R. and Land, R. B. (1974) The effect of lactation on the resumption of reproductive activity and the pre-ovulatory release of LH in Finn x Dorset ewes. *J. Reprod. Fert.* **38,** 369–378.

Signoret, J. P. and Cognie, Y. (1975) Determination of the moment of ovulation in ewe and sow. Influence of environment and hormonal treatment. *Ann. Biol. Anim. Biochim. Biophys.* **15,** 205–214.

Speedy, A. W. and Fitzsimons, J. (1977) The reproductive performance of Finnish landrace x Dorset horn and Border Leicester x Scottish Blackface ewes mated three times in 2 years. *Anim. Prod.* **24,** 189–196.

Theriez, M. and Molenat, G. (1975) Intensive management of sheep. Fecundity rate of ewes inseminated every 6 months as influenced by drying-off immediately after part. *Ann. Zootech.* **24**(4), 729–742.

Thimonier, J. and Cognie, Y. (1977) Application of control of reproduction of sheep in France. In, *Management of Reproduction in Sheep and Goats, Symp. Univ. Wisconsin,* pp. 109–118.

Thimonier, J., Mauleon, P., Cognie, Y. and Otravant, R. (1968) Induction of oestrus and pregnancy in ewes during post-partum anoestrus with the aid of vaginal sponges impregnated with fluorogestone acetate. *Ann. Zootech.* **17,** 257–273.

Thimonier, J., Cognie, Y., Cornu, C., Schneberger, J. and Vernusse, G. (1975) Intensive lamb production. *Ann. Biol. Anim. Biochim, Biophys.* **51**(2), 365–367.

Van Niekerk, C. H. (1976) Limitations to female reproductive efficiency. *Proc. Int. Congr. Sheep. Breed. Muresk,* 299–309.

Veress, L., Stosz, J. and Lovas, L. (1976) *Proc. 27th Mt. EAAP (Zurich).*

Wagner, J. F. and Veenhuizen, E. L. (1968) Effect of lactation on reproductive performance in the ewe. *J. Anim. Sci.* **27,** 1198 (Abs).

Walton, J. S., McNeilly, J. R., McNeilly, A. S. and Cunningham, F. J. (1977) Changes in concentrations of follicle-stimulating hormone, luteinizing hormone, prolactin and proges-terone in the plasma of ewes during the transition from anoestrus to breeding activity. *J. Endocr.* **75,** 127–136.

Wheeler, A. G. and Land, R. B. (1977) Seasonal variation in oestrus an ovarian activity of Finnish Landrace, Tasmanian Merino and Scottish Blackface ewes. *Anim. Prod.* **24,** 363–376.

Wilson, P. N. (1968) Biological ceilings and economic efficiencies for the production of animal protein, A.D. 2000. *Chem. Ind.* 899.

Wright, P. J., Geytenbeek, P. E., Clarke, I. J. and Findlay, J. K. (1980) Pituitary responsiveness to LH-RH, the occurrence of oestradiol-17$_B$-induced LH-positive feedback and the resumption of oestrous cycles in ewes post-partum. *J. Reprod. Fert.* **60,** 171–176.

Wright, P. J., Geytenbeek, P. E., Clarke, I. J. and Findlay, J. K. (1981a). Evidence for a change in oestradiol negative feedback and LH pulse frequency in post-partum ewes. *J. Reprod. Fert.* **61,** 98–102.

Wright, P. J., Stelmasiak, T. and Chamley, W. A. (1981b) Pituitary responsiveness to LH-RH in post-partum ewes treated with oestradiol.17$_B$ and failing to show a plasma LH surge. *Aust. J. Biol. Sci.* **33,** 465–469.

CHAPTER 16

Induction of Multiple Births

16.1 INTRODUCTION

In fat-lamb production, it is not only essential to achieve high conception rates in sheep subjected to controlled breeding procedures but important that most ewes produce twins rather than single lambs. Economic studies in lowland sheep over the years have clearly shown the importance of high fertility as a major determinant of profitability in the enterprise. A small difference in the proportion of ewes carrying multiples may make a large difference to the net income yielded by the flock.

In farming situations where the full genetic potential of a particular breed is being achieved and a further improvement in litter-size is considered desirable, then the introduction of a more prolific breed, selection of ewes within a breed or the artificial control of litter-size by the use of exogenous gonadotrophin are among several of the options available. In the Irish Republic, in which about a million of the 1.6 million breeding ewes are located on the lowlands, about 0.6 million of these are Galways, a breed in terms of size and lambing performance much like the Romney Marsh sheep in England. A survey of more than 10 000 Galway ewes on 354 farms by Daly (1966) revealed an average litter-size of 1.28; on the other hand, under other experimental farm conditions, a litter-size of 1.67 has been shown for the same breed (Curran and McGloughlin, 1964).

Although it would appear possible that the Galways's reproductive performance can be markedly improved by adjustments in feed and management, an alternative approach has been by way of incorporating 25–50% of Finn genes into the breed; results show a very useful improvement in litter-size from 1.4 to 2.0 (Timon, 1971). There has been a slow uptake by farmers of this particular option as yet.

16.2 ENDOCRINE AND OVARIAN EVENTS

As well as the generally recognized effects of feeding, management and environment on ovulation rate in the ewe, administration of gonadotrophins at particular stages of the oestrous cycle will induce multiple ovulations and by that means increase the number of lambs born. It is therefore of interest to look at what is

Fig. 16.1. The Galway ewe — the main lowland sheep breed in the Irish Republic. The Galway is a large (22.5 kg mature body weight) long-wooled sheep which is used primarily as a fat-lamb mother in matings with a Suffolk ram. Although its growth potential and wool characteristics are good, the litter-size could be improved. One advantage in promoting a Sheep AI Service in Galway flocks is the fact that the progestagen-PMSG treatment can result in a higher-than-usual litter-size among ewes that hold to the AI

known to underlie the normal variations in ovulation rate in the species.

The total follicle population in the sheep's ovary consists of a large reserve of primordial and small follicles and a much smaller number of larger vesicular follicles in the growth phase; a direct relationship has been found to exist between the number of follicles in the growth phase and ovulation rate (Cahill et al., 1979). In some reports, three categories of follicles are recognized, these being dormant, transitory and growing follicles; there is evidence that recruitment of follicles in the transitory phase to the growth phase is under the control of the pituitary gonadotrophins (Dufour et al., 1979). There are indications that follicles in the transitory phase acquire FSH receptors (Ryle, 1971) and then selectively enter the growth phase

under gonadotrophic control; however, the recruitment of follicles from the dormant to the transitory category remains unresolved and it has been suggested that such recruitment may operate by an intraovarian mechanism independent of gonadotrophin.

In Merinos, it is believed that some three to four follicles are recruited each day into the growing follicle population (Turnbull et al., 1977); the number of follicles which finally ovulate 6 months later is determined by the rate of atresia occurring during this growth phase. It would appear, according to the studies of Cahill and Mauleon (1980) that prior to antrum formation in the ovarian follicle, growth is very slow (130 days) but that this speeds up considerably in the rapid growth phase (45 days); the long growth period of the follicle means that follicles ovulating in the breeding season must have begun their growth during the seasonal anoestrus, 6 months previously. The fact that the number of developing pre-antral follicles is increasing in anoestrus and decreasing in the breeding season has led some to suggest that anoestrus may constitute an essential recovery period for the ovary (Cahill and Mauleon, 1980).

16.2.1 Follicles and ovulation rate

Finn and Romanov sheep have high ovulation rates and various workers have examined ovarian and oestrous activity in these breeds as compared to other sheep. In the U.K., the proportion of follicles at birth in Finn × Welsh and in Finn × Blackface lambs is greater than that in purebred Welsh or Blackface animals (Land, 1979); it has also been found that later in life the duration of oestrus is greater in the Finn crossbreds than in the purebreds.

16.2.2 Gonadotrophin levels

Relating gonadotrophin levels to follicular growth and development is made difficult by the large variations found in FSH concentrations within and between animals (Findlay and Cumming, 1976) and the lack of knowledge about when the gonadotrophin-susceptible phases of follicle growth occur. At least one phase is believed to occur on days 12–14 of the oestrous cycle when gonadotrophin levels are important in determining ovulation rate at the subsequent oestrus (Findlay and Cumming, 1976). A comparison of FSH levels in groups of ewes, on different planes of nutrition which influenced ovulation rates, revealed relatively greater FSH levels on days 13–14 compared to day-1 (Brien et al., 1976); in contrast, differences were not evident when FSH concentrations in ewes at different stages of the cycle were compared by Findlay and Cumming (1976) and elsewhere attempts to correlate the level of FSH with the ovulation rate shown by the adult ewe were not successful (Bindon et al., 1975).

There is evidence indicating that there are two peaks of FSH during the oestrous cycle, the first coincident with the preovulatory surge of LH and the second occurring 20–30 h after the LH peak (L'Hermite et al., 1972; Cahill and Dufour, 1979); the second FSH peak appeared to be correlated with the number of vesicular follicles present at the next heat period (Cahill and Dufour, 1979). The only characteristic of the preovulatory LH surge that can be correlated with ovulation rate appears to be the interval between the onset of oestrus and the start of the discharge of LH (Thimonier and Pelletier, 1971; Land et al., 1973; Bindon et al., 1975).

16.2.3 Predicting ovulation rates

Circulating LH concentrations have been studied in prepubertal ewe lambs as a possible means of making an early assessment of an individual's potential fertility (Thimonier and Pelletier, 1971; Bindon and Turner, 1974); unfortunately, measurement of LH is complicated by fluctuations in peripheral plasma LH concentrations throughout the day (Bindon and Turner, 1974); it has been shown, however, that selection for increased female fertility could be aided by the use of certain male characteristics, the most promising of which appears to be testis size (Bindon and Piper, 1976; Land, 1980).

16.3 ENVIRONMENTAL INFLUENCES

Well-established factors that may affect litter-size in sheep, such as breed, age and environmental conditions have been discussed at length by many authors over the years (Heape, 1899; Marshall and Potts, 1924; McKenzie and Terrill, 1937; Hammond, 1944; Gordon, 1958a, b). In the U.K., with its considerable array of sheep breeds and established crossbreds, average litter-sizes, as reported in the literature range all the way from 1.1 in Welsh Mountains to 2.4 in the Finnish Landrace (Donald and Read, 1967); as observed by Robinson et al. (1977), there is ample breeding material in the country to select for flocks that give a wide range of litter-sizes. As noted earlier for the Galway in Ireland, the ability of many traditional breeds of sheep in the U.K. to produce multiple births is now to be often in excess of what their feeding and management will allow them to show (Gunn et al., 1972; Gunn and Doney, 1975).

16.3.1 Seasonal effects

There is ample evidence from several breeds of sheep that ovulation rate increases after the commencement of the breeding season and then falls away towards the end (McKenzie and Terrill, 1937; Hammond, 1944; Johansson and Hansson, 1943; Averill, 1955, 1959; Hulet and Foote, 1967; Fletcher and Geytenbeek, 1970; Wheeler and Land, 1977; Lees, 1978; Gunn et al., 1979). This variation in the ovulation rate is usually reflected in a similar pattern of multiple births at lambing time which suggests that fertilization rate and the incidence of embryonic mortality may not be subject to seasonal variation.

The extent of the decline in ovulation rate and average litter-size in the later stages of the breeding season may be influenced by body condition of the ewes, those in good condition suffering more of a decline than those in thin condition (Newton et al., 1980). It is possible that some of the reduction in ovulation rate with advancing season may be the result of stress, particularly weather stress, since the later stages of the season tend to include the periods of worsening weather; stress has been shown to have an adverse effect on the ovulation rate (Griffiths et al., 1970; Doney et al., 1976).

16.4 NUTRITION AND 'FLUSHING'

Ovulation rate in the ewe in the usual autumn breeding season is determined by factors which operate up to the time of mating. Nutritionally, the most influential period is probably that between the previous lambing (or more accurately, the end of lactation) and the time of mating; this can be regarded as the recovery period when the sheep's reserves that were depleted during pregnancy and lactation are replenished. There are two considerations in looking at the nutrition of the ewe during this recovery period; the first is the long-term one

which largely determines the body condition and weight of the ewe at mating time, the second is the short-term, "flushing" effect operating at the time of mating. A direct link between body condition and ovulation rate was established in sheep almost 50 years ago (Clark, 1934) but most of the reports since then have been concerned with the short-term "flushing" effect. Coop (1966) in New Zealand was one of the first to try to define the nutritional effect more precisely; he used the terms "static" and "dynamic" to describe the nutritional effects. Static effect was seen to be a matter of body condition, liveweight and size of the ewe; dynamic effect was defined as a change in liveweight during a 6-week period prior to mating.

16.4.1 Body condition and ovulations.

Body weight of the ewe at mating, representing the static effect, has been shown to influence subsequent litter-size (Coop, 1962, 1966; Allison, 1968); the effect is mainly a result of differences in ovulation rate (Killeen, 1967; Guerra et al., 1971) but with some involvement in the extent of embryonic mortality (Edey, 1969a, b). The bodyweight of the ewe has two components, basic skeletal size of the sheep on the one hand and the degree of fatness (i.e. body condition) on the other (Geisler and Fenlon, 1979). In Australia, where flocks are large, and ewes are usually of similar genetic constitution, live-weight alone has been found to be a more accurate predictor of ovulation rate than body condition (Cumming, 1977); in general, heavier ewes within a flock have more ovulations than the lighter ones, showing about 2.5–3.0% increase for each 1.0 kg increase in liveweight.

16.4.2 "Flushing"

The concept of "flushing", the dynamic effect, has been recognized in sheep farming since at least the 19th century; it is generally taken to mean that the ewe should be in a rapidly improving body condition at mating time. As noted by several investigators, research is still required to elucidate the neural and hormonal mechanisms which can relate factors such as mature skeletal size, tissue fat and protein reserves to ovulation rate (Cumming, 1977; Doney, 1979). It is known, for instance, that there can be certain components of a ewe's nutrition which can have a marked effect on ovulation rate with little change in liveweight (Knight et al., 1975; Smith et al., 1979).

Fresh information on the relationship between nutrition and ovulation rate came from studies in Australia during the 1970s. The feeding of high protein supplements such as lupin grains (Knight et al., 1975) and soyabean meal (Davis and Cumming, 1976) has resulted in significant increases in ovulation rate. It seems that the response can vary according to environment and season (Lightfoot and Marshall, 1974; Rizzol et al., 1976). In Western Australia, responses in ovulation rate can be substantial and can occur within a week of starting lupin feeding (Lindsay, 1976). It has been suggested that in such an environment, a short-term lupin feeding programme could be integrated to advantage with an oestrus synchronization programme (Cumming, 1976); in other environments, however, possibly because normal pasture protein levels are higher, there may not be an acceptable response.

Hormone assay studies produced evidence that ewes supplemented with lupin grains had higher FSH concentrations in plasma than controls 5 days prior to oestrus (Brien et al., 1976). One interesting fact, as observed by Lindsay (1976), was that ewes did not have to change in bodyweight when supplemented with lupins to show significant changes in ovulation rate; the response was sudden and dramatic once the ewe settled into its new nutritional regimen and it ceased soon after lupin supplement was withdrawn.

16.4.3 Net nutritional status

Lindsay (1976) suggested that ovulation rate in ewes is related to what he termed "net nutritional status", which is taken to be the sum of nutrients available from body reserves and those taken up daily from the digestive tract. According to this, heavy ewes given poor feeding may still show a good ovulation rate because they have a reasonable endogenous source of energy and protein. On the other hand, poor ewes temporarily well-fed will also ovulate well because of the contribution of exogenous source of nutrients.

16.4.4 "Flushing" ewe lambs

Earlier evidence that "flushing" prior to mating had no clear effect upon ovulation rate in ewe lambs (Williams, 1954; Allen and Lamming, 1961a, b) was not borne out in the results of Keane (1974, 1975) in Ireland and Downing and Lees (1977) in Wales who showed definite enough evidence of a response in this category of animal.

16.4.5 Embryonic mortality

As to the effect of nutrition on early embryonic mortality in sheep, most reports would seem to relate to studies involving severe undernutrition, with investigators showing that fasting for periods varying from 2 days to a week or more, during very early pregnancy, can result in some degree of embryonic mortality (Edey, 1966; Van Niekerk et al., 1968; Blockey et al., 1974). In view of the drastic nature of the undernutrition treatments applied in such studies and the relatively minor effect recorded in most of them, Lindsay (1976) was led to conclude that it is unlikely that normal nutritional fluctuations play any serious part in influencing embryonic mortality in the ewe. Certainly, there have been reports in which mild forms of undernutrition have been applied without the survival of embryos being affected in any way (Bennett et al., 1970; Braden, 1971).

16.4.6 Lucerne and phyto-oestrogens

Coop and Clark (1960) in a series of trials at Lincoln in New Zealand, found that barrenness in sheep was increased by 2%, multiple-births decreased by 10% and the mean lambing date delayed by several days in sheep flushed and mated on lucerne in comparison with those on grass pasture; later work at Lincoln by Coop (1977) showed a depression in litter-size of 20% and confirmed the existence of a real problem when lucerne is used. These reports and those of other workers (Thompson and Jagusch, 1976; Scales et al., 1977; Smith et al.,1979) indicate a need for investigations to determine the factors which influence the level of phyto-oestrogens in lucerne so that the relative safety or danger of the plant can be predicted. Smith *et al.* (1979) related the decrease in ovulation rate to the level of coumestans in the lucerne; they suggested that the coumestans exert their effect by disturbing the release of FSH.

16.4.7 Breed and nutrition interactions

Cumming and Findlay (1977) have drawn attention to the fact that certain sheep breeds have evolved a more responsive relationship between liveweight and ovulation rate than others; it has also been noted that some breeds (e.g. Booroola and Romney) are less responsive to nutrition (Allison and Kelly, 1979). Elsewhere it has been shown that certain breeds may be more responsive to the effects of nutrition at certain weights; Scottish Blackface ewes have been found to be particularly responsive between 40 and 50 kg (Gunn and Doney, 1975).

16.5 BREED AND AGE EFFECTS

According to Cumming and Findlay (1977), the Finn Landrace breed has been developed by systematic selection, starting some 60 years ago; the sheep are thought to be derived from the Mouflon unimproved breed. If this can be achieved for Finns, then improved litter-size should not be impossible to achieve in other breeds with intense selection. Certainly, in Australia, by a process of such intense selection, dramatic increases in ovulation rate were achieved in one strain of Merino (Turner, 1968); the fertile Booroola strain apparently arose from a single gene mutation in one flock of Merinos.

It is generally accepted, however, that selection for increased litter size can be a slow process, with annual improvements of no more than about 2 lambs per 100 ewes (Land, 1978). As noted by Robinson *et al.* (1977), since the mid-sixties, the highly prolific Finn Landrace sheep has been imported directly from Finland by no less than 24 countries which now employ the breed as a means of increasing fertility and productivity of new synthetic breeds; much the same is true for the equally prolific Romanov

breed which has been spreading rapidly through various countries of Western Europe.

A similar crossing procedure has been adopted in improving the litter-size of the Awassi in the Middle East and North Africa by crossing with the moderately prolific Chios breed from Greece (Fox *et al.*, 1976); another breed in North Africa regarded as useful for crossing purposes is the D'man (Bouix 1975). The use of breeds such as the Finn has contributed to the establishment of new synthetic breeds, such as the Cambridge (Owen, 1969), which is capable of a remarkable reproductive performance.

16.5.1 Breed differences in gonadotrophin levels

It has been shown by some workers that breed differences exist in the LH response of ewe lambs to oestradiol challenge (Bindon *et al.*, 1974) and Gn-RH challenge (Stelmasiak *et al.*, 1978). However, it would not seem that consistent individual differences exist within breeds which could provide the basis of any selection process (Tyrell *et al.*, 1980); the view seems to be that differences, if they do exist, are masked by several factors, including age, sex and season.

16.5.2 Age

Among factors that are known to have a definite effect on ovulation rate is age; ample evidence that young ewes tend to have lower ovulation rates and litter-sizes than mature ewes at similar liveweights (Jones and Rouse, 1920; McKenzie and Terrill, 1937; Gordon, 1967b; Brien *et al.*, 1976).

16.6 ENDOCRINOLOGICAL "FLUSHING"

There are undoubtedly many sheep farming situations in which a simple technique for increasing the twinning percentage would be of economic advantage. As already mentioned, selective breeding, feeding and management and the use of highly prolific imported breeds of sheep can all help in this. However, there are instances in which the hormonal induction of multiples may be considered, especially in sheep flocks that show a low twinning percentage and are not following any selective breeding programme to try to increase litter-size.

The hormonal induction of multiple-births in sheep received much of its early attention in Soviet Russia although methods and results were difficult to interpret for a number of reasons; a monograph by Zavadovskii (1941) indicated that PMSG was being used at that time, apparently on some scale and especially among Karakul sheep. Elsewhere, serious efforts to examine the possibility of augmenting sheep fertility by gonadotrophins date from the studies of Robinson (1951) at Cambridge; he employed a technique, using PMSG, in which a single dose was administered during the follicular phase (day 12/13 usually) of the ewe's oestrous cycle. The procedure was effective in inducing additional ovulations, with a dose–response relationship evident over the range 500 – 2000 i.u.; the Cambridge work formed the basis of several subsequent studies in New Zealand (Wallace et al., 1954; Wallace, 1956, 1962), South America (Larrea and Piguillam, 1956), Germany (Haring et al., 1961), Iceland (Palsson, 1956, 1962), North

America (Gosset et al., 1965; Neville and Neathers, 1964) and the U.K. (Newton and Betts, 1966, 1968; Newton et al., 1970; Boaz and Tempest, 1975).

Elsewhere in Britain and Ireland, trials with several thousand sheep showed evidence of significant increases in litter size after administration of PMSG doses ranging from 250 to 1000 i.u. (Gordon, 1958a, 1967a,). Conception rate to first and later services was not affected but the practical success of the application under commercial farming conditions was very much a question of how far perinatal lamb mortality could be minimized, especially in instances of triplets, quadruplets and quintuplets. The most useful practical results were in those lowland flocks normally producing very few twins; among ewes such as Cluns and Suffolks, which usually produced 50% of twins on more, little if any benefit could be demonstrated. For farming situations that are not geared to cope with triplets, the birth of such sets may prove to be an embarrassment when they occur on any scale.

Reports of applications of this type of

Table 16.1. *Endocrinological flushing of sheep — using PMSG in the normal oestrous cycle to increase the litter-size in sheep*

PMSG Dose (i.u.)	Treated		Controls		References
	No. ewes	Lambs/ ewe	No. ewes	Lambs/ ewe	
500	15	1.67	15	1.47	Robinson (1951)
500	131	1.38	132	1.17	Wallace et al. (1954)
1000	94	1.76	103	1.07	
500	20	1.80	20	1.15	Palsson (1956)
750	20	2.05	20	1.20	
250–500	452	1.71	435	1.52	Gordon (1958)
750–1000	595	1.89	562	1.49	
500	614	1.78	475	1.16	Palsson (1962)
5 i.u./lb. Bodyweight	57	1.95	59	1.25	Gordon (1967a)

Figures here relate to ewes lambing to first services. In all cases, the method of treatment involved a single subcutaneous injection of PMSG in the follicular phase (days 12/13) of the ewe's natural oestrous cycle. The timing of PMSG administration was by running sterile teaser rams with the ewes beforehand.

treatment in Soviet Russia, mainly among Karakul sheep, appeared in the literature during the fifties and sixties (Zavadovskii, 1954, 1957; Belevickii, 1959; Savov et al., 1961; Amarbaev, 1964; Juzlikaev, 1965). Elsewhere, work in Australia with high and low fertility strains of Merinos (Bindon et al., 1971) and in New Zealand with high and low fertility strains of Romneys (Smith, 1976) showed that the high fertility animals responded to a greater extent than the low to a given dose of PMSG.

From the sheep farmer's point of view, the PMSG technique involved running vasectomized teaser rams with the flock beforehand in order to work out the appropriate dates for administering the gonadotrophin. The high cost of labour makes the use of teasers and regular checking for heats difficult and expensive to apply in normal farm practice; there may be the difficulty that ewes cannot be bred at their first oestrus if this is taken up with the teaser ram service. For these and other reasons, thoughts turned increasingly towards the possibility of developing a technique in which progestagen is first employed to synchronize oestrus and gonadotrophin then administered independently of the oestrous cycle. It was felt that a method of augmenting fertility, simultaneously with oestrus synchronization, could permit the practical benefits of artificial insemination, compact lambings and twinning to be usefully combined.

16.6.1 PMSG in conjunction with synchronizing treatments

Early efforts by Wallace (1955) in New Zealand involved multiple doses of progesterone by injection for an 8-day period prior to giving PMSG; most ewes were in oestrus within 7 days and litter-size was 1.5 in the PMSG group and 1.1 in the controls. Gordon (1958b, 1963) and Howell and Woolfitt (1964) also employed similar progesterone-PMSG regimes with some evidence of an increase in the incidence of multiple-births. Nonetheless, the inconvenience of administering progesterone in several doses made the procedure impracticable for commercial application and it was only with the advent of the progestagen impregnated sponge

pessary that the approach was able to receive serious consideration. In Ireland, studies with Galway sheep, showed that FGA-PMSG treatment (750 i.u. doses) was effective in the induction of a consistently high litter-size under field conditions (Gordon, 1975; Smith, 1977); ample evidence, based on direct inspection of the ovaries, was also available to show that the use of the gonadotrophin in conjunction with progestagen (FGA/MAP/SC-21009) could markedly increase the number of eggs shed at the controlled oestrus (Boland et al., 1979).

Although one approach to increasing litter-size in Galway sheep is by introducing Finn blood, there are opportunities for employing the progestagen-PMSG technique; it is a matter of being able to provide the treatment at a sufficiently low cost to be attractive to the farmer. In New Zealand, Allison (1974) estimated that the application of the progestagen-PMSG technique could be a cheaper way of improving lamb output in low liveweight Romney ewes than by additional pre-mating feeding. In Canada, as part of their sheep research and development work, Ainsworth et al. (1977) did report a significant ovulatory response in ewes to a 500 i.u. dose of PMSG given at the end of intravaginal-FGA treatment.

16.6.2 Prostaglandins and PMSG

As one means of synchronizing oestrus in cyclic sheep, prostaglandin $F_{2\alpha}$ or one of its analogues has been employed, as mentioned elsewhere. Studies in which PMSG has been administered at the time of the second of two luteolytic doses of prostaglandin have been reported by Boland et al. (1978a, b); results did suggest that a mild superovulatory effect could be achieved by this routine.

16.6.3 Gonadotrophins in the early cycle

An alternative to using a single dose of PMSG in the follicular phase of the cycle has been suggested by Cahill and Dufour (1979); they found it possible to get a response when the gonadotrophin was administered during the early luteal phase (day-2). One apparent merit of giving the PMSG at day-2 rather than day-12, according to Cahill and Dufour (1979) is that the variation in ovulatory response is decreased and there is less likelihood of undesirably high ovulation rates and litter-sizes. This method, even if its promise should be fulfilled in further work, would still demand the accurate recognition of a specific stage of the sheep's oestrous cycle and this would seem to be a severe limitation to its application in commerical practice. The treatment is apparently based on information showing a correlation between a peak in FSH at the start of the cycle and the number of follicles ovulating at the next heat period (Cahill and Dufour, 1979).

16.7 USE OF Gn-RH

A further approach to the matter of controlling follicular development was examined by Findlay and Cumming (1976) in Australia and by workers elsewhere; an analogue of Gn-RH (Hoe 766; Hoechst) was used to bring about the release of gonadotrophin towards the end of the sheep's oestrous cycle. According to Australian evidence, when given about day-12 of the normal cycle, Gn-RH increased the mean ovulation rate without sheep releasing more than two eggs. It appears that the method was applied in a large-scale field programme in Western Australia; the suggestion was that the administration of the analogue on either day-12 or 13 after a previous synchronized heat would increase ovulation rates by more than 20% (Findlay et al., 1976). Although the Australian studies did suggest that the enhanced ovulation rate was a result of increased follicle growth due to FSH being released in response to the Gn-RH analogue, studies in Ireland by Quirke et al. (1979), who employed the agent with intravaginal pro-gestagen, showed that the quantity of LH released was sufficiently great to trigger ovulation in many ewes regardless of the time the analogue was administered. Certainly, the conclusion drawn from the Irish work was that further investigations were necessary before Gn-RH or its analogues could be considered as practical aids to control the ovulation rate in sheep.

16.8 MODIFYING HORMONAL FEEDBACK EFFECTS

The normal process of ovulation, in sheep as in other mammals, depends on the balance between the stimulatory effects of pituitary gonadotrophins on developing vesicular follicles in the ovaries and the feedback effects of steroid hormones (oestradiol being the major steroid involved) from these follicles that suppress the release of the gonadotrophins. The amount of oestradiol produced by the ovary depends on the number and stage of maturation of the follicles (Moor, 1973); ewes with higher ovulation rates have more developing follicles and hence secrete more oestradiol. Cumming and Findlay (1977) have suggested that the higher ovulation rates found in the prolific breeds of sheep (Finns and Romanovs) may be the result of decreased sensitivity of the hypothalmic – pituitary axis to the negative feedback effects of oestradiol, allowing gonadotrophin levels to be maintained or enhanced at critical times to support the growth and development of a greater number of vesicular follicles. It is known that the largest one or two vesicular follicles are the main source of the oestrogen which is exerting the negative feedback effect (Baird and Scaramuzzi, 1976); there are several ways in which it may be possible to reduce the feedback effects of ovarian steroids on the pituitary.

One possibility is to reduce feedback action by using either an anti-oestrogen or a very weak oestrogen, which would decrease the inhibitory effects of the endogenous oestrogen produced by the ovarian follicles; the compound clomiphene citrate (an anti-oestrogen) has been one such agent used quite commonly in human medicine to induce ovulation in infertility cases (Cox, 1975). In Australia, Lindsay and Robinson (1970) used a dose range of 1–90 mg clomiphene in ewes but at all dose levels they observed oestrogenic rather than anti-oestrogenic effects; the indications were that these doses were too high. Markedly lower doses (25 μg) were employed in the efforts of Land and Scaramuzzi (1979) in sheep of several breeds; responses in the ewes were minor and variable and it was generally felt that the agent had no place in controlled breeding applications.

16.9 IMMUNIZATION AGAINST OVARIAN STEROIDS

An alternative to the anti-oestrogen approach is to reduce the feedback effects of ovarian steroids by immunizing the ewe against them. Active immunization against potentially important hormones has been widely used as a method of investigating their effects, and has been employed in examining the actions of steroids, polypeptides and prostaglandins. The ovaries of the ewe are believed to secrete at least nine different steroids, including androgens such as testosterone and androstenedione and oestrogens such as oestradiol and oestrone (Baird, 1978).

The ability of exogenous testosterone to induce oestrus (Robinson, 1951), the release of LH (Pant, 1977; Clarke and Scaramuzzi, 1978) and ovulation (Radford and Wallace, 1971) in ewes suggested to researchers that the steroid as secreted by the ovary has some biological function; a high proportion of ewes immunized

Fig. 16.2. New methods of increasing litter size in the ewe. One recent development in agricultural research has been the application of active and passive immunization procedures to neutralize certain biological effects of steroid hormones. Evidence which is now building up in several countries indicates that immunization against steroids such as oestrone may have considerable potential for increasing the lambing performance of flocks. There would be plenty of opportunity for the application of such techniques, should they prove to be both consistent and effective.

against testosterone became anovulatory in studies reported by Scaramuzzi et al. (1981), without the mechanism underlying such ovulatory failure being evident.

Active immunization against oestrogens (oestradiol or oestrone) has been observed to produce a castration-like effect on pituitary function (Scaramuzzi et al., 1977; Pant et al., 1978; Rawlings et al., 1978); in this, the basal levels both of LH and FSH and the frequency of pulsatile LH surges increase to levels that are only seen in ovariectomized ewes. In some reports, immunized sheep rapidly developed an anovulatory condition, apparently due to a failure of positive feedback mechanisms or showed an increased ovulation rate (Cox et al., 1976); Scaramuzzi et al., 1977, 1980; Smith et al., 1981). In New Zealand, it has been shown that an increased ovulation rate after immunization against oestrone was followed by a 27% increase in the number of lambs that were weaned from Coopworth and Romney ewes. Clearly, there is a need to follow up such findings in further work.

Although little is known of the physiological function of the androgen, androstenedione, ewes immunized against this particular ovarian steroid have shown increases in ovulation rate (Scaramuzzi et al., 1977; Van Look et al., 1978; Martin et al., 1978, 1979: Quirke and Gosling, 1981) in the levels of LH and progesterone and a decrease in the level of FSH (Martensz and Scaramuzzi, 1979). Such reports are taken as indicating that androstenedione is an active regulator of ovarian activity by way of its feedback action on the hypothalamic–pituitary axis. Scaramuzzi et al. (1980) suggested that immunization against androstenedione reduces the availability of that hormone, which effectively decreased the sensitivity of the hypothalamic-pituitary axis to the negative feedback effect of oestrogen, resulting in a higher concentration of tonic LH and permitting greater follicle development. Elsewhere, Bon Durant et al. (1980) in the U.S.A. failed to find an effect, either on LH level or on the ovulation rate of ewes which they immunized against androstenedione. There is also, from the practical viewpoint, the fact that increased ovulation rates after androstenedione have not often been followed by increased litter-sizes at lambing (Van Look et al., 1978; Martin et al., 1978, 1979; Smith et al., 1981). Before the immunization approach can be recommended for the farm, there would seem to be a need for much further information about ovarian and lambing response, both long-term as well as short-term. It may be that such work will show that the approach does have great potential for increasing lambing percentages (Smith et al., 1981).

16.10 LITTERS AND LAMB MORTALITY

Perinatal lamb mortality is a major cause of reduced productivity in sheep, with figures of 10, 15% and even 20% deaths recorded in the literature. Most of the lamb deaths occur in the first few days of life and it is recognized that the major causes are nutritional, behavioural and physiological rather than infectious (Moule, 1954; Gordon, 1967a, b; Dennis, 1974). According to figures available from the M.L.C. in Britain, about 12–13% of lambs die in lowland flocks operating at litter-sizes of 1.5 or so.

In general, as lamb birthweight increases within a particular breed type, mortality declines to a minimum for lambs of average or somewhat greater than average birthweight, and then as a result of difficult births, rises again for the high birthweights.

16.10.1 Litters and problems

In a normal flock situation, in which the average litter-size is 1.5, the proportion of litters consisting of more than two lambs would be small; with a flock averaging 2.5, on the other hand, there may well be 40% triplets and 15% quadruplets and quintuplets (Robinson et al., 1977) with a consequent increase in lamb mortality. Lees (1978), working in Wales with Clun Forest ewes, suggests that two lambs per ewe is what to aim for; he concludes, on the basis of an analysis of the literature, that the efforts of workers who aim at much larger litter-sizes may be largely self-defeating because of the increases in lamb mortality when prolificacy exceeds two lambs per ewe. In dealing with triplets and such

lambs, the number reared may actually decline as litter-size goes beyond a certain point; there is also the question of the increased costs of feeding, labour and attention, as well as the poorer viability and growth rates of lambs. All this is true enough, but the essential point is that management must be geared to deal effectively with litters if the farmer is to gain the benefits of an increased litter-size.

The results of workers such as Robinson (1979) dealing with highly prolific sheep show that lamb mortality can be kept very low if the management system is appropriate; at the Rowett, it has been routine practice to administer, by stomach catheter and syringe and as soon after birth as possible, about 60 ml of either ewe or cow colostrum to each lamb from a large litter, a quick, easy procedure which has reduced perinatal mortality in such litters to a very low figure. It has been shown, from studies on the anatomical development of the ovine foetus that the small lamb from a large litter is better developed than its birthweight might otherwise indicate (McDonald et al., 1977); thus, it is not at risk of dying from under-development per se, providing it gets colostrum soon after birth. Retained meconium is another situation in weakly lambs, deprived of, or receiving insufficient quantities of colostrum, which Robinson (1981) has alleviated, using a discarded stomach tube to administer an enema.

16.10.2 Large litters and the ewe

A large litter can lead to some degree of stress in the ewe during late pregnancy; Robinson (1979) has shown in the Finn x Dorset ewe that the total lamb weight produced by this prolific sheep is considerably greater in relation to her body size than that which occurs in any other farm animal. As mentioned earlier, for those sheep that are to be used in frequent breeding programmes, the ideal would probably be litters of two lambs rather than more than two.

As to the ability of the ewe to deal with large litters in relation to breed, Robinson et al., (1977) noted some indication in published figures that lambs from the Romanov and its first crosses may have a lower mortality rate than lambs from the Finn and its crosses.

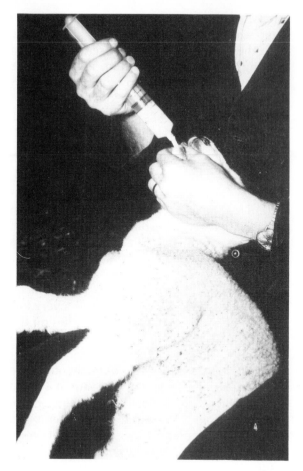

Fig. 16.3. Using the stomach tube as a means of saving weakly lambs. Workers at the Rowett at Aberdeen have clearly shown the value of the stomach tube in saving small lambs that would otherwise almost certainly die through lack of energy. The method has been actively promoted among farmers in the North-East of Scotland as a means of saving lambs by advisory officers from Aberdeen. Further afield, the method has been recognized by New Zealand sheep farmers for some time as a valuable practical aid at lambing time.

16.11 REFERENCES

Ainsworth, L., Hacket, A. J., Heaney, D. P., Langford, G. A. and Peters, H. F. (1977) A multidisciplinary approach to the development of controlled breeding, and intensive production systems for sheep. *In, Management of Reproduction in Sheep and Goats, Symp. Univ. Wisconsin,* pp.101–108.

Allen, D. M. and Lamming, G. E. (1961a) Some effects of nutrition on the growth and sexual development of ewe lambs. *J. Agric. Sci., Camb.* **57,** 87–95.

Allen, D. M. and Lamming, G. E. (1961b) Nutrition and reproduction in the ewe. *J. Agric. Sci. Camb.* **56,** 69–79.

Allison, A. J. (1968) The influence of liveweight on ovulation rate in the ewe. *Proc. N. Z. Soc. Anim. Prod.* **28,** 115.

Allison, A. J. (1974) Some techniques for increasing reproductive rates in sheep and their application in the industry. *Proc. N. Z. Soc. Anim. Prod.* **34,** 167–174.

Allison, A. J. and Kelly, R. W. (1979) Effects of differential nutrition on the incidence of oestrus and ovulation rate in Booroola X Romney and Romney ewes. *Proc. N. Z. Soc. Anim. Prod. 39th Ann. Conf.* **39,** 43–49.

Amarbaev. A. M. (1964) It is necessary to simplify PMS treatment of ewes. *Ovcevodstvo* **9** (7) 29–31.

Averill, R. L. W. (1955) Fertility of the ewe. *Proc. Soc. Study Fert.* **7,** 139–148.

Averill, R. L. W. (1959) Ovulatory activity in mature ewes in Otago. *N. Z. J. Agric. Res.* **2,** 575–583.

Baird, D. T. (1978) Pulsatile secretion of LH and ovarian estradiol during the follicular phase of the sheep estrous cycle. *Biol Reprod.*

Baird, D. T. and Scaramuzzi, R. J. (1976) The source of ovarian oestradiol androstendione in the sheep during the luteal phase. *Acta. Endocr.* **83,** 402–409.

Belevickii, G. S. (1959) A three-year Exp. in treating Karakul ewes with PMS. *Trud. veseojuz. nauc-issled Inst. Zivotn.* **23,** 525–541.

Bennett, D., Nadin, J. B. and Axelsen, A. (1970). The effect of undernutrition during early pregnancy in merino ewes. *Proc. Aust. Soc. Anim. Prod.* **8,** 362.

Bindon, B. M. and Piper, L. R. (1976) Assessment of New and Traditional techniques of selection for reproduction rate. *Proc. Int. Congr. Sheep Breed., Muresk.* 357–371. Waite Press, Perth.

Bindon, B. M. and Turner, H. N. (1974) Plasma LH of the prepubertal lamb: a possible indicator of fecundity. *J. Reprod. Fert.* **39,** 85–88.

Bindon, B. M., Chang, T. S. and Turner, H. N. (1971) Ovarian response to gonadotrophin by Merino ewes selected for fecundity. *Aust. J. agric. Res.* **22,** 809–820.

Bindon, B. M., Chang, T. S. and Evans, R. E. (1974). Genetic effects on LH release by oestradiol and Gn-RH in prepubertal lambs. *J. Reprod. Fert.* **36,** 477.

Bindon, B. M., Blanc, M. R., Pelletier, J, Terqui, M. and Thimonier, J. (1975) Preovulatory gonadotrophin and ovarian steroid changes in French sheep breeds differing in fecundity. Does FSH stimulate follicles? *Proc. Endocr. Soc. Aust.* **18,** 64.

Blockey, M. A. deB., Cumming, I. A. and Baxter, R. W. (1974) The effect of short term fasting in ewes on early embryonic mortality. *Proc. Aust. Soc. Anim. Prod.* **10,** 265–269.

Boaz, T. G. and Tempest, W. M. (1975) Some consequences of high flock prolificacy in an intensive grassland sheep production system. *Anim. Prod.* **20,** 219–232.

Boland, M. P., Gordon, I. and Kelleher, D. L. (1978a) The effect of treatment of prostaglandin analogue (ICI 80996) or progestagen (SC 9880) on ovulation and fertilization in cyclic sheep. *J. Agric. Sci., Camb.* **91,** 727–730.

Boland, M. P., Lemainque, F. and Gordon, I. (1978b) Comparison of lambing outcome in ewes after synchronization of oestrus by progestagen or prostaglandin treatment. *J. agric. Sci., Camb.* **91,** 765–766.

Boland, M. P., Kelleher, D. and Gordon, I. (1979). Comparison of control of oestrus and ovulation in sheep by an ear implant (SC 21009) or by intravaginal sponge. *Anim. Reprod. Sci.* **1** (4), 275–283.

BonDurant, R. H., Torell, D., Layton, L and Munro, C. (1980) Attempted increase in twinning rates via immunization of ewes against androstenedione. *J. Anim. Sci.* **51** (Suppl 1), 438 (Abs).

Bouix, J. (1975). Un des elements majeurs de la mise en valeur des palmergies: la race ovine D'man. *Options Mediterr.* **26,** 87–93.

Braden, A. W. H. (1971). Effect of undernutrition of ewes during joining. *Aust. J. Exp. Agric. Anim. Husb.* **11,** 375–378.

Brien, F. D., Baxter, R. W., Findlay, J. K. and Cumming, I. A. (1976) Effect of lupin grain supplementation on ovulation rate and plasma follicle stimulating hormone (FSH) concentration in maiden and mature Merino ewes. *Proc. Aust. Soc. Anima. Prod.,* **11,** 237–244

Cahill, L. P. and Dufour, J. (1979) Follicular populations in the ewe under different gonadotrophin levels. *Ann. Biol. Anim. Bioch. Biophys.* **19** (5) 1475–1481.

Cahill, L. P. and Mauleon, P. (1980) Influences of season, cycle and breed on follicular growth rates in sheep. *J. Reprod. Fert.* **58,** 321–328.

Cahill, L. P., Mariana, J. C. and Mauleon, P. (1979) Total follicular populations in ewes of high and low ovulation rates. *J. Reprod. Fert.* **55,** 27–36.

Clark, R. T. (1934) The ovulation rate of the ewe as affected by the plane of nutrition. *Anat. Rec.* **60,** 125.

Clarke, I. J. and Scaramuzzi, R. J. (1978) Sexual behaviour and LH secretion in sprayed androgenized ewes after a single injection of testosterone or oestradiol-17$_\beta$. *J. Reprod. Fert.* **52,** 313–320.

Coop, I. E. (1962) Liveweight and reproduction. *N.Z.J. Agric. Res.* **5,** 249.

Coop, I. E. (1966) Effect of flushing on reproductive performance of ewes. *J. Agric. Sci. Camb.* **67,** 305.

Coop, I. E. (1977) Depression of lambing percentage from mating on lucerne. *Proc. N. Z. Soc. Anim. Prod.* **37,** 149–151.

Coop, I. E. and Clark, V. R. (1960) The reproductive performance of ewes mated on lucerne. *N. Z. Jl. Agric. Res.* **3,** 922–933.

Cox, L. W. (1975) Infertility: a comprehensive programme. *Br. J. Obstet. Gynaec.* **82,** 2–6.

Cox, R. I., Wilson, P. A. and Mattner, P. E. (1976) Immunization of ewes to oestrogens: effects on the oestrous cycle and parturition. *Theriogen.* **6,** 607.

Cumming, I. A. (1976) Synchronization of ovulation. *Proc. Int. Congr. Sheep Breed. Muresk.* 430–448. Waite Press, Perth.

Cumming, I. A. (1977) Relationships in the sheep of ovulation rate with liveweight, breed, season and plane of nutrition. *Aust. J. exp. Agric. Anim. Husb.* **17,** 234–241.

Cumming, I. A. and Findlay, J. K. (1977) Evolution of ovarian function in sheep and cattle. *Reprod. and Evolution, 4th Int. Symp. Compl Biol. Reprod. Canberra),* pp 225–233.

Daly, P. J. (1966) *Sheep Husbandry Survey in Kilmaine, Co. Mayo.* An Foras Taluntais. Dublin.

Davis, I. F. and Cumming, I. A. (1976). Effect of feeding legume grain supplements on ovulation rate in Border Leicester × Merino ewes. *Proc. Aust. Soc. Reprod. Biol.* **8,** 28.

Dennis, S. M. (1974) Perinatal lamb mortality in Western Australia. I. General procedures and results. *Aust. Vet. J.* **50,** 433–449.

Donald, H. P. and Read, J. L. (1967) The performance of Finnish Landrace sheep in Britain, *Anim. Prod.* **9,** 471–476.

Doney, J. M. (1979) Nutrition and the reproductive function in female sheep. *In The Management and Diseases of Sheep.* pp 152–160. *Comm. Agric. Bur. Slough.*

Doney, J. M., Gunn, R. G. and Smith, W. F. (1976) Effects of pre-mating environmental stress, ACTH, Cortisone

Acetate of Metyrapone on oestrus and ovulation in sheep. *J. Agric. Sci., Camb.* **87,** 127–132.

Downing, J. and Lees, J. L. (1977) Unpublished data cited by J. L. Lees in a paper read at the *Brit. Council No. 729, Edinburgh, March, 1978.*

Dufour, J., Cahill, L. P. and Mauleon, P. (1979) Short and long-term effects of hypophysectomy and unilateral ovariectomy on ovarian follicular populations in sheep. *J. Reprod. Fert.* **57,** 301–309.

Edey, T. N. (1966) Nutritional stress and pre-implantation embryonic mortality in Merino sheep. *J. Agric. Sci., Camb.* **67,** 287–293.

Edey, T. N. (1969a) Prenatal mortality in sheep: a review. *Anim. Breed. Abser.,* **37,** 173–190.

Edey, T. N. (1969b) Fertilization and pregnancy. In *Anim. Reprod.* ed. James, B. J. F. Ed., *Cheshire, Melbourne,* pp. 63–69.

Findlay, J. K. and Cumming, I. A. (1976) Increase in ovulation rate in sheep following administration of an LH-RH analogue. *Biol. Reprod.* **15,** 115–117.

Fletcher, I. and Geytenbeck, P. E. (1970) Seasonal variation in the ovarian activity of Merino ewes. *Aust. J. Exp. Agric. Anim. Husb.* **10,** 267–270.

Fox, C. W., Chouciti, E. and Chabaan, R. (1976). *E.A.A.P. 27th Ann. Mting. Zurich.*

Geisler, P. A. and Fenlon, J. S. (1979) The effects of body weight and its components on lambing performance in some commercial flocks in Britain. *Anim. Prod.* **28,** 245–255.

Gordon, I. (1958a) The hormonal augmentation of fertility in the ewe during the breeding season. *J. Agric. Sci., Camb.* **50,** 123.

Gordon, I. (1958b). Studies in the extra-seasonal production of lambs. *J. Agric. Sci., Camb.* **50,** 125.

Gordon, I. (1963) The induction of pregnancy in the anoestrous ewe by hormonal therapy. I. Progesterone-PMS therapy during the breeding season. *J. Agric. Sci., Camb.* **60,** 31.

Gordon, I. (1967a) Research in the use of hormones in animal reproduction. *J. Ir. Dept. Agric. Dublin,* **64,** 51.

Gordon, I. (1967b). Aspects of reproduction and neonatal mortality in ewe lambs and adult sheep. *J. Ir. Dept. Agric. Dublin* **64,** 76–130.

Gordon, I. (1975) Oestrus synchronization in sheep and its application in practice. *Proc. Symp Detection and Control of Breeding Activity in Farm Animals, Aberdeen Univ.,* 40–54.

Gosset, J. W., Kiracofe, G. H., Graham, P. P. and Baker, B. (1965) Effects of equine gonadotrophin on ewe reproductivity. *Tech. Bull. Va. agric. Exp. Sta.* No. 164.

Griffiths, J. G., Gunn, R. G. and Doney, J. M. (1970) Fertility in Scottish blackface ewes as influenced by climatic stress. *J. Agric. Sci., Camb.* **75,** 485–488.

Guerra, J. C., Thwaites, C. J. Edey, T. N. (1971) The effects of liveweight on the ovarian response to PMSG and on embryo mortality in the ewe. *J. Agric. Sci., Camb.* **76,** 177–178.

Gunn, R. G. and Doney, J. M. (1975) The interaction of nutrition and body condition at mating on ovulation rate and early embryo mortality in Scottish Blackface ewes. *J. Agric. Sci. Camb.* **85,** 465–470.

Gunn, R. G., Doney, J. M. and Tussell, A. J. F. (1972) Embryo mortality in Scottish Blackface ewes as influenced by body condition at mating and by post-mating nutrition. *J. Agric. Sci., Camb.* **79,** 19–25.

Gunn, R. G. Doney, J. M. and Smith, W. F. (1979) The effect of time of mating on ovulation rate and potential lambing rate of Greyface ewes. *Anim. Prod.* **29,** 277–282.

Hammond, J. Jr. (1944) On the breeding season in the sheep. *J. Agric. Sci. Camb.* **34,** 97–105.

Haring, F., Weniger, J. H. and Engelke, F. (1961) Increase in the number of multiple births in sheep by PMS. *Zucth. ort. Phistor. Besam, Hasutuere,* **5,** 59.

Heape, W. (1899) Abortion, barrenness and fertility in sheep. *J. Roy. Agric. Engl.* Series 111, **10,** 217

Howell, W. E. and Woolfitt, W. C. (1964) Hormonal control of estrus and its effect on fertility in cycling ewes. *Can. J. Anim. Sci.* **44,** 195–199.

Hulet C. V. and Foote, W. C. (1967) Physiological factors affecting frequency and rate of lambing. *J. Anim. Sci.* **26,** 553–562.

Johansson, I. and Hansson, A. (1943) The sex ratio and multiple births in sheep. *Landbrhogsk. Ann.,* 145–171.

Jones, S. V. H. and Rouse, J. E. (1920) The relation of age of dam to observed fecundity. *J Dairy Sci.* **3,** 260.

Juzlikaev, R. D. (1965) The dose of PMS should be related to the weight of the ewe. *Ovcevodstvo,* **11** (7) 23.

Keane, M. G. (1974) Factors affecting the occurrence of puberty and reproduction in ewe lambs. *Ph.D. Thesis, N. U. I., Dublin.*

Keane, M. G. (1975) Effect of nutrition and dose level of PMS on oestrous response and ovulation rate in progestagen treated non-cyclic Suffolk X Galway ewe lambs. *J. Agric. Sci., Camb.* **84,** 507–511.

Killeen, I. D. (1967) The effects of body weight and level of nutrition befpre. during and after joining on ewe fertility. *Aust. J. Exp. Agric. Anim. Husb.* **7,** 126–136.

Knight, T. W., Oldham, C. M. and Lindsay, D. R. (1975) Studies in ovine infertility in agricultural regions in Western Australia: the influence of a supplement of lupins at joining on the reproductive performance of ewes. *Aust. J. Agric. Res.* **26,** 567–575.

Land, R. B. (1978) Reproduction in young sheep: some genetic and environmental sources of variation. *J. Reprod. Fert.* **57,** 427–436.

Land, R. B. (1979) Genetic and physiological variation in reproductive performance. *In Management and Diseases of Sheep.* pp 114–123 Comm. Agric. Bur. Slough.

Land, R. B. (1980) Genetic control of ovulation rate. *Proc. 9th Int. Congr. Anim. Reprod. A. I. (Madrid),* **2,** 63–70.

Land, R. B. and Scaramuzzi, R. J. (1979) A note on the ovulation rate of sheep following treatment with clomiphene citrate. *Anim. Prod.* **28,** 131–134.

Land, R. B., Pelletier, J., Thimonier, J. and Mauleon, P. (1973) A quantitative study of genetic differences in the incidence of oestrus, ovulation and plasma LH concentration in the sheep. *J. Endocr.* **53,** 305–317.

Larrae, I. A. and Piguillon, E. (1956) Effect of treatment with gonadotrophic hormone during the mating season on superovulation and superfoetation in sheep. *A.I.A. Rev. Assoc. Ing Agron Montevideo* **25,** 3.

Lees, J. L. (1978) Functional infertility in sheep. *Vet. Rec.* **102,** 232–236.

Lightfoot, R. J. and Marshall, T. (1974) *J. Agric. W. Aust.,* **15,** 29.

Lindsay, D. R. (1976) The usefulness to the animal producer of research findings in nutrition on reproduction. *Proc. Aust. Soc. Anim. Prod.* **11,** 217–224.

Lindsay, D. R. and Robinson, T. J. (1970) The action of clomiphene in the ewe. *J. Reprod. Fert.* **23,** 277–283.

L'Hermite, M., Niswender, G. D., Reichert, J. L. E. and Midgley, A. R. (1972) Serum FSH in sheep as measured by radioimmunoassay. *Biol. Reprod.* **6,** 325–332.

McDonald, I., Wenham, G. and Robinson, J. J. (1977) Studies on reproduction in prolific ewes. 3. The development in size and shape of the foetal skeleton. *J. Agric. Sci., Camb.* **89,** 373–391.

McKenzie, F. F. and Terrill, E. (1937) Estrus, ovulation and related phenomena in the ewe. *Res. Bull Mo. Agri. Exp. Sta.* No. 264.

Marshall, F. H. A. and Potts, C. G. (1924). *Bull. U.S.D.A.* No. 996.

Martin, G. B., Scaramuzzi, R. J., Cox, R. I. and Gherardi, P. B. (1979) Effects of active immunization against androstenedione or oestrone on oestrus, ovulation and lambing in Merino ewes. *Aust. J. Exp. Agric. Anim. Husb.* **19,** 673–678.

Martin, T. E., Henricks, D. M., Hill, J. R., Jr. and Rawlings, N. C. (1978) Active immunization of the cow against oestradiol-17$_\beta$. *J. Reprod. Fert.* **53,** 173–178.

Moor, R. M. (1973) Oestrogen production by individual follicles explanted from ovaries of sheep. *J. Reprod. Fert.* **32,** 545–548.

Moule, G. R. (1954) Observations on mortality amongst lambs in Queensland *Aust. Vet. J.* **30,** 153–171.

Neville, W. E. and Neathery, M. W. (1964) Effects of PMS and triodothyroxine on percent lamb crop. *J. Anim. Sci.* **23,** 36, (Abs).

Newton, J. E. and Betts, J. E. (1966) Factors affecting litter size in the Scotch Half-bred ewe. I. Treatment with PMS and progesterone. *J. Reprod. Fert.* **12,** 167.

Newton, J. E. and Betts, J. E. (1968) Factors affecting litter-size in the Scotch half-bred ewe. II. Superovulation and synchronization of oestrus. *J. Reprod. Fert.* **17,** 485–493.

Newton, J. E., Betts, J. E. and Large, R. V. (1970) Increasing litter size in three breeds of sheep by superovulation. *J. Agric. Sci., Camb.* **75,** 355–360.

Newton, J. E., Betts, J. E. and Wilde, Renee. (1980). The effect of body condition and time of mating on the reproductive performance of Masham ewes. *Anim. Prod.* **30,** 253–260.

Owen, J. B. (1969). Sheep Production, View of the Future. Seale-Hayne Agric. College, Newton Abbot, Devon.

Palsson, H. (1956) Augmentation of fertility of Iceland ewes. *Proc. 3rd. Int. Congr. Physiol. Path. Anim. Prod. A. I. (Cambridge),* **1,** 112.

Palsson, H. (1962) Augmentation of fertility in Iceland ewes with PMS in successive years. *J. Reprod. Fert.* **3,** 55.

Pant, H. C. (1977) Effect of oestradiol infusion on plasma gonadotrophins and ovarian activity in progesterone-primed and un-primed anoestrous ewes. *J. Endocr.* **75,** 233.

Pant, H. C., Dobson, H. and Ward, W. R. (1978) Effect of active immunization against oestrogens on plasma gonadotrophins in the ewe and the response to synthetic oestrogen of LH. *J. Reprod. Fert.* **53,** 241–248.

Quirke, J. F., Jennings, J. J., Hanrahan, J. P. and Gosling, J. P. (1979) Oestrus, Time of ovulation, ovulation rate and conception rate in progestagen-treated ewes given Gn-RH analogues and gonadotrophins. *J. Reprod. Fert.* **56,** 479–488.

Quirke, J. F. and Gosling, J. P. (1981) Effect of immunization against androstenedione on ovulation rate in Galway and Finnish Landrace ewes. *Ann. Rep. An Foras Taluntais, Anim. Prod. Res.* **1980,** 94–95.

Radford, H. M. and Wallace, A. L. C. (1971) The effect of testosterone propionate on ovarian activity in sheep. *J. Reprod. Fert.* **24,** 439–440.

Rawlings, N. C. Kennedy, S. W. and Henricks, D. M. (1978) Effect of active immunisation of the cyclic ewe against oestradiol-17ᵦ. *J. Endocr.* **76,** 11–19.

Rizzoli, D. J., Reeve, J. L., Baxter, R. W. and Cumming, I. A. (1976) Variation between years in seasonal ovulation rate of Border Leicester x Merino ewes receiving lupin grain supplement. *Theriog.* **6,** 623.

Robinson, J. J. (1974) Intensifying ewe productivity. *Proc. Br. Soc. Anim. Prod.* **3,** 31–40.

Robinson, J. J. (1979). Intensive systems. *In, Management and Diseases of sheep. pp. 431–446. Comm. Agric. Bur., Slough.*

Robinson, J. J. (1981). Prenatal growth and development in the sheep and its implications for the viability of the newborn lamb. *Livestock Prod. Sci.,* **8,** 273–281.

Robinson, J. J. Fraser, C. and McHattie, I. (1977). Development of systems for lambing sheep more frequently than once per year. *Techn. Publ. U.S. Feed Grains Council,* 5–33.

Robinson, T. J. (1951) The augmentation of fertility by gonadotrophin treatment of the ewe in the normal breeding season. *J. Agric. Sci., Camb.* **41,** 6.

Ryle, M. (1971). The growth "in vitro" of mouse ovarian follicles of different sizes in response to purified gonadotrophins. *J. Reprod. Fert.* **30,** 395–405.

Savov, R., Prahov, R. and Evtimova, L. (1961) Increasing the incidence of multiple births in sheep. *Izv. Cent. Naucissled. Inst. Zivotn. G. Dinitrov, Kostinbrod* **12,** 207–221

Scales, G. H., Moss, R. A. and Kelly, R. W. (1977) Reproductive performance of ewes mated on lucerne. *Proc. N. Z. Soc. Anim. Prod.* **37,** 152–157.

Scaramuzzi, R. J., Davidson, W. G. and Van Look, P. F. A. (1977) Increasing ovulation rate in sheep by active immunization against an ovarian steroid andro-stene-dione. *Nature,* **269,** 817.

Scaramuzzi, R. J., Martensz, N. D. and Van Look, P. F. A. (1980) Ovarian morphology and the concentration of steroids, and of gonadotrophins during the breeding season in ewes actively immunized against oestradiol-17ᵦ or oestrone. *J. Reprod. Fert.* **59,** 303–310.

Scaramuzzi, R. J., Baird, D. T., Masrtensz, N. D., Turnbull, K. E. and Van Look, P. F. A. (1981) Ovarian function in the ewe after active immunization against testosterone. *J. Reprod. Fert.* **61,** 1–9.

Smith, J. F. (1976) Selection of fertility and response to PMSG in Romney ewes. *Proc. N. Z. Soc. Anim. Prod.* **36,** 247–251.

Smith, J. F., Jagusch, K. T., Brunswick, L. F. C. and Kelly, R. W. (1979) Coumestans in lucerne and ovulation in ewes. *N. Z. Jl. Agric. Res.* **22,** 411–416.

Smith, J. F., Cox, R. I., McGowan, T. L., Wilson, P. A. and Hoskinson, R. M. (1981) Increasing the ovulation rate in ewes by immunisation. *Proc. N. Z. Soc. Anim. Prod.* **41,** 193–197.

Smith, P. A. (1977). Studies in the artificial insemination of sheep. *Ph. D. Thesis, N.U.I., Dublin.*

Stelmasiak, T. and Cumming, I. A. (1977) Two pools of pituitary LH. An hypothesis explaining the control of the preovulatory surge of LH in the ewe. *Theriogen.* **8** (4), 131.

Thimonier, J. and Pelletier, J. (1971) Difference genetique dans la decharge ovulante (LH) chez les brebis de race Ile-de-France; relations avec le nombre d'ovulations. *Ann. Biol. Anim. Biochim. Biophys.* **11,** 559–567.

Thompson, N. A. and Jagusch, K. T. (1976) Effect of lambing date on the utilization of grass/clover and lucerne pastures during mating. *Proc. N. Z. Soc. Anim. Prod.* **36,** 184–189.

Timon, V. M. (1971) Improved breeding and production methods for the intensification of Irish sheep production. *Lamb Product. U.S. Feed Grains Council Misc. Publ.* 69–78.

Turnbull, K. E., Braden, A. W. H. and Mattner, P. E. (1977) The pattern of follicular growth and atresia in the ovine ovary. *Aust. J. Biol. Sci.* **30,** 229–241.

Turner, H. N. (1968) *Proc. of U.S. Sheep Development Program on Physiology of reproduction in sheep. Scott, G.,* Stillwater, Oklahoma.

Tyrrell, R. N., Starr, B. G., Restall, B. J. and Donnelly, J. B. (1980) Repeatability of LH responses by lambs to monthly challenge with synthetic gonadotrophin releasing hormone (GnRH). *Anim. Reprod. Sci.* **3,** 155–160.

Van Look, P. F. A., Clarke, I. J., Davidson, W. G. and Scaramuzzi, R. J. (1978) Ovulation and lambing rates in ewes actively immunized against androstenedione. *J. Reprod. Fert.* **53,** 129–130.

Van Niekerk, C. H., Belonje, P. G. and Hunter, G. L. (1968) Early embryonic mortality and resorption in Merino ewes due to malnutrition. *6th Congr. Int. Reprod. Anim. Insem. Artif. (Paris),* **1,** 455–458.

Vesely, J. A. and Bowden, D. M. (1980). Effect of various light regimes on lamb production by Rambouillet and Suffolk ewes. *Anim. Prod.,* **31,** 163–169.

Wallace, L. R. (1955). *Rpt. Ruakura Fmrs' Conf.* No. 38.

Wallace, L. R., Lambourne, L. J. and Sinclair, D. P. (1954) Effect of PMS on the reproductive performance of Romney ewes. *N. Z. Jl. Sci. Tech. Agric.,* **55,** 421.

Wheeler, A. G. and Land, R. B. (1977) Seasonal variation in oestrus and ovarian activity of Finnish landrace, Tasmanian Merino and Scottish Blackface ewes. *Anim. Prod.* **24,** 363–376.

Williams, S. M. (1954). Fertility in Clun Forest sheep. *J. Agric. Sci. Camb.* **45,** 202–228.

Zavadovskii, M. M. (1941) *Hormonal Stimulation of Multi-foetation in Sheep. Agiz. Seljhozgiz, Moscow.*

Zavadoskii, M. M. (1954) Frontal variant in hormonal induction of multifoetation in sheep. *Dokl. Akad. Seljskohoz. Nauk. Lenin,* **19** (3), 20–24.

Zavadovskii, M. M. (1957) The effect of treatment with PMS on Karakul ewes, and on the embryonic development and quality of newborn lambs. *Trud. vsesojuz. nauc-issled. Inst. Ziovotn.* **21,** 167–179.

CHAPTER 17

Pregnancy Testing in Sheep

17.1 INTRODUCTION

A practical and economical method for the early diagnosis of pregnancy in sheep has been sought for some time; it is a question of practical importance in sheep farming as well as being of scientific interest in the study of reproduction and fertility in the species. There would be several practical advantages in knowing in advance whether sheep are pregnant or not: (a) it would eliminate the cost and labour involved in providing expensive supplementary feed to barren sheep; (b) barren ewes could be culled and sold earlier than otherwise would be possible; (c) meal feeding and attention could be restricted to pregnant sheep as they approach lambing and not wasted on the barren animals. There is the additional consideration of determining whether the pregnant sheep is carrying a single lamb or multiple foetuses; this could permit the farmer to direct feed and attention to where it is needed most.

The usual method of checking for early pregnancy in sheep in the autumn breeding season is by noting whether the ewe returns in oestrus after a previous breeding; to aid in detecting oestrous sheep, the farmer can employ raddle paste (or block) or the marking harness with crayons, based on the device first described by Radford et al. (1960). In the ewe anoestrus, on the other hand, pregnancy diagnosis on the basis of non-return of oestrus is not possible and this is when there is a particular need for a suitable test. With the greater adoption of controlled breeding techniques, particularly those used in more frequent lambing systems and involving out-of-season matings, the question of separating out ewes that are pregnant, especially as they approach the time for meal feeding in late pregnancy, becomes important.

17.1.1 Distinguishing singles from twins

As already noted, the incidence of perinatal mortality in sheep is related to size and birthweight of the lamb; this, in turn is influenced by litter-size and the particular nutritional regime enjoyed by the ewe in late pregnancy. Provision of appropriate amounts of supplementary feed to ewes carrying multiple foetuses could ensure that these reach the maximum size at birth and therefore ensure their survival. On the other hand, reducing the amount of feed provided to single-bearing ewes could control birthweights and help to minimize lamb losses arising from difficult lambings. For farmers breeding their own flock replacements, if ewes could be grouped before lambing into those that are carrying twins and triplets and those carrying

Fig. 17.1. Using the marking harness as a method of identifying ewes that fail to become pregnant. Australian workers were the first to come up with the ram marking harness. Unfortunately, these can be quite expensive and the crayons are also costly. In much of the work in controlled breeding in sheep conducted from Lyons Farm, raddle paste is the standard product used in marking rams.

single lambs, then subsequent selection for natural twinning ability of the ewes could be made that much easier in flocks where no record of individual ewes is maintained. In devising appropriate tests for pregnancy diagnosis it is clearly a great advantage to be dealing with a group of ewes all of which are at known stages of pregnancy; this can now be easily arranged by way of oestrus control measures.

One of the first critical reviews of the literature on pregnancy testing in sheep was the report of Richardson (1972b); The author described 24 methods which had been employed up to that time and gave first hand information on 17 which she had checked out herself. More recently, literature has also been reviewed by others (Memon and Ott, 1980; Plant, 1980). The present discussion is mainly confined to those methods which may be regarded as sufficiently accurate and feasible to be employed as part of a controlled breeding service, which might be operated from some appropriate centre; to satisfy these requirements, techniques must be simple, rapid and accurate.

17.2 RADIOGRAPHIC TECHNIQUES

Radiography has been successfully used at research institutions for some time; in studies on frequent lambing systems in sheep at the Rowett in Scotland, the technique has been used routinely to obtain an accurate diagnosis of pregnancy and numbers of foetuses (Wenham and Robinson, 1972). Earlier than that, Benzie (1951) had reported accurate X-ray diagnosis in the ewe after the 55th day.

In Australia, there have been those who have maintained that if X-ray diagnoses were available in commercial flocks, feed resources available in late pregnancy could be used more efficiently (Rizzoli et al., 1976); they demonstrated that with specially designed handling equipment it was technically feasible to use radiography in sheep on a farm scale to determine number of foetuses with a high degree of accuracy during the fourth month of gestation (90% accuracy at 100 to 120 days in diagnosing twin-pregnancies). Using the unit under farm conditions, the Australians were able to deal with 400–600 ewes per day; the hope was that the twin-bearing ewes, with the greater nutritional requirements in late pregnancy, could be fed at a more appropriate level and that lambs would be saved by this and by preferential husbandry at lambing.

17.3 ULTRASONIC TECHNIQUES

Extensive use has already been made of ultrasonics in human medicine in dealing with various aspects of pregnancy; diagnostic ultrasound has involved the use of either the Doppler technique (detection of the foetal pulse) or the A-mode (amplitude-depth) technique (detection of the fluid-filled uterus).

17.3.1 Foetal pulse detection

This Doppler technique utilizes ultrasound at frequencies similar to the A-mode method; in this approach, the ultrasound which is transmitted into the ewe and received back by the transducer after meeting rapidly moving particles (i.e. blood in the foetal heart and umbilical vessels) is slightly shifted in frequency; such sound is converted into audible signals by the equipment whereas sound returning from motionless structures has exactly the same frequency as transmitted sound and cannot be heard.

The Doppler method for use in sheep has been reported by several workers in Britain (Fraser and Robertson, 1967, 1968; Wilson and Newton, 1969; Fraser et al., 1971; Richardson, 1972a, b) Ireland (Keane, 1969) the United States (Lindahl, 1968, 1969, 1970, 1971; Shelton, 1968; Hulet, 1969) France (Bosc, 1971a, b) and New Zealand (Allison, 1971). The ewe is examined in either a sitting or standing position; the surface of the transducer is smeared with oil (to ensure good contact) and placed on the bare area of skin close to the udder. Such external application of the doppler technique can result in a high accuracy of diagnosis when employed during the second half of pregnancy.

17.3.2 Rectal probe doppler

The intra-rectal Doppler technique has been reported to be more accurate and permits determinations of pregnancy to be made sooner than with the external transducer (Lindahl, 1971, 1972; Deas, 1977; Horvath et al., 1979; Ott et al., 1980). According to early work reported by Lindahl (1971, 1972) covering more than 2000 ewes, pregnancy could be determined at mid-pregnancy with an accuracy of 90% or more. In the U.K., Deas (1977) dealt with 1396 sheep by the intra-rectal technique, examining them at 20–30, 31–40, 41–60, 61–90, 81–100 and 100–120 days after mating; the percentages of correct positive diagnoses were 58, 80, 88, 96 and 97, respectively.

An accuracy of diagnosis at 46 days of pregnancy of 95% was reported by Horvath et al. (1979), working with 674 sheep; a faster diagnosis (1–2 min per sheep) was possible at 60 days when the Doppler signals were easily recognizable.

17.3.3 Detection of fluid filled uterus

Work reported over several years by a number of investigators has shown the examination of ewes by A-mode sound to be quick, convenient and simple (Lindahl, 1966, 1969; Thompson et al., 1979; Trapp and Slyter, 1979; Wroth and McCallum, 1979; Bon Durant, 1980; Langford et al., 1980; Meredith and Madoni, 1980). The ewe is usually dealt with in the standing position; the transducer is smeared with oil and placed on the bare skin of the belly about 50 mm in front of the udder on th ewe's right side. When the narrow beam of ultrasound meets tissue which has a different acoustic value (e.g. fluid filled, pregnant uterus), it is reflected at the boundary of the object; the echoes are received by the transducer and converted into signals which are amplified and displayed on a cathode ray screen or in some other visual form.

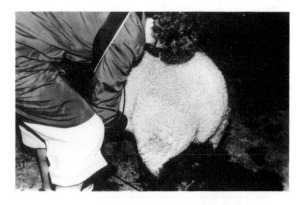

Fig. 17.2. The use of ultrasonics in establishing pregnancy in the ewe. There are many occasions when it would be useful to identify ewes that are pregnant other than by using methods involving the ram. One such occasion would be among ewes that are treated for the induction of pregnancy in the spring months of the year. By the use of ultrasonics, it is now possible to pick out those sheep which have become pregnant with a high degree of accuracy, certainly by the third month of pregnancy. It should be noted, however, that these instruments can be costly and quite beyond the means of the normal run of sheep farmer in the Irish Republic.

The general experience would seem to be that the ewe must be into the second half of pregnancy if a highly accurate diagnosis is to be made; Bon Durant (1980) recorded an accuracy of 91% in sheep greater than 65 days pregnant and 35% in ewes examined before that time. The speed of testing can be much greater than when using the Doppler technique; with good facilities, three operators have easily been able to test about 160 sheep an hour (Wroth and McCallum, 1979).

17.3.4 Ultrasonics and detecting multiples

A commercial animal "scanner" for determining backfat and loin-eye areas in pigs and rib-eye areas in cattle was first reported as a possibility in pregnancy testing in sheep by Stouffer et al. (1969a, b); subsequently, Lindahl (1976) used this equipment to generate a two-dimensional image which was then photographed with a Polaroid® camera. Abdominal scanning as close as possible to the udder resulted in detection of 100% of ewes that were pregnant, when this was done after mid-term (day 70 or beyond); an accuracy of 84% was achieved in distinguishing between single and multiple foetuses, but this was not regarded as sufficiently high to warrant the expense and labour involved.

As noted by Plant (1980), talking of Australian and similar conditions, one disadvantage of ultrasonics is the initial cost of the equipment and the need for maintenance and recharging of batteries if they are to be used in isolated areas or when mains electricity is not available. However, for sheep farmers looking for an early answer on the pregnancy status of ewes, the ultrasonic approach would not appear to provide the answer.

17.4 RECTAL–ABDOMINAL PALPATION

A rectal–abdominal palpation technique for pregnancy diagnosis in sheep was first described by Hulet (1972, 1973; Hulet and Shupe, 1973). The method is based on detecting the enlarged pregnant uterus by means of a probe inserted into the rectum of the ewe; in the hands of an experienced operator the procedure is reliable

after mid-pregnancy and it is possible to deal with 120 or more sheep per hour (Plant, 1980). However, the possibility of problems arising with inexperienced operators, resulting in rectal perforation, has been a matter of concern; some abortions and ewe-deaths, apparently the result of rectal perforation and subsequent infections have been recorded (Morcan, 1973; Plant and Tyrell, 1974; Turner and Hindson, 1975; Weigl et al., 1975; Tyrrell and Plant, 1979). As against this, Plant (1980) has employed the method in many flocks without problems of abortion or ewe mortality; the probe can be easy to make, is inexpensive and needs no maintenance.

The examination is easier if feed and water is withheld from ewes overnight; the sheep are placed in laparotomy cradles or in tilting squeeze chutes for examination. The probe, as described by Plant (1980), can take the form of a bright steel rod (50 cm in length with an outside diameter of 50 mm) fitted with a hardened aluminium knob (3 cm in diameter with a bullet-shaped tip). The rounded tip of the probe is lubricated and inserted into the rectum to a distance of 30–35 cm. While one hand manipulates the rod, the other is placed on the posterior abdomen; manipulation continues until the pregnant uterus is encountered and palpated against the abdominal wall. At mid-pregnancy, the uterus is felt as a round object about 15 cm in diameter in the midline region (Plant, 1980); in later pregnancy, the uterus may be felt as a large mass between the shaft of the probe and the ventral abdominal wall. In order to gain experience in inserting and handling the probe, Plant (1980) suggests that non-pregnant ewes or even wethers are used for practice, as this will enable the operator to become familiar with the feel of the abdominal organs in non-pregnant animals.

17.5 PROGESTERONE AND HORMONAL TESTS

Early pregnancy diagnosis in the ewe, based on plasma progesterone levels at a fixed time after mating, has been reported by several groups of workers, starting more than a decade ago (Bassett et al., 1969; Thorburn et al., 1969; Robertson and Sarda, 1971; Shemesh et al., 1973; McDonnell,

1974, 1976). As in cattle, the technique relies on the fact that plasma progesterone concentrations are much lower in the cyclic ewe at oestrus than in the pregnant sheep. In France, early pregnancy testing in sheep is generally used as a complementary technique to controlled breeding, especially when this has been applied during the ewe anoestrus (Thimonier and Cognie, 1977). Thimonier et al. (1977) measured progesterone levels at day-18 after breeding; almost all ewes diagnosed non-pregnant failed to lamb, whereas only 83.5% of those diagnosed pregnant actually gave birth. Robinson (1980), using the day-18 test in frequent lambing systems, has been one to express concern at the number of false positives, presumably arising from embryonic mortality; as in cattle, it is necessary to regard the progesterone test as a method for detecting non-pregnancy rather than pregnancy.

17.5.1 Progesterone in milk

Efforts in Israel by Shemesh et al. (1979) to base progesterone determinations on milk rather than blood plasma proved successful when dealing with Awassi milking ewes in the natural breeding season (92–100% accuracy in detecting non-pregnancy); during the seasonal anoestrus, however, the accuracy in diagnosing pregnancy was found to be unusually low and it was thought that this may have been due to a higher level of a particular protein in the milk which interfered with the assay.

17.5.2 Progesterone testing in ewes at unknown stages

A pregnancy testing method applicable to situations in which the mating dates for individual ewes are not known is described by Tyrrell et al. (1980); the technique, which gave a very accurate diagnosis, involves taking three progesterone samples from each ewe over a 12-day period. Such a procedure would usually be limited to research applications.

17.5.3 Progesterone and litter size

Placental production of progesterone is known to increase markedly between days 70–100 of gestation in the ewe, after the placenta has reached its maximum weight (Thorburn et al.,

1977); in the ewe, unlike the goat, it is possible to make some estimate of the number of foetuses by progesterone determinations because the steroid level is related to litter-size. In the U.K., Gadsby et al. (1972) attempted to classify litter-size in prolific sheep by progesterone determinations carried out between days 91 and 105, but the success rate of 65% was too low for the method to have practical relevance.

17.5.4 Oestrogen tests

Oestrogens are synthesized in the placenta and are present either in the foetal blood or in the maternal circulation. Total oestrogens in the maternal peripheral blood are known to increase as pregnancy progresses in the ewe; Thimonier et al. (1977) tested ewes at days 100–110 of gestation and determined pregnancy with an accuracy of 99% (>0.3 ng/ml oestrogen was evidence of pregnancy). On the basis of studies by Terqui and Delouis (1975), it became clear that the concentration of total oestrogen in the maternal peripheral blood of sheep increases with total birth weight and this held out the possibility of estimating foetal number by oestrogen concentration. Thimonier et al. (1977) found, however, that determining litter-size with any reasonable degree of accuracy required prior knowledge of the maternal oestrogen pattern for the particular breed or type of crossbred examined. Although the same authors found no evidence of a seasonal variation in total oestrogen levels, they did consider that nutritional status of the dam and the genotype of the foetuses themselves may affect maternal oestrogen concentrations.

17.5.5 Ovine placental lactogen

Placental lactogenic activity in sheep has been demonstrated and an ovine placental lactogen (oPL) has been purified and characterized (Chan et al., 1976); the hormone appears to have mammogenic, lactogenic and growth promoting activities and for this reason is also known as ovine chorionic somatomammotrophin (Kelly et al., 1974). Thimonier et al. (1977) in France and Robertson et al. (1980a) in Canada have described pregnancy tests for sheep based on the detection of this pregnancy-specific agent in the blood after 80 days and 57 days, respectively. A further report by Robertson et al. (1980b) confirmed that an extremely accurate diagnosis of pregnancy and non-pregnancy could be attained when blood samples were taken later than day-55 of pregnancy; the incidence of foetal loss beyond that stage of gestation was found to be extremely small (>3%).

On the matter of relating oPL concentrations to litter-size, studies reported by Taylor et al. (1980) showed that the mean concentrations of the hormone to be 718±227, 1387±160 and 1510±459 ng ml-1 for single, twin and triplet pregnancies, respectively; however, peak concentrations of oPL were observed at days 130 to 139, which would be rather too late to be of practical value.

17.6 IMMUNOLOGICAL TESTS

Antigens associated with pregnancy in the ewe have been described by Findlay et al. (1979) in Australia, these workers placing particular emphasis on determining the distribution and site of production of these antigens; elsewhere, progress towards the characterization of these antigens has been reported by Clarke et al. (1980). The antigens have been detected in the maternal circulation of the pregnant ewe as early as 24 h after mating (Morton et al., 1979); it would appear that a factor is released into the maternal circulation of the ewe soon after fertilization and possibly acts by modifying lymphocyte activity in order to protect the fertilized egg from rejection by the maternal tissues.

Egg mortality has been detected by testing sheep serum within 48 h of death occurring (Evison et al., 1977; Nancarrow et al., 1979) so that new opportunities are available on a research basis for measuring the extent of this problem in sheep. The rosette inhibition test presently employed to detect the "early-pregnancy factor" is, unfortunately, much too involved for any thought of routine use and a simpler method has to be devised.

Other workers have reported the detection of antigens specific to pregnancy in the first week after mating (Cerini et al., 1976); appropriate immunological tests have been developed (Lawson et al., 1976; Cerini et al., 1976; Staples et al., 1976) but their accuracy does not appear to be sufficiently high to justify field use at this stage.

17.7 MANUAL EXAMINATIONS

Several techniques can be used in late pregnancy in order to sort out pregnant from non-pregnant animals. Pratt and Hopkins (1975) reported accuracies of 80–95% in ewes examined by abdominal palpation at 90–130 days of gestation. With this method, the ewe is normally restrained in a sitting position, one hand is placed against the left side of the sheep's abdomen, the other being palpated using the fingertips. The foetus should be felt as a floating body that is pushed away and then returns to the fingertips (Plant, 1980).

17.8 OTHER METHODS

For research purposes, laparotomy has been reported as a diagnostic method in Australia (Lamond and Urquhart, 1961, 1963) and in the U.S.A. by Hulet and Foote (1966); pregnancy was accurately detected during the fourth to sixth week of gestation and a skilled operator was able to perform 25–30 examinations per hour.

17.8.1 Vaginal biopsy

The vaginal biopsy method was reported on by Richardson (1972b); the technique had an accuracy of 90% in ewes pregnant more than 60 days. Although the method is quick and easy to carry out, the biopsy sample has to be processed in the laboratory and it is several days before results are known.

17.9 REFERENCES

Allison, A. J. (1971) Ultrasonics for pregnancy detection. N. Z. Jl. Agric. 123(1), 25.

Bassett, J. M., Oxborrow, T. H., Smith, I. D. and Thorburn, G. D. (1969) The concentration of progesterone in the peripheral plasma of the pregnant ewe. J. Endocrin. 45, 449–457.

Benzie, D. (1951). Br. Vet. J. 107, 3.

Bon Durant, R. H. (1980) Pregnancy diagnosis in sheep and goats: Field tests with an ultrasound unit. *California Vet.* **34,** 26–28.

Bosc, M. J. (1971a) The control of parturition in the ewe. *J. Reprod. Fert.* **27,** 491.

Bosc. M. J. (1971b) A study of pregnancy diagnosis in the ewe based on ultrasonics and the doppler effect. *Ann. Zootech.* **20,** 107–110.

Cerini, M., Findlay, J. K. and Lawson, R. A. S. (1976) Pregnancy-specific antigens in the sheep. *J. Reprod. Fert.* **46,** 65–69.

Chan, J. S. D., Robertson, H. A. and Friesen, H. G. (1978) Maternal and foetal concentration of ovine placental lactogen measured by RIA. *Endocrinology* **102,** 1606–1613.

Clarke, F. M., Morton, H., Rolfe, B. E. and Clunie, G. J. A. (1980) Partial characterisation of early pregnancy factor in the sheep. *J. Reprod. Immunol.* **2,** 151–162.

Deas, D. W. (1977) Pregnancy diagnosis in the ewe by an ultrasonic rectal probe. *Vet. Rec.* **101,** 113–115.

Evison, B., Nancarrow, C., Morton, H., Scaramuzzi, R. and Clunie, J. A. (1977) Detection of early pregnancy and embryo mortality in sheep by the Rosette inhibition test. *Theriogen.* **8**(4), 157.

Findlay, J. K., Cerini, M., Sheers, M., Staples, L. D. and Cumming, I. A. (1979) The nature and role of pregnancy-associated antigens and the endocrinology of early pregnancy in the ewe. *Ciba Foundation Conf.*

Fraser, A. F. and Robertson, J. G. (1967) The direction of foetal life in ewes and sows. *Vet. Rec.* **85,** 28.

Fraser, A. F. and Robertson, J. G. (1968) pregnancy diagnosis and detection of foetal life in sheep and pigs by an ultrasonic method. *Br. Vet. J.* **124,** 239–244.

Fraser, A. F., Nagaratham, V. and Callicot, R. B. (1971) The comprehensive use of Doppler ultra-sound in farm animal reproduction. *Vet. Rec.* 202–205.

Gadsby, J. E., Heap, R. B., Powell, D. G. and Walters, D. E. (1972) Diagnosis of pregnancy and of the number of foetuses in sheep from plasma progesterone concentrations. *Vet. Rec.* **90,** 339–342.

Horvath, M., Mottl, K. and Szabo, L. (1979) Early diagnosis of pregnancy in sheep by ultrasonic doppler method. *Anim. Breed. Abstr.* **47,** 320.

Hulet, C. V. (1969) Pregnancy diagnosis in the ewe using an ultrasonic doppler instrument. *J. Anim. Sci.* **28,** 44–47.

Hulet, C. V. (1972) A rectal-abdominal palpation technique for diagnosing pregnancy in the ewe. *J. Anim. Sci.* **35,** 814–819.

Hulet, C. V. (1973) Determining fetal numbers in pregnant ewes. *J. Anim. Sci.* **36,** 325–330.

Hulet, C. V. and Foote, W. C. (1966) *J. Anim. Sci.* **25,** 584.

Hulet, C. G. and Shupe, W. L. (1973) Predicting multiple births in sheep by rectal-abdominal palpation. *J. Anim. Sci.* **36,** 1202–1203 (Abs).

Keane, M. G. (1969) Pregnancy diagnosis in the sheep by an ultrasonic method. *Ir. Vet. J.* **23,** 194–196.

Kelly, P. A., Robertson, H. A. and Friesen, H. G. (1974) Temporal pattern of placental lactogen and progesterone secretion in sheep. *Nature,* Lond. **248,** 435–437.

Lamond, D. R. and Urquhart, E. J. (1961) Sheep laparotomy cradle. *Aust. Vet. J.* **37,** 430.

Lamond, D. R. and Urquhart, E. J. (1963) Diagnosis of early pregnancy in ewes. *Aust. Vet. J.* **39,** 192.

Langford, G. A., Fiser, P. S., Heaney, D. P. and Ainsworth, L. (1980) Ultrasonic diagnoses of pregnancy in confined sheep. *J. Anim. Sci.* **51**(Suppl. 1), 295 (Abs).

Lawson, R. A. S., Cerini, M. and Findlay, J. K. (1976) Immunological test for pregnancy in the ewe. *J. Reprod. Fert.* **46,** 523–533.

Lindahl, I. L. (1966) Detection of pregnancy in sheep by means of ultra-sound. *Nature, Lond.* **212,** 642–643.

Lindahl, I. L. (1968) Pregnancy diagnosis in ewes in continual breeding. *J. Anim. Sci.* **27,** 1511.

Lindhal, I. L. (1969) Comparison of ultrasonic techniques for the detection of pregnancy in ewes. *J. Reprod. Fert.* **18,** 117–120.

Lindahl, I. L. (1970) Intra-rectal detection of pregnancy in ewes. *J. Anim. Sci.* **31,** 225 (Abs).

Lindahl, I. L. (1971) Pregnancy diagnosis in the ewe by intra-rectal doppler. *J. Anim. Sci.* **32,** 992–995.

Lindahl, I. L. (1972) Early pregnancy detection in ewes by intra-rectal reflection echo ultrasound. *J. Anim. Sci.* **34,** 772–775.

Lindahl, I. L. (1976) Pregnancy diagnosis in ewes by ultrasonic scanning. *J. Anim. Sci.* **43,** 1135–1140.

McDonnell, H. (1974) A pregnancy test using progesterone binding protein by a competitive binding technique: A preliminary report of its application to ewes. *Ir. Vet. J.* **28,** 1–10.

McDonnell, H. (1976) Peripheral plasma progesterone in the ewe. Its application to the diagnosis of early pregnancy following oestrus synchronization treatment. *Ir. Vet. J.* **30,** 11–15.

Memon, M. A. and Ott, R. S. (1980) Methods of pregnancy diagnosis in sheep and goats. *Cornell Vet.* **70,** 226–231.

Meredith, M. J. and Madani, M. O. K. (1980) The detection of pregnancy in sheep by a-mode ultrasound. *Br. Vet. J.* **136,** 325–330.

Morcan, L. (1973) pregnancy detection in ewes — a new technique. *N.Z. Jl. Agric.* **126,** 15.

Morton, H., Clunie, G. J. A. and Shaw, F. D. (1979) A test for early pregnancy in sheep. *Res. Vet Sci.* **26,** 261–262.

Morton, H., Nancarrow, C. D., Scaramuzzi, R. J., Evison, B. M. and Clunie, G. J. A. (1979) Detection of early pregnancy in sheep by the Rosette inhibition test. *J. Reprod. Fert.* **56,** 75–80.

Nancarrow, C. D., Evison, B. N., Scaramuzzi, R. J. and Turnbull, K. E. (1979) Detection of induced death of embryos in sheep by the Rosette inhibition test. *J. Reprod. Fert.* **57,** 385–389.

Plant, J. W. (1980) Pregnancy diagnosis in the ewe. *World Anim. Rev.* **36,** 44–47.

Plant, J. W. and Tyrrell, R. N. (1974) Evaluation of a rectal-abdominal palpation technique for pregnancy diagnosis in sheep. *Aust. Vet. J.* **50,** 178–179.

Pratt, M. S. and Hopkins, P. S. (1975) The diagnosis of pregnancy in sheep by abdominal palpation. *Aust. Vet. J.* **49,** 378–380.

Radford, H. M., Watson, R. H. and Wood, G. C. (1960) A crayon and associated harness for the detection of mating under field conditions. *Aust. Vet. J.* **36,** 57–66.

Richardson, G. (1972a) Pregnancy testing in ewes. *Agriculture* **79,** 63–67.

Richardson, C. (1972b) Pregnancy diagnosis in the ewe. A review. *Vet. Rec.* **90,** 264–275.

Rizzoli, D. J., Winfield, C. G., Howard, T. J. and England, I. K. H. (1976) Diagnosis of multiple pregnancy in ewes on a field scale. *J. Agric. Sci., Camb.* **87,** 67–677.

Robertson, H. A. and Sarda, I. R. (1971) A very early pregnancy test for mammals; its application to the cow, ewe and sow. *J. Endocr.* **49,** 407–419.

Robertson, H. A., Chan, J. S. D., Hackett, A. J., Marcus, G. J. and Friesen, H. G. (1980a) Diagnosis of pregnancy in the ewe at mid-gestation. *Anim. Reprod. Sci.* **3,** 69–71.

Robertson, H. A., Chan, J. S. D. and Friesen, H. G. (1980b) The use of a pregnancy-specific antigen, chorionic somatom-ammotrophin, as an indicator of pregnancy in sheep. *J. Reprod. Fert.* **58,** 279–281.

Robinson, T. J. (1980) Programmed year-round sheep breeding. *Aust. J. Exp. Agric. Anim. Husb.* **20,** 667–673.

Shelton, M. (1968) An evaluation of the Doppler shift principle for pregnancy diagnosis in sheep. *Proc. Second Wld. Conf. Anim. Prod.,* p. 435, Bruces, St. Paul.

Shemesh, M., Ayalon, N. and Lindner, H. R. (1973) Early pregnancy diagnosis based upon plasma progesterone levels in the cow and ewe. *J. Anim. Sci.* **36,** 726–729.

Shemesh, M., Ayalon, N. and Mazor, T. (1979) Early pregnancy diagnosis in the ewe, based on milk progesterone levels. *J. Reprod. Fert.* **56,** 301–304.

Stouffer, J. R., Lindahl, I., Hogue, D. E. and White, W. R. C. (1969a) Ewe pregnancy check with ultrasonic scanner and doppler. *J. Anim. Sci.* **29,** 103 (Abs).

Stouffer, J. R., White, W. R. G., Hogue, D. E., Hunt, G. L. (1969b) Ultrasonic scanner for detection of single or multiple pregnancy in sheep. *J. Anim. Sci.* **29,** 104 (Abs).

Taylor, M. J., Jenkin, G., Robinson, J. S., Thorburn, G. D., Friesen, H., and Han, J. S. D. (1980) Concentrations of placental lactogen in chronically catheterized ewes and fetuses in late pregnancy. *J. Endocr.* **85,** 27–34.

Terqui, M. and Delouis, C. (1975) Les oestrogenes au cours de la gestation et de la parturition. *Ie res J. de la Recherche ovine et caprine.* pp. 332–341. INRA Publn. Paris.

Thimonier, J. and Cognie, Y. (1977) Application of control of reproduction of sheep in France. In, *Management and Reproduction in Sheep and Goats.* Symp. Univ. Madison, Wisconsin. S.I.D. Publn.

Thimonier, J., Bosc, M., Djiane, J., Martal, J. and Terqui, M.

(1977) Hormonal diagnosis of pregnancy and number of fetuses in sheep and goats. In, *Management and reproductions in Sheep and Goats,* Symp. Univ. Wisconsin, 79–88. S.I.D. Publn.

Thompson, P., Shelton, M. and Ahlschwede, G. (1978) A pregnancy detection device, *Tex. Agr. Exp. Sta.* PR 3498.

Thorburn, G. D., Bassett, J. M. and Smith, I. D. (1969) Progesterone concentration in the peripheral plasma of sheep during the oestrus cycle. *J. Endocrin.* **45,** 459–469.

Thorburn, G. D., Challis, J. R. and Currie, W. B. (1977) Control of parturition in domestic animals. *Biol. Reprod.* **16,** 18–27.

Trapp. M. J. and Slyter, A. L. (1979) Pregnancy diagnosis in the ewe. *Sth. Dakota State Univ. Agric. Exten. Ser.* No. 79, 11–17.

Turner, G. B. and Hindson, H. G. (1975) An assessment of a method of manual pregnancy diagnosis in the ewe. *Vet. Rec.* **96,** 56–58.

Tyrrell, R. N. and Plant, J. W. (1979) Rectal damage in ewes following pregnancy diagnosis by rectal-abdominal palpation. *J. Anim. Sci.* **48**(2), 348–350.

Tyrrell, R. N., Gleeson, A. R., Peter, D. A. and Connell, P. J. (1980) early identification of non-pregnant and pregnant ewes in the field using circulating progesterone concentration. *Anim. Reprod. Sci.* **3,** 149–153.

Weigl, R. M., Tilton, J. E., Light, M. R., Hauges, C. N. and Buchanan, M. L. (1975) Pregnancy diagnosis in the ewe. I. Rectal-abdominal palpation. *Nth. Dakota Farm Res.* **33**(2), 8–10.

Wenham, G. and Robinson, J. J. (1972) Radiographic pregnancy diagnosis in sheep. *J. Agric. Sci., Camb.* **78,** 233–238.

Wilson, I. A. N. and Newton, J. E. (1969) Pregnancy diagnosis in the ewe: A method for use on the farm. *Vet. Rec.* **84,** 356–358.

Wroth, R. H. and McCallum, M. J. (1979) Diagnosing pregnancy in sheep — the "Scanopreg". *J. (W. Aust),* **20,** 85.

CHAPTER 18

Control of Lambing

18.1 INTRODUCTION

The more widespread application of con-
rolled breeding techniques, by which a flock of
ewes can be bred by natural or artificial
inseminination as a group rather than as
individuals, makes the possibility of using
controlled lambing techniques in practical
farming much easier. Clearly, if most ewes in the
farmer's flock are at an identical stage of
gestation, it is relatively simple to gather the
sheep on a given day in late pregnancy and
administer an agent which will initiate parturition. As already mentioned, the highly
sophisticated intensive sheep systems employed
at the Nouzilly research centre in France aim at
programmed lambing of artificially-bred oestrus-
synchronized ewes during mid-week by initiating lambing in the last week of gestation; this can
ensure a minimum of weekend and holiday work.

In the context of making the most efficient use
of labour, ultra-compact synchronized lambing
may prove to be an economic proposition in
many practical situations. It means that in flocks
kept for fat-lamb production, oestrus synchronized ewes which would normally lamb down
within the space of 7–10 days can be further
aligned to give birth within a 48 h period, with
most lambs being born during daytime. Induced
parturition in sheep may have some unusual

applications; in Karakul flocks, in which the pelt
of the unborn foetus is of primary economic
importance, premature induction rather than
Caesarian may be employed to advantage.

18.2 DURATION OF GESTATION IN SHEEP

It is well established that the duration of
pregnancy in sheep can vary according to several
factors; these include, the number of lambs in the
conceptus, the sex of the lambs, the sire breed,
the breed of ewe and its age (Terrill and Hazel,
1947; Dickinson et al., 1962; Forbes, 1967).
Reviewing variation in gestation length according to breed types, Terrill (1968) distinguished
three categories; the early maturing mutton
breeds (e.g. Southdown, Suffolk, Hampshire,
Dorset Horn) with gestation periods varying from
144 to 147; the slow-maturing fine-wool breeds
(e.g. Merino, Rambouillet) with periods averaging 149–151 days; crossbred long-wool
breeds (e.g. Columbia, Corriedale) with periods
in the intermediate range. It is generally
recognized that the duration of gestation in the
ewe is extremely stable (Forbes, 1967).

In Britain, dealing in the main with long-wool
mutton breeds such as the Romney, an average
gestation period of 147.8 days for 515 ewes was
recorded (Gordon, 1958a); in Ireland, lowland

Table 18.1. *Duration of gestation period in relation to litter-size in Clun sheep*

		Single	Twin	Triplet	Quadruplet
No. of ewes		176	164	31	10
Gestation length	Range	138–153	142–152	142–152	140–150
	Mean	147.5	146.8	146.7	144.8

Data from a Clun Forest flock located in Suffolk *Gordon (unpublished data)*

breeds of ewes, mainly Galways and their crosses showed a period of 147.7 days for 5726 ewes (Cadden, 1973).

18.2.1 Season and gestation length

In the U.K., there was some suggestion that summer pregnancies were of shorter duration than those occurring in the usual autumn/winter period (Gordon, 1958b); ewes lambing in the autumn after a summer pregnancy carried their lambs on average for 144.7 days whereas those lambing in spring carried their young for 147.8 days. Elsewhere, however, it has been reported that under a decreasing daylight pattern and low environmental temperatures during late pregnancy in Finn-cross ewes was shorter than under the opposite environmental conditions (Amir *et al.*, 1980.

18.3 ENDOCRINOLOGY OF PARTURITION

The past decade has witnessed a substantial increase in knowledge dealing with the hormonal regulation of parturition in the mammal and much of this is due to studies conducted with the ewe as the experimental model. The classic experiments of Liggins (1968) and Liggins *et al.* (1973, 1977) established the role of the foetal pituitary-adrenal axis in the initiation of parturition in the sheep; ablation of the foetal pituitary was found to result in an indefinite prolongation of pregnancy, whereas infusion of synthetic adrenocorticotrophin (ACTH) or glucocorticoids into the foetus caused premature delivery.

18.3.1 Foetal adrenal activity

The observations of Comline and Silver (1961) that the foetal adrenals increased in size

markedly in the last 2 weeks of gestation and those of Bassett and Thorburn (1969) showing that the plasma concentration and secretion rate of the corticosteroids such as cortisol also increased at that time agreed with a view that activation of the foetal pituitary–adrenal axis initiated parturition. It is not clear whether increased concentration of cortisol is due to an increase in trophic stimulation of the foetal adrenal or to a maturational change in the foetal adrenals in the presence of the basal level of ACTH; there are lines of evidence indicating that an increase in adrenal sensitivity probably does play a role in the initiation of parturition, although doubt exists about the cause of this (Thorburn, 1978).

18.3.2 Production of cortisol

Although stimulation of the foetal adrenal to produce cortisol was originally thought to be a question of ACTH from the foetal pituitary, it now seems possible that other substances, perhaps of pituitary origin, are responsible for the initial stimulation of cortisol secretion by the foetal adrenals and for increasing the sensitivity of the adrenals to ACTH (First, 1979); certainly, the final surge of cortisol is believed to be a result of ACTH action. The belief is that in the ewe, this cortisol stimulates placental enzymes which are responsible for the conversion of placental progesterone into oestrogen; this placental oestrogen acts on a uterus which is no longer under progesterone influence, causing the synthesis of $PGF_{2\alpha}$ and uterine contractions (First, 1979).

18.3.3 Placental lactogen

It has been suggested that placental lactogen (oPL) may play an important role in the control of pregnancy in the sheep by inhibiting the synthesis of PG and that the rise in foetal cortisol before parturition may switch off oPL (Thorburn, 1978).

18.4 LAMB MORTALITY CONSIDERATIONS

Delivery of the lamb is but one of several coordinated events occurring at parturition; other events include lung maturation, closing of the ductus arteriosus, softening of the cervix, milk-formation, milk ejection and separation of the foetal membranes from the uterine wall. Treatments for the control of lambing should obviously not result in a failure in any of the several mechanisms which normally operate at parturition.

18.4.1 Incidence of lamb deaths

As mentioned already, under some sheep farming conditions, up to 20% of lambs may fail to survive the early weeks of life. Looking at the situation in sheep flocks in Ireland and the U.K., it has been noted that perinatal lamb losses can account for 15% or more lambs born, though in well-managed flocks the losses can be as low as 7–10% (Gordon, 1958a; 1967; Kilkenny and Read, 1974). Elsewhere, and at an earlier time, an analysis of data covering 25 years by Bell (1947) in the U.S.A. had shown a 20% loss of lambs up to 2 months of age. Moule and Jackson (1949) in Australia, recorded a 13% mortality rate in Merino lambs in the first 2 weeks of life; a similar figure (13%) was given by Wallace (1949) for New Zealand Romney lambs in the first month. In Wales, dealing with the Clun Forest, Williams (1954) records an incidence of 9–10% mortality. There is general agreement among authors that much of this lamb mortality is avoidable by improvements in the management and nutrition of the lambing flock. It is very rare for death of the lamb to occur prior to the start of parturition; survival of the live-born lamb rests mainly on its ability to withstand environmental stress, cold and starvation.

As previously mentioned, lambs at both low and high birthweights may be at a disadvantage; in the one case, it would be because the lamb's energy resources may be inadequate and in the other because of difficulties in the birth process.

Fig. 18.1. Most lamb deaths occur in the first few days after birth. Lamb mortality around the time of parturition is a major cause of reduced productivity in sheep. Under many conditions, lamb mortality can operate at a level of 10–15% or even higher. The loss figure can be reduced markedly by better feeding, housing and more attentive shepherding — but all this costs money. The ability to control the time of lambing in sheep with precision should permit the necessary attention to be provided in small sheep flocks in a more systematic manner.

Management should obviously be geared to ensuring that all lambs are as close as possible to the optimum birthweight. Multiple births usually have the disadvantage of lower than optimum birthweights and it would obviously be beneficial if ewes could be separated during the last 2 months of pregnancy according to the number of lambs they are carrying and fed on an appropriate plane of nutrition to minimize losses at birth.

18.4.2 Compact lambings

Part of the reason for interest in compact matings and lambings is in being able to reduce lamb mortality by the application of well-proven management techniques for ensuring survival of the lambs. The use of the stomach tube for feeding weakly lambs and cross-fostering crates (lamb adopters) for fostering triplet lambs on to ewes producing singles are among such techniques; overnight housing and shelter can also be expected to increase the number of lambs reared by way of reductions in losses arising from starvation and exposure.

18.5 INDUCTION BY CORTICOSTEROIDS

There are two ways in which the timing of lambing may be influenced by exogenous hormones; it may be a matter of prolonging gestation or shortening it. In regard to shortening the gestation period, there are known limitations to how far this may be taken; Dawes and Parry (1965) concluded on the basis of their evidence that lambs of gestational age less than 95% of normal are not of normal viability. In practical terms, if the lambs are to survive, an induction treatment should not be applied earlier than about 1 week before the average date for lambing in the sheep in question.

Although the administration of progesterone, which has a well-recognized inhibitory effect on uterine motility (Csapo, 1977), could possibly delay parturition, the problem is likely to be the large increase in perinatal mortality which is associated with prolonged gestation, as this occurs in normal circumstances. Apart from an isolated report suggesting that oral doses of MAP-progestagen may be employed in the terminal stages of gestation to control the initiation of lambing (Garm and Nedkvitne, 1968), most of the reports appearing in the literature have been concerned with using agents to shorten rather than prolong the pregnancy period.

18.5.1 Corticosteroids

As already observed, the perfusion of the foetal lamb with ACTH or with cortisol can result in premature parturition; after finding that cortisol was effective in this way, highly potent corticosteroid analogues have glucocorticoid or mineralocorticoid activity have been used. Dexamethasone, a glucocorticoid with about 25 times greater potency than cortisol, has been found to be very effective an an induction agent (Bosc, 1972); other studies have employed flumethasone (Skinner et al., 1970; Emadi and Noakes, 1973) or betamethasone (Lucas and Notman, 1974) as alternative glucocorticoids of extremely high potency.

It is assumed that injection of synthetic steroids can simulate one step in the normal sequence of events which occurs at birth. There is no evidence that dexamethasone directly stimulates uterine motility in the preparturient ewe (Prud'Homme and Bosc, 1977); there is, instead, a sharp increase in oestrogen levels (Bosc et al., 1977) and a

decrease in progesterone concentration (Fylling, 1971; Emadi and Noakes, 1973). The mechanism by which the exogenous glucocorticoid leads to increased oestrogen concentrations and decreased progesterone levels is presumably that involving the placental enzymes already referred to.

It is known that the foetal cortisol level is substantially depressed after administering dexamethasone to the ewe in late pregnancy; this inhibition lasts for less than 24 h, the initial foetal cortisol levels being recovered by that time and thereafter rising to higher concentrations than those of the controls 36 h after the injection (Bosc and Fevre, 1974). In view of evidence that the secretion of cortisol by the foetal adrenals depends on their stage of maturation at the time of the treatment, the effect of a single dose of corticosteroid in bringing about the subsequent surge of foetal cortisol cannot be expected until within about a week of the average duration of gestation. The inhibition of foetal cortisol secretion for some hours after administering a synthetic corticosteroid is believed to be involved in the well recognized lull of about a day before lambings commence (Bosc, 1972; Martin and Espinosa, 1972; Joyce, 1974). However, those ewes which have already embarked on the parturition process can be expected to go ahead; it is known that labour normally begins about 12 h before the expulsion of the foetus (Hindson et al., 1968), so that ewes that have already started into labour at time of injection will be expected to deliver on schedule.

It might be just as well to note that certain environmental effects can influence the time of day at which the ewe gives birth. It has been said that although the lamb foetus decides the day on which it is to be born it is the mother that decides the hour. Such mechanisms would have an obvious survival value among sheep in the wild state. With domesticated sheep, a relationship between the distribution of lambings and certain farm routines has been found (Sharafeldin et al., 1971); the lowest incidence of lambings was observed during the period of concentrate feeding and the indications were that imminent lambings were postponed as a result of increased adrenalin levels at the time of feeding.

18.5.2 Corticosteroid doses and responses

The usual dose level of dexamethasone employed is 15–20 mg; the more potent flumethasone is employed at a dose level of 2 mg. The actual day of the gestation period when the agent is given can be expected to vary with the gestation length of the breed in question; generally, it would be about 4–5 days ahead of the mean gestation length for the breed. Even the time of day when the corticosteroid is injected may be a consideration; ewes treated in the evening (20.00 h) have tended to lamb sooner and over a shorter space of time than those treated at 08.00 h on the same day (Bosc, 1972, 1973).

It would not appear that parity of the ewe, litter-size or sex of the lamb influences the response to the corticosteroid (Bosc et al., 1977).

It may be worth quoting an example of how the induction treatment may be expected to operate in a normal commercial-type situation taken from work at the Rowett in Scotland; Finn x Dorset ewes were bred after oestrus synchronization on a Thursday; on Saturday evening, at 21.00 h, 142 days later, they were each given a dose of 15 mg dexamethasone to induce lambing, which started in the early morning of the following Monday and finished in the evening of the Tuesday (Robinson, 1979). In summary, the use of dexamethasone results in a characteristic delay of 24–36 h with a peak over the next 36 h and lambings virtually completed by 72 h. It should be noted that evidence supports the view that the viability and growth rates of lambs and the health and subsequent fertility of ewes after corticosteroid induction are normal (Bosc et al., 1977).

18.6 USE OF OESTROGENS

It is well established for many mammals that the level of oestrogen in the maternal circulation increases as pregnancy progresses (Thorburn, 1980). In the ewe, the rise in oestrogen concentration which occurs prior to parturition has been well documented (Challis, 1971; Challis et al., 1972; Obst and Seamark, 1972); it appears that this increase occurs for a few days prior to

lambing with the major rise observed within 48 h of parturition (Bedford et al., 1972). As already mentioned, there is clear evidence that the last major increase in circulating oestrogen is an important part of the hormonal events associated with the initiation of lambing.

Early reports showing that parturition could be induced in sheep include those of Hindson et al. (1968) and Liggins et al. (1973) using the synthetic oestrogen, diethylstilboestrol (DES). Studies with the natural steroid showed that oestradiol benzoate (ODB) at the 15–20 mg dose level, administered in the last week of gestation, was also effective in the induction of parturition (Cahill et al., 1976; Louis et al., 1976; Thimonier et al., 1977; Robinson, 1980). Where the stage of gestation is known accurately, Robinson (1980) suggested, on the basis of comparative evidence, that the use of ODB to synchronize lambings may be preferable to dexamethasone; with 20 mg ODB, lambing of 125/128 ewes was virtually completed within 48 h with very few lambs lost at parturition and none in the following 72 h. It should be noted that in some oestradiol induction studies, there have been sheep which did not respond (Cahill et al., 1976); these ewes apparently suffered a higher incidence of dystocia and there was a greater perinatal mortality.

A positive effect of oestradiol treatment on lactation has been observed in some of these studies (Delouis et al., 1976; Currie, 1977; Thimonier et al., 1977), increased milk yield being reflected in greater weight gains by the lambs in the early weeks of life (Delouis et al., 1976). In view of reports of dystocia and higher lamb mortality in some instances, it would be necessary to evaluate ODB treatment much further; it may, however, offer a simple and inexpensive form of treatment to apply in farm practice.

18.7 PROSTAGLANDINS FOR INDUCTION

Liggins and Grieves (1971) produced evidence implicating $F_{2\alpha}$ as a factor in normal parturition in the sheep; although there is a large increase in prostaglandin in the maternal utero-ovarian

Table 18.2. *Induction of parturition (day 143/144) using different agents from Boland et al. (1982)*

	Oestradiol Benzoate (20 mg)	Dexamethasone (16 mg)	Prostaglandin (15 mg)	Saline
Ewes	39	41	40	39
Interval to parturition (h)	38.6	44.2	83.5	82.9

Both oestradiol and dexamethasone have been successfully employed to induce lambings on the University farm in recent years. The injection of prostaglandin, on the other hand, has generally proved to be ineffective.

venous plasma of the ewe during the final 24 h of gestation (Challis *et al.*, 1976), $F_{2\alpha}$ has proved relatively ineffective in initiating parturition earlier than about a week from full-term (Oakes *et al.*, 1973). In one comparison between corticosteroid (2 mg flumethasone) and a normal luteolytic dose of prostaglandin (15 mg $F_{2\alpha}$) administered on day-141 of gestation, 89 and 33% of ewes, respectively, delivered lambs within 72 h (Harman and Slyter, 1970); in studies reported by Barta *et al.* (1980) in the U.S.A. Cloprostenol was used at the 250 μg dose level without the agent being effective.

18.8 AGENTS FOR TERMINATING PREGNANCY

Although it is possible to use prostaglandin $F_2\alpha$, or one of its analogues, to terminate pregnancy in cattle in the early months of gestation, the results are much less clearcut in sheep (Inskeep *et al.*, 1975; Reid and Crothers, 1980). A success rate of about 67% was reported for ewes aborted by prostaglandin in the first month of pregnancy in one report (Bottomley, 1980); there has been a suggestion that the failure of ewes to respond may be due to an anti-luteolytic effect arising from the conceptus which is capable of overcoming the action of prostaglandin (Inskeep *et al.*, 1975; Pratt *et al.*, 1977).

Further evidence along these lines is in the results of Tyrrell *et al.* (1981) who showed that a single dose of 125 μg Cloprostenol was not always effective in terminating pregnancy in ewes during the first trimester of pregnancy; the authors suggested giving a second dose of PG after a 7-day interval to ewes which were expected to be carrying multiples, on the assumption that the anti-luteolytic effect of the embryos is related to the number present.

18.8.1 Oestrogen and terminating pregnancy

The use of oestrogen as the agent for synchronizing lambings in sheep could be hazardous if the farmer is not quite certain of the mating dates of the ewes. The action of oestradiol, employed in doses ranging from 10 to 40 mg in the final trimester of pregnancy has been reported on (Restall *et al.*, 1976); 40–70% of ewes aborted within 3 days when injected between day 126 and 130. If thinking in terms of the relative safety of agents used for synchronizing lambings, then it should be noted that the administration of a single dose of corticosteroid, earlier than the last week or so of gestation, is usually without effect (Bosc, 1973; Restall *et al.*, 1976). As already mentioned, the studies of Dawes and Parry (1965) led these workers to conclude that lambs of a gestational age less than 95% of normal show poor viability.

In using corticosteroids, rather than oestrogen, there is the safeguard that the treatment is unlikely to result in the delivery of lambs through inadvertently administering the agent to sheep several weeks away from full-term.

18.9 FUTURE OF INDUCED LAMBINGS

As a follow-on to controlled matings, especially in sheep where a very high conception rate to first service can be expected, the synchronization of lambings by corticosteroid or oestrogen would seem to be of good practical appeal. In view of the fact that lambs are often born during the inclement winter weather and many of them

Fig. 18.2. Induced lambings permit very compact lambings in flocks that are bred after oestrus synchronization. Where ewes have been bred after oestrus synchronization and it is known that a high percentage have conceived to first service, then it is possible to get almost all lambs born upon a chosen day. One farmer in Gloucestershire in the U.K. with a flock of some 60 Finn × Dorset ewes planned to have lambings confined to Easter Monday in one particular year and that is how it eventually turned out. Induced lambings would only have practical appeal at a certain range of flock sizes — and only when a good conception rate to the controlled oestrus was achieved.

in the night, controlled lambings would seem to hold out the hope of the shepherd being on the spot while the ewes are giving birth, thereby saving more of the lambs and improving labour efficiency during the lambing season.

18.10 REFERENCES

Amir, D., Genizi, A. and Schindler, H (1980) Seasonal and other changes in the gestation duration. *J. Agric. Sci. Camb.* **95,** 47–49.

Barta, M., Wallace, A. K., Humes, E., Williams, J. C. and Godke, R. A. (1980) Attempts to induce parturition in domestic ewes and goats using cloprostenol (ICI 80996). *J. Anim. Sci.* **5,** (Suppl. 1), 257 (Abs).

Bassett, J. M. and Thorburn, G. D. (1969) Fetal plasma corticosteroids and the initiation of parturition in the sheep. *J. Endocrin.* **44,** 285–286.

Bedford, C. A., Harrison, F. A. and Heap, R. B. (1972) The metabolic clearance rate and production rate of progesterone and the conversion of progesterone to 20x-hydroxypregn.-4-en-3-one in the sheep. *J. Endocrin.* **55,** 105–118.

Bell, D. S. (1947) Dead lambs do tell tales. *The Sheepman* **17,** 466.

Bosc, M. J. (1972) The induction of synchronization of lambing with the aid of dexamethasone. *J. Reprod. Fert.* **28,** 347–357.

Bosc, M. J. (1973) Review of methods of inducing parturition in the ewe and cow. *Rec. Med. Vet.* **149**(ii), 1463–1480.

Bosc, M. J. and Feure, J. (1974) Etude du mode d'action de la dexamethasone utilisee pour induire l'agnelage chez la brebis. *C. R. Acad. Sci. Paris,* **278,** D, 315–318.

Bosc, M. J., De Louis, C. and Terqui, M. (1977) Control of the time of parturition of sheep and goats. In, *Manag. and action of Reprod. Sheep and Goats. Symp. Univ. Wisconsin.* pp. 89–100.

Cadden, J. (1973) Studies relating to pregnancy and neonatal mortality in sheep. *M. Agr. Sc., Thesis, Univ. College Dublin.*

Cahill, L. P., Knee, B. W. and Lawson, R. A. S. (1976) Induction of parturition in ewes with a single injection of oestradiol benzoate. *Theriogen.* 5 (6), 289–294.

Challis, R. R. C. (1971) Sharp increase in free circulating oestrogens immediately before parturition in sheep. *Nature, Lond.* **229,** 208–209.

Challis, J. R. G., Harrison, F. A., Heap, R. B., Horton, E. W. and Pyser, N. L. (1972) A possible role of oestrogens in the stimulation of prostaglandin $F_{2\alpha}$ output at the time of parturition in a sheep. *J. Reprod. Fert.* **30**, 485–488.

Challis, J. R. G., Dilley, S. R., Robinson, J. S. and Thorburn, G. D. (1976) Prostaglandins in the circulation of the foetal lamb. *Prostaglandins* **11**, 1041.

Comline, R. S. and Silver, M. (1961) The release of adrenaline and non-adrenaline from the adrenal glands of the foetal sheep. *J. Physiol., Lond.* **156**, 424–444.

Csapo, A. I. (1977) From uterine actomyosin to parturition. In, *Search and Discovery*, Kaminer, B. Ed. Academic Press, New York.

Currie, W. B. (1977) Endocrinology of pregnancy and parturition in sheep and goats. In, *Manage. Reprod. Sheep and Goats.* Univ. Wisconsin. (Madison), pp. 72–78.

Dawes, G. S. and Parry, H. B. (1965) Premature delivery and survival of lambs. *Nature, Lond.* **207**, 330.

Dickinson, A. G., Hancock, J. L., Hovell, J. R., Taylor, St. C. S. and Wiener, G. (1962) The size of lambs at birth — a study involving egg transfer. *Anim. Prod.* **4**, 64–79.

Emadi, M. and Noakes, D. E. (1973) The pharmacological control of the time of parturition in the ewe. *Vet. Rec.* **93**, 76.

First, N. L. (1979) Mechanisms controlling parturition in farm animals. In, *Anim. Reprod.* BARC. Symp No. 3. Hawk, H. Ed. pp. 215–257. Allenheld. Osmun.

Forbes, J. W. (1967) Factors affecting the gestation length in sheep. *J. Agric. Sci., Camb.* **68**, 191–194.

Fylling, P. (1971) Premature parturition following dexamethasone administration to pregnant ewes. *Acta Endocr.* **66**, 289–295.

Garm, O. and Nedkvitne, O. (1968) Synchronization of parturition in ewe groups of the Norwegian Dalabreed. *Proc. 6th Int. Congr. Reprod. and A.I. (Paris)*, 273.

Gordon, I. (1958a) Hormonal augmentation of fertility in the ewe during the breeding season. *J. Agric. Sci., Camb.* **50**, 123.

Gordon, I. (1958b) Studies in the extra-seasonal production of lambs. *J. Agric. Sci., Camb.* **50**, 152.

Gordon, I. (1967) Aspects of reproduction and neonatal mortality in ewe lambs and adult sheep. *J. Ir. Dept. Agric. Dublin* 64–76.

Harman, E. L. and Slyter, A. L. (1980) Induction of parturition in the ewe. *J. Anim. Sci.* **50**, 391–393.

Hindson, J. G., Scofield, B. M. and Turner, C. G. (1968) Parturient pressure in the ovine uterus. *J. Physiol. Lon.* 195–198.

Inskeep, E. K., Smutny, W. J. and Butcher, R. L. (1975) Effects of intrafollicular injections of prostaglandins in non-pregnant and pregnant ewes. *J. Anim. Sci.* **41**, 1098–1104.

Joyce, M. J. B. (1974) The use of dexamethasone to induce parturition in ewes. *Ir. vet. J.* **28**, 127–131.

Kilkenny, J. B. and Read, J. L. (1974) British sheep production economics. *Livest. Prod. Sci.* **1**, 165–178.

Liggins, G. C. (1968) Premature parturition after infusion of corticotrophin or cortisol into foetal lambs. *J. Endocrin.* **42**, 323–329.

Liggins, G. C. and Grieves, S. (1971) Possible role of $PGF_{2\alpha}$ in parturition in sheep. *Nature, Lond.* **232**, 629.

Liggins, G. C., Fairclough, R. J., Grieves, S. A., Kendall, J. Z. and Knox, B. S. (1973) The mechanism of initiation of parturition in the ewe. *Rec. Prog. Horm. Res.* **29**, 111–159.

Liggins, G. C., Foster, C. S., Grieves, S. A. and Schwartz, A. L. (1977) Control of parturition in man. *Biol. Reprod.* **16**, 39–56.

Louis, T. M., Challis, J. R. G., Robinson, J. S. and Thorburn, G. D. (1976) Rapid increase of foetal corticosteroids after prostaglandin E_2. *Nature, Lond.* **264**, 797–799.

Lucas, J. M. S. and Notman, A. (1974) The use of corticosteroids to synchronize parturition in sheep. *Br. Vet. J.* **130**, I–V.

Martin, E. and Espinosa (1972) *Proc. 8th Int. Congr. Anim. Reprod. A.I. (Paris), Summaries*, 174.

Moule, G. R. and Jackson, M. N. S. (1949) Studies on lamb mortality. *Qd. Agric. J.* **69**, 235.

Oakes, G., Mofid, M., Brinkman, C. R. and Assali, N. S. (1971) Insensitivity of the sheep to prostaglandins. *Proc. Soc. Exp. Biol. Med.* **142**, 194.

Obst. J. M. and Seamark, R. F. (1972) Plasma oestrogen concentrations in ewes during parturition. *J. Reprod. Fert.* **28**, 161–162.

Pratt, B. R., Butcher, R. L. and Inskeep, E. K. (1977) Antiluteolytic effect of the conceptus and of PGE_2 in ewes. *J. Anim. Sci.* **46**, 784–791.

Prud'Homme, N. and Bosc, M. J. (1977) Uterine activity in ewe before during and after spontaneous parturition or after dexamethasone priming. *Ann. Biol. Anim. Bioch. Biophys.* **17**(1), 9–19.

Reid, R. N. D. and Crothers, I. (1980) Prostaglandin $F_{2\alpha}$ for oestrus synchronization or abortion in polwarth ewes. *Aust. Vet. J.* **56**, 22–24.

Restall, B. J., Herdegen, J. and Carberry, P. (1976) Induction of parturition in sheep using oestradiol benzoate. *Aust. J. Exp. Agric. Anim. Husb.* **16**, 462–466.

Robinson J. J. (1979) Intensive systems. In, *Manage and Diseases of Sheep* pp. 431–446. Comm. Agric. Buck. Slough.

Robinson, T. J. (1980) Programmed year-round sheep breeding. *Aust. J. Exp. Agric. Anim. Husb.* **20**, 667–673.

Sharafeldin, M. A., Ragab, M. T. and Kandeel, A. A. (1971) Behaviour of ewes during parturition. *J. Agric. Sci., Camb.* **76**, 419–422.

Skinner, J. D., Jochle, W. and Nel, J. W. (1970) Induction of parturition in Karakul and cross-bred ewes with flumethasone. *Agroanimalio*, **2**, 99–100.

Terrill, C. E. (1968) In, *Reproduction of Farm Animals.* Hafez, E. S. E. Ed. pp. 265–278. Lea and Febiger, Philadelphia.

Terrill, C. and Hazel, L. N. (1947) Length of gestation in range sheep. *Am. J. Vet. Res.* **8**, 66–72.

Thimonier, J., Bosc, M., Djiane, J., Martal, J. and Terqui, M. (1977) Hormonal diagnosis of pregnancy and number of fetuses in sheep and goats. *Manag, Reprod. Sheep and Goats, Symp.* (Univ. Wisconsin), 79–88.

Thorburn, G. D. (1978) Hormonal control of parturition in sheep and goat. *Seminar in Perinathology.* **2**(3), 235–245.

Thorburn, G. D. (1980) Physiology and control of parturition; reflections on the past and ideas for the future. *Anim. Reprod. Sci.* **2**, 1–27.

Tyrrell, R. N., Lane, J. G., Nancarrow, C. D. and Connell, P. J. (1981) Termination of early pregnancy in ewes by use of a prostaglandin analogue and subsequent fertility. *Aust. Vet. J.*, **57**, 76–78.

Wallace, L. R. (1949). Parturition in ewes and lamb mortality. *Massey Agric. Coll. Sheep Farming Annual*, **2**, 5.

Williams, S. M. (1954). Fertility in Clun Forest Sheep. *J. Agric. Sci., Camb.* **45**, 202–228.

CHAPTER 19

Embryo Transfer in Sheep

19.1 INTRODUCTION

Although small-scale studies in sheep embryo transfer were reported in the 1930's and subsequently (Warwick et al., 1934; Casida et al. 1944; Warwick and Berry, 1949; Lopyrin et al., 1950, 1951) results were usually disappointing with no report showing more than 35% of recipient ewes producing lambs after transfer. It was not until the work of the Cambridge group (Hunter et al., 1955; Averill et al., 1955; Averill, 1956, 1958; Rowson and Adam, 1957; Averill and Rowson, 1958) that the possibilities of the technique were clearly demonstrated, with the authors reporting much higher survival rates for the transferred eggs; Averill (1958) showed, for example, that 24/30 (80%) of embryos transferred to 16 recipients developed into viable lambs.

The methods employed in the mid-fifties by the Cambridge workers remain the same basic procedures used in sheep embryo transfer today; the practical application of the technique would only be of interest in rather exceptional circumstances. One area of commercial interest has been in employing the method to boost the population of a particular breed (e.g. the Texel breed in Ireland); a further consideration is in using the procedure in exporting and importing

sheep in the form of embryos rather than as live animals. For those investigating various aspects of sheep reproduction, the transfer technique is of considerable importance.

19.2 SUPEROVULATION TECHNIQUES

In the sheep, the induction of superovulation follows much the same lines as those employed in cattle; a follicle-stimulating preparation is administered either towards the end of the sheep's normal oestrous cycle (days 11–13) or around the end of a progestagen treatment which is employed to control oestrus. Unlike the donor cow, the seasonally breeding ewe may not always be showing oestrous cycles; for that reason, progestagen treatment preceding the gonadotrophin part of the regimen may be more usual in dealing with the sheep.

Superovulation has been attempted using a variety of gonadotrophins, particularly PMSG (Hunter et al., 1955; Rowson and Adams, 1957; Averill, 1958; Averill and Rowson, 1958; Moore et al., 1960; Hancock and Hovell, 1961; Cumming and McDonald, 1967; Lawson et al., 1972) and there is evidence of a dose–response relationship when the preparation is administered in the cyclic sheep. About 2000 i.u. PMSG would be regarded as the highest permissible dose level; in some reports, doses have been employed on a bodyweight basis at the rate of 20–45 i.u. kg.

19.2.1 HAP vs PMSG

Of the various anterior pituitary preparations employed, that obtained from the horse, horse anterior pituitary (HAP), has probably been most frequently used, generally with good success when given in the form of several consecutive daily injections in the follicular phase of the natural cycle (Moore and Shelton, 1962a, 1964). Whereas with high PMSG dose levels there is a tendency towards increased numbers of unruptured luteinized follicles in sheep, this is not the case with HAP. Optimum responses to the horse preparation, as observed by Moore and Shelton (1964), were in ewes that came in oestrus 24–48 h after the end of treatment, when an average of more than nine fertilized eggs per ewe were

obtained with less variability than found with PMSG.

19.2.2 Prostaglandin and gonadotrophin

The use of prostaglandin $F_{2\alpha}$ or one of its analogues may be employed as part of the superovulation regimen. The analogue Cloprostenol employed to induce luteolysis after ovarian stimulation in sheep at Cambridge has been described by Trounson et al. (1976); in this 100 μg Cloprostenol was administered to sheep treated 24–72 hours previously with PMSG, the regimen resulting in most ewes coming into oestrus within 36 h. However, according to Willadsen (1979), a major drawback to the use of prostaglandin in PMSG-treated ewes is the high incidence of premature regression of the corpora lutea formed as a result of superovulation. This premature regression, which was also observed by Lawson (1977), apparently occurs between days 5 and 7 in some 50% or more of ewes;

Fig. 19.1. Texel ewes as donors in an embryo transfer programme. Embryo transfer in sheep has been carried out at Lyons Farms since 1968. In recent years, a transfer service for Texel Sheep breeders in the Republic has been provided with breeders providing five recipient ewes for every Texel donor entered for superovulation treatment.

although it appears that the uterus is implicated, the exact reasons for the demise of the corpora lutea are unknown. However, the ewes can be expected to return in oestrus after corpus luteum regression and for any embryos to be expelled from the uterus; for that reason, it is necessary not to postpone collection of embryos beyond day-4 or alternatively that sheep should be treated with progestagen until the day of collection (Willadsen, 1979). Although a similar phenomenon of corpus luteum regression has been observed in superovulation studies in cattle (Booth et al., 1975; Bouters et al., 1977), the timing of the regression and the low incidence of its occurence do not pose problems.

Whyman and Moore (1980) examined the use of the analogue Cloprostenol, administered at an interval after giving PMSG on day-12 of the natural cycle, but the treatment did not show any advantage over the regimen in which no PG was given.

19.2.3 Progestagen and gonadotrophin

Many of the superovulation treatments used in sheep attempt to combine ovarian stimulation with control of oestrus. As noted previously, superovulation and oestrus at a predetermined time can be induced by PMSG or pituitary extracts given in conjunction with progestagens, as described in several reports (Robinson, 1959; Gordon, 1969; Moore, 1970; Bradford et al., 1972, 1974; Boland, 1973; O'Reilly and O'Byrne, 1973; Quirke and Hanrahan, 1975; Boland and Gordon, 1978; Crosby et al., 1980; Wright et al., 1980). In these treatments, PMSG has usually been given as a single injection 24 h before, or at the time of, the last injection or removal of sponge pessaries, pituitary preparations such as HAP are usually given in the form of several daily injections, the final one of which coincides with the termination of progestagen treatment. Superovulated donors can usually be expected to exhibit oestrus some 24–48 h after terminating the progestagen treatment.

19.2.4 Need for ovulating hormone.

There appears to be no clear justification for administering an ovulating hormone as part of a treatment regimen in the belief that this will increase the ovulation rate. Wright et al. (1980) administered an LH preparation in the early hours of oestrus to ewes treated with progestagen and gonadotrophin without noting any effect. Earlier work, in which gonadotrophin-treated ewes were given hCG (750 i.u.) within 3 h of the start of oestrus, did indicate an increase in the proportion of follicles ovulating (Killeen and Moore, 1970). The use of hCG at a set-time relative to the termination of an intravaginal treatment gave variable results according to season in other work (Welch, 1969). The general view is that the sheep possesses sufficient endogenous LH to cope with the needs of superovulation.

19.3 PREPUBERTAL LAMB AS A SOURCE OF EGGS

Mansour (1959), working at Cambridge, was one of the first to attempt the induction of ovulation in young lambs; he treated lambs varying in age from 1 to 22 weeks with PMSG and hCG, but observed an absence of ovulation in the animals until 16 weeks or more. Elsewhere, however, Land and McGovern (1968) and Worthington and Kennedy (1979) did achieve ovulations at earlier ages (6–9 week-old lambs) with PMSG and hCG. Nonetheless, even when superovulation can be induced and fertilized eggs recovered (surgical inseminations required), there is evidence to show that prepubertal ewe-lambs may not always yield eggs with the same potential for continued development as do older sheep; studies when such eggs have been cultured in vitro (Wright et al., 1976) or transferred to adult recipients (Quirke and Hanrahan, 1977) have shown evidence of marked differences. It would seem that questions of embryonic mortality arise in prepubertal lambs that are not found in the postpubertal animals.

19.3.1 Repeated superovulation

One of the requirements of a successful superovulation and embryo transfer technique is that donor females should be capable of responding to gonadotrophin treatment on several occasions. In Australia, Moore and

Shelton (1962b) induced superovulation at intervals of 1 year in sheep without finding any significant decrease in the ovulatory response. Palsson (1962), working with a once-yearly treatment with PMSG in Icelandic sheep over a 3-year period, likewise found no evidence of a reduced response. In Ireland, studies with PMSG (Lynch, 1968) and HAP (Boland, 1973) showed that sheep could be superovulated on three occasions in the course of a 6–9 month period; this including treatment during the ewe anoestrus as well as in the breeding season.

In Australia, a study reported by Gherardi and Martin (1978) examined the responsiveness of Merino ewes given PMSG (1000 i.u.) regularly every cycle for 12 months; the results clearly showed that the sheep did not become progressively less responsive to the hormone. Such evidence is encouraging to those who may be concerned with sheep embryo transfer, using the same donors on several occasions. It does not, of course, solve the major problem associated with repeated surgery, that of a build-up of adhesions; the general rule would be that not much in excess of three surgical interventions would be possible, and that with pregnancies intervening between the successive attempts. It would seem worth considering the possibility of using laparoscopic techniques for the recovery of eggs to avoid the need for repeated surgery on the sheep.

19.4 BREEDING BY NATURAL AND ARTIFICIAL INSEMINATION

Regardless of the superovulation regimen employed, fertilization failure frequently occurs in superovulated ewes; according to Willadsen (1979) fertilization after mating is the exception rather than the rule with donors having more than about 10 ovulations. However, it has been demonstrated that high fertilization rates can be achieved in superovulated sheep by the direct deposition of semen into the uterine horns (Trounson and Moore (1974a); Boland and Gordon, 1978). Studies show that fertilization rates in excess of 90% can be achieved by depositing small volumes of semen into the uterine horns at the time of oestrus; unfortunately, it is also true that the subsequent rate of embryo recovery may be significantly decreased by this procedure (Boland and Gordon, 1978), although it has been maintained by Tounson and Moore (1974a) that the lower recovery rate is more than compensated for by the very high fertilization rates.

It has been noted that surgical insemination may also hasten egg transport and advance the time of ovulation (Killeen and Moore, 1971; Trounson and Moore, (1974a); Boland and Gordon, 1978). According to Willadsen (1979), stress and careless insemination late in oestrus may result in a high loss of eggs in sheep bred by intrauterine insemination; the author suggests that AI should be done as soon as possible in oestrus and as gently as possible, without touching the ovaries or oviducts.

It is evident that eggs fertilized by uterine insemination are viable and capable of normal development when transferred to recipients (Killeen and Moore, 1971); it remains for the problem of decreased egg recovery rate to be satisfactorily resolved. One possibility may be to use laparoscopy rather than laparotomy in carrying out the uterine insemination; manipulation of the tract may otherwise be responsible for adversely affecting egg transport to the detriment of recovery rates.

Using orthodox artificial and natural insemination procedures to breed the donor sheep, it would be usual practice to mate by handservice or perform cervical AI at 12 h intervals during the heat period; oestrus may be more prolonged than normal for the breed in question, presumably by a result of the greater oestrogen concentrations arising from the stimulated ovaries. One advantage of breeding by AI, especially uterine insemination, is that ewes which do not exhibit oestrus will be dealt with as well as those that do show heat, assuming that progestagen is employed to control the timing of ovulation within predictable limits; Moore (1980) mentioned that some 10–15% of donors usually fail to come in oestrus after superovulation but that they are capable of yielding normal fertilized eggs after surgical AI.

19.5 RECOVERING EGGS

Sheep eggs and embryos are usually obtained from the reproductive organs using the flushing methods first described by Hunter et al. (1955). In this, collection is carried out under general anaesthesia with the ovaries, oviducts and uterus exposed by a mid-ventral incision; oviducts are cannulated via the fimbrae and part or all of the reproductive tract is flushed by gently expressing the recovery medium along the uterine horns and through the Fallopian tubes. In the ewe, the egg enters the uterus around the third to fourth day after the end of oestrus (Holst and Braden, 1972; Holst, 1974) regardless of the timing of collection in the donor, flushing of medium back through the oviducts can result in a high (around 80%) rate of egg recovery (Moore and Shelton, 1962a, b, 1964; Trounson and Moore, 1974a–c).

In an attempt to reduce the incidence and severity of reproductive tract adhesions, Tervit and Havik (1976) employed a uterine-flush technique which involved inserting a urethral catheter into the lumen of the uterine horn, inflating the catheter cuff and then flushing the horn with medium injected near the uterine tip; the egg recovery rate from the technique (83%) was comparable to that achieved after orthodox tubal flushing (78%) and it could be employed in repeated recovery attempts. The possibility of non-surgical recovery along the lines of that employed in cattle is generally thought to be excluded in the sheep because of the tortuous nature of the cervical canal; however, it may be

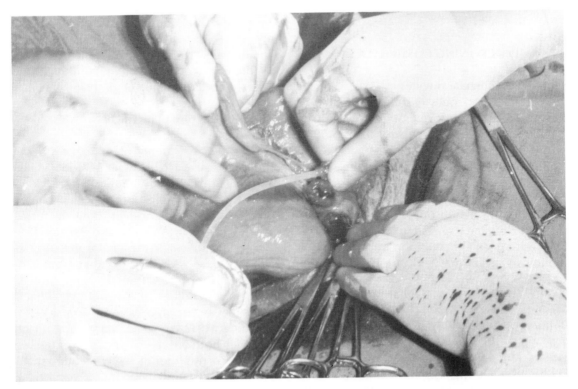

Fig. 19.2 Collecting eggs from the ewe after cannulating the fallopian tube. There is just no simple way of collecting eggs from the superovulated donor ewe other than by surgical intervention. Horse pituitary extract, prepared from material collected locally, is used at U.C.D. Lyons Farm as the main source of FSH for inducing superovulation. In sheep, the use of horse pituitary rather than PMSG does help to cut down on the number of large unovulated follicles in the ovaries of donor sheep. The main problem remains one of getting a high fertilization rate in donor ewes.

that satisfactory instrumentation can be devised to do this.

19.5.1 Media for recovery

Different forms of media, ranging from complex tissue culture media (e.g. Medium 199) to simple balanced salt solutions enriched with sheep serum, or serum albumin of sheep or cattle origin, have been used for the collection and holding of sheep embryos. Early work generally involved the use of sheep serum with trace amounts of antibiotics added (Hunter et al., 1955; Averill and Rowson, 1958; Moore et al., 1960; Hancock and Hovell, 1961). With the development of successful methods for culturing sheep embryos, serum has been wholly or partly replaced by bicarbonate or phosphate-buffered solutions enriched with either 2–3% sheep or cattle serum albumin or 10–20% sheep serum. For collection and transfer, the phosphate buffers (e.g. Dulbecco's phosphate buffer) have proved to be particularly useful.

19.6 CLONING POSSIBILITIES

19.6.1 Use of follicular oocytes

Although sheep oocytes released from the follicle readily undergo meiotic maturation in vitro (Edwards, 1965; Quirke and Gordon, 1971; Crosby and Gordon, 1971; Jagiello et al. 1974), it has been shown that the presence of a second meiotic metaphase figure in cultured oocytes is not necessarily synonymous with oocyte maturation (Moore and Trounson, 1977); it is important that early cleavage stages should not be used as a measure of normal maturation because defects in the organism may not be evident until blastulation.

As mentioned already, abnormalities in protein synthesis in extrafollicular oocytes during maturation have been identified (Warnes et al., 1977). It has been suggested that it is the absence of new proteins synthesized during the later stages of normal oocyte maturation that is responsible for the developmental incompetence observed with most cultured oocytes (Moor and Trounson, 1977). In contrast to consistent failure to induce normal maturation

in sheep oocytes released from vesicular follicles, Moor and Trounson (1977) in sheep and Thibault and Gerard (1973) in goats found that oocytes from preovulatory follicles matured within intact follicles in vitro subsequently developed normally to term; the Cambridge work also showed that the potential for complete maturation in vitro is not restricted to the preovulatory follicle but can be induced in sheep oocytes from non-atretic and atretic follicles obtained at any stage of the cycle.

Normal oocyte maturation within the follicle, according to Moor and Trounson (1977), is regulated by both gonadotrophins and by steroids; this view is in agreement with that of Baker and Neal (1972) who considered that oestrogen and gonadotrophin acted synergistically when added to cultured mouse Graafian follicles. Elsewhere, there are indications that increasing levels of intrafollicular oestrogen are associated with normal maturation and fertilization of pig oocytes (Hunter et al., 1976) and that the acquisition of a "male pronucleus growth factor" (MPGF) in mammalian oocytes (Thibault and Gerard, 1973) may be facilitated by oestradiol in conjunction with other steroids (Thibault et al., 1975).

19.6.2 Production of identical twins and multiples

The normal incidence of monozygotic twins in sheep is believed to be extremely low. Johansson and Hansson (1943), examining extensive data on sex ratio and multiple-births in sheep, could find no statistical evidence of their occurrence. Morley (1949) in Australia and Barton (1950) in New Zealand, also on the basis of analysing sheep lambing data also conclude that identicals are either absent or extremely rare. Studies in prenatal physiology in sheep suggest that such twins may occur on occasions; Cohrs (1934) and Henning (1937), dealing with slaughterhouse material, both observed twins in ewes possessing a single corpus luteum and concluded that they were monozygotic. In more recent times, Rowson and Moor (1964), in examining 424 sheep embryos ranging from early blastocysts (6–7 day old) to elongating gastrulae (day-14), found four with two embryonic areas. Testing by skin

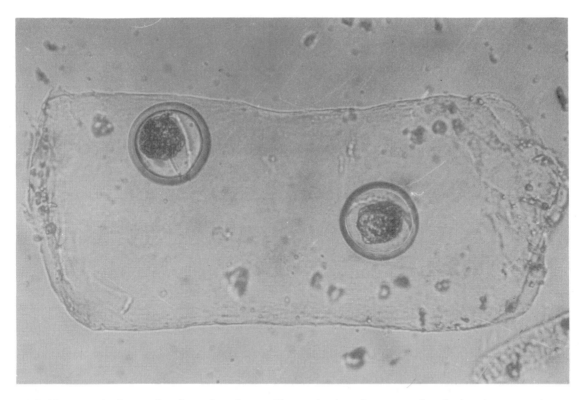

Fig. 19.3. Monozygotic sheep twins after culture in agar. The production of monozygotic twins by microsurgery is an area currently being researched at Lyons. This has involved taking eggs at the 2, 4 or 8 cell stages and after arranging the blastomers into two groups in a pair of zonae pellucidae putting into agar for culture in the oviduct of the ewe or rabbit. The picture shows a monozygotic pair of sheep embryos after recovery from the sheep oviduct—still imbedded in the agar.

grafting techniques provides a highly critical test for monozygotics in sheep.

As already mentioned, the potential of single blastomeres from early embryos to develop normally to term has been demonstrated in several mammals (Nicholas and Hall, 1942; Seidel, 1952; Tarkowskii, 1959; Tarkowskii and Wroblewska, 1967; Moore et al., 1968, 1969) and single blastomeres of two, four and eight-cell rabbit and sheep eggs did develop into normal young after transfer to recipients (Seidel, 1952; Moore et al., 1968; Moore, 1974). An attempt to produce identicals by mechanically dividing 4-, 6- and 7-day old sheep embryos was reported by Trounson and Moore (1974c); although some 25% of the halved 6- and 7-day embryos developed during culture into blastocysts which appeared to be normal, only two lambs were born from 19 blastocysts which were transferred

into recipient sheep. Then came the report of Willadsen (1979), who developed a technique for producing identicals in sheep which involved the microsurgical separation of the blastomeres of 2-cell eggs, their insertion into foreign zonae pellucidae, embedding in a protective cylinder of agar and culture in ligated sheep oviducts. The viability of late morulae or early blastocysts produced by this method was about 50%, the lower than normal survival rate being attributed primarily to mechanical damage resulting from the manipulative procedure by which the agar was removed from the embryo before transfer to the recipient.

In a later report, Willadsen (1980) showed that two blastomeres of a 4-cell egg and four blastomeres of an 8-cell egg developed into early blastocysts which were as normal as those produced by isolated blastomeres from 2-cell eggs; pregnancy rate (79%) and embryo survival rate (80%) was as high on this occasion as that recorded after the transfer of ordinary sheep embryos (Moore and Shelton, 1964; Rowson and Moor, 1966a,b). As mentioned with reference to cattle embryo transfer, the artificial production of identical twinning is likely to be of considerable value in many areas of farm animal research and marks an important milestone in mammalian embryo transfer research.

19.7 EVALUATION OF SHEEP EMBRYOS

There is ample evidence available on the normal process of fertilization and early development of sheep eggs (Averill, 1958; Moore et al., 1960; Moore and Shelton, 1964) which are known to enter the uterus about 60 h after ovulation (Holst and Braden, 1972; Holst, 1974). The first cleavage takes place in the egg about 15–18 hours after sperm penetration, the second some 12 h later to give a 4-cell egg by 48 h after ovulation (day-3 after oestrus onset); from then on, the blastomeres cleave roughly every 16–24 hours, with 4–8-cell eggs being typical of day-4 and 24–32 cell morulae typical of day-5 (Willadsen, 1979). By day-6, most eggs would have developed into compacted late morulae of some 40 cells which are difficult to distinguish individually, or into early blastocysts containing up to 60 cells; on day-7, the majority are early or expanding blastocysts. After day-7, it may be difficult to distinguish embryos from aggregations of oviducal cells in flushing medium, especially on day-8 or day-9 when they have shed the zona pellucida; after hatching, there is a tendency for the blastocyst to contract temporarily into a compact ball of cells.

Usually, day-3 to day-7 eggs are used in transfers; relatively under-developed eggs are probably best left out of transfer attempts (Moore, 1976). Morphological abnormalities in sheep embryos have been observed by several investigators (Averill, 1958; Hancock and Hovell, 1961; Tervit and McDonald, 1969) but their effect on embryo survival is not always clear. Killeen and Moore (1971) noted that sheep eggs possessing one of more anucleate cells could still develop normally and suggested that these should be regarded as atypical rather than abnormal. Gross abnormalities involving the nuclear elements of sheep embryos have also been decribed (Braden, 1964; Killeen and Moore, 1970, 1971) but the incidence is low (<2%).

19.8 SHORT-TERM STORAGE METHODS

The use of sterile sheep blood serum (usually with trace amounts of antibiotics added) as the recovery and storage medium for eggs, together with transfers only to those recipients closely synchronized with their respective donors, probably accounts for much of the success by Cambridge workers among ewes in the 1950's (Hunter et al., 1955; Averill et al., 1955; Averill, 1956, 1958; Averill and Rowson, 1958, 1959).

Although it was shown to be possible, almost 30 years ago, to ship rabbit eggs in blood serum at 10°C from one continent to another and get acceptable survival rates (Marden and Chang, 1952), the fertilized eggs of farm animals proved much less amenable to such treatment. However, a fortunate discovery in the mid-fifties by Cambridge workers showed that sheep eggs, at an early stage of cleavage, could be stored for several days in the rabbit oviduct and retain their ability to survive after re-transfer to the ewe (Averill et al., 1955; Averill, 1956); this subsequently enabled sheep embryos to be trans ported between England and South Africa and between Australia and New Zealand (Adams et al., 1961; Hunter et al., 1962; Welch, 1969). More recent studies have shown that in preserving early-cleavage sheep eggs destined for re-transfer, the rabbit oviduct would appear to provide a satisfactory environment for up to 5 days (Lawson et al., 1972).

19.8.1 In vitro culture

Methods of culturing sheep embryos in vitro at 37–38°C have been developed and these can be used in assessing the capacity of embryos for further development (Moore, 1970; Moor and Cragle, 1971; Moore and Spry, 1972; Tervit and

Rowson, 1974; Wright *et al.*, 1976; Tervit and Goold, 1978). Sheep embryos, in common with those of a number of other species, hesitate at a particular stage of their development (Moore, 1973) and require specific conditions in culture before they pass through this stage. In the sheep, the "block" to continued development in culture occurs around the 8-cell stage; incubation under reduced oxygen tension enables embryos to progress through and beyond the 8-cell stage (Tervit *et al.*, 1972; Trounson and Moore, 1974).

According to Moore (1976), apparently normal development of the sheep embryo in culture can provide a reliable indication of the potential for further development *in vivo* and hence culture allows the rapid assessment of embryos after they have been exposed to different treatments. There is also the use of the technique for the long-distance transport of embryos; Baker *et al.* (1971) successfully transported sheep embryos by air between the U.S.A. and Canada in medium within silicon rubber tubing.

Fig. 19.4. Pure bred Texel lamb with its Suffolk × mother. It should prove possible to get 60–80% of recipient ewes pregnant after transfer of eggs. In the work at Lyons Farm, oestrus is synchronized both in donors and recipients by way of the intravaginal sponge inserted for a 12-day treatment period. Horse pituitary extract is administered during the final 3 days of the intravaginal treatment to donors and a low dose of PMSG given to recipients at sponge withdrawal.

19.8.2 Storage at reduced temperature

In vitro culture at 37–38°C, as already described, can provide a means of short-term storage, but one which is only effective for a limited time. Storing embryos at a reduced temperature may have advantages, one of these being the inhibition of continued cleavage, which would permit synchronization of donor and recipient ewes to be based on the age of the embryo at the start of storage. In sheep, some evidence has shown that the early cleavage egg (2–16-cell) may be more sensitive to cooling to 0°C than morulae stages (Willadsen *et al.*, 1976) although there are several reports which suggest that 8–16-cell sheep eggs can be stored without a marked decrease in viability at temperatures varying from 0 to 13°C for periods of up to 10 days (Averill and Rowson, 1959; Loginova, 1961; Kardymowicz *et al.*, 1963, 1966, 1971; Kardymowicz, 1972; Renard *et al.*, 1976). On the basis of embryo survival after transfer to recipients, Moore and Bilton (1973) found that only one of seven embryos stored for 2 days at 5°C continued development; embryos checked by *in vitro* culture after storage at this temperature showed evidence of reduced viability after 3 days.

19.9 FREEZING THE EMBRYO

Although commercial interest in the low temperature storage of sheep embryos is limited in comparison to that shown in cattle, from the research viewpoint, the sheep has often been used in testing methods because of its relative cheapness as an experimental animal. The first lamb born after transfer of a frozen–thawed embryo was born in Cambridge (Willadsen *et al.*, 1974) and this was followed by similar success in Australia (Moore and Bilton, 1976) and in Poland (Smorag *et al.*, 1978). Among the compounds with cryoprotectant characteristics examined are dimethylsulphoxide (DMSO), glycerol and polyvynyl pyrrolidone (PVB). At Cambridge, Willadsen *et al.* (1976a, b) successfully stored sheep embryos in media containing 1.5 M. DMSO; Australian workers also obtained apparently normal development in culture and lambs from embryos frozen in media containing 1.0–2.0 M. DMSO (Bilton and Moore, 1976). Glycerol has been employed at a concentration of 1.4 M and results suggest that this agent may be preferable to DMSO (Willadsen, 1980).

Phosphate buffered saline forms the basis of media for deep-freezing and for storage of embryos for the few hours that elapse from the time of collection until freezing; the sheep embryo does not apparently show the same sensitivity to reduced temperatures in the early-cleavage stages as the cattle embryo (Willadsen, 1980). Although after storage for 24 h in PBS at room temperature the viability of fresh sheep embryos does not appear to be affected, the same is not true of embryos thawed after a period of frozen storage (Willadsen et al., 1976a, b). Protection against freezing/thawing, regardless of whether DMSO or glycerol is employed, appears to depend on the presence of the cryoprotectant intracellularly.

Freezing and thawing methods applicable in both sheep and cattle have been described by Willadsen (1980b); the Cambridge studies have shown that even when only about half the normal cell number is present at the early blastocyst stage (in the experimental production of identical sheep twins), a normal lamb may still be produced after freezing and thawing (Willadsen, 1980a); fully expanded and hatched blastocysts appear to survive less readily, probably because of their relatively large size. The essential fact, in all of this is, however, that reasonably efficient freezing techniques are now available for late morulae and early blastocysts of sheep.

19.10 SYNCHRONIZING DONORS AND RECIPIENTS

It is well accepted that the occurrence of oestrus in donor and recipient ewes must be closely synchronized if the maximum rate of survival of transferred embryos is to be obtained (Hunter et al., 1955; Averill and Rowson, 1958; Moore et al., 1960; Hancock and Hovell, 1961; Moore and Shelton, 1964; Rowson and Moore, 1966a, b; Lynch, 1968). In Australia, Shelton and Moore (1964) examined synchronization requirements in the sheep, transferring embryos to recipients in oestrus 48 h before to 48 h after their respective donors; optimum results, in terms of pregnancy rates and embryo survival rates, were found among recipients in heat 12 h before to

12 h after donor sheep. Rowson and Moor (1966a, b) confirmed and extended these observations, recording that 75% of their recipients became pregnant when oestrus was exactly synchronized; a difference of ±2 days was tolerated reasonably well but with a difference of ±3 days, only 8% of recipient ewes became pregnant. The results of Wilmut and Sales (1981) at Edinburgh in more recent times has shown that sheep embryos transferred into an advanced asynchronous recipient fail to implant because their development is so modified that they fail to inhibit luteolysis.

19.10.1 Oestrus control in recipients

Early studies in sheep embryo transfer, in which doses of progesterone were administered daily to control oestrus in recipient sheep, indicated that this form of synchronization treatment did not adversely affect pregnancy and embryo survival rates (Hunter et al., 1955; Shelton and Moore, 1955); the same appears to be true when progestagens such as FGA and MAP are administered to recipient ewes by the intra-vaginal route (Tervit et al., 1976; Crosby et al., 1980). At Cambridge, Willadsen (1979) reported that practically all prostaglandin-treated recipients (125 μg Cloprostenol at 10–12 day intervals) came in oestrus 24–48 h after the second dose of the agent and that this was a satisfactory method of oestrus control in such sheep; in view of difficulties reported elsewhere with prostaglandin (early regression of corpora lutea; low oestrus response), it may be worth treating this agent in recipients with some caution.

19.11 TRANSFER TECHNIQUES

The ewe, because of its small size and ease of handling in comparison with cattle and pigs, is a species which does permit large numbers of transfers to be attempted daily. The developmental stages of eggs which have been transferred in sheep research studies have varied from follicular oocytes (transferred to mated recipients) and one-cell eggs late on the day of oestrus (Lopyrin et al., 1951; Woody and Ulberg,

Fig. 19.5. Transferring embryos to the tip of the uterine horn of the recipient ewe. Sheep embryos are transferred singly or one to each uterine horn by pipette, as shown in this. It would be useful to explore the application of laparascopic techniques to transfer the embryo in sheep rather than using surgery. The ability to promote identical sheep twins, which can be extremely valuable in certain lines of research in parasitology, for example, is one reason why there is a renewal of interest in sheep embryo transfer at the University farm.

1963) to elongated blastocysts on day-12 (Moor and Rowson, 1966).

The effect of age of embryo, number of embryos transferred and the site of transfer have been reported on by several investigators (Moore and Shelton, 1964; Rowson and Moor, 1966a,b; McDonald, 1975; Killeen, 1976). Eggs recovered about 4 days after oestrus are suitable for transfer to the uterus. The usual procedure is to transfer two embryos to each recipient (one to each uterine horn) although single egg transfers can give acceptable pregnancy rates (Crosby et al., 1980). Transfer in all instances requires surgical intervention, the work being conducted under general anesthesia, or under local anaesthesia with the sheep restrained in a laparotomy cradle, as described by Lamond and Urquhart (1961). Transfer using the cradle has the advantages of speed and economy. Access to the reproductive tract to effect transfer is invariably by mid-ventral incision and there would appear to be little advantage in exploring alternative approaches; Moore (1977) does suggest, however, that transfer using laparoscopic techniques might provide an attractive alternative to laparotomy.

19.12 REFERENCES

Adams, C. E., Rowson, L. E. A., Hunter, G. L. and Bishop, G. P. (1961) Long distance transport of sheep ova. *Proc. 4th Int. Congr. Anim. Reprod. The Hague*, **2**, 381–382.
Averill, R. L. W. (1956) The transfer and storage of sheep ova. *Proc. 3rd. Int. Congr. Anim. Reprod. Camb.* **3**, 7–9.
Averill, R. L. W. (1958) The production of living sheep eggs. *J. Agric. Sci., Camb.,* **50**, 17–33.
Averill, R. L. W. and Rowson, L. E. A. (1958) Ovum transfer in sheep. *J. Endocr.* **16**, 326–336.
Averill, R. L. W. and Rowson, L. E. A. (1959) Attempts at

storage of sheep ova at low temperatures. *J. Agric. Sci., Camb.* **52,** 392–395.

Averill, R. L. W., Adams, C. E. and Rowson, L. E. A. (1955) Transfer of mammalian ova between species. *Nature, Lond,* **176,** 167.

Baker, T. G. and Neal, P. (1972) Gonadotrophin-induced maturation of mouse graafian follicles in organ culture. In, *Oogenesis* Biggers, and Schultz, Ed., pp. 377–396. Univ. Press, Baltimore.

Baker, R. D., Webel, S., Ellicott, A. and Dziuk, P. J. (1971) Arial transport of sheep embryos in vitro. *Can. J. Anim. Sci.* **51,** 542–543.

Barton, R. A. (1950) A note on sex ratios in a Romney Marsh Stud flock. *N.Z. J. Sci. Tech. Agric.* **31**(3), 24.

Boland, M. P. (1973) Studies related to egg transfer in sheep. *Ph. D. Thesis, N.U.I., Dublin.*

Boland, M. P. and Gordon, I. (1978) Recovery and fertilization of eggs following natural service and uterine insemination in the Galway ewe. *Ir. Vet. J.* **32**(7), 123–125.

Booth, W. D., Newcomb, R., Strange, H., Rowson, L. E. A. and Sacher, H. B. (1975) Plasma oestrogen and progesterone in relation to superovulation and egg recovery in the cow. *Vet. Rec.* **97,** 366–369.

Bouters, R., Moyaert, I., Coryn, M., Spincemaille, J. and Vandeplasse, M. (1980) Premature regression of the corpora lutea in superovulated cows. *Theriogenology.* **14,** 207–216.

Braden, A. W. H. (1964) The incidence of morphologically abnormal ova in sheep. *Aust. J. Biol. Sci.* **17,** 499.

Bradford, G. E., Hart, R., Quirke, J. F. and Land, R. B. (1972) Genetic control of the duration of gestation in sheep. *J. Reprod. Fertil.* **30,** 459–463.

Bradford, G. E., Taylor St. C. S., Quirke, J. F. and Hart, R. (1974) Egg transfer study of litter size, birthweight and lamb survival. *Anim. Prod.* **18,** 249–263.

Casida, L. E., Warwick, E. J. and Meyer, R. K. (1944) Survival of multiple-pregnancy in the ewe following treatment with pituitary gonadotrophins. *J. Anim. Sci.* **3,** 22.

Cherardi, P. G. and Martin, G. B. (1978) The effect of multiple injections of pregnant mares serum gona-dotrophin on the ovarian activity of Merino ewes. *Proc. Aust. Soc. Anim. Prod.* **12,** 260.

Cohrs, P. (1934) Uniovular twins in the sheep and pig and binovular unifollicular twins in the sheep. *Z. Anat. Enw.* **102,** 584–593.

Crosby, T. F. and Gordon, I. (1971) II. Timing of nuclear maturation in oocytes cultured in growth medium. *J. Agric. Sci., Camb.,* **76,** 373–374.

Crosby, T. F., Boland, M. P., El-Kamali, A. A. and Gordon, I. (1980) Superovulation in the ewe using HAP. *Theriogen.* **13,** 92.

Cumming, I. A. and McDonald, M. F. (1967) The production of ova by N.Z. Romney ewes following hormonal stimulation. *N.Z.J. Agric. Res.* **10,** 226.

Edwards, R. G. (1965) Maturation in vitro of mouse, sheep, cow, pig rhesus monkey and human ovarian oocytes. *Nature, Lond.* **206,** 349.

Gordon, I. (1969) Controlled reproduction in sheep and cattle. *J. Ir. Dept. Agric. Dublin.* **66,** 184–211.

Hancock, J. L. and Hovell, G. H. R. (1961) Transfer of sheep ova. *J. Reprod. Fert.* **2,** 295–306.

Henning, W. L. (1937) A double pregnancy with a single corpus luteum. *J. Hered.* **28,** 61–62.

Holst, P. H. (1974) The time of entry of ova into the uterus of the ewe. *J. Reprod. Fert.* **36,** 427–428.

Holst, P. H. and Braden A. W. H. (1972) Ovum transport in the ewe. *Aust. J. Biol. Sci.* **25,** 167.

Hunter, G. L., Adams, C. E. and Rowson, L. E. A. (1955) Interbreed ovum transfer in sheep. *J. Agric. Sci., Camb.* **46,** 143–149.

Hunter, G. L., Biship, G. P., Adams, C. E. and Rowson, L. E. A. (1962) Successful long-distance aerial transport of fertilized sheep ova. *J. Reprod. Fert.* **3,** 33–40.

Hunter, R. H. F., Cook, B. and Baker, T. G. (1976) Dissociation of response to injected gonadotrophin between the graafian follicle and oocyte in pigs. *Nature, Lond.* **260,** 150–158.

Jagiello, G. M., Miller, W. A., Ducayen, M. B. and Lin, J. S. (1974) Chiasma frequency and disjunctional behaviour of ewe and cow oocytes matured in vitro. *Biol. Reprod.* **10,** 354–363.

Johansson, I. and Hansson, A. (1943) The sex ratio and multiple births in sheep. *Ladtbr. Hogsk. Ann.* **11,** 145–171.

Kardymowicz, M., Kardymowicz, O., Kohl, W. and Lada, A. (1963) Storage of fertilized sheep ova for 5 days. *Acta Biol. Cracov. Ser. Zool.* **9,** 117–119.

Kardymowicz, M., Kardymowicz, O. and Grochowalski, K. (1966) A study on the effect of cooling of sheep ova at 10>C on their capability of further development. *Acta Biol. Cracow. Ser. Zool.* **9,** 113–116.

Kardymowicz, O. (1972) Successful in vitro storage of fertilized sheep ova for ten days. *Proc. 7th Int. Congr. Anim. Reprod. A.I. Munich.* **1,** 499–502.

Kardymowicz, O. (1972) A method of vital staining for determining the viability of fertilized sheep ova stored in vitro. *Proc. 7th Int. Congr. Anim. Reprod. A.I. (Munich).* **1,** 503–506.

Killeen, I. D. (1976) The effects of age of egg and site of transfer on survival of transferred eggs in the ewe. *Theriogen.* **6,** 637.

Killeen, I. D., Moore, N. W. (1970) The effect of pregnant mare serum gonadotrophin and human chorionic gonadotrophin on ovulation and fertility in the ewe. *Aust. J. Agric. Res.* **21,** 807–814.

Killeen, I. D. and Moore, N. W. (1971) The morphological appearance and development of sheep ova fertilized by surgical insemination. *J. Reprod. Fert.* **24,** 63–70.

Lamond, D. R. and Urquhart, E. J. (1961) Sheep laparotomy cradle. *Aust. Vet. J.* **37,** 430–431.

Lampkin, G. H. (1953) Intolerance of dizygotic twin lambs to skin homografts. *Nature, Lond.* **171,** 975–976.

Land, R. B. and McGovern, P. T. (1968) Ovulation and fertilization in the lamb. *J. Reprod. Fert.* **15,** 325–327.

Lawson, R. A. S., Adams, G. E. and Rowson, L. E. A. (1972) The development of sheep eggs in the rabbit oviduct and their viability after re-transfer to ewes. *J. Reprod. Fert.* **29,** 105–116.

Loginova, N. W. (1961) Transfer of 10 ova (sheep) stored 1 day at 0°C. *Ovtsevodstvo.* **8,** 10–20.

Lopyrin, A. I., Loginova, N. V. and Karpov, P. L. (1950) *Sovetsk. Zooteckh.* **8,** 50.

Lopyrin, A. I., Loginova, N. V. and Karpov, P. L. (1951) *Sovetsk. Zooteckh.* **9,** 83.

Lynch, J. J. (1968) Superovulation and egg transfer in sheep. *M. Agr. Sci. Thesis, U.C.D. Dublin.*

McDonald, M. F. (1975) Progress in the transfer of eggs between sheep. *Sheep Farming Ann. 1975, Massey Univ.* 145–149.

Mansour, A. M. (1959) The hormonal control of ovulation in the immature lamb *J. Agric. Sci. Camb.* **52,** 87–94.

Marden, W. G. R. and Chang, M. C. (1952) The aerial transport of mammalian ova for transplantation. *Science.* **115,** 705.

Moore, N. W. (1970) Fertilization in ewes treated with progesterone and equine anterior pituitary extract. *J. Endocr.* **46,** 121.

Moore, N. W. (1973) Ovum development and transfer. *J. Reprod. Fert.* (Suppl. 18), 111–116.

Moore, N. W. (1976) Culture, storage and transfer of sheep embryos. *Proc. Int. Congr. Sheep Breed. Muresk,* 495–499.

Moore, N. W. (1977) Embryo transfer methods. *In: Embryo Transfer in Farm Animals (K Betteridge, Ed.) Monograph 16, pp 40, Canada Dept Agriculture Publn.*

Moore, N. W. (1980) Procedures and results obtainable in sheep and goats. In: Current Therapy in Theriogenology *(Ed. Morrow, D. A.),* 89–94.

Moore, N. W. and Shelton, N. J. (1962a). Oestrous and ovarian response of the ewe to a horse anterior pituitary extract. *Nature, Lond.* **194,** 1283–1284.

Moore, N. W., and Shelton, J. N. (1962b). Application of the technique of egg transfer to sheep breeding. *Aust. J. Agric. Res.* **13,** 718–724.

Moore, N. W. and Shelton, J. N. (1964) Response of ewe to a horse anterior pituitary extract. *J. Reprod. Fert.* **7,** 79–87.

Moore, N. W. and Bilton, R. J. (1973) The storage of fertilized sheep ova at 5°C. *Aust. J. Biol. Sci.* **26,** 1421–1427.

Moore, N. W. and Bilton, R. J. (1976) Storage, culture and transfer of embryos of domestic animals. *Proc. 8th Int. Congr. Anim. Reprod. A.I. (Kracow),* **3,** 306.

Moore, N. W. and Spry, G. A. (1972) The culture of fertilized sheep ova. *J. Reprod. Fert.* **28,** 139.

Moore, N. W., Rowson, L. E. A. and Short, R. V. (1960) Egg transfer in sheep. Factors affecting the survival and development of transferred eggs. *J. Reprod. Fert.* **1,** 332–349.

Moore, N. W., Adams, C. E. and Rowson, L. E. A. (1968) Developmental potential of single blastomeres of the rabbit egg. *J. Reprod. Fert.* **17,** 527.

Moore, N. W., Polge, C. and Rowson, L. E. A. (1969) The survival of single blastomeres of pig eggs transferred to recipient gilts. *Aust. J. Biol. Sci.* **22,** 979.

Moor, R. M. and Cragle, R. G. (1971) The sheep eggs; enzymatic removal of the zona pellucida and culture of eggs *in vitro. J. Reprod. Fert.* **27,** 401.

Moor, R. M. and Rowson, L. E. A. (1966) The corpus luteum of the sheep: functional relationship between the embryo and the corpus luteum. *J. Endocr.* **34,** 233–239.

Moor, R. M. and Trounson, A. O. (1977) Hormonal and follicular factors affecting maturation of sheep oocytes *in vitro* and their subsequent developmental capacity. *J. Reprod. Fert.* **49,** 101–109.

Morley, F. H. W. (1949) The occurrence of identical twins among Merino sheep. *Aust. Vet. J.* **24,** 72.

Nicholas, J. S. and Hall, V. B. (1942) Experiments on developing rats. II. The development of isolated blastomeres and fused eggs. *J. Exp. Zool.* **90,** 441.

O'Reilly, P. H. and O'Byrne, E. (1973) Ovum transfer in the Galway ewe synchronized with intravaginal pessaries. *Ir. Vet. J.,* **27,** 117–179.

Palsson, H. (1962) Hormonal augmentation of fertility in sheep by PMS. *J. Reprod. Fert.* **3,** 55–63.

Quirke, J. G. and Gordon, I. (1971) Culture and fertilization of sheep ovarian oocytes. I. Effect of culture medium on resumption of meiosis. *J. Agric. Sci., Camb.* **76,** 369–372.

Quirke, J. F. and Hanrahan, J. P. (1975) Effect of gonadotrophin-releasing hormone and human chorionic gonadotrophin on the response of the ewe to pregnant mare serum gonadotrophin. *J. Reprod. Fert.* **43,** 167–170.

Quirke, J. F. and Hanrahan, J. P. (1977) Comparison of the survival in the uteri of adult ewes of cleaved ova from adult ewes and ewe lambs. *J. Reprod. Fert.* **51,** 487–489.

Renard, J. P., Wintenberger-Torres, S. and Du Mesnil du Buisson, F. (1976) Storage of ewe and cow eggs at 10°C. In, *Egg Transf. in Cattle.* Rowson, L. E. A. Ed., pp. 165–171. Commiss. Europ. Communit. Luxembourg.

Robinson, T. J. (1959) The estrous cycle of the ewe and doe. In, *Reprod. in Domestic Ann.* 1st Ed., Cole, H. H. Ed., and Cupps, P. T. pp. 291–333. Acad. Press. NY.

Rowson, L. E. A. and Adams, C. E. (1957) An egg transfer experiment in sheep. *Vet. Rec.* **69,** 849.

Rowson, L. E. A. and Moor, R. M. (1964) Occurrence and development of identical twins in sheep. *Nature, Lond.* **201,** 521–522.

Rowson, L. E. A. and Moor, R. M. (1966a). Development of the sheep conceptus during the first 14 days. *J. Anat.* **100,** 777–785.

Rowson, L. E. A. and Moor, R. M. (1966b) Embryo transfer in the sheep: the significance of synchronizing oestrus in donor and recipient animal. *J. Reprod. Fert.* **11,** 207–212.

Seidel, F. (1952) Die entwicklung spotenzen einer isolierken blastomere des zweizeilenstadiums im saugetierei. *Naturwissenschaften.* **39,** 355.

Shelton, J. N. and Moore, N. W. (1966) Survival of fertilized eggs transferred to ewes after progesterone treatment. *J. Reprod. Fert.* **11,** 149–151.

Smorag, Z., Wierzbowski, S. and Wierzchos, E. (1978) Results of transplanting 3-6-, and 7-day old frozen sheep embryos. *Bull. Acad. Pol. Sci. Sci. Biblo.* **26**(4), 273–275.

Tarkowski, A. K. (1959) Experience on the development of isolated blastomeres of mouse eggs. *Nature, Lond.* **184,** 1286.

Tarkowski, A. K. and Wroblewska, J. (1967) Development of blastomeres to mouse eggs isolated at the 4 and 8 cell stage. *J. Embryol. Exp. Morphol.* **18,** 155.

Tervit, H. R. and McDonald, M. F. (1969). Culture and transplantation of sheep ova. *N.Z. J. Agric. Res.* **12,** 313.

Tervit, H. R. and Good, P. G. (1978) The culture of sheep embryos in either a bicarbonate-buffered medium or a phosphate-buffered medium enriched with serum. *Theriogen.* **9**(3), 251–257.

Tervit, H. R. and Havik, P. G. (1976) A modified technique for flushing ova from the sheep uterus. *N.Z. Vet. J.* **24,** 138–140.

Tervit, H. R. and Rowson, L. E. A. (1974) Birth of lambs after culture of sheep ova in vitro for up to 6 days. *J. Reprod. Fert.* **38,** 117.

Tervit, H. R., Whittingham, D. G. and Rowson, L. E. A. (1972) Successful culture in vitro of sheep and cattle ova. *J. Reprod. Fert.* **30,** 493–497.

Thibault, C. and Gerard, M. (1973) Cytoplasmic and nuclear maturation of rabbit oocytes *in vitro. Ann. Biol. Anim. Biochim. Biophys.* **13,** Suppl. 145–156.

Thibault, C., Gerard, M. and Menezo, Y. (1975) In vitro acquired ability of rabbit and cow oocyte to ensure sperm nucleus decondensation during fertilization (MPGF). *Ann. Biol. Anim. Biochim. Biophys.* **15,** 705–714.

Trounson, A. O. and Moore, N. W. (1974a) Fertilization in the ewe following multiple ovulation and uterine insemination. *Aust. J. Biol. Sci.* **27,** 301–304.

Trounson, A. O. and Moore, N. W. (1974b). The survival and

development of sheep eggs following complete or partial removal of the zona pellicuda. *J. Reprod. Fert.* **41,** 97–105.

Trounson, A. O. and Moore, N. W. (1974c) Attempts to produce identical offspring in the sheep by mechanical division of the ovum. *Aust. J. Biol. Sci.* **27,** 505–510.

Trounson, A. O., Willadsen, S. M. and Moor, R. N. (1976) Effect of prostaglandin analogue Cloprostenol and oestrus, ovulation and embryonic viability in sheep. *J. Agric. Sci., Camb.* **86,** 609–611.

Warnes, G. N., Moor, R. N. and Johnson, M. H. (1977) Changes in protein synthesis during maturation of sheep oocytes *in vivo* and *in vitro. J. Reprod. Fert.* **49,** 331–335.

Warwick, B. L. and Berry, R. O. (1949) Inter-generic and intra-specific embryo transfers. *J. Hered.* **40,** 297–303.

Warwick, B. L., Berry, R. O. and Horlacher, W. R. (1934) Results of mating rams to Angora female goats. *Proc. 27th Ann. Meet. Amer. Soc. Anim. Prod.,* 225–227.

Welch, R. A. S. (1969) Transport of sheep ova in rabbits. *Proc. N.Z. Soc. Anim. Prod.* **29,** 87–94.

Whyman, D. and Moore, R. W. (1980) Effects of PMSG and the prostaglandin $F_{2\alpha}$ analogue, Cloprostenol, on superovulation, fertilization and egg transport in the ewe. *J. Reprod. Fert.* **60,** 267–272.

Willadsen, S. M. (1979) Embryo transplantation in sheep. In, *Management and Diseases of Sheep.* pp. 69–85. Comm. Agric. Buc. Slough.

Willadsen, S. M. (1980a) The viability of early cleavage stages containing half the normal number of blastomeres in the sheep. *J. Reprod. Fert.* **59,** 357–362.

Willadsen, S. M. (1980b) Deep freezing of embryos in the large domestic species. *Proc. 9th Int. Congr. Anim. Reprod. A.K. (Madrid),* 255–261.

Willadsen, S. M., Polge, C., Rowson, L. E. A. and Moor, R. M. (1976a) Deep freezing of sheep embryos in liquid nitrogen. *Cryobiol.* **11,** 560 (Abs).

Willadsen, S. M., Polge, C., Rowson, L. E. A. and Moor, R. M. (1976b) Deep freezing of sheep embryos. *J. Reprod. Fert.* **46,** 151–154.

Wilmut, I. and Sales, D. I. (1981) Effect of an asynchronous environment on embryonic development in sheep. *J. Reprod. Fert.* **61,** 179–184.

Woody, C. O. and Ulberg, L. C. (1963) Transfer and viability of one-cell ova in sheep. *J. Reprod. Fert.* **5,** 203–208.

Worthington, C. A. and Kennedy, J. P. (1979) Ovarian response to exogenous hormones in six-week old lambs. *Aust. J. Biol. Sci.* **32,** 91–95.

Wright, R. W. Jr., Anderson, G. B., Cupps, P. T., Drost, M. and Bradford, G. E. (1976) In vitro culture of embryos from adult and prepuberal ewes. *J. Anim. Sci.* **42,** 912–917.

Wright, R. W. Jr., Bondioli, K. R., Grammer, J. C., Kuzan, F. B. and Menino, A. R. Jr., (1980) FSH or FSH+ LH superovulation in ewes following estrus synchronization with medroxyprogesterone acetate pessaries. *J. Anim. Sci.* **51** (Suppl. 1), 339 (Abs).

CHAPTER 20

Breeding Sheep at Younger Ages

20.1 INTRODUCTION

For those involved in formulating proposals for improving the productivity of lowland sheep, breeding the ewe as early as possible would be an obvious consideration. Farmers who are attempting to increase output and to counter rising costs are likely to adopt early breeding practices more readily if they feel the outcome is likely to be successful. The worldwide advantages and disadvantages of breeding sheep as ewe-lambs have been reviewed by Dyrmundsson (1973); the author observes that for this practice to be acceptable to farmers, the ewe-lamb's reproductive performance must be satisfactory without subsequent lifetime performance being adversely affected.

Certainly, in lowland flocks, in countries such as Ireland, under conditions of good feeding and management, there is every reason for arguing that ewes should be selected, managed and bred to lamb first at 1 year of age. The obvious advantages to breeding 7–8-month old ewe-lambs to give birth at about a year, include; reduced maintenance costs before the start of reproduction, a shortened generation interval that results in more rapid genetic gains from selection and increased lifetime production (Hulet, 1977). However, the success rate in breeding ewe-lambs can vary markedly, according to bodyweight and size, according to breed type and age and according to the time of year chosen for breeding. The fact is that most sheep farmers throughout the world breed ewes for the first time at the yearling stage. There is, however, growing interest in sexual development and reproductive performance in ewe-lambs, particularly in relation to systems of intensified sheep production.

Controlled breeding can be applied to ewe lambs at 7–10 months of age to advance their breeding season by several weeks, to synchronize oestrus in those that have already reached puberty and to induce oestrus in lambs that may not have mated at all during their first year of life. There is even the possibility of delaying the induction of oestrus until the sheep is 1 year or more of age and getting the first lambs born in the early autumn when the sheep is some 18 months old.

20.1.1. Puberty and sexual maturity

Although sexual maturity is a term occasionally used as an alternative to puberty, it should be noted that the terms do relate to two different situations in sheep; puberty is the time at which reproduction first becomes possible whereas sexual maturity is not reached until the animal expresses its full reproductive potential. In ewe-lambs such a distinction is important, since ewes do not acquire their full reproductive capacity until the adult stage is reached.

20.2 ENDOCRINOLOGY OF PUBERTY

Puberty is the process whereby the young female sheep becomes capable of spontaneous ovulation and a fertile mating; in sheep, such events occur as a consequence of activation of the gonadotrophin surge mechanism by the positive (stimulatory) feedback action of oest-radiol (Goding et al., 1969; Scaramuzzi et al., 1971). In sheep, competency to respond to oestradiol positive feedback becomes estab-lished within a few weeks of birth (Land et al., 1970; Squires et al., 1972; Foster and Karsh, 1975) and the magnitude of the LH discharge in response to exogenous oestradiol is similar to that of the adult sheep by 27 weeks of age (Chu et al., 1979). The evidence is that many of the endocrine mechanisms are capable of operating long before they are called on to function in the ewe-lamb.

In contrast to the inactivity of the mechanism governing LH surge in the prepubertal lamb, that regulating tonic LH secretion is relatively active throughout the prepubertal period. Although tonic LH production in the lamb is characterized by pulsatile releases of the gonadotrophin from the pituitary (Bindon and Turner, 1974; Foster et al., 1975) this apparently does not apply to FSH (Foster et al., 1975); the indications are that the mechanisms which regulate the tonic secretion of LH and FSH in the growing ewe-lamb differ appreciably (Foster et al., 1975). Evidence suggests that tonic LH levels increase from the early weeks after birth, but reports do not extend beyond 12 weeks of age (Land et al., 1970; Foster et al., 1972; Echternkamp and Laster, 1976; Hanrahan et al., 1977).

Tonic LH secretion occurs in the form of pulsatile releases, the pulse rate being less than one per hour in the developing lamb. Puberty is the time during the ewe lamb's development when hourly LH pulses are first permitted to occur, a situation which appears to be due to a reduction in the negative feedback action of oestradiol produced by the ovaries; what is still not clear, as observed by Quirke (1981), is the nature of the stimulus for the critical decrease in response to oestradiol feedback.

20.2.1 Events at puberty

There is a sustained rise, which occurs in the space of a few days, in the tonic LH baseline at the onset of puberty, which is believed to be due to an increase in rate of pulsatile LH discharges to about one per hour; this results in one or more follicles developing towards the preovulatory stage and in a steady increase in oestradiol production, which eventually activates the LH surge mechanism.

As already noted, it has been suggested by Foster and Ryan (1979) that puberty occurs because of a marked decrease in the response of the hypothalamic–pituitary axis to the negative feedback action of oestradiol on tonic LH secretion. There is evidence showing that removing the ovaries of the young lamb increases the LH pulse rate to once per hour (Foster et al., 1975); other work has shown that artificially producing such a rapid LH pulse rate (by administering LH hourly will result in an LH surge and ovulation (Foster and Ryan, 1979).

Such data are taken to indicate that the young lamb is readily capable of producing the hourly pulses of LH if inhibitory ovarian steroids are removed and to show that the ovaries are capable of producing oestradiol in amounts sufficient to invoke the LH surge, if they are artificially exposed to more frequent LH stimulation. The similarity of puberty in the ewe-lamb and the onset of the breeding season in adult sheep, in which there is evidence that the season starts because of a marked reduction in response to the inhibitory feedback effect of oestradiol on tonic LH (Legan et al., 1977) has suggested to the Michigan workers that hypersensitivity to oestradiol feedback on LH secretion was the final common mechanism at work in both the prepubertal ewe-lamb and the anoestrous ewe.

Karsh and Foster (1975) postulated that the growing lamb becomes less inhibited by oestradiol as it ages, this eventually enabling tonic LH pulses to occur with sufficient frequency to cause follicle development, oestrogen production and the LH surge which leads to the first ovulation and initiates puberty.

20.2.2 First ovulations and corpora lutea

Although to the farmer, puberty is indicated by the ewe lamb exhibiting its first oestrus, in endocrinological terms, this is by no means the first important event occurring at that time. The probability is that two preliminary ovarian cycles actually precede the first heat period; in the immediately preceding cycle, there has been the well-established normal luteal phase after a silent heat (Robinson, 1959) and before that another short cycle (Ryan and Foster, 1978). The initial short-cycle is less than half the length of the normal cycle and is apparently initiated by the first LH surge. This sequence of events is not unique to ewe-lambs at puberty; already mentioned is the fact that short cycles may occur before the commencement of cyclical breeding activity in adult ewes after ram introduction in the ewe anoestrus (Oldham et al., 1979; Oldham and Martin, 1979).

20.3 ENVIRONMENTAL AND OTHER EFFECTS AND PUBERTY

On the basis of a comprehensive review article, covering more than 50 published reports on puberty and early reproductive performance in ewe lambs, Dyrmundsson (1973) concluded that there is no fixed age, bodyweight or time of year at which ewe-lambs experience their first heat period, this being a result of the complex interaction between these factors and the time of birth. Certainly, the reproductive performance of ewe-lambs, in terms of oestrous response, conception rate and litter-size, differs markedly from that of the adult sheep.

20.3.1 Daylight environment

There is plenty of evidence showing that in certain breeds a proportion of ewe-lambs may fail to attain puberty (i.e. show oestrus) before the changing day length environment in winter inhibits sexual activity. Hammond (1944) and Hafez (1952) at Cambridge in the U.K. found that lambs born later in the lambing season (normally births occurring in February to April period) were unlikely to exhibit oestrus in their first autumn. As well as that, lambs with a low rate of growth during the summer months had an increased chance of remaining prepubertal until their second autumn season (Hafez, 1952; Allen and Lamming, 1961).

Fig. 20.1. Care necessary in using intravaginal sponges in the ewe lamb. Provided the ewe-lamb is sufficiently grown, the use of intravaginal sponges, usually with a dose of PMSG at the end of treatment, can be extremely useful in bringing these young females into oestrus. Care must be taken during the insertion and removal of sponges because of the relatively smaller size of the vagina compared with adult ewes — and these are not tasks to be undertaken by inexperienced personnel. Controlled breeding in ewe lambs can be useful in enabling the time of lambing to be precisely known — so that supervision can be given at that time to keep lamb losses with this category of sheep as low as possible.

20.3.2 Conceptions and silent heats

In those ewe-lambs that do come in oestrus and mate, the percentage conceiving can often be markedly below the 92% or so figure expected in adult sheep of the same breed; the barrenness rate in the young animals is commonly within the range 20–40% (Gordon, 1967; Dyrmundsson, 1973; Keane, 1974, 1975; Forest and Bichard, 1974; MLC, 1977; Edey et al., 1978). Female lambs which do attain puberty in their first year of life may show a high incidence of silent heats; a high frequency of multiple cycle intervals during the breeding season of ewe lambs at Cambridge was interpreted by Hafez (1952) as evidence of silent heats.

20.3.3 "Flushing" and the ewe-lamb

Although some evidence did suggest that nutritional "flushing" prior to mating did not have a clear effect on ovulation rate in ewe lambs (Allen and Lamming, 1961; Southam et al., 1971) such an effect has been reported by others (Keane, 1974a; Downing and Lees, 1977). The sheep farmer may, however, be more interested in avoiding twins rather than promoting them in the young ewe (Dyrmundsson, 1981).

20.3.4 Breed effects

Several reports suggest that genetic factors can contribute to the variable reproductive perform- ance of ewe-lambs. Laster et al. (1972) conducted a study involving 19 genetic groups and recorded lambing results varying from 33% for purebred Corriedales to 100% in Finn-crossbreds (percent lambing of those bred); Rambouillet crossbreds and Finn-crosses reproduced significantly better than did purebred lambs from a range of domestic breeds. These American workers found that the performance of Finn-crosses exceeded that of any other sheep examined; differences between genetic groups and high lambing rates in Finn-cross sheep have been recorded in other studies (Donald et al., 1968; Southam et al., 1971; Quirke, 1978, 1979a, b).

20.3.5 Bodyweight effects

As already mentioned, the effect of increasing liveweight of the adult sheep on its reproductive performance is well recorded; in the young ewe- lamb, bodyweight is of even greater significance because the occurrence of puberty is likely to be dependent on the animal attaining a certain critical liveweight in its first autumn. Most reports agree that reproductive performance in the ewe lamb improves with increasing liveweight (Spencer et al., 1942; Williams, 1954; Bowman, 1966; McGuirke et al., 1968; Bichard et al., 1974; Keane, 1974a); much of this improvement ap- pears to have arisen from an increase in the proportion of ewe-lambs that came into oestrus.

In general, first oestrus in ewe-lambs is attained at weights varying from 50 to 70% of adult bodyweight (Hafez, 1952; Dyrmundsson, 1973). However, the liveweight may also depend on the season; in Irish Suffolk-cross lambs, for instance, the threshold of bodyweight at puberty declines from 44 kg in early October to 33 kg in later December (Keane, 1974b). Lightweight ewe- lambs are not a good prospect for breeding because they will attain puberty late in the year or may not attain puberty at all, in which case they are precluded entirely from mating and lambing.

20.3.6 Age of lamb

An increase in the ewe-lamb's age at mating has been found by some to result in a significant increase in conception and lambing rates (Laster et al., 1972; Christenson et al., 1976); Keane (1974a), on the other hand, found that date of birth, within the range January to early April, had no influence on the reproductive performance of ewe lambs which were of similar liveweight at the start of the breeding season.

The season of birth can markedly influence the age at which puberty occurs; work reported by Foster (1980) indicated that in lambs born out of their natural birth season, environmental factors delay puberty by delaying the reduction in negative feedback responsiveness to oestrogen until the developing female enters an appro- priate season for reproduction.

20.3.7 Ram effect

Although well recognized in adult sheep, the ram effect on attainment of puberty in ewe-lambs is very limited. Dyrmundsson and Lees (1972) did report, however, that the sudden introduction of rams to ewe-lambs in the normal period of transition from their prepubertal to pubertal condition resulted in a high degree of synchronization of first matings.

20.3.8 Temperature effect

Little information is to be found in the literature on the direct effect of temperature on sexual development in ewe-lambs. There is evidence that removal of the fleece towards the end of anoestrus may bring forward the start of the sexual season in adult sheep (Lees, 1967); after autumn shearing treatment, however, there was no clear effect on the onset of puberty among ewe-lambs in studies in Wales (Drymundsson and Lees, 1972).

20.4 HORMONAL INDUCTION OF PUBERTY

Although there is a considerable literature now available on the control and induction of oestrus in adult sheep, there are relatively few reports dealing with the use of controlled breeding in the ewe lamb. Dyrmundsson (1973) did review papers published up to that time and concluded that there was a very high degree of variability in the proportion of ewe-lambs which respond successfully to treatment; hormone treatments were generally more effective when applied close to the time of the natural onset of breeding activity.

In the U.S.A., work reported by Foote and Matthews (1969) clearly showed the possibility of inducing puberty by exogenous steroid and gonadotrophin treatment; elsewhere, however, there were those who pointed to the need for the sheep at 1 year to have adequate size to bear normal healthy young and to produce enough milk to nourish them (Hulet, 1977); under most circumstances, a better management practice would be to put this size on the lambs in early life, an approach which would enhance the natural occurrence of oestrus and in many instances eliminate the need for the use of exogenous hormones.

In France, where controlled breeding is now used on some scale in ewe-lambs, the sheep for the intravaginal-FGA-PMSG regimen employed must be older than 7 months and heavier than 60–65% of their adult weight (Thimonier et al., 1968; Thimonier and Cognie, 1977); there is obviously little merit in inducing oestrus and ovulation among sheep that are incapable of rearing lambs after birth because of small size and general unsuitability. The French do employ an FGA-impregnated pessary which is specifically designed for ewe-lambs.

20.4.1 Irish studies

In certain sheep breeds, and this would apply to the Galway in Ireland, because of their genetic constitution, there can be a failure of many well-grown ewe-lambs to exhibit oestrus in their first year (Gordon, 1967; Quirke, 1978, 1979a, b); conception rates at the first mating usually proved to be less than 50%. The use of the progestagen-impregnated intravaginal sponge (FGA or MAP) and PMSG (400–500 i.u.) has been employed to induce oestrus in Galway, Suffolk-cross and other sheep (Keane, 1974a; Quirke, 1978, 1979a, b).

Proper placement of the progestagen sponge within the vagina may occasionally be impeded by the presence of a muscular constriction (Quirke, 1979a, b); forcing either the sponge or speculum past this constriction can cause tissue damage in the vagina which may render the subsequent removal of the device either difficult or impossible (1.7% impossible in Keane, 1974; 0.8% in Quirke, 1979a, b). However, care should be taken to avoid treating such sheep and there is no merit in simply depositing the sponge in the posterior vagina; Ch'ang et al. (1968) did record a loss rate of 26% in New Zealand Romney ewe-lambs which was apparently due to a failure to lodge the device in the anterior vagina in many instances.

With ewe-lambs, it is necessary that PMSG should be routinely used, because of the uncertainty of knowing whether the sheep are prepubertal or cyclic. With intravaginal progestagen and PMSG, 90% or more of ewe-lambs can be expected to mate within 2–3 days of treatment (Keane, 1974a, b; Quirke, 1978); the interval between progestagen withdrawal and oestrus onset is rather longer in ewe-lambs than in adults (Quirke, 1979) and the heat period lasts as long in the young sheep as in the adult ewe. Ovulation without oestrus (3%) and oestrus without ovulation (7%) has been observed in Galways in some work (Quirke, 1979).

As well as using intravaginal sponges, Keane (1974a) also employed subcutaneous progesterone implants (375 mg Sil-Estrus) in conjunction with PMSG; the implant did circumvent the occasional difficulty experienced in sponge insertion. Elsewhere, some workers have included oestrogens as part of the treatment regimen applied in the ewe-lamb; those who have reviewed such work have found no evidence suggesting an improvement over the normal progestagen-PMSG treatment (Quirke, 1981).

20.4.2 Breeding at 1-year of age

Getting the young sheep to accept the ram in its first autumn is not the only opportunity that exists for earlier breeding. The availability of pro-gestagen-PMSG treatments can permit sheep to be bred in spring at a year of age and to lamb for the first time in the late summer or autumn (Gordon, 1958, 1963); this has the advantage of the animal being that much older at the time of its first lambing. Against this is the fact that the spring conception rate can be variable and the autumn lambs would need to be taken off the sheep if they are to come in oestrus and reproduce normally at that time.

20.5 SUBFERTILITY IN EWE LAMBS

As already mentioned, fertility is much more variable and lower for ewe-lambs than for adult sheep; conception rates as low as 16% (Watson and Gamble, 1961) and as high as 76% (Dyrmundsson and Lees, 1972) have been recorded. In Ireland, work by Keane (1974a) with Suffolk-cross ewe-lambs showed conception rates varying from 37 to 58%. Unlike adult sheep, ewe-lambs which do not conceive immediately very often fail to return to service and this contributes to the reduced reproductive per-formance (Gordon, 1967; Hulet et al., 1969; Keane, 1974). The poor fertility, it should be noted, applies to ewe-lambs that mate after progestagen-PMSG treatment as it does to those that breed naturally (Bichard et al., 1974; Forest and Bichard, 1974; Edey et al., 1978; Dyrmundsson, 1981); it is evident that progestagen-PMSG can induce oestrus but will not improve fertility in sheep which in the normal way have a poor genetic potential for becoming pregnant as ewe-lambs.

20.5.1 Causes of infertility

Oestrus without ovulation (anovulatory oestrus), although regarded as rare in adult sheep, has been observed in normal and hormone-treated lambs. Edey et al. (1978)

recorded an incidence of anovulatory oestrus of between 7 and 33% in groups of Merino and Perendale lambs; Quirke (1979) observed a similar phenomenon in 7% of Galway ewe-lambs. Studies by Quirke et al. (1980) suggest that reduced fertility in Galway ewe-lambs is unlikely to be the result of an unfavourable relationship between the timing of ovulation and behavioural oestrus; they found the duration of heat to be 30.0 ± 1.2 h and that ovulation occurred in most lambs around the end of oestrus, as recorded elsewhere for adult sheep (Robinson, 1959; Holst and Braden, 1972).

20.5.2 Fertilization rates

Several authors have attempted to estimate the fertilization rate in ewe-lambs as part of their investigations into the problem of reduced reproductive performance; figures for untreated ewe-lambs have varied from 77 to 90% (Allen and Lamming, 1961; Keane, 1974; Hamra and Bryant, 1979) and for hormone-treated animals from 78 to 93% (Bradford et al., 1971; Quirke and Hanrahan, 1977; Quirke, 1979). Although it is possible that the particular behavioural responses of ewe-lambs to rams can be a factor resulting in fertilization failure (Edey et al., 1978) and in Ireland it has been possible to attribute certain instances of fertilization failure to lack of insemination (Quirke, 1981), the general con-clusion is that fertilization failure is unlikely to be the source of the major difference in conception and pregnancy rates between ewe-lambs and adult sheep.

20.5.3 Embryonic mortality

With fertilization rates high and lambing rates low, it follows that the level of embryonic mortality must contribute substantially to the problem; Quirke (1979a, b) estimated an embryo survival rate of 37% in one study involving 556 ewe-lambs, as against the 75% or so suggested for adults on the basis of the literature (Edey, 1969). The factors involved in this have yet to be precisely defined, but the evidence strongly suggests that the problem lies with the embryos themselves rather than with unfavourable uterine conditions (Quirke and Hanrahan, 1977; Quirke et al., 1978); embryo transfer studies have shown that ewe-lamb and adult ewe uteri are equally capable of supporting normal adult sheep eggs.

20.5.4 Oestrogen production in ewe-lambs

Although those who have examined various characteristics of the oestrous cycle in the ewe-lamb and adult sheep have found them to be very similar (Smith et al., 1977; Quirke et al., 1981), there is some evidence from the Irish work of a different pattern of oestrogen secretion by the preovulatory ovarian follicles (Quirke et al., 1981); this would appear to be in agreement with some earlier data reported by Trounson et al. (1977) in work involving the culture of isolated follicles in vitro. There would seem to be indications that conditions in the developing follicle or in the reproductive tract between ovulation and before the 8–16 cell stage are related to the reduced fertility of ewe-lambs.

20.6 LAMB MORTALITY CONSIDERATIONS

Lamb mortality, especially in the perinatal period, is known to be substantially greater in the offspring of ewe-lambs than in that of older sheep (Gordon, 1967; Donald et al., 1968). Losses may be especially high among the twin-born lambs because of low birthweight and associated lack of vitality (Yalcin and Bichard, 1964; Gordon, 1967; Donald et al., 1968; Southam et al., 1971; Dyrmundsson, 1973, 1976; Bichard et al., 1974). In sheep that are carrying singles, on the other hand, generous feeding of the immature ewes during the late stages of pregnancy may result in the birth of too large offspring causing lambing difficulties (Laster et al., 1972; Lees and Eltan, 1978); it would seem that proper feeding in late pregnancy may be even more critical in the ewe-lamb than in the adult sheep.

There is evidence suggesting that the pattern of nutrient utilization of pregnant ewe-lambs differs from that of adult ewes (Robinson et al., 1971; Christenson et al., 1976; Quirke et al., 1978). Although the maintenance of net bodyweight during the final trimester of pregnancy may be a reliable indicator of nutritional adequacy in adult sheep, there may be the need to ensure that the net maternal weight of the young ewe increased during this period if there is not to be a reduction in lamb birthweight.

20.6.1 Mothering qualities of young sheep

Ewe-lambs which give birth at a year of age acquire their mothering experience earlier and usually with the advantage of having to care for only single lambs; the sheep have the chance to become better mothers sooner and before they have the responsibility of larger litters. Although some ewe-lambs may well exhibit poor mothering abilities after lambing, yearlings previously bred as lambs tend to be more reliable breeders, better mothers and to have fewer lambing troubles (Lewis, 1959; Eltan, 1974; Lees and Eltan, 1978).

20.7 REFERENCES

Allen, D. M. and Lamming, G. E. (1961) Some effects of nutrition on the growth and sexual development of ewe lambs. J. Agric. Sci., Camb. **57**, 87–95.

Bichard, M., Younis, A. A., Forrest, P. A. and Cumberland, P. H. (1974) Analysis of production records from a lowland sheep flock. 4. Factors affecting the incidence of successful pregnancy in young females. Anim. Prod. **19**, 177–191.

Bindon, B. M. and Turner, H. N. (1974) Plasma LH of the prepubertal lamb: A possible early indicator of fecundity. J. Reprod. Fert. **39**, 85–88.

Bowman, J. C. (1966) Meat from sheep. Anim. Breed. Abs. **34**(3), 293–319.

Bradford, G. E., Quirke, J. F. and Hart, R. (1971) Natural and induced ovulation rate of Finnish Landrace and other breeds of sheep. Anim. Prod. **13**, 627–635.

Ch'ang, T. S., McDonald, M. F. and Wong, E. D. (1968) Induction of oestrus and ovulation in Romney ewe hoggets with a progestagen. N.Z. Jl. Agric. Res. **11**, 525–532.

Christenson, P. K., Laster, D. B. and Glimp, H. A. (1976) Influence of dietary energy and protein on reproductive performance of Finn-cross ewe lambs. J. Anim. Sci. **42**, 448–454.

Chu, T. J., Edey, T. N. and Findlay, J. K. (1979) Pituitary response of prepuberal lambs to oestradiol-17β Aust. J. Biol. Sci. **32**, 463–467.

Donald, H. P., Read, J. L. and Russell, W. S. (1968) A comparative trial of crossbred ewes by Finnish Landrace and other sires. Anim. Prod. **10**, 413–421.

Downing, J. and Lees, J. L. (1977) Unpublished data cited by J. L. Lees in paper given to British Council Course No. 729, Edinburgh.

Dyrmundsson, O. R. (1973) Puberty and early reproductive performance in sheep. Anim. Breed. Abs. **41**, 273–280.

Dyrmundsson, O. R. (1976) Breeding from ewe lambs — a common practice in Iceland. Bull. No. 24 Res. Inst. Nedri-As, Hueragerdi, Iceland. 12 pp.

Dyrmundsson, O. R. (1981) Natural factors affecting puberty

and reproductive performance in ewe lambs: A review. *Livestock Prod. Sci.* **8,** 55–65.

Dyrmundsson, O. R. and Lees, J. L. (1972) Attainment of puberty and reproductive performance in Clun Forest ewe lambs. *J. Agric. Sci., Camb.* **78,** 39–45.

Dyrmundsson, O. R. and Lees, J. L. (1972) A note on factors affecting puberty in Clun Forest female lambs. *Anim. Prod.* **15,** 311–314.

Echternkamp, S. E. and Laster, D. E. (1976) Plasma LH concentrations for prepubertal, postpubertal, anoestrous and cyclic ewes of varying fecundity. *J. Anim. Sci.* **42,** 444–447.

Edey, T. N., Kilgour, R. and Bremner, K. (1978) Sexual behaviour and reproductive performance of ewe lambs at and after puberty. *J. Agric. Sci., Camb.* **90,** 83–91.

Eltan, O. (1974) Studies on lambing behaviour. *Ph. D. Thesis, University of Wales.*

Foote, W. C. and Matthews, D. H. (1969) Hormonal induction of precocious puberty and related phenomena in the ewe. *J. Anim. Sci.* **29,** 189 (Abs).

Forrest, P. and Bichard, N. (1974) Analysis of production records from a lowland flock. 2. Flock statistics and reproductive performance. *Anim. Prod.* **19,** 25–32.

Foster, D. L. (1980) Does season of birth alter the age of the pubertal reduction in response to steroid negative feedback in the lamb? *Biol. Reprod.* **22** (Suppl. 1), 89A.

Foster, D. L. and Karsch, F. J. (1975) Development of the mechanism(s) regulating the preovulatory LH surge in female sheep. *Endocrin. Soc. 57th Ann. Meet.*

Foster, D. and Ryan, K. (1979) Mechanisms governing onset of ovarian cyclicity at puberty in the lamb. *Ann. Biol. Anim. Bioch. Biophys.* **19**(4b), 1369–1380.

Foster, D. L., Jackson, G. L., Cook, B. and Nalbandov, A. V. (1972) Regulation of luterinizing hormone (LH) in the fetal and neonatal lamb. IV. Levels of LH releasing activity in the hypothalamus. *Endocrin.* **90,** 684–690.

Foster, D. L., Lemons, J. A., Jaffe, R. B. and Niswender, G. D. (1975) Sequential patterns of circulating luteinizing hormone and follicle-stimulating hormone in female sheep from early post-natal life through the first estrous cycles. *Endocrin.* **97,** 985–993.

Goding, J. R., Catt, K. J., Brown, J. M., Kaltenbach, C. C., Cummings, I. A. and Mole, B. J. (1969). RIA for ovine LH secretion of LH during estrus and following estrogen administration in the sheep. *Endocrin.* **85,** 133–142.

Gordon, I. (1958) Studies in the extra-seasonal production of lambs. *J. Agric. Sci., Camb.* **50,** 152–197.

Gordon, I. (1963) The induction of pregnancy in the anoestrous ewe by hormonal therapy. *J. Agric. Sci., Camb.* **60,** 31–87.

Gordon, I. (1967) Aspects of reproduction and neonatal mortality in ewe lambs and adult sheep. *J. Dept. Agric., Ireland* **64,** 76–127.

Hafez, E. S. E. (1952) Studies on the breeding season and reproduction of the ewe. *J. Agric. Sci., Camb.* **42,** 189–265.

Hammond, J. Jr. (1944) On the breeding season in the sheep. *J. Agric. Sci., Camb.* **34,** 97–105.

Hamra, A. N. and Bryant, M. J. (1979) Reproductive performance during mating and early pregnancy in young female sheep. *Anim. Prod.* **28,** 235–243.

Hanrahan, J. P., Quirke, J. F. and Gosling, J. P. (1977) Genetic and non-genetic effects on plasma LH concentrations in lambs at 4 and 8 weeks of age. *J. Reprod. Fert.* **51,** 343–349.

Holst, P. J. and Braden, A. W. H. (1972) Ovum transport in the ewe. *Aust. J. Biol. Sci.* **25,** 167–173.

Hulet, C. V. (1977) Management of reproduction in sheep. In, *Management of Reproduction in Sheep and Goats.* Symp. Univ. Wisconsin (Madison), pp. 119–133.

Hulet, C. V., Wiggins, E. L. and Ercanbrack, S. K. (1969) Oestrus in range ewe lambs and its relationship to lifetime reproductive performance. *J. Anim. Sci.* **28,** 246–252.

Karsch, F. J. and Foster, D. L. (1975) Sexual differentiation of the mechanism controlling the preovulatory discharge of luteinizing hormone in sheep. *Endocrin.* **97,** 373–379.

Keane, M. G. (1974a) Factors affecting the occurrence of puberty and reproduction in ewe lambs. *Ph.D. Thesis, NUI Dublin.*

Keane, M. G. (1974b) Effect of bodyweight on attainment of puberty and reproductive performance in Suffolk-X Galway ewe lambs. *Ir. J. Agric. Res.* **13,** 263–274.

Land, R. B., Thimonier, J. and Pelletier, J. (1970) Possibilite d'induction d'une decharge de LH par une injection d'estrogen chez l'agnou femelle en fondion de l'age. *C. R. Acad Sci.* Ser. D. **271,** 1549–1551.

Laster, D. B., Glimp, H. A. and Dickerson, G. E. (1972) Factors affecting reproduction in ewe lambs. *J. Anim. Sci.* **35,** 79–83.

Lees, J. L. (1967) Effect of time of shearing on the onset of breeding activity in the ewe. *Nature, Lond.* **214,** 743–744.

Lees, J. L. and Elton, O. (1978) Unpublished data cited by J. L. Lees in a paper given to British Council Course No. 729, Edinburgh, Mar. 1978.

Legan, S. J., Karsch, F. J. and Foster, D. L. (1977) The endocrine control of seasonal reproductive function in the ewe: a marked change in response to negative feedback action of estradiol on LH secretion. *Endocrin.* **101,** 800.

Lewis, K. H. C. (1959) Mating of hoggets. *Proc. N.Z. Soc. Anim. Prod.* **19,** 111.

McGuirk, B. J., Bell, A. K. and Smith, D. M. (1968) The effect of bodyweight at joining on the reproductive performance of young crossbred ewes. *Proc. Aust. Soc. Anim. Prod.* **70,** 220–222.

Meat & Livestock Commission (1977) Data sheets on lowland and upland sheep production. Mimeo, MLC, Bletchley, Bucks, U.K.

Oldham, C. M. and Martin, G. B. (1979) Stimulation of seasonally anovular Merino ewes by rams. II. Premature regression of ram-induced corpora lutea. *Anim. Reprod. Sci.* **1,** 291–295.

Oldham, C. M., Martin, G. B. and Knight, T. W. (1979) Stimulation of seasonally anovular Merino ewes by rams. I. Time from introduction of rams to the preovulatory LH surge and ovulation. *Anim. Reprod. Sci.* **1,** 283–290.

Quirke, J. F. (1977) Studies related to the reproductive performance of adult and immature sheep. *Ph.D. Thesis, NUI, Dublin.*

Quirke, J. F. (1978) Onset of puberty and oestrous activity in Galway, Finnish landrace and Finn-cross ewe lambs during their first breeding season. *Ir. J. Agric. Res.* **17,** 15–23.

Quirke, J. F. (1979a) Control of reproduction in adult ewes and ewe lambs and estimation of reproductive wastage in ewe lambs following treatment with progestagen impregnated sponges and PMSG. *Livest. Prod. Sci.* **6,** 295–305.

Quirke, J. F. (1979b) Oestrus, ovulation, fertilization and early embryo mortality in progestagen-PMSG treated Galway ewe lambs. *Ir. J. Agric. Res.* **18,** 1–11.

Quirke, J. F. (1981) Regulation of puberty and reproduction in female lambs: A Review. *Livestock Prod. Sci.* **8,** 37–53.

Quirke, J. F. and Hanrahan, J. P. (1977) Comparison of the survival in the uteri of adult ewes of cleaved ova from adult ewes and ewe lambs. *J. Reprod. Fert.* **51,** 487–489.

Quirke, J. F., Hanrahan, J. P. and Gosling, J. P. (1978a) Reproduction in ewe lambs. *Anim. Prod. Res. Rpt. An Foras Taluntais*, 155–159.

Quirke, J. F., Sheehan, W. and Lawlor, M. J. (1978b) The growth of pregnant female lambs and their progeny in relation to dietory protein and energy during pregnancy. *Ir. J. Agric. Res.* **17**, 33–42.

Quirke, J. F., Hanrahan, J. P. and Gosling, J. P. (1981) Duration of oestrus, ovulation rate, time of ovulation and plasma LH, total oestrogen and progesterone in Galway adult ewes and ewe lambs. *J. Reprod. Fert.* **61**, 265–272.

Robinson, T. J. (1959) Estrous cycle of the ewe and doe. In, *Reproduction in Domestic Animals* Cole, H. H. and Cupps P. T., Eds., Acad. Press, New York.

Robinson, J. J., Fraser, C., Corse, E. L. and Gill, J. C. (1971) Reproductive performance and protein utilization in pregnancy of sheep conceiving at eight months of age. *Anim. Prod.* **13**, 653–660.

Ryan, K. D. and Foster, D. L. (1978) Necessity for a decrease in negative feedback of ovarian steroids on LH secretion at puberty in the lamb. *Proc. 60th Ann. Meet. Endocr. Soc.*, Abst. No. 507.

Scaramuzzi, R. J., Tillson, S. A., Thorneycroft, H. and Caldwell, B. V. (1971) Action of exogenous progesterone and estrogen on behavioural estrus and LH levels in the ovariectomized ewe. *Endocrin.* **88**, 1184–1189.

Smith, J. F., Frost, H., Fairclough, R. J., Peterson, A. J. and

Tervit, H. R. (1977) Effect of age on peripheral levels of progesterone and oestradiol $17\text{-}\beta$ and duration of oestrus in Romney Marsh ewes. *N.Z. Jl. Agric. Res.* **19**, 277–280.

Southam, E. R., Hulet, C. V. and Botkin, M. P. (1971) Factors influencing reproduction in ewe lambs. *J. Anim. Sci.* **33**, 1282–1287.

Spencer, D. A., Scott, R. G., Phillips, R. W. and Aune, B. (1942) Performance of ewes bred first as lambs compared with ewes bred first as yearlings. *J. Anim. Sci.* **1**, 27–33.

Squires, E. L., Scaramuzzi, R. J., Caldwell, B. V. and Inskeep, E. K. (1972) LH release and ovulation in the prepuberal lamb. *J. Anim. Sci.* **34**, 614–619.

Thimonier, J., Mauleon, P., Cognie, Y. and Ortavant, R. (1968) Induction of oestrus in ewe lambs with the aid of vaginal sponges impregnated with fluorogestone acetate. *Ann. Zootech.* **17**, 275–288.

Trounson, A., Willadsen, S. M. and Moor, R. M. (1977) Reproductive function in prepubertal lambs: ovulation, embryo development and ovarian steroidogenesis. *J. Reprod. Fert.* **49**, 69–75.

Watson, R. H. and Gamble, L. C. (1961) Puberty in the Merino ewe with special reference to the influence of season of birth on its occurrence. *Aust. J. Agric. Res.* **12**, 124–138.

Williams, S. M. (1954) Fertility in Clun Forest sheep. *J. Agric. Sci., Camb.* **45**, 202–228.

Yalcin, B. C. and Michard, M. (1964) Crossbred sheep production. 1. Factors affecting production from the crossbred ewe flock. *Anim. Prod.* **6**, 73–84.

PART III

The Control and Manipulation of Reproduction in Pigs

CHAPTER 21

Introduction to Controlled Breeding in Pigs

21.1 INTRODUCTION

In contrast to cattle and sheep, which have a relatively low reproductive output annually, the pig has the ability to produce a large number of young in a short space of time; certainly, given appropriate management, housing and nutrition, pigs can prove to be among the most profitable of the meat-producing animals.

The usual method of assessing reproductive performance, which can vary markedly from farm to farm, is to examine the number of young produced each year by the sow. This characteristic comprises two important components: litter-size and the number of litters produced each year. The fact that there can be considerable variation from herd to herd suggests that many factors are involved and that some of these are under the control of the farmer; it is clearly important to understand the effect of factors such as breeding, feeding and management on reproductive performance under normal commercial conditions. As well as that, there is the need to examine carefully any new technique which may be capable of increasing the reproductive efficiency of the pig herd.

21.1.1 Larger-sized pig units

The pig industry in Ireland, in common with that in many other countries, is continually moving in the direction of fewer and larger units; Irish figures certainly show a marked decrease in the number of farmers keeping pigs in the recent decade. Elsewhere, units with 500 sows or more, once a rarity, are becoming commonplace; capital investment in buildings and equipment has increased greatly. Fowler (1980), looking at the U.K. scene, points to signs that feedstuff concerns, producer groups and processors are forming business arrangements which will put the British pig industry well on the road towards the vertically integrated structures of the poultry industry; the same author notes that the tendency towards larger units is likely to increase because they do offer considerable scope for highly efficient management. The disposal of effluent, which is one of the major problems with

Fig. 21.1. View of the Pig Unit on the University Farm at Lyons Estate. The objectives of the work conducted on the 500 ha farm are two-fold: to extend knowledge relating to animal and crop science and to provide undergraduate teaching and post-graduate research programmes. The pig unit, with more than 100 breeding sows, provides facilities for various lines of work in pig reproduction. A high quality Large White herd is maintained but a few years ago the Landrace herd was phased out to use the sows as the foundation stock for a hybrid herd (Large White × Landrace) with a criss-crossing breeding policy using Landrace and Large Whites employed subsequently.

pig units, large or small, should be eased by large-scale units, since these are the ones best able to justify the cost of installations for the anaerobic digestion of waste to methane.

As pig units do become larger and more specialized, the needs of production will place increased demands on reproductive performance; at the same time, larger-scale confinement production itself may well raise new problems which have to be solved in order to achieve optimum reproductive performance and certainly makes precise scheduling of events in the pig unit increasingly important.

21.1.2 Animal welfare considerations

Although it is generally recognized that considerable potential exists for increasing the efficiency of pig production, including reproductive efficiency, it is essential to keep a watchful eye on animal welfare considerations (Anon. 1981; Fox, 1981), and not to confine thinking merely to the production aspects alone. In densely populated countries, such as the U.K., pig production units with their odours and effluents are likely to become a frequent target for the attentions of the urban-dwelling environmentalists. Public concern about the conditions which animals reared in intensive units endure has resulted in Codes of Practice and Welfare regulations in some number of countries; this concern must be shared by farmers and those who tend the stock, if the more extravagant demands for regulations governing animal production are to be countered effectively by the livestock industry.

21.2 AREAS OF CONTROLLED BREEDING

Controlled breeding in pigs, as the term is employed in the present discussion, covers a range of possibilities. In the main, these possibilities relate to reproductive performance in the gilt or sow, but it is recognized that many factors can influence the efficiency of the boar in reproduction (Leman and Rodeffer, 1976). It should perhaps be kept in mind that reproductive efficiency in pigs can be influenced, in a way much less apparent in the other farm species, by the association of the sexes, whether this is in matters such as the elicitation of the full immobilization reflex in the oestrous sow or in triggering the onset of puberty in the gilt.

When considering controlled breeding within its several areas, it is as well to note that certain of the control measures could probably be integrated to provide an enhanced effect. Effective oestrus procedures, fixed-time artificial insemination and farrowing control would allow for all-in all-out systems that would improve the efficiency of labour use, reduce the incidence of disease and the risk of stress and enable the farmer to schedule his entire pig operation.

In attempting to control the farrowing process in gilts within the working week and more especially, within the working day, it would be an obvious advantage to have control both of the day of mating as well as that of parturition. If effective controlled farrowing in a herd requires the administration of prostaglandin on day-114 of gestation, then this would be made that much easier if, in the first instance, the actual date of mating is controlled with that in mind. Thus, the full advantage of a technique for precisely controlling time of parturition in gilts may only be obtained when an effective method for controlling oestrus and ovulation is employed.

21.3 PIG FERTILITY AND MEASURES OF EFFICIENCY

In view of the fact that the profitability of the pig enterprise is largely a matter of the number of pigs weaned per sow annually, techniques, whether they are controlled breeding procedures or otherwise, that may improve conception rates, reduce the incidence of embryonic mortality, decrease the farrowing interval and improve the rate of piglet survival are likely to be of considerable commercial interest.

An efficient level of reproduction in present-day breeding units means a sow producing 2–2.4 litters of young annually and rearing 18–24 pigs in that period; still some way short of the known biological limits of the species (Wilson, 1968) yet some way in excess of the level of efficiency attained by a proportion of pig producers. The rewards for achieving higher output per sow are generally clear to see; food constitutes 70–80% of the costs in pig production and the amount of feed consumed by a sow in a year is much the same whether she rears 12 or 24 young per year (English, 1978). For many producers, it may well be that the only way to stay in profit in pigs is by way of larger and more frequent litters and a reduction in piglet mortality; controlled breeding techniques could eventually be of value in achieving worthwhile improvements in these different aspects. It should also be noted that it is the degree of fertility which is of greatest interest in pigs; as in cattle and sheep, total failure to reproduce is rare and a problem of minor practical importance in the sow.

21.3.1 Fertility and temperature

A condition known as summer infertility, characterized by a decline in the pig's reproductive performance during hot weather,

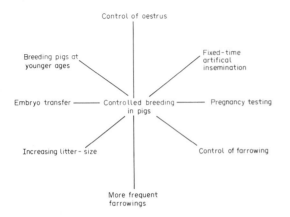

Fig. 21.2. Areas of controlled breeding in pigs.

has been recognized by pig producers and veterinarians in many parts of the world. Aumaitre et al. (1976) in France found that sows farrowing from July to September had a 10-day longer weaning to conception interval than sows farrowing at other times of the year; in the U.S.A. several reports have also shown the farrowing interval may be markedly prolonged for sows farrowing in the June to August period, compared with other months of the year (Hurtgen, 1976; Hurtgen and Leman, 1981). It is also evident that primiparous sows are more prone to the summer infertility than older pigs.

Nearer home, in the U.K., five large pig herds were the subject of studies by Stork (1979) who found that reproductive efficiency was related to temperatures in excess of 20°C; in practical terms, pigs mated in summer in July and August showed an increase in returns to service. On the other hand, in the climate of West Scotland, in which the cool summer months offer little chance for heat stress to occur, evidence of seasonal variation in reproductive efficiency was not found by Pepper and Taylor (1981) in an analysis of 3631 farrowings throughout a 12-month period. In general, it would be true to say that annual sow reproductive performance differs between countries in colder climates and those in the tropics where annual output is estimated to be 15–20% lower (Maner, 1974; Steinbach, 1976); these differences persist even when similar breeds and husbandry methods are employed.

In Australia, annual output of pigs per breeding sow is substantially below that achieved in various of the European countries; Penny et al. (1971) estimated that Australian sows produce about 3.4 pigs less per year than those in the U.K. According to Lindsay (1974), this difference is mainly the result of small litters, which may almost be two piglets below the average litter-size in the U.K. Within Europe itself, the number of pigs slaughtered per sow per year is much higher in northern European countries than those in the south (King, 1970).

21.3.2 Temperature research studies

Experimentally, elevated ambient temperatures have been shown to increase the incidence of anoestrus in gilts (Teague, 1970) and reduce

conception rate and embryo survival in others (Warnick et al., 1965; Thibault et al., 1966; Tompkins et al., 1967; Edwards et al., 1968). Many of these investigators reached the conclusion that the effect of heat stress is on the sow's fertility but there are those who suggest that heat may stress the boar and reduce semen quality and fertility (Thibault et al., 1966; Signoret and Du Mesnil du Buisson, 1968; McNitt and First, 1970; Wetteman et al., 1976). However, there does not appear to be any evidence that semen quality in boars is markedly affected by season of year (Cameron, 1980; Hurtgen et al., 1980).

21.3.3 Sow culling

Authors such as Pattison (1980) have drawn attention to the low breeding-life expectancy of sows in many commercial herds, resulting from a high culling rate (30–50% in the early parities; such high culling levels involve substantial economic loss (Dagorn and Aumaitre, 1979; Kroes and Van Male, 1979; Pattison, 1980). The fact that the average age at culling lies somewhere between the second and fourth litter obviously means that a high proportion of sows are culled before they reach their peak in terms of litter-size; this will be to the detriment of the overall herd performance.

Whether the culling of sows for reproductive problems at levels of 30–50% is always justified is another matter. Dubois et al. (1980) in France examined 550 breeding tracts from sows culled by producers and concluded that 38% of the pigs had been culled for unjustified reasons; it appears that culling errors had often occurred because of faulty oestrus detection, especially in herds where boars were housed independently of sows and where the stockman attempted to detect heats in the absence of a boar.

21.3.4 Reproduction and the lean pig

The point has been made by Bichard (1980) that in making the modern bacon pig so much leaner, the sows of today are probably not so well buffered against fluctuating energy demands as those of yesteryear; for that reason, lean sows may require a higher standard of management if they are to be kept at peak performance throughout their lives.

Fig. 21.3. The lean, low appetite, highly productive young pig may not have the fat reserves to cope with difficult reproductive situations. In concentrating much attention on getting the lean pig, the reserves which the animal has to draw upon may not always be so readily available, and this may have relevance to what may be expected of the animal in reproduction. In the matter of very early weaning of the pig after producing her first litter there may be scope for the use of high-oil feed supplements as a means of rebuilding body fat reserves quickly enough to permit efficient rebreeding of the animal.

21.3.5 Measuring reproductive efficiency

The number of pigs weaned, or sold, per sow annually is the most important measure of sow productivity and has a large effect on overall profitability; production efficiency is also influenced by the age structure of the sow herd and by the patterns of culling. As large, efficiently managed, pig units have developed in different countries, accurate observations and recording systems have provided data on reproductive efficiency. In the U.S.A., one report suggests that reproductive efficiency has remained essentially unchanged during the 1970's (Gerrits et al., 1979); the figures quoted show an average of 7.2 pigs marketed per litter, with each sow farrowing about 1.8 litters per year. A reasonable objective, according to these authors, would be two litters per sow annually and 10 pigs per litter marketed. It should be noted that this is some way below what the pig is capable of producing; a mature sow herd has the potential of reproducing at the rate of 2.6 normal-sized litters per year. Still in the United States, Day (1979) notes that the weaning of 16 pigs annually per breeding pig would represent a considerable improvement in the present levels of reproductive performance of the average herd. According to Cunha (1980), by the year 2000, the goal should be 24 pigs raised per dam per year, with producers being able to wean 90–95% of all the pigs born.

21.3.6 Economics of sow performance

In the U.K., English et al. (1977) analysed figures from the Meat and Livestock Commission for a 3-year period (1974–1976) and showed that units with an annual output of 14 weaners per sow were losing money, whereas those producing 18 and 20 weaners were showing increasing profitability. In Norway, Skjervold (1975) showed that an increase in litter-size not only reduced part of the sow's maintenance cost per piglet but also increased total production without extra capital expenditure; an increase in litter-size by one piglet resulted in a decrease in the amount of feed per slaughtered pig by as much as 5 kg. Also in Norway, a survey by Aagard and Studstrop (1977) produced evidence showing that a relatively small increase in the number of pigs weaned per sow annually increased the profit per sow by more than 50%.

21.4 SOCIAL ENVIRONMENT AND REPRODUCTION

It has been recognized for many years that social environment can exert a marked influence on reproduction in the pig. There also is evidence suggesting that some of the difficulties encountered in modern pig production may be the result of a sub-optimal social environment; it would follow from this that improvements in reproductive efficiency are likely to be achieved by utilizing and increasing the existing knowledge of the role of the social environment on the processes of the animal.

Although there has been a general awareness that the relationship formed between the stockman and his animals may be an important factor determining their productivity (Kiley-Worthington, 1977), there has been a lack of objective data to show the importance of the effect. In cattle, Seabrook (1972) found that the type of personality of the dairyman, which appeared to influence the man–cow relationship, was associated with the milk yield of the herd. In pigs, Hemsworth *et al.* (1981) have provided strong evidence that the reproductive performance of pigs on a farm may be associated with the relationship developed between the stockman and his breeding animals; the suggestion was made that where the relationship between the stockman and his pigs is poor, the sows may show a stress response in the presence of the stockman to the extent that reproductive failure may occur.

21.4.1 Stress and performance

Studies with laboratory species have indicated that the quality of animal handling can influence the physiological stress responses of the animal (Denenberg, 1963; Newton and Levine, 1968) and the literature concerned with the effect of stress on reproductive failure in the sow has been reviewed a few years ago by Wrathall (1975). As noted by Hemsworth *et al.* (1981), research is needed in order to identify the factors that influence the pig–man relationship; a fuller understanding of this relationship is likely to have considerable practical implications.

21.4.2 Performance and welfare

Undoubtedly, improvements in the reproductive efficiency of pigs would result from a greater awareness in the industry of the causes of reproductive failure or of decreased reproductive performance. The fact that it is not only a matter of buildings and feeding levels but also one of the relationship between stockman and the pigs should help in the adoption of recommended, industry-wide management practices relating to the conditions under which the animals are kept. The pig industry will have to face, as mentioned by Bichard (1980), an increasing number of charges from informed and perhaps uninformed opinion from the welfare lobby; the practices that operate in pig units are likely to have to meet the approval of the farm workers themselves and by society at large. However, the fact that a good relationship between the stockman and the breeding animal is an important factor determining reproductive performance, makes it all the more essential that the animal's welfare is given adequate consideration.

Fig. 21.4. Accurate records are essential for efficiency in pig production. In the breeding unit, individual sow records are vital to the breeding programme and as the basis for culling of sows. In the Irish Republic, the number of farms with pigs has halved during recent years whereas the average number of pigs per farm has doubled. Within the present reduced number of pig farms, a small core of highly specialized units dominates. The application of computer science to the various aspects of record keeping in the pig industry is likely to be one of the features of the 1980s.

21.5 PLACE OF ARTIFICIAL INSEMINATION

The current extent of pig AI throughout the world has been estimated at about 7 million pigs bred annually (Reed, 1981); the use made of the technique has, however, varied widely from region to region. In North America, as noted by Pursel (1979) pig AI has been very little used; in contrast, the technique has been employed fairly extensively in certain Eastern and Western European countries and Japan. In Soviet Russia and Eastern Europe (4 million or so bred by AI) artificial insemination under the labour and management conditions of the large collective farms is regarded as economically advantageous and simpler than natural service. The interest in Japan in AI arose because of the fact that farms were small and contained no more than one or two sows and the farmer could not afford a boar. In the Netherlands, the breeding technique was employed extensively after a Foot-and-Mouth out-break and in Belgium after *Brucella sui* as the means of preventing the transmission of disease organisms from farm to farm.

In a review of the European scene, Willems (1978) reported that more than a million pigs were being bred at that time in Western Europe;

expansion has been especially rapid in certain countries, notably Denmark (32% bred by AI) and the Netherlands (26% bred). In terms of the actual proportion of breeding pigs inseminated, the greatest was to be found in Norway (41%) and Finland (33%), but for most countries, including Ireland, the percentage of pigs bred by AI is still very small. The semen delivery service has been employed to the greatest extent in the U.K., where it represents most of the AI used; semen delivery services appeared to be expanding at a more rapid rate than the inseminator service in most of the European countries surveyed by Willems (1978). It might be mentioned, however, that the best results after AI, in terms of conception rates and litter-sizes, were generally to be found in those countries where AI was based on a full-time inseminator service.

21.5.1 Advantages of pig AI

Artificial insemination for pigs is regarded as having a number of possible advantages, both at the national and at the individual herd level. From the national viewpoint, for instance, the technique enables widespread dissemination of top quality genes from genetically superior boars, with obvious advantages in terms of national productivity; as observed in a review by Wrathall (1975), it also offers the better control of certain infectious diseases. Individual pig producers may benefit as a result of AI providing them with the opportunity of introducing new blood lines into their herds with relative safety and at low cost. There is also the fact that AI is now being used increasingly for the production of slaughter generation pigs as well as for replacement breeding stock.

21.5.2 Litter-size and conception rate after AI

In the early days of pig AI, conception rates and to some extent litter sizes, tended to be disappointing but they have gradually improved, so that they now can, with certain provisos, approach those of natural matings. Average farrowing rates reported from pig AI organizations in different countries vary from 60 to 85% (Willems, 1978); this would be against the figure of 90% or less that would be expected with natural service.

Comparisons of litter-size after natural mating and AI show consistent evidence of smaller litters with the insemination technique (Skjervold, 1975; Ral et al., 1977, 1980). There has been a tendency to regard this as due to inadequacies in the detection of oestrus and in the timing of the inseminations. It is more difficult to determine oestrus among gilts than in sows and this might be one reason for the poorer results in gilt litters using AI rather than natural mating (Ral et al., 1978).

21.5.3 Hetereospermic AI and addition of cellular antigens

The observation that insemination with a mixture of semen from two boars (hetereospermy) would increase conception rates in sows by 9% and in gilts by 7% was reported by Pacova and Dupal (1978) in Yugoslavia. In Norway, Skjervold et al. (1979) were able to provide some evidence of an immunological effect on litter-size; an improvement in litter-size was achieved by addition of leucocytes to semen (from the same or different boars) when gilts were bred by AI. Further, more comprehensive findings about this approach were published by Almlid (1981), which showed that litter-size was increased by 12.4% when gilts were inseminated with boar semen containing leucocytes of various origin. The addition of cellular antigens to semen as an approach towards more efficient AI is worth investigating much further and not only in relation to pigs.

21.5.4 AI and oestrus

Establishing when service should take place is important with natural mating; with AI as the breeding method, the situation is even more critical (especially where the "boar effect" is absent or minimal), because heat periods can be missed, or even when detected, for the timing of insemination to be inappropriate. Certainly, the problem of oestrus detection has been one factor limiting the uptake of AI in the average herd; however, several developments over the years have helped to ease the difficulty of performing the inseminations at the correct time.

The use of two inseminations rather than just one insemination during the heat period, applied at an interval of 12–24 h, was found to increase the rate of conception by almost 20% in the U.K. in the early seventies (58% after a single insemination and 76% after double AI: Reed et al., 1971). More recent evidence for Britain, quoted by Smith (1976), indicates an average conception rate to first service of about 75% for pigs inseminated from pig AI centres or dealt with by way of the semen delivery service (using the split-dose technique). The fact that ovulation does not occur at a consistent time after the onset of oestrus probably accounts for the improvement in fertility that occurs when sows are inseminated twice compared to only once in the heat period. A further aid in commercial pig AI has been the use of synthetic boar odour (pheromone), which is now available and can be employed to improve the response of the oestrous sow, especially when there is no boar in the vicinity (Melrose et al., 1971; Willems and Jong, 1972 Reed et al., 1974). In several instances, authors had reported reduced conception rates and smaller litter-sizes in gilts and sows which failed to display the full immobilization or standing reflex at insemination (Wermuch, 1967; Einarsson, 1968), a difficulty which may now be eased by way of the "bottled pheromone".

21.5.5 Semen diluents

As well as the question of oestrus detection, a further factor which has limited the development of pig AI has been the inability to store semen for more than a few days. Of the various diluents currently employed in commercial practice, the most widely used is one based on ethylene diamine tetra-acetate (EDTA) and referred to usually as the Kiev diluent (also Merck or Varohm diluent); the Kiev diluent is popular because it is simple to prepare and boar semen diluted in it can be used for up to 3 days without any appreciable loss in fertility. There would not appear to be published evidence to suggest that semen diluted and stored in any of the current diluents for more than 3 days can be used without some reduction in conception rate and litter-size occurring.

Over the years, the preservation of boar semen has presented several problems which are different from those experienced with bull and ram semen. In early studies, it became evident that boar sperm were particularly susceptible to cooling below 15°C (Polge, 1956). Despite that difficulty, substantial progress was made during the sixties with the preservation of boar semen at ambient temperature in a modified Illinois Variable Temperature (IVT) diluent (Reed, 1969); it was on the basis of such work that commercial pig AI was established, and has continued up to the present time. For much of the work, diluents have been based on glucose solutions with citrate, bicarbonate or milk supplying buffering capacity. Although short-term storage in these diluents, some of which have included egg-yolk, has been generally satisfactory (Watson, 1979), since about 1970, the Kiev diluent has replaced the IVT and others as the predominant diluent in the U.K. and Western European countries.

It would seem true to say that in parts of the world where economic or disease factors do not bring about an acceptance of pig AI as an alternative to natural service, the lack of methods which will consistently preserve the fertilizing capacity of pig sperm during storage and transportation to the farm has been a major deterrent to the uptake of AI by the average commercial pig farmer. It would appear to be highly desirable that research into semen preservation, by the use of metabolic inhibitors and otherwise, should continue in an effort to improve on this aspect of pig AI.

It should be mentioned that a sperm dose of 2–3 x 10^9 is commonly employed in pig AI in European countries; synthetic boar pheromone (Boarmate) has been employed in those countries in which an inseminator service is in widespread use particularly where no boar is present or where only a single insemination is carried out.

21.5.6 Expansion of pig AI services

The future expansion of the AI technique in Europe is likely to depend on the structure of the pig industry in the different countries. The view is that provided AI is no more costly than natural service and is as effective and convenient, there could be a marked expansion in its use for the production of slaughter generation pigs; because of increasing herd size, together with a move towards "closed" herds, health control measures could also influence producers to use artificial rather than natural insemination.

Pig AI in Europe is presently operated mainly by way of an inseminator service, but increases in salaries and travelling costs, together with the use of AI in larger herds, especially if they are "closed" to avoid disease risks, is seen as favouring expansion of the semen delivery service, with boar semen being used on the farm by the producer's own staff. The extent to which this would occur would depend on the transport facilities available and the size of the herds in the countries concerned. In the U.K., the introduction of high-speed trains means that pig producers as far away as Wales and the South West of England can order boar semen in the morning from the pig AI centre not far from London (Reading Centre) and receive it the same day. Clearly, in all of this, one of the factors which could encourage more producers to use AI would be improvements in fertility, so further efforts in this direction are well worthwhile.

21.6 DETECTION OF OESTRUS

The effectiveness of oestrus detection will depend on several factors, the most important of which would be the presence of a boar and the skill and experience of the stockman. As noted by Winfield (1980), the only certain way of detecting heat is to ensure that the gilt or sow has daily contact with an active boar in a setting as free as possible from distractions; it is probably better to take sows to the boar when oestrus is expected rather than the boar to the sow. This means that the boar pen must be situated reasonably close to the females, which in itself, is likely to be a factor in facilitating the full expression of oestrus.

21.6.1 Detection in the absence of the boar

Without the boar, the stockman's skill becomes all-important and he must know the behavioural and other characteristics which are associated with heat in the female pig. A behavioural characteristic which is often used as the basis of oestrus detection is the animal's response to the "riding-test", which takes the form of the standing heat reflex in which the pig stands quite still, arches her back and pricks up her ears; according to Signoret (1972), at most 50–60% of oestrous pigs are likely to be detected in this way, in the absence of the boar. A further aid to the riding test may be to manually simulate the nosing activity of the boar along the flanks of the sow, while applying pressure to the sow's back (Winfield, 1980).

Already mentioned is the question of boar odour. Two of the steroids produced by the boar testis (3a-androstenol and 5α-androstenone) are concentrated in the submaxillary gland of the mature boar and secreted into the saliva, whereupon they act as pheromones to facilitate the induction of the mating stance in the oestrus sow (Melrose et al., 1971); this knowledge led eventually to the availability of the pheromones in aerosol form which can be used as an aid in heat detection where there is no boar.

21.7 FROZEN BOAR SEMEN

Although researchers successfully froze bull sperm more than 30 years ago, the same freezing procedures applied to the boar have resulted in a loss of fertilizing capacity of the sperm. A decade or so ago, Polge et al. (1970) did achieve success by way of surgical insemination in the pig; up until then, attempts to establish pregnancies on a consistent basis with frozen boar semen either met with failure or at best unrepeatable and isolated instances of success, despite the recovery of good motility by sperm after thawing. Shortly afterwards, several other research groups (Crabo and Einarsson, 1971; Graham et al., 1971; Pursel and Johnson, 1971) independently reported fertility when frozen boar semen was employed by cervical insemination. These reports had the one feature in common of rapid freezing by the pellet technique, which enabled concentrations of no more than 3% glycerol to be employed in the diluted semen.

However, the successful results achieved at that time, involved methods unsuitable for commercial pig AI; reviews dealing with these early freezing efforts and their practical application have been presented by several authors (Einarsson, 1973; Paquignon and du Mesnil du Buisson, 1973; Schmidt et al., 1974). After the first successful studies, numerous investigations were conducted to adapt the techniques for practical use and to gain deeper knowledge about factors affecting the fertility of frozen–thawed boar sperm; much of this has also been dealt with in various review articles (Goffaux, 1977; Larsson, 1978; Watson, 1979).

21.7.1 Current techniques

At present, a number of freezing methods have been developed and tested for field use (Pursel and Johnson, 1975; Westendorf et al., 1975; Paquignon and Courot, 1976; Larsson et al., 1977) all of these include concentration of semen by centrifugation, because of the large volume and low sperm concentration of the boar ejaculate. Centrifugation is potentially damaging to sperm, so the force applied and the duration of the effect must be kept low.

The diluents employed before freezing have a low ionic strength which is known to minimize cellular damage (Crabo et al., 1972), glycerol levels are kept low (as compared to those commonly used in bull semen) as a result of studies showing that this cryoprotective agent can have a detrimental effect on boar sperm (Crabo et al., 1971; Bower et al., 1973; Wilmut and Polge, 1974). The freezing methods have all been developed with consideration to the specific sensitivity of the boar sperm cell in terms of composition of diluent, exposure to glycerol and cooling rates. It is also clear that several factors can influence the fertility of the semen after thawing.

At Cambridge, as noted earlier, Polge et al. (1970) employed surgical inseminations in the oviducts to achieve their early success with frozen–thawed semen; subsequent efforts, involving several hundred gilts, showed that rapid freezing of boar semen in media containing sugars, egg-yolk and a low concentration (1%) of glycerol, followed by rapid thawing, could result in acceptable fertility levels after cervical insemination (Polge, 1976). In other studies, in which fertility was achieved after cervical

inseminations (Einarsson and Viring, 1973; Viring et al., 1974) it was shown that sperm thawed in boar seminal plasma remained viable for a longer time in the uterus and in the oviducts than did sperm thawed in protein-free thawing diluents.

Although a number of semen processing/ freezing methods have been reported in the literature, only one of these, the Beltsville method (BFS), appears to be used to any extent commercially in the U.S.A. for the international exchange of blood lines. In France, Paquignon et al. (1980) described a freezing process and single insemination technique which they felt gave an acceptable conception rate and litter-size (58% conceptions; 9.3 piglets, litter-size); the results were inferior by about 10% compared to those from their fresh semen work (67.8% and 10.3 piglets).

21.7.2 Future prospects

It is generally agreed that the frozen semen technique for pigs has still some way to go in becoming a commercially attractive technique. Semen has to be used at a much lower dilution when frozen and this can mean only 4 or 5 sows are bred from a single ejeculate, compared with the 30–35 which can be inseminated if the semen is used fresh. In view of the additional costs arising from freezing and storage, it is perhaps doubtful whether frozen semen would ever be routinely employed in commercial practice in the way that bull semen is used; it could be useful in stockpiling semen from outstanding boars to allow the pig AI centre to provide the farmer with special bloodlines. However, from an international viewpoint, the prospects for continued and increasing exchange of semen would appear to be good (Pursel et al., 1980); should the freezing of pig embryos eventually prove to be a viable proposition, then that particular approach to the international exchange may become the method of choice. In the meantime, the development of internationally recognized standards for the exchange of frozen pig semen is regarded as particularly desirable (Pursel et al., 1980).

On the research side, it would be extremely useful if laboratory criteria used in assessing the viability of frozen–thawed boar sperm were to be more highly correlated with fertilizing capacity (Pursel, 1979); there certainly are boars whose semen will freeze better than that of others and it would be valuable to recognize such males at an early stage. It should always be recognized, however, that the real test of success in frozen pig AI must be in terms of farrowing rates.

It has been suggested that there are other aspects of pig AI which may be of greater importance than the freezing of semen (Reed, 1978); it is possible that extending the shelf life of fresh semen may have a much greater impact on the expansion of AI services than would a breakthrough in frozen semen techniques. As mentioned earlier, one difficulty with pig AI is in carrying out the insemination at the most appropriate time in oestrus; this becomes all the more important when frozen semen is employed (Larsson, 1979); the question of having a boar in the background or employing boar pheromone would apply with even greater emphasis if it is to be insemination with frozen rather than fresh semen.

21.8 ASPECTS OF BOAR FERTILITY

In commercial pig farming, difficulties can arise as a result of mating failure and from varying degrees of infertility in boars; objective methods whereby the reproductive performance of the boar can be predicted are not particularly well developed at this time. Certain of the Australian studies reported in recent years emphasize the important part that stimulation from the female pig has on the sexual behaviour of the boar (Hemsworth et al., 1977, 1981). It is evident from these studies that boars isolated from female pigs can achieve fewer matings and display less courting behaviour than boars housed near sexually receptive sows; the practical lesson in this is that producers and those operating pig AI centres can optimize the sexual behaviour of their breeding boars as well as intensifying the use of genetically superior males by housing the boars near female pigs.

In breeding pigs under normal farm conditions, there is need for accurate heat detection to ensure that all the females are bred on the chosen

date; because the heat period may last for 2 or even 3 days, and ovulation is known to occur about 40 h or so after its onset, it is also important to know the optimum time for breeding (natural or artificial insemination) within the heat period. For achieving high fertilization rates, the general view is that sperm should be in the oviducts about 12 h before ovulation; this has been shown by inseminating sows at known intervals before and after ovulation (Hunter, 1966; Willemse and Boender, 1967; Hunter and Dzuik, 1968).

Fig. 21.5. Use of the boar in natural service. One of the Large White stock boars at the Pig Unit on the University Farm. The boar has an important role in determining the reproductive efficiency of the pig breeding herd. Over and under-use of boars is regarded as critical — the usual practice is 2–3 double services per week from the male. The mating of sows and gilts on 2 consecutive days of oestrus is generally held to improve conception rate by 10% or more and increase litter-size slightly as well. When a different boar is used for the second service within the same heat period, some evidence suggests additional improvements in conception rate and litter-size as compared with double mating with a single boar. In Irish herds, Large White and Landrace are the dominant boar breeds, with equal proportions in commercial herds.

Although a single service at the optimum time during oestrus should be sufficient to ensure a high fertilization rate, in practice, as noted by Wrathall (1975), the observation of oestrus onset is seldom accurate enough to enable service to be delayed with confidence until the second day of oestrus. The best policy is to try and ensure that sows are served once on each day that they stand for the boar. In the majority of pigs, this means two matings, but for those sows that are not detected until the second day, a high conception rate would still be ensured. Herds in which sows routinely receive two services per heat period have conception rates 5–10% higher, and also show a tendency for larger litter-sizes, than those which receive only the one service (Henry, 1972).

As well as that, Willemse and Boender (1967) did show that the litter-sizes of gilts inseminated only once at unfavourable times during the heat period (i.e. very early or late in oestrus) were much below those of gilts bred at optimum times. If breeding occurs too late in the heat period (which can happen because oestrus may extend for up to 24 h beyond ovulation) then this can result in a reduced conception rate, a lower incidence of normal fertilization and significant embryonic loss (Hunter, 1977), these latter effects being evident ultimately in a reduced litter-size.

21.8.1 Use of boar

As observed by Walker (1980), there is evidence to show that both overworking and underworking can cause the boar to sire smaller than optimal litters; the same author looked at data based on more than 2000 farrowings in Northern Ireland and England and concluded that resting the boar between sows does increase litter-size unless the rest period is longer than a month. Others have pointed to the loss of fertility in the boar through over-use; Rasbech (1969) suggested that young boars should not be used more than once daily and Leman and Rodeffer (1976) observed that boars with an unsatisfactory fertility record were often young males used excessively while under 8 months of age.

Hughes and Varley (1980) suggest that a boar should serve two sows per week, on the assumption that this involves double-service on each occasion; the same authors also make the point that it is essential to introduce young boars carefully and gradually to their duties if their fertility and libido is to be maintained at a high level. It is obviously important that unsatisfactory boars should be eliminated from the breeding scene at the earliest opportunity; in this connection, there is an obvious relevance of early pregnancy diagnosis techniques that can be used in the female to show up the boar's competence.

21.9 REFERENCES

Anon (1978) Agriculture Select Committee. *1st Rpt Animal Welfare in Poultry, Pig and Veal Calf Production.* Cmnd. 406 H.M.S.O. Lond.

Aagard, R. and Studstrop, N (1977) *Suineholdsokonomi. Landsudualget for driftsokonomi.* Denmark.

Almlid, T. (1981) Does enhanced antigenicity of semen increase the litter size in pigs. *Z. Tierzuchtg. Zuchtgsbiol.* **98**, 1–10.

Aumaitre, A., Dagorn, J., Legault, C. and LeDenmat, M. (1976) Influence on farm management and breed types on sow's conception — weaning interval and productivity in France. *Livestock Prod. Sci.* **3**, 75–83.

Bichard, M. (1980) The breeding sow — today and tomorrow. *Rept. Agric. Econom. Unit. Univ. Exeter,* **209**, 31–53.

Bower, R. E., Crabo, B. G., Pace, M. M. and Graham, E. F. (1973) Effects of dilution and glycerol on the release of GOT from boar spermatozoa. *J. Anim. Sci.* **36**, 319–324.

Cameron, R. D. A. (1980) The effect of heat stress on reproductive efficiency in breeding pigs. *Vet. Ann.* **20**, 259–64.

Crabo, B. and Einarsson, S. (1971) Fertility of deep frozen boar spermatozoa. *Acta Vet. Scand.* **12**, 125–127.

Crabo, B. G., Brown, K. I. and Graham, E. F. (1972) Effects of some buffers on storage and freezing of boar spermatozoa. *J. Anim. Sci.* **35**, 377–82.

Cunha, T. J. (1980) Action programs to advance swine production efficiency. *J. Anim. Sci.* **51**, 1429–1433.

Dagorn, J. and Aumaitre, A. (1979) Sow culling: reasons and effect on productivity. *Livestock Prod. Sci.* **6**, 167–177.

Day, B. N. (1979) Reproductive problems in swine. In, *Anim Reprod.* BARC Symp No. 3, Hawk, H. Ed., pp. 41–50. Allenheld, Osmun. Montclair.

Denenberg, V. H. (1963) Early experience and emotional development. *Sci. Am.* **208**, 2–7.

Dubois, A. et al. (1980). Sow cullings: results of an enquiry. *Proc. Int. Pig Veterinary Society (Copenhagen),* 45.

Edwards, R. L., Omtvedt, I. T., Tarman, E. J., Stephens, D. F. and Mahoney, G. W. A. (1968). Reproductive performance of gilts following heat stress prior to breeding and early gestation. *J. Anim. Sci.* **27**, 1634–1637.

Einarsson, S. (1968) Fertility and serving ability of Swedish landrace and Swedish Yorkshire boars. *Nord. Vet. Med.* **20**, 616–621.

Einarsson, S. (1973) Deep freezing of boar spermatozoa. *Wld. Rev. Anim. Prod.* **9**(1), 45–51.

Einarsson, S. and Viring, S. (1973) Distribution of frozen spermatozoa in the reproductive tract of gilts at different time intervals after insemination. *J. Reprod. Fert.* **32**, 117–120.

English, P. R. (1978) Husbandry in high producing sow herds. *Moorepark Farming Conf. Rept. An Foras Taluntais,* Dublin, 21–27.

English, P. R., Smith, W. and MacLean, A. (1977) *The Sow*–Improving Her Efficiency. Farming Press, Suffolk.

Fowler, V. R. (1980) The future of the pig as a meat animal. *Proc. Nutr. Soc.* **39**, 151–159.

Fox, M. W. (1981) The question of animal rights. *Vet. Rec.* **109**, 37–39.

Gerrits, R. J., Blosser, T. H., Purchase, H. G., Gerill, C. E. and Warwick, E. J. (1979) Economics of improving reproductive efficiency in farm animals. In, Anim. Reprod. BARC Symp No.3 Hawk, H. Ed., pp. 413–421. Allenheld, Osmun. Montclair.

Goffaux, M. (1977) *Elevage Insemination* No. 159, 23.

Graham, E. F., Rahamannan, A. H. J., Schinehel, M. K. L., Waki-Laorial, N. and Bower, R. E. (1971) Preliminary report on procedure and rationale for freezing boar semen. *A.I. Dig.* **19**, 12–14.

Hemsworth, P. H., Donnelly, J., Findlay, J. K. and Galloway, D. B. (1977) The effects of prostaglandin $F_{2\alpha}$ on sperm output in boars. *Prostaglandins* **13**(5), 933–941.

Hemsworth, P. H., Brand, A. and Willems, P. (1981) The behavioural response of sows to the presence of human beings and its relation to productivity. *Livestock Prod. Sci.* **8**, 67–74.

Henry, D. P. (1972) Mating management in pigs. *Aust. Vet. J.* **46**, 258–262.

Hughes, P. and Varley, M. (1980) *Reproduction in the Pig.* Butterworths, London.

Hunter, R. H. F. (1966) Luteal phase ovulation and fertility in the pig. *J. Anim. Sci.* **25**, 925.

Hunter, R. H. F. (1977) Physiological factors influencing ovulation, fertilization, early embryonic development and establishment of pregnancy in pigs. *Brit. Vet. J.*, **133**, 461–470.

Hunter, R. H. F. and Dziuk, P. J. (1968) Sperm penetration of pig eggs in relation to the timing of ovulation and insemination. *J. Reprod. Fert.* **15**, 199–208.

Hurtgen, J. P. (1976) Seasonal anestrus in a Minnesota swine breeding herd. *Proc. Int. Pig. Vet. Soc., Ames, Iowa, D.22.*

Hurtgen, J. P. and Lemen, A. D. (1981) Effect of parity and season of farrowing on the subsequent farrowing interval of sows. *Vet. Rec.* **108**, 32–34.

Hurtgen, J. P., Lemen, A. D. and Crabo, B. (1980) Seasonal influence of estrous activity in sows and gilts. *J. Am. Vet. Med. Assoc.* **170**, 199–123.

Kiley-Worthington, M. (1977) *Behavioural Problems of Farm Animals.* Oriel Press, Lond.

King, J. W. B. (1970) Organisation and practice of pig improvement in European countries. *Anim. Breed. Abs.* **38**, 523–536.

Kroes, Y. and Van Male, J. P. (1979) Reproductive lifetime of sow in relation to economy of production. *Livestock Prod. Sci.* **6**, 179–183.

Larsson, K. (1978) Current research on the deep freezing of boar semen. *Wld. Rev. Anim. Prod.* **14** (4), 59–64.

Larsson, K., Einarsson, S. and Swensson, T. (1977). The development of a practical method for deep freezing of boar spermatozoa. *Nord. Vet. Med.* **29**, 113–118.

Leman, A. D. and Rodeffer, H. E. (1976) Boar Management. *Vet. Rec.* **98**, 457–459.

Lindsay, D. (1974) *Pig Production.* West Aust. Inst. of Technol. Press, Perth.

McNitt, J. I. and First, N. L. (1970) Effects of 72-hour heat stress semen quality in boars. *Int. J. Biometeor.* **14**, 373–380.

Maner, J. H. (1974) In, *Animal Production in the Tropics.* Loosli, J. K. et al., Eds., pp. 177–199. Heinemann Educat. Books. Ibadan, Nigeria.

Melrose, D. R., Reed, H. C. B. and Patterson, R. L. S. (1971) Androgen steroids associated with boar odour as an aid to the detection of oestrus in pig A.I. *Brit. Vet. J.* **127**, 497–502.

Newton, G. and Levine, S. (1968) *Early Experience and Behaviour. The Physchobiology of Development.* Thomas, C. Springfield.

Pacova, J. and Dupal, J. (1978) The effect of heterospermy on the conception rate and fertility of inseminated sows and gilts. *Zivocisna Vyroba* **23**, (10), 735–741.

Paquignon, M. and Courot, M. (1976). Fertility capacity of frozen boar spermatozoa. *Proc. 8th Int. Congr. Anim. Reprod. A. I. (Kracow),* **4**, 1041–1044.

Paquignon, M., Bussiere, J., Bariteau, F. and Courot, M. (1980) Effectiveness of frozen boar semen under practical conditions of artificial insemination. *Theriogen.* **14**, 217–226.

Paquignon, M. and du Mesnil du Buisson, F. (1973) Fertilite et prolificite de tr vies inseminees avec du sperme congel. *J. Rech. Porcine en France,* 49–57.

Pattison, H. D. (1980) Patterns of sow culling. *Pig News Inf.* **1**, (3), 215–218.

Penny, R. H. C., Edwards, M. J. and Mulley, R. (1971) Reproductive efficiency of pigs in Australia with particular reference to litter size. *Aust. Vet. J.* **47**, 194–198.

Pepper, T. A. and Taylor, D. J. (1981) Farrowing intervals of sows. *Vet. Rec.* **108**, 195.

Polge, C. (1956) Artificial insemination in pigs. *Vet. Rec.* **68**, 62–76.

Polge, C. (1976). The fertilizing capacity of boar spermatozoa following freezing and thawing. *Proc. 8th Int. Congr. Anim. Reprod. A.I. (Cracow),* **4**, 1061–1064.

Polge, C., Salamon, S. and Wilmut, I. (1970) Fertilizing capacity of frozen boar semen following surgical insemination. *Vet. Rec.* **87**, 424–428.

Pursel, V. G. (1979) Advances in preservation of swine spermatozoa. *Anim. Reprod.* BARC Symp. No. 3 Hawk, H. Ed. pp. 145–157. Allenheld. Osmun, Montclair.

Pursel, V. G. and Johnson, L. A. (1971a) Fertility with frozen boar spermatozoa *J. Anim. Sci.* **33**, 265.

Pursel, V. G. and Johnson, L. A. (1971b) Procedure for the preservation of boar spermatozoa by freezing. *U.S. Dept. Agric. ARS.* **44**, 227.

Pursel, V. G. and Johnson, L. A. (1976) Frozen boar spermatozoa: methods of thawing pellets. *J. Anim. Sci.* **42**, (4), 927–931.

Pursel, V. G., McVicar, J. W., George, A. E. and Waters, H. A. (1980) Guideline for international exchange of swine semen and embryos. *Proc. 9th Int. Congr. Anim. Reprod. A.I. (Madrid),* **2**, 301–308.

Ral, G., Andersson, K. and Kihlberg, M. (1977) Litter size in AI and natural mating in the Swedish data litter-recording. *Rep. Agric. Coll. Swed.* A, 281, 19.

Ral, G., Andersson, K. and Kihlberg, M. (1980) Differences in litter size arising between artificially inseminated and naturally mated pigs in everyday production. *Swed. J. Agric. Res.* **8**, 21–24.

Rasbech, N. O. (1969) A review of the causes of reproductive failure in swine. *Br. Vet. J.* **12**, 599–616.

Reed, H. C. B. (1969) Application of controlled ovulation in the A.I. of pigs. *Vet. Rec.* **85**, 271.

Reed, H. C. B. (1981) Artificial insemination In, *Control of Pig Reproduction,* Butterworths, London.

Reed, H. C. B., Barlow, M. and Pratt, J. P. H. (1971) Use of a two-part insemination technique in the pig A.I. semen delivery service. *Anim. Prod.* **13**, 393.

Reed, H. C. B., Melrose, D. R., and Patterson, R. L. S. (1974) Androgen steroids as an aid to the detection of oestrus in pig artificial insemination. *Br. Vet. J.* **130**, 61.

Schmidt, D., Winifried, P., Mudra, K. and Kanze, C. (1974) Untersuchugnen zut Gefrierkonservierung von Ébersperma. 3. Mittelung: Prufung der Beefruchtungsfahigkeit. *Arch. Tier.,* **17**, 335–343.

Seabrook, N. F. (1972) A study to determine the influence of the herdsmans personality on milk yield. *J. Agric. Labour Sci.* **1**, 1–45.

Signoret, J. P. (1972) The mating behaviour of the sow. In, *Pig Production.* Cole, D. J. A. Ed. Butterworths, London.

Signoret, J. P. and du Mesnil du Buisson, F. (1968) Influence of the housing conditions of boars on farrowing rate after A.I. In. *Proc. 6th Intr. Congr. Anim. Reprod. A.I. (Paris)*, 74.

Skjervold, H. (1975) Comparisons of litter size by use of natural and artificial mating in pigs. *Z. Tierzuchtg. Zuchtgsbiol.* **92**, 252–259.

Skjerwold, H., Almlid, T., Onstad, O. and Fossum, K. (1979) Evidence of immunological influence on the number of live embryos in pigs. *Z. Tierzuchtg. Zuchtgsbiol.* **96**, 235–236.

Smith, D. H. (1976) The role of the British MLC in pig improvement. *Wld. Rec. Anim. Prod.* **12**(3), 21–34.

Steinbach, J. (1976) Effect of season and stage of the oestrous cycle on the growth of the oviduct epithelium of the gilt. *Proc. 8th Int. Congr. Anim. Reprod. A.I. (Kracow)* **3**, 220–223.

Stork, M. G. (1979) Seasonal reproductive inefficiency in large pig breeding units in Britain. *Vet. Rec.* **104**, 49–52.

Teague, H. S. (1970) Effect of temperature and humidity on reproduction. *In Symp. Proced. Effect of Disease and stress on reproductive efficiency in swine.* Univ. Nabraska, 21–26.

Thibault, C., Courot, M., Martinet, L., Mauleon, P. de Mesnil du Buisson, F., Ortavant, R., Pelletier, J. and Signoret, J. P. (1966) Regulation of breeding season and estrous cycles by light and external stimuli in some mammals. Environmental Influences on Reproductive Processes. Proc. 7th. Bienn. Symp. Anim. Reprod. 1965. *J. Anim. Sci.* **25**, 119–142.

Tompkins, E. C., Heidenreich, C. J. and Stob, M. (1967) Effect of post-breeding thermal stress on embryo survival in gilts. *J. Anim. Sci.* **26**, 377–380.

Viring, S., Einarsson, S. and Larsson, K. (1974). Proc. 12th Nord. Vet. Congr. (Reykjavik), 149.

Walker, N. (1980) Pigs per litter depend on the boar. *Agric. N. Ire.* **55**, (5), 135–137.

Warnick, A. C., Wallace, H. D., Palmer, A. Z., Sosa, E., Deverse, D. J. and Caldwell, V. E- (1965) Effect of temperature on early embryo survival in gilts *J. Anim. Sci.* **24**, 89–92.

Watson, P. F. (1979) The preservation of semen in mammals. *Oxford Rev. in Biol.* Vol. 1, Finn, C. A. Ed., pp. 283–350. Clarendon Press, Oxford.

Wermuth, C. (1967) Untersuchungen uber die schweinebesamung an der besamungsstation fur rinder und schweine in Schwarzenbeck-Holstein *D.V.M. Dissertation,* Hanover.

Westendorf, P., Richter, L. and Treu, H. (1975) Zur Tiefgefrierung von Ebersperma labor und besamungsergebhisse mit dem Holstnberger Pailletton-Verfahien. *Dtsch. Tierarztl. Wschr.* **82**, 261–267.

Wettemann, R. P., Wells, M. E., Omtvedt, I. T., Pope, C. E. and Turman, E. J. (1976) Influence of elevated ambient temperature on reproductive performance of boars. *J. Anim. Sci.* **42**, 664–669.

Willems, C. M. (1978) Development of artificial insemination in pigs in E.A.A.P. countries. *Livest. Prod. Sci.* **5**, 285–291.

Willems, C. M. and de Jong, J. B. (1972) The use of pheromones in the practice of pig A.I. *Proc. 8th Int. Congr. Anim. Reprod. A.I. (Munich)*, **2**, 1661–1663.

Willemse, A. H. and Boender, J. (1967) The relation between the time of insemination and fertility in gilts. *Tijdschr. Diergeneesk.* **92**, 18–34.

Wilmut, I. and Polge, G. (1974) The fertilizing capacity of boar semen stored in the presence of glycerol at 20.5 and 79°C. *J. Reprod. Fert.* **38**, 105–113.

Winfield, C. G. (1980) Oestrus detection in pigs. In, *Behaviour in relation to Reprod. Management and Welfare of Farm Animals.* Revs. Rural Sci. **4**, 83–86.

Wilson, P. N. (1968) Biological ceilings and economic efficiencies for the production of animal protein, A. D. 2000: *Chem. Ind.* 899.

Wilson, P. N. (1981) Animal welfare on the farm. *Span.* **24**(3), 121–123.

Wrathall, A. E. (1975) *Reproductive Disorders in Pigs.* Com. Agric. Bureaux. Farnham Royal.

CHAPTER 22

The Sow's Oestrous Cycle

22.1 INTRODUCTION

Of the various farm mammals, the pig is the species which has been influenced to the greatest extent by conditions of modern intensive husbandry. As noted by Signoret (1980), permanent housing in controlled environments has resulted in marked changes in the pig's natural social interactions, and this is especially true in talking of reproduction. In contrast to events in the permanently cyclic domestic sow, in the wild pig, sexual activity only occurred during autumn and farrowing at the end of the winter. It has been observed, however, that rutting activity can be very well synchronized in wild herds (Meynhardt, 1979), resulting in a highly synchronized farrowing period; such simultaneous farrowing has an obvious survival value in view of the fact that cross-suckling of the young is often observed. In dealing with the reproductive behavioural patterns and endocrinology of sexual activity in the female pig, it is obviously as well to keep in mind that the domesticated sow faces a situation far removed from that of her wild ancestor, although she has to work with the same basic hypothalamic–pituitary–ovarian mechanisms.

22.2 OESTRUS AND THE OESTROUS CYCLE

The domestic pig does not show any evidence of a breeding season, and in the absence of pregnancy the sow can be expected to exhibit oestrus at intervals of 21 days (range 19–23 days) throughout the year (McKenzie, 1926; Asdell, 1964). Although the expected average interval between heats is normally 21 days, Dziuk (1977) has shown that when a large number of oestrous cycles is recorded in mated gilts, there are two peaks in the frequency of these intervals — one occurs near 21 days and the other at 26 days. Of interest is the fact that similar 26-day intervals have been reported in mated gilts possessing only one to four fertilized eggs (Polge et al., 1966); the indications are that a small number of embryos prolongs the normal 21-day interval but does not initiate a full-term pregnancy. It may be just as well that the stockman should be aware of such occurrences.

As already noted, oestrous cycles are generally thought of as occurring throughout the year without any obvious seasonality (Asdell, 1964; Dziuk, 1977); however, there is evidence of a tendency, at least in some sows, to show cyclical breeding activity rather less consistently during the late summer (Hurtgen, 1976; Hurtgen and Leman, 1980; Stork, 1979). Although the duration of the normal cycle remains relatively constant at 21 days there are minor individual and breed variations; cycle length should not be affected by factors such as feeding and management (Wrathall, 1980).

22.2.1 Oestrus in the pig

The start of the heat period is characterized by gradual changes in the pig's behaviour which may not always be easily recognized (increased restlessness, reduced appetite, mounting other animals, malelike sexual behaviour, lordosis response) and the physiological changes that may also be missed (swelling and colour changes of the vulva, occasionally a cloudy mucus discharge). The duration of sexual receptivity has been reported on by many authors; McKenzie and Miller (1930) gave the average as 40–46 h in the normal sow and a half-century later Anderson (1980) reported a figure of 40–60 h. Other authors simply report that oestrus lasts 2–3 days, but that variation from 1 to 4 days is common (Day, 1968; Wrathall, 1980).

Gilts frequently fail to show oestrus for more than a day, whereas sows usually show sexual receptivity for 2 days or longer (Day, 1968). *Post-*

Fig. 22.1. Oestrus in the sow and gilt — behaviour and other signs. The onset and disappearance of the heat period is gradual in the pig. The real criterion of oestrus is acceptance of the boar and during the period the sow and gilt should also be responsive to a riding test, especially in the presence of the boar. In the riding test, it is a matter of pressing down of the pig's back with both hands and sitting astride the animal. If she stands firm for this, there is every reason to believe she is in oestrus.

partum oestrus has been recorded in some proportion of sows in the period, 2 to 5 days after farrowing (Warnick et al., 1950; Burger, 1952; Baker et al., 1953); in view of the fact that there is no marked development in the ovaries at this time, it is assumed that an extra-ovarian source of oestrogen is responsible for this anovulatory heat. It would appear that this oestrus is the result of circulating oestrogens derived from the foetuses rather than from the ovaries (Fevre, 1970; Ash et al., 1973; Holness and Hunter, 1975).

Ovulation usually occurs about 40 h after the onset of oestrus when the heat period lasts about 2 days; when the duration is longer than 2 days, after about 75% of the heat period has elapsed (Willemse, 1967). In normal cyclic gilts, the interval from release of preovulatory LH to ovulation is about 40 h, the release of the LH being at the onset of oestrus (Niswender et al., 1970); the LH surge induces ovulation, the differentiation of follicular cells and the formation of corpora lutea. The number of eggs released from the ovaries varies, usually within the range 10–24, depending on factors such as age, breed, parity and nutrition (Wrathall, 1971). At the first oestrus occurring at puberty, ovulation rate tends to be low, but there may be a marked increase of up to three ovulations at the second heat, and a further less substantial increase at the third period (Robertson et al., 1951, Warnick et al., 1951).

The duration of ovulation, i.e. time taken to shed all the eggs, is reported to vary from about 1 to 6 h (Betteridge and Raeside, 1962; du Mesnil du Buisson and Signoret, 1970) but frequent stimulation of the sow by the boar during pro-oestrus and the early hours of the heat period may concentrate the ovulation process (Signoret et al., 1972; Hunter, 1977); ovulations have also been observed to occur about 4 h earlier in mated than in unmated animals (Signoret et al., 1972).

22.3 HORMONES OF THE OESTROUS CYCLE

The published literature on the levels of steroid hormones that operate during the oestrous cycle of the pig suggests many similarities with cattle and sheep.

22.3.1 Gonadotrophins

Niswender et al. (1970) were the first to report on an RIA procedure for LH in the pig and to publish evidence on plasma levels; subsequently the results of other RIAs for LH were also reported (Rayford et al., 1970; Wilfinger, 1974; Parvizi et al., 1976); there appears to be good agreement among workers in the plasma levels reported. As noted by Brinkley (1981), the most dramatic feature of the sow's gonadotrophin profile is the preovulatory LH surge, which begins to rise in the early hours of oestrus (reaching a peak of 8 ng ml^{-1} or more) and returns to basal levels (1–2 ng ml^{-1}) some 30 h later; the long duration of the LH surge is in contrast to what occurs in cattle and sheep.

The LH surge at the start of oestrus initiates both maturation of the oocyte and rupture of the follicle wall. In the follicle destined for ovulation, the primary oocyte commences its first meiotic division about 20 h after the LH peak, and proceeds to its reduction division, with formation of the first polar body, about 2 hours prior to ovulation (Spalding et al., 1955; Hunter and Polge, 1966; Hunter, 1977).

Data presented by Brinkley (1981) show an average of 8.5 ng ml^{-1} (range 5–14) fluctuation in the concentration of tonic LH through the luteal phase of the cycle; most of these luteal surges had an average duration of about 12 h and it is evident that plasma progesterone concentrations during the maximum functional state of the corpora lutea do not inhibit the secretion of LH.

22.3.2 Pulsatile release of LH

The presence of LH pulses at certain stages of the pig's oestrous cycle is discussed by Brinkley (1981), who during the mid-luteal phase found these to be of 60–80 min duration and in which LH concentrations could rise to be almost as high as those found in the preovulatory LH surge. In the follicular phase of the cycle, on the other hand, there appeared to be an absence of pulses and this persisted until the onset of the preovulatory surge; during the long period of the preovulatory surge of LH, it would seem that no pulses have been observed. It is known that the release of LH can be brought about by administering Gn-RH (Foxcroft et al., 1975) and that this release is in the form of a pulse of short duration (60–240 min) and

certainly not a prolonged response extending for many hours.

22.3.3 Oestradiol control of LH

It is known that exogenous oestradiol can be used to inhibit LH secretion in the spayed sow (Hoover et al., 1977) and in prepubertal gilts (Foxcroft et al., 1975). There is also the fact that tonic LH concentrations are lowest during the follicular phase (Wilfinger, 1974) and no LH pulses are exhibited at this time of high oestradiol levels (Hoover and Young, 1979); the evidence is strong that follicular oestradiol suppresses the appearance of LH pulses in the late stages of the cycle.

22.3.4 Role of LH pulses

As noted by Brinkley (1981), the role of the LH pulses in the cycle is not clear. Although the gonadotrophin can stimulate the release of progesterone from both the granulosa cells of follicles and the luteal cells of corpora lutea (Watson and Maule Walker, 1978) it is also known that the corpora lutea can persist without the support of pituitary LH (Brinkley et al., 1964); if the sow does not become pregnant, a luteolytic mechanism of uterine origin is responsible for bringing about luteal regression.

22.3.5 Gonadotrophins and follicles

The vesicular follicles in the pig's ovaries do require gonadotrophins for their support; the presence of mid-luteal plasma LH pulses would seem to be associated with the process of atresia and follicular maturation which is found to be operating during the later stages of the cycle. In the follicular phase, those Graafian follicles which are destined to ovulate grow from about 4–5 mm diameter on day-15 to an ovulatory diameter of 9–11 mm.

As with LH, plasma FSH concentrations are known to be low during the follicular phase (Wilfinger, 1974) and it is also evident that oestrogens will suppress FSH concentrations (Hoover et al., 1977). The period of low plasma FSH ocurs during the highest and most prolonged period of oestradiol concentration in the cycle and is followed by the LH surge, the main FSH surge and the onset of oestrus. It is in the follicular phase that follicles mature, granulosa cells in these follicles proliferate rapidly and produce the oestradiol, plasma levels of this steroid increasing to a peak of 60–90 pg ml[-1] on about day-19 of the cycle (Shearer et al., 1971; Henricks et al., 1972; Hunter et al., 1972). It would seem that oestradiol initially suppresses both plasma LH and FSH concentrations, but later induces the preovulatory surge of the two gonadotrophins; Brinkley (1981) speculates that these surges of LH and FSH initiate and sustain major changes (luteal cell function and follicular growth), whereas pulses of LH, and probably FSH, initiate, sustain and regulate physiological changes in the cells prepared by the surges.

22.3.6 Prolactin in the cycle

There is no clear evidence that prolactin is involved in ovarian function in the sow, although Rolland et al. (1976) and Dusza-Krzymowska (1979) have suggested that it may play a role in the regulation of the cycle. Brinkley (1981) found that prolactin surges do occur in the pig's cycle and that there is one during oestrus which coincides in time with the main FSH surge rather than with the preovulatory LH surge; there was other evidence suggesting that prolactin surges occurred during those phases of the oestrous cycle when plasma concentration is known to be highest (during the follicular phase and oestrus).

22.4 PROGESTERONE IN THE CYCLE

After ovulation, there is a rapid proliferation of primarily granulosa and a few thecal cells lining the collapsed follicle wall; these cells, as a result of the preovulatory LH surge, become luteinized to form luteal tissue, a process which involves rapid functional changeover from oestrogen to progesterone production (Henderson, 1979) and morphological differentiation into more typical steroidogenic cells. The process of luteinization proceeds rapidly, so that within 6 to 8 days the corpus luteum has become a mass of luteal cells with an overall diameter of 8–11 mm. By that time, healing of the follicle rupture points by stromal connective tissue has usually occurred, but reorganization of the blood coagulum filled central cavity takes longer; eventually, and certainly if the pig becomes pregnant, the central cavity is obliterated by connective tissue and luteal cell hypertrophy.

22.4.1 Maintenance of corpora lutea

Once initiated by the preovulatory surge of LH, subsequent formation and function of the corpus luteum in the sow is believed to proceed independently of further gonadotrophic hormone influence, for at least the duration of its oestrous cycle activity. If sows are hypophysectomized on the first day of oestrus, the corpora lutea are formed and remain active for about 15 days (Anderson and Melampy, 1967; Anderson et al., 1967). Provided that ovulation takes place, failure of a ruptured follicle to form a corpus luteum would seem to be a remote possibility (Wrathall, 1980). Premature failure of corpora lutea during the oestrous cycle is also unlikely because they are insensitive to known luteolytic factors such as prostaglandin $F_{2\alpha}$ until they are at least 10 days old (Gleeson, 1974; Guthrie and Polge, 1976), which only leaves about 4 days before the onset of normal cyclic regression.

The use of RIA's has shown that plasma progesterone concentrations usually reach a peak in the region of 25–35 ng ml at about days 8–10 of the cycle (Edqvist and Lamm, 1971; Shearer et al., 1971; Henricks et al., 1972); the level is maintained until day-14 or 15 when a steady decline in progesterone level occurs, with the concentration of the steroid getting down to preovulatory levels by day-16.

22.5 PROSTAGLANDINS AND LUTEOLYSIS

About 14 days after its formation, the lifespan of the corpus luteum is decided; the lifespan will be extended in the pregnant animal whereas in the non-pregnant cyclic pig, there is rapid regression of the corpora lutea, maturation of a further crop of Graafian follicles and a new oestrous cycle. Morphological regression of the corpora lutea is paralleled by cessation of luteal function, the concentrations of plasma progesterone falling rapidly within a period of 1 or 2 days.

The mechanisms involved in terminating or (in the case of the pregnant pig) extending the lifespan of the corpora lutea are complex and as yet not fully understood. The regression of the corpora lutea is associated with the presence of the uterus (Puglisi et al., 1978); if the organ is removed this will permit the corpora lutea to persist. On the basis of several lines of evidence, it is believed that prostaglandin $F_{2\alpha}$ of uterine origin passes to the ipsilateral ovary and induces regression of the corpora lutea (Bazer and Thatcher, 1977). The pathway taken by the prostaglandin in getting to the ovary has been the subject of several reports; a counter-current exchange of uterine $PGF_{2\alpha}$ between the anterior uterine vein and the ovarian artery (Krzymowski et al., 1978) or by way of the lymphatic circulation (Kotwica, 1980) has been suggested.

In the sow, a sustained release of $PGF_{2\alpha}$ begins several days prior to luteolysis (Gleeson et al., 1974; Moeljono et al., 1977; Shille et al., 1979); the reason for the early initiation of prostaglandin release in the sow is not apparent, because at the time this is first occurring it is difficult to destroy the corpora lutea with exogeneous $PGF_{2\alpha}$.

22.5.1 Oestrogen and maintenance of corpora lutea

When the pig becomes pregnant, the corpora lutea persist until the end of the gestation period. Oestrogens are luteotrophic, even in non-pregnant sows (Frank et al., 1978) and it seems that they act by inhibiting the release of prostaglandins from the uterine endometrium.

In the pregnant sow, there is evidence that the developing embryos synthesize oestrogens (Moeljono et al., 1977), which probably prevents the movement of $PGF_{2\alpha}$ to the anterior uterine vein (Bazer and Thatcher, 1977; Robertson et al., 1978) and thereby avoids the transport of the agent to the corpora lutea.

22.6 REFERENCES

Anderson, L. L. (1980) Pigs. In, Reprod. in Farm animals (4th edit). Hafez, E. S. E. Ed., pp. 358–386. Lea and Febiger, Philadelphia.

Anderson, L. L. and Melampy, R. M. (1967) Hypophysial and uterine influences on pig luteal function. In, Reprod. in Female Mammal Lamming G. E. and Amoroso E. C. Ed., pp. 285–316. Butterworths, London.

Anderson, L. L., Dyck, G. W., Mori, H., Henricks, D. M. and Melampy, R. M. (1967) Ovarian function in pigs following hypophysial stalk transection or hypophysectomy. Am. J. Physiol. 212, 1188.

Asdell, S. A. (1964) Patterns of Mammalian Reproduction. (2nd Edit.). Cornell Univ. Press. Ithaca, New York.

Ash, R. W., Banks, P., Broad, S. and Heap, R. B. (1973) Plasma oestrogen, progesterone and corticosteroid concentrations in the pregnant parturient and lactating sows. J. Reprod. Fert. 33, 359–360.

Baker, L. N., Woehling, H. L., Casida, L. E. and Grummer, R. H. (1953) Occurrence of oestrus in sows following parturition. J. Anim. Sci. 12, 33–38.

Bazer, F. W. and Thatcher, W. W. (1977) Theory of maternal recognition of pregnancy in swine based on estrogen controlled endocrine versus exocrine secretion of prostaglandin $F_{2\alpha}$ by the uterine endometrium. Prostaglandins, 14(2), 379–401.

Betteridge, K. J. and Raeside, J. I. (1962) Observation of the ovary by peritoneal cannulation in pigs. Res. Vet. Sci. 3, 390–398.

Brinkley, H. J. (1981) Endocrine signaling and female reproduction. Biol. Reprod. 24, 22–43.

Brinkley, H. J., Norton, H. W. and Nalbandov, A. V. (1964) Role of a hypophysical luteotrophic substance in the function of porcine corpora lutea. Endocrin. 74, 9–13.

Burger, J. F. (1952) Sex physiology of pigs. Ondestepoort J. Vet. Res. Suppl. 2, 1–218.

Day, B. N. (1968) Reproduction of wine. In, Reprod. in Farm Animals (2nd edit.). Hafez, E. S. E. Ed., pp. 279–288. Lea and Febiger, Philadelphia.

Du Mesnil du Buisson, F. and Signoret, J. P. (1970) Reproductive physiology and A.I. in pigs. Vet. Rec. 87, 562–568.

Dusza, L. and Krzymowska, H. (1979) Plasma prolactin concentrations during the oestrous cycle of sows. J. Reprod. Fert. 57, 511–514.

Dziuk, P. J. (1977) Reproduction in Pigs. In, Reprod. in Domestic Animal. Cole and Cupps Ed., 3rd Ed. Academ. Press, New York, pp. 456–476.

Edqvist, L. E. and Lamm, A. M. (1971) Progesterone levels in plasma during the oestrous cycle of the sow measured by a rapid competitive protein binding technique. J. Reprod. Fert. 25, 447–449.

Fevre, J. (1970) Conversion en oestrone de quelques steroides C–19 chez la truie gestante. Annls. Biol. Anim. Biochim. Biophys. 10, 25–35.

Foxcroft, G. R., Pomerantz, D. K. and Nalbandov, A. V. (1975) Effects of estradiol-17β on LH-RH/FSH-RH-induced, and spontaneous, LH release in prepubertal female pigs. Endocrinology, 96(3), 551–557.

Frank, M., Brazer, F. W., Thatcher, W. E. and Wilcox, C. J. (1978) A study of prostaglandin $F_{2\alpha}$ as the luteolysin in swine; IV an explanation for the luteotrophic effects of estradiol. Prostaglandins, 15(1), 151–160.

Gleeson, A. R. (1974) Luteal function in the cyclic sow after infusion of prostaglandin $F_{2\alpha}$ through a uterine vein. J. Reprod. Fert. 36, 487–488.

Gleeson, A. R., Thorburn, G. D. and Cox, R. I. (1974) Prostaglandin F. concentrations in the utero-ovarian venous plasma of the sow during the late luteal phase of the oestrous cycle. Prostaglandins, 5(6), 521–529.

Guthrie, H. D. and Polge, C. (1976) Luteal function and oestrus in gilts treated with a synthetic analogue of prostaglandin $F_{2\alpha}$ (ICI 79939) at various times during the oestrous cycle. *J. Reprod. Fert.* **48**, 423–425.

Henderson, K. M. (1979) Gonadotrophic regulation of ovarian activity. *Brit. Med. Bull.* **35**, 161–166.

Henricks, D. M., Guthrie, H. D. and Handlin, D. L. (1972) Plasma oestrogen progesterone and LH levels during the estrus cycle in pigs. *Biol. Reprod.* **6**, 210–218.

Holness, D. H. and Hunter, R. H. F. (1975) Post-partum oestrus in the sow in relation to the concentration of plasma oestrogens. *J. Reprod. Fert.* **45**, 15–20.

Hoover, D. J., Brinkley, H., Rayford, P. L. and Young, E. P. (1977) Effect of injected progesterone, estradiol and estrone on serum LH, FSH and PRL in ovariectomized (ovs) sows. *69th Ann. Meet. Amer. Soc. Anim. Sci.* 171.

Hunter, R. H. F. (1977) Physiological factors influencing ovulation, fertilization, early embryonic development and establishment of pregnancy in pigs. *Brit. Vet. J.* **133**, 461–470.

Hunter, R. H. F., Hall, J. P., Cook, B and Taylor, P. D. (1972) Oestrogens and progesterone in porcine peripheral plasma before and after induced ovulation. *J. Reprod. Fert.* **31**, 499–501.

Hunter, R. H. F. and Polge, C. (1966) Maturation of follicular oocytes in the pig after injection of LCG. *J. Reprod. Fert.* **12**, 525–531.

Hurtgen, J. P. (1976) Seasonal anestrus in a Minnesota swine herd. *Proc. 4th Int. Pig Vet. Soc.*, D. 22.

Hurtgen, J. P. and Lemen, A. D. (1980) Seasonal influence on the fertility of sows and gilts. *J. Am. Vet. Med. Assoc.* **177**, 631–635.

Krzymowski, T., Kotwica, J., Okrasa, S., Doboszynska, T. and Ziecik, A. (1978) Luteal function in sows after unilateral infusion of $PGF_{2\alpha}$ into the anterior uterine vein on different days of the oestrous cycle. *J. Reprod. Fert.* **54**, 21–47.

McKenzie, F. F. (1926) The normal estrous cycle in the sow. *Mo. Agric. Exp. Sta. Res. Bull.* No. 86.

McKenzie, F. F. and Miller, J. C. (1930) Length of the period of heat in gilts and sows and the length of the interval between heat periods. *M. Agr. Exp. Sta. Res. Bull.* 285.

Meynhardt, H. (1979) Schwarzwild Report, Leipsig.

Moeljono, M. P. E., Thatcher, W. W., Bazer, F. W., Frank, M., Owens, L. J. and Wilcox, C. J. (1977) A study of prostaglandin $F_{2\alpha}$ as the luteolysin in swine. II Characterization and comparison of prostaglandin F. estrogens and progestin concentrations in utero-ovarian vein plasma of non-pregnant gilts. *Prostaglandins*, **14**(3), 543–555.

Niswender, G. D., Reichert, L. E. and Zimmerman, D. R. (1970) RIA of serum levels of LH throughout the estrous cycle in pigs. *Endrocrin.* **37**, 576–580.

Puglisi, T. A., Rampacek, G. B. and Kraeling, R. R. (1978) Corpus luteum function following subtotal hysterectomy in the prepuberal gilt. *J. Anim. Sci.* **46**, 707–710.

Robertson, G. L., Grummar, R. H., Casida, L. E. and Chapman, A. B. (1951) Age at puberty and related phenomena in outbred Chesta White and Poland China gilts. *J. Anim. Sci.* **10**, 647–656.

Robertson, H. A., King, G. J. and Dyck, G. W. (1978) The appearance of oestrone sulphate in the peripheral plasma of the pig early in pregnancy. *J. Reprod. Fert.* **52**, 337–338.

Rolland, R., Gunsalus, G. L. and Hammond, J. M. (1976) Demonstration of specific binding of prolactin by porcine corpora lutea. *Endocrin.* **98**, 1083–1091.

Shearer, I. J., Haynes, N. B. and Crighton, D. B. (1971) Peripheral steroid hormone levels and nitrogen retention in the gilt from prepuberty to parturition. *J. Reprod. Fert.* **27**, 491–492.

Shearer, I. J., Purvis, K., Jenkin, G. and Haynes, N. B. (1972) Peripheral plasma progesterone and oestradiol-17_β levels before and after puberty in gilts. *J. Reprod. Fert.* **30**, 347.

Signoret, J. P. (1980) Endocrine basis of reproductive behaviour in female domestic mammals. In, *Behaviour in Relation to Reprod. Management Welfare of Farm Animals. Revs. Rural Sci.* **4**, 3–9.

Signoret, J. P., de Mesnil du Buisson, F. and Mauleon, P. (1972) Effect of mating on the onset and duration of ovulation in the sow. *J. Reprod. Fert.* **31**, 327–330.

Stork, M. G. (1979) Seasonal reproductive inefficiency in large pig breeding units. *Vet. Rec.* **104**, 49–52.

Warnick, A. C., Casida, L. E. and Grummer, R. H. (1950) The occurrence of oestrus and ovulation in post-partum sows. *J. Anim. Sci.* **9**, 66–72

Warnick, A. C., Wiggins, E. L., Casida, L. E., Grummer, R. H. and Chapman, A. B. (1951) Variations in puberty phenomena in inbred gilts. *J. Anim. Sci.* **10**, 479–493.

Watson, J. and Maule Walker, F. M. (1978) Progesterone secretion by the corpus luteum of the early pregnant pig during superfusion in vitro with $PGF_{2\alpha}$ LH and oestradiol. *J. Reprod. Fert.* **52**, 209–212.

Wilfinger, W. S. (1974) Plasma concentrations of LH, FSH and prolactin in ovariectomized hysterectomized and intace swine. Dissertation. Univ. Maryland, U.S.A.

Willemse, A. H. (1967) The relation between the moment of ovulation and the duration of oestrus in gilts. *Tijdschr. Drergenecsk.* **92**, 1144–1148.

Wrathall, A. E. (1971) *Ovulation Rate and Influence on Prenatal Survival and Litter-size in Pigs.* Commonwealth Agric. Bur. Farnham Royal.

Wrathall, A. E. (1980) Ovarian disorders in the sow. *Vet. Bull.* **50**, 253–272.

CHAPTER 23

Artificial Control of Oestrus and Ovulation

23.1 INTRODUCTION

The development of effective hormonal procedures for oestrus control would enable the pig producer to plan all aspects of his breeding programme on a time basis, with all matings or inseminations in a particular group of pigs being concentrated into a few days. It is at the cyclic gilt that controlled breeding techniques have been aimed rather than at the sow, which can be controlled to some extent by management procedures. Unfortunately, although a very effective oestrus control procedure was developed and made commercially available in the U.K. and in other countries during the 1960s, the pituitary inhibitor employed, methallibure, was subsequently withdrawn from the market by the British manufacturing company. For all that, it appears to be still in use in Eastern countries, so it is perhaps relevant to include it in the present discussion.

23.2 OESTRUS CONTROL BY MANAGEMENT

In contrast to what can be done with the farm ruminants, a considerable measure of oestrus control is possible in pigs by management. In sows, the post-weaning oestrus can be expected to occur 4–5 days after weaning, although this may not always be the predictable event that some authors might suggest. Among post-pubertal gilts, on the other hand, oestrus occurs at random throughout a 3-week period and management alone is not more likely to be effective in achieving its synchronization that it is in cattle and sheep.

Sows weaned after lactations of 4–8 weeks duration can be expected to return in oestrus 3–7 days later; absence of oestrus for more than 10 days is often regarded as a reproductive disorder (Rasbech, 1969; Meredith, 1979). There is plenty of evidence to show that factors such as breed, age, parity, season and nutrition may all influence the duration of the interval between weaning and oestrus (Brooks and Cole, 1972; Brooks et al., 1975; Hughes and Varley, 1980; Benjaminsen and Karlberg, 1981); there is general agreement that the interval progressively increases as the duration of lactation is shortened from about 6 weeks down to within a week of farrowing (Cole et al., 1975). Absence of heat after weaning indicates ovarian activity, although silent heats may also be a possibility (Love, 1979; Stork, 1979).

One aspect which has relevance to oestrus control by management is the withholding of feed and/or water during the day after weaning. Brooks and Cole (1972) found no improvement in the reproductive performance by withholding

Fig. 23.1. Weaning and the return of oestrus in the sow. The age at which the piglets are weaned will depend on the general level of feeding, housing, disease control and management. There is no need to look for anything other than abrupt weaning of the sow and it is not necessary to withdraw either water or food from the pig at this time. Some workers suggest that housing weaned sows in small groups of four to eight will encourage oestrus more than putting them straight from the farrowing pen into cubicles or stalls.

feed for 24 h after weaning; according to Hughes and Varley (1980), it is now established that there is also no benefit in withholding water from the sow in the period just after weaning.

23.2.1 Oestrus control in lactating sows

Although it is generally accepted that the sow does not show heat during lactation, there do appear to be certain circumstances under which it is possible to overcome the inhibitory effect on ovarian activity. A system of management involving the grouping of sows, together with their litters, in the presence of a boar and feeding them *ad lib.* has proved successful in getting lactating sows in oestrus about 5 weeks after parturition (Rowlinson *et al.*, 1975; Rowlinson and Bryant, 1975). This would seem to be a clear example of how the pig's reproductive processes can be profoundly affected by short-term environmental factors. Although it has been

suggested that oestrus can be stimulated to occur in lactating sows by the temporary removal of the piglets from the mother for a few hours each day, this has not always been shown experimentally; in one study, the separation of sows and litters for 12 h each day, starting between 5 and 31 days after parturition, failed to induce oestrus (Burger, 1952).

23.3 WEANING TO OESTRUS INTERVAL

Some attempt has been made to apply fixed-time AI in breeding the sow after gonadotrophin treatment in conjunction with weaning the animal. Ohio workers and investigators elsewhere have reported on such gonadotrophin treatments (PMSG at weaning; hCG after a further 2–4 days) which were held to be reasonably satisfactory in controlling ovulation in pigs weaned after 3–6 weeks of lactation; artificial insemination was applied, without heat detection, 1 day after the hCG administration and promising results were obtained (Longenecker and Day, 1968; Christenson and Teague, 1975; Soma and Spear, 1975).

23.4 EARLY PROGESTAGEN WORK

The occurrence of oestrus and ovulation in the pig, as in cattle and sheep, may be controlled either by employing compounds which interrupt or agents that prolong the normal oestrous cycle. These hormonal preparations may act either by suppressing the release of the pituitary gonadotrophins and delaying oestrus or by inducing premature regression of the corpora lutea; after employing such agents, follicular development and oestrous symptoms can be expected to occur some 4–8 days after the treatment (Webel, 1978). Progesterone or synthetic progestagens have been the compounds most commonly employed to inhibit ovarian activity. Daily doses of progesterone given by injection have been used to suppress oestrus and, when the dosage level has been adequate, this has resulted in acceptable fertility upon withdrawal (Ulberg et al., 1951; Baker et al., 1954; Gerrits et al., 1963).

Several of the synthetic progestagens, when administered in oral doses or by injection have been shown to be capable of inhibiting oestrus and ovarian activity; however, there have been difficulties resulting from inadequate suppression of oestrus, reduced fertility on treatment withdrawal and the formation of cystic follicles (Webel, 1978). Medroxy-progesterone acetate (MAP) is one progestagen which was employed and reported on by several investigators (Baker et al., 1954; Dziuk 1960, 1964; Nellor, 1960; Nellor et al., 1961; Dziuk and Baker, 1962; First et al., 1963; Dziuk and Polge, 1965); provided a sufficiently high dose level was used, MAP inhibited oestrus without producing cystic follicles, but heat was not always well synchronized and litter-size could be decreased. The use of other synthetic progestagens, including CAP (Ray and Seerley, 1960; Wagner and Seerley, 1961; Veenhuizen et al., 1965) and norethandrolone (Martinat-Botte,

1975) have given results similar to those achieved with MAP.

Studies showed the pig to be very sensitive to the dose of progestagen employed; cystic follicles have resulted from levels of progestagen that were either too high or too low. From the work that was done in the fifties and sixties, it came to be generally accepted that progesterone and the progestagens described (e.g. MAP, CAP) were not suitable agents for use in oestrus control because of the decreased fertility evident at the synchronized heat, an increased incidence of cystic follicles and the lack of precise synchronization.

23.5 THE METHALLIBURE ERA

Of the various farm mammals, it was with the pig that the first very precise control of ovulation was achieved, using a non-steroidal pituitary inhibitor, methallibure (ICI-33828; dithiocarbamoyl-hydrazine derivative). Apparently, a chance observation led to the discovery that the agent would inhibit the release of pituitary gonadotrophins in rats and experiments soon afterwards showed methallibure to be highly effective in suppressing the occurrence of oestrus and ovulation in cyclic pigs. When methallibure was administered orally in appropriate daily doses (100 mg) for an 18–20-day treatment period, follicular growth and maturation was very effectively suppressed, although the lifespan of the corpora lutea was not affected; after the end of treatment, follicular development was resumed, leading to oestrus in most animals 5–7 days after withdrawal of the agent (Polge, 1964).

Fertility was not affected when methallibure was used (Polge, 1965, 1966; Gerrits and Johnson, 1965; Stratman and First, 1965; Groves, 1967; Polge et al., 1968) and unlike the experiences with the progestational compounds, cystic follicles were not observed. ALthough the precise mode of action of methallibure is still not fully understood, it appears that it acts on the hypothalamus to induce an effective suppression of gonadotrophin release without having any direct effect on the pig's reproductive tract. It was unfortunate, for those using the agent in commercial farming in several countries, that an adverse side-effect led to the compound's withdrawal from the market by the manufacturers; work in Canada was the first to show that methallibure could result in malformations in the foetuses of sows consuming the agent in early pregnancy (King, 1969). The agent continues to be used in Eastern European countries, where it is administered under strictly regulated conditions (Jochle and Lamond, 1980).

23.6 MORE RECENT PROGESTAGEN WORK

Although progestational compounds were tried and generally found wanting because of undesirable effects on fertility in the pre-methallibure era, there has been a revival of interest in the progestagen approach with the withdrawal of methallibure and the failure of prostaglandins to provide an acceptable alternative to oestrus control. As pig production systems become increasingly cost and labour conscious, the need to arrange reproductive events into a predetermined schedule becomes more and more important. Over the last 6 years, a new synthetic progestagen (allyl-trenbolone; Regumate) has been employed in gilts (Davis et al., 1976, 1979; Knight et al., 1976; Webel, 1976, 1978; O'Reilly et al., 1979; Boland and Gordon, 1981); results from the various studies conducted indicate that allyltrenbolone, when fed at the level of 12.5–15 mg/gilt daily for 18 consecutive days, effectively controls the occurrence of oestrus.

In some studies, it has been found that fertilization rate is not adversely affected by

treatment (O'Reilly et al., 1979) but the incidence of follicles in other trials has been sufficiently high to warrant some concern (Davis et al., 1979). In the light of other lines of evidence (Webel, 1976, 1978), the cystic follicle problem may have arisen from an insufficient dose of progestagen due to unknown environmental or social factors or to individual animal differences in the threshold dose necessary to prevent cystic follicles. The onset of oestrus after withdrawal of the progestagen has been reported as 4–10 days, with most heats occurring between days 5 and 7 (Davis et al., 1979; O'Reilly et al., 1979); the heat period itself appears to be of normal duration. In studies at Cambridge, doses of 12–15 mg Regumate have been employed over an 18-day period in 250 gilts (Polge, 1981); most gilts were in oestrus between 5 and 7 days after treatment and produced litters of normal size. Unlike treatment with methallibure, the use of Regumate in pigs does not depress appetite.

23.7 USE OF PROSTAGLANDINS

The synchronization of oestrus, using two spaced doses of prostaglandin $F_{2\alpha}$ as carried out in cattle, or even in sheep, is just not possible in pigs. This is because of the long refractory period of the sow's corpus luteum which does not respond to prostaglandin $F_{2\alpha}$ or its analogues until day-12 or so of the oestrous cycle (Diehl and Day, 1974; Hallford et al., 1975; Guthrie and Polge, 1976; Lindoff et al., 1976; Elze et al., 1979). There has been some suggestion that the saturation of regulatory units on cells of the newly formed corpus luteum by the preovulatory LH peak protects them from luteolysis (Henderson and McNatty, 1975); however, it has been found difficult to reconcile the longer refractory period of the pig with its less dramatic preovulatory LH peak when comparisons are made with similar data for cattle and sheep (Anderson, 1974).

It has also been suggested that it may be the luteotrophic effect of oestrogen which supports the young corpus luteum. It does appear that higher doses of prostaglandin are required during the refractory period or that a longer duration of luteolytic effect is needed; Jackson

Table 23.1. *Synchronization of oestrus following the use of allyl trenbolone.* From Boland and Gordon (1981).

Dose level (mg)		Nil	15	20
No. gilts treated		20	17	18
No. in oestrus within 10 days of progestagen withdrawal		12	16	18
Total no. in oestrus		20	17	18
Interval (days)	Mean	8.4	5.5	5.5
for all gilts	± S.E	1.1	1.2	1.0

and Hutchinson (1980) employed higher than normal doses of prostaglandin analogue (Cloprostenol) in gilts at mid-cycle in slow release formulations with or without an anti-oestrogen, but treatments proved to be ineffective in the induction of luteal regression.

23.7.1 Prostaglandin after oestrogens

The administration of oestrogen in the pig with active corpora lutea can have a luteotrophic rather than a luteolytic effect and if administered towards the end of the luteal phase (days 10 to 14), may result in persistence of the corpora lutea (Kidder et al., 1955; Gardner et al., 1963; Dziuk, 1964; Garbers and First, 1969, Chakraborty et al., 1972; Guthrie, 1975; Schilling and Cerne, 1975); such corpora lutea which are maintained beyond their normal life-span will regress synchronously after prostaglandin treatment (Guthrie, 1975; Guthrie and Polge, 1976).

Quite apart from any thought of oestrus control, it is as well to keep the possible effect of oestrogenic agents on the pig's cycle in mind in dealing with breeding animals. According to Hughes and Varley (1980) there have been many reports from Eastern Europe suggesting that the administration of high levels of oestrogens may suppress oestrus in the sow for several months. It is also noted by Wrathall (1980) that if oestrogenic preparations are inadvertently given to sows with active corpora lutea, prolonged anoestrus may occur. It is also believed that feedstuffs containing the oestrogenic mycotoxin zearalenone could have similar effects (Etienne and Jemmali, 1979); when diagnosed, sows with persistent corpora lutea arising from such causes can be treated effectively with $PGF_{2\alpha}$ (Guthrie, 1975).

23.7.2 Accessory corpora lutea

An approach to regulating the oestrous cycle, possible in pigs, but not in the other farm animals, lies in the induction of accessory corpora lutea in cyclic gilts and then allowing these bodies to regress normally. The administration of PMSG followed by hCG will induce ovulation and the formation of accessory corpora at any stage of the oestrous cycle; these accessory bodies then regress after a normal lifespan with oestrus occurring 18–24 days after the hCG injection (Neill and Day, 1964; Day et al., 1965; Caldwell et al., 1969; Cleary and Lawson, 1978). Although this approach gives some measure of control, it is far from precise because of the variability in the duration of luteal function and the early regression of accessory corpora lutea induced during the first 6 days of the cycle. A refinement of this procedure is to employ prostaglandin when the accessory corpora lutea reach 12 days of age and become susceptible to the action of that agent (Cleary and Lawson, 1978).

23.7.3 Pregnancy and the luteal phase

In mentioning ways of employing prostaglandins in pigs that possess susceptible corpora lutea, there is even the possibility of prolonging the luteal phase by initiating pregnancy and then inducing regression of these corpora lutea in the early weeks of gestation. Such a devious means of assembling a group of gilts with susceptible corpora lutea would not appeal to practical pig producers but may be of some interest on the research station when it is necessary to have a group synchronized.

23.8 FIXED-TIME AI POSSIBILITIES

It was in pigs, using methallibure in conjunction with PMSG and hCG that fixed-time AI was first shown to be a highly effective means of getting farm animals pregnant without reference to oestrus (Polge et al., 1968); after receiving 100 mg methallibure daily for 20 days, gilts were given PMSG 24 h after that treatment and 4 days later injected with hCG. The Cambridge work showed a 90% conception rate and normal litter-sizes in gilts inseminated 24 h after the injection of hCG without reference to oestrus. These studies constituted the first real breakthrough in oestrus/ovulation control in farm animals; so far as pig AI was concerned, it appeared that the methallibure–PMSG–hCG regimen had removed a major obstacle to the exploitation of the technique on the farm. It came as a serious blow for methallibure to be subsequently removed from the market by the manufacturers because administration to pregnant pigs was occasionally found to result in developmental anomalies in the piglets. The withdrawal of the agent has left a vacuum which has not been filled up to the present time, in so far as the commercial application of fixed-time pig AI is concerned. Of course, it is right and proper that any substance employed in animals that are subsequently consumed by humans should be subjected to the most stringent rules and tests; the fact remains, however, that methallibure is employed in Eastern European countries and information about its use continues to be available in the literature from that quarter.

Elsewhere, in the absence of methallibure, the synthetic progestagen allyl-trenbolone has been employed; Webel (1978) did investigate the possibility of using it in fixed-time pig AI, employing PMSG and hCG after withdrawing the progestagen (AI carried out 24–30 h after hCG). As an alternative to using exogenous gonadotrophins, Webel (1978) also studied the use of a Gn-RH analogue; encouraging results were obtained after pigs were given the analogue about 5 days after the last feeding of Regumate and then inseminated 30 h later. However, in this whole area of fixed-time AI, the amount of data is far too small to permit any firm conclusions; clearly the need exists for much further investigation in order to perfect suitable treatment combinations.

23.9 REFERENCES

Anderson, L. L. (1974) Pigs. In, *Reproduction in Farm Animals*. 3rd ed) E. S. E. Hafez, Ed., Lea & Febiger, Philadelphia.

Baker, L. N., Ulberg, L. C., Grummer, R. H. and Casida, L. E. (1954) Inhibition of heat by progesterone and its effect on subsequent fertility in gilts. *J. Anim. Sci.* **13**, 648–657.

Benjaminsen and Karlberg (1981) Post weaning oestrus and luteal function in primiparous and pluriparous sows. *Res. in Vet. Sci.*, **30**, 318–322.

Boland, M. P. and Gordon, I. (1981) Attempts to control the oestrous cycle in the gilt. *Irish Vet. J.* **35**, 82–85.

Brooks, P. H. and Cole, D. J. A. (1972) Studies in sow reproduction. I. The effect of nutrition between weaning and remating on the reproductive performance of primiparous sows. *Anim. Prod.* **15**, 259–264.

Brooks, P. H., Cole, D. J. A. and Rowlinson, P. (1975) Studies in sow reproduction. 3. The effect of nutrition between weaning and remating on the reproductive performance of multiparous sows. *Anim. Prod.* **20**, 407–412.

Burger, J. F. (1952) Sex physiology of pigs. *Onderstepoort J. Vet. Res.* Suppl. No. 2.

Caldwell, B. V., Moor, R. M., Wilmut, I., Polge, C. and Rowson, L. E. A. (1969) The relationship between day of formation and functional life span of induced corpora lutea in the pig. *J. Reprod. Fert.* **18**, 107–113.

Chakraborty, P. K., England, D. C. and Stormshak, F. (1972) Effect of 17-β estradiol on pituitary gonadotrophins and luteal function in gilts. *J. Anim. Sci.* **34**, 427–429.

Christenson, R. K. and Teague, H. S. (1975) Synchronization of ovulation and artificial insemination of sows after lactation. *J. Anim. Sci.* **41**, 560–563.

Cleary, G. V. and Lawson, R .A. S. (1978) Synchronization of oestrus in gilts using a prostaglandin analogue (Estrumate ICI). *Proc. Aust. Soc. Anim. Prod.* **12**, 254.

Cole, D. J. A., Varley, M. A. and Hughes, P. E. (1975) Studies in sow reproduction. 2. The effect of lactation length on subsequent reproductive performance of the sow. *Anim. Prod.* **20**, 401–406.

Day, B. N., Neill, J. D., Oxenreider, S. L., Waite, A. M. and Lasley, J. F. (1965) Use of gonadotropins to synchronize estrous cycles in swine. *J. Anim. Sci.* **24**, 1075–1079.

Davis, D. L., Killian, D. E. and Day, B. N. (1976) Control of estrus in gilts with compound A-35957. *J. Anim. Sci.* **42**, 1358 (Abs).

Davis, D. L., Knight, J. W., Killian, D. B. and Day, B. N. (1979) Control of estrus in gilts with a progestagen. *J. Anim. Sci.* **49**, 1505–1509.

Diehl, J. R. and Day, B. N. (1974) Effect of prostaglandin F$_{2\alpha}$ on luteal function in swine. *J. Anim. Sci.* **39**, 392–396.

Dziuk, P. J. (1960) Influence of orally administered progestin on estrus and ovulation in swine. *J. Anim. Sci.* **19**, 1319–1320.

Dziuk, P. J. (1964) Response of sheep and swine to treatments for control of ovulation. *Proc. Conf. on Estrus Cycle Control in Domestic Animals*, U.S.D.A. Misc. Publ. 1005, 50–57.

Dziuk, P. J. and Baker, R. D. (1962) Induction and control of ovulation in swine. *J. Anim. Sci.* **21**, 697–699.

Dziuk, P. J. and Polge, C. (1965) Fertility in gilts following induced ovulation. *Vet. Rec.* **77**, 236–239.

Efienne, M. and Jemmali, M. (1979) Consequences de l'ingestion de mais fusarie par la truie reproductrice C. R. Hebd. Seanc. *Acad. Sci. Paris* **288D**, 779–782.

Elze, K., Schnurrbusch, U., Hagner, H. J. and Erices, J. (1979) Use of F$_{2\alpha}$ prostaglandin to induce oestrus in gilts. *Arch. exp. Vet. med. Leipzig* **33**, 151–160.

First, N. L., Stratman, F. W., Rigor, E. M. and Casida, L. E. (1963) Factors affecting ovulation and follicular cyst formation in sows and gilts fed 6-methyl-17-acetoxyprogesterone. *J. Anim. Sci.* **22**, 66–71.

Garbers, D. L. and First, N. L. (1969 Effect of various dose levels of ICI 33828 on gilt ovarian function. *J. Anim. Sci.* **28**, 227–229.

Gardner, M. L., First, N. L. and Casida, L. E. (1963) Effect of exogenous oestrogens on corpus luteum maintenance in gilts. *J. Anim. Sci.* **22**, 132–134.

Gerrits, R. J. and Johnson, L. A. (1965) Synchronization of estrus in gilts fed two levels of ICI 33828 and the effect of fertility, embryo survival and litter size. *J. Anim. Sci.* **24**, 917–918.

Gerrits, R. J., Fahning, M. L., Meade, R. J. and Graham, E. F. (1963) Effect of synchronization of estrus on fertility in gilts. *J. Anim. Sci.* **21**, 1022.

Groves, T. W. (1967) Methallibure in the synchronization of oestrus in gilts. *Vet. Rec.* **80**, 470–475.

Guthrie, H. D. (1975) Estrous synchronization and fertility in gilts treated with estradiol-benzoate and prostaglandin F$_{2\alpha}$. *Theriogen.* **4**, 69–75.

Guthrie, H. D. and Polge, C. (1976) Luteal function and oestrus in gilts treated with a synthetic analogue of prostaglandin $F_{2\alpha}$ (ICI 79939) at various times during the oestrous cycle. *J. Reprod. Fert.* **48**, 423–425.

Hallford, D. M., Wetteman, R. P., Turman, E. J. and Omtvedt, I. T. (1975) Luteal function in gilts after prostaglandin $F_{2\alpha}$. *J. Anim. Sci.* **41**, 1706–1710.

Hughes, P. and Varley, M. (1980) *Reproduction in the Pig.* Butterworths, London.

Jackson, P. S. and Hutchinson, F. G. (1980) Slow release formulations of prostaglandin and luteolysis in the pig. *Vet. Rec.* **106**, 33–34.

Jochle, W. and Lamond, D. R. (1980) *Control of Reproductive Functions in Domestic Animals.* Gustav Fischer Verlag, Jena, 248 pp.

Kidder, H. E., Casida, L. E. and Grummer, R. H. (1955) Some effects of oestrogen injections on the estrual cycle of gilts. *J. Anim. Sci.* **14**, 470–474.

King, G. J. (1969) Deformities in piglets following administration of methallibure during specific stages of gestation. *J. Reprod. Fert.* **20**, 551–553.

Knight, J. W., Davis, D. L. and Day, B. N. (1976) Estrus synchronization in gilts with a progestogen. *J. Anim. Sci.* **42**, 1358–1359 (Abs).

Lindloff, G., Holtz, W., Eslaesser, F., Kriekenbaum, K. and Smidt, D. (1976) The effect of prostaglandin $F_{2\alpha}$ on corpus luteum function in the Gottingen miniature pig. *Biol. Reprod.* **15**, 303–310.

Longenecker, D. E. and Day, B. N. (1968) Fertility level of sows superovulated at post-weaning oestrus. *J. Anim. Sci.* **27**, 709–711.

Love, R. J. (1979) Reproductive performance of first parity sows. *Aust. Adv. Vet Sci. Cooper MG* (ed) 42.

Martinat-Botte, F. (1975) Estrus control in gilts with norethandrolone injections and an analogue of prostaglandins (ICI 80996). *Ann. Biol. Anim. Biochim. Biophys.* **15**, 383–384.

Meredith, M. J. (1979) The treatment of anoestrus in the pig: A review. *Vet. Rec.* **104**, 25–27.

Neill, J. D. and Day, B. N. (1964) Relationship of developmental stage to regression of the corpus luteum in swine. *Endocrin.* **74**, 355–360.

Nellor, J. E. (1960) Control of estrus and ovulation in gilts by orally effective progestational compounds. *J. Anim. Sci.* **19**, 412–420. (ABA 28, 2116).

Nellor, J. E., Ahrenhold, J. E., First, N. L. and Hoefer, J. A. (1961) Control of estrus and ovulation in gilts by orally effective progestational compounds. *J. Anim. Sci.* **20**, 22–30.

O'Reilly, P. H., McCormack, R., O'Mahony, K. and Murphy, C. (1979) Estrus synchronization and fertility in gilts using a synthetic progestagen (allyl. trenbolone) and inseminated with fresh stored or frozen semen. *Theriogen.* **12**, 131–137.

Polge, C. (1964) Synchronization of oestrus in pigs by oral administration of ICI compound, 33,828. *Proc. 5th Int. Congr. Anim. Reprod. A.I. (Trento),* 388.

Polge, C. (1965) Effective synchronization of oestrus in pigs after treatment with ICI compound 33,828. *Vet. Rec.* **77**, 232–236.

Polge, C. (1966) Recent advances in controlled breeding of pigs. *Outlook Agric.* **5**, 44–48.

Polge, C. (1981) Embryo transplantation and preservation. In, *Control of Pig Reproduction,* Butterworths, London.

Polge, C., Day, B. N. and Groves, T. W. (1968) Synchronization of ovulation and artificial insemination in pigs. *Vet. Rec.* **83**, 136–142.

Rasbech, N. O. (1969) A review of the causes of reproductive failure in swine. *Brit. Vet. J.* **12**, 599–616.

Ray, D. E. and Seerley, R. W. (1960) Oestrus and ovarian morphology in gilts following treatment with orally effective steroids. *Nature, Lond.* **211**, 1102–1103.

Rowlinson, P. and Bryant, M. J. (1975) Effect of the interval between farrowing and grouping on the incidence and timing of oestrus in sows during lactation. *Proc. Br. Soc. Anim. Prod.* **4**, 103–104.

Rowlinson, P., Boughton, H. G. and Bryant, M. J. (1975) Mating of sows during lactation: Observations from a commercial unit. *Anim. Prod.* **21**, 233–241.

Schilling, E. and Cerne, F. (1975) Nacht teilige wirkung von oestradiol bei dessen Verwendungzur hormonalen Trachtigkeitsf estellung beim Schwein. *Berl. Munch. tierarztl. Wschr.* **88**, 385–386.

Soma, J. A. and Speer, V. C. (1975) Effects of pregnant mare serum and chlorotetracycline on the reproductive efficiency of sows. *J. Anim. Sci.* **41**, 100–105.

Stork, M. G. (1979) Seasonal reproductive inefficiency in large pig breeding units in Britain. *Vet. Rec.* **104**, 49–52.

Stratman, F. W. and First, N. L. (1965) Estrus inhibition gilts fed a dithiocarbamoylhydrazine (ICI 33,828). *J. Anim. Sci.* **24**, 930.

Ulberg, L. C., Grummer, R. H. and Casida, L. E. (1951) The effects of progesterone upon ovarian function in gilts. *J. Anim. Sci.* **10**, 665–671.

Veenhuizen, E. L., Wagner, J. F., Waite, W. P. and Tonkinson, L. (1965) Estrous control in gilts treated sequentially with DES and CAP. *J. Anim. Sci.* **24**, 931.

Wagner, J. F. and Seerley, R. W. (1961) Synchronization of estrus in gilts with an orally active progestin. *J. Anim. Sci.* **20**, 980–981.

Webel, J. K. (1976) Estrous control in swine with a progestogen. *J. Anim. Sci.* **42**, 1358 (Abs).

Webel, S. K. (1978) Ovulation control in the pig. In, *Control of Ovulation,* Crighton, Foxcroft, Haynes and Lamming, Ed. pp. 421–434. Butterworths, London.

Wrathall, A. E. (1980) Ovarian disorders in the sow. *Vet. Bull.* **50**, 253–272.

CHAPTER 24

Pregnancy Testing in Pigs

24.1 INTRODUCTION

Even in the most effective of breeding herds, about 10% of services may turn out to be unsuccessful; the early and accurate detection of non-pregnant sows would be really useful to the pig producer. Traditionally, sows and gilts that do not return to oestrus 18–26 days after service are presumed to be pregnant; detection of heat is carried out at that time by the stockman with or without the use of a boar and perhaps again at 6 weeks after breeding. As already mentioned, the tendency is increasingly for pig breeding herds to become larger, there has been a growth in the use of artificial insemination and labour costs have increased; all these factors are likely to increase the demand for a more refined system of diagnosing pregnancy.

Routine testing is likely to be most applicable in large herds, in pig units in which there is a high barren cull rate, on farms with high in-pig gilt sales and under conditions in which AI is practised. Whatever the reason, the diagnostic technique needs to have a high degree of accuracy in distinguishing between pregnant and non-pregnant pigs and should be capable of being applied as early as possible in pregnancy. Unfortunately, at present, the only method available to the pig producer which permits the diagnosis to be made in time to allow rebreeding

at 3 weeks is the traditional one of detecting oestrus.

Methods that have been employed to diagnose pregnancy in the sow include, the measurement of urinary oestrogens (Grunsell and Robertson, 1953; Velle, 1960; Sanada et al., 1975), the induction of oestrus by oestrogen injection (Nishikawa et al., 1955), the examination of vaginal or cervical mucus (Betteridge and Raeside, 1962; Horvath, 1961; Matsukawa, 1967), radiography (Rapic, 1961; Wintzer, 1964; Walker, 1972). Among the more practical methods for use in the commercial pig unit are techniques such as vaginal biopsy, rectal examination, the ultrasonic detection of early foetal life and hormone assay of plasma hormones.

24.2 ENDOCRINOLOGY OF EARLY PREGNANCY

During pregnancy, which has a duration averaging about 114–116 days (usual range 110–120 days) in the sow, cyclic ovarian activity and ovulation is normally suppressed; for this reason, as in cattle and sheep, it is possible to determine the number of eggs shed by examining the ovaries at any stage of pregnancy (Longenecker et al., 1968). The appearance of the ovary in pregnancy is similar to that of mid-cycle;

there may be minor follicular growth and atresia taking place, particularly during the first half of gestation (Dufour and Fahmy, 1974) and, on rare occasions, oestrus itself may apparently be observed in the pregnant sow, as has been reported in cattle and sheep.

Plasma hormone levels in pregnancy have been reported on by many authors using RIA and other techniques (Guthrie et al., 1972; Edqvist et al., 1974; Robertson and King, 1974; Ash and Heap, 1975; Baldwin and Stabenfeldt, 1975; Parvizi et al., 1976; Robertson et al., 1978). Progesterone concentration declines quite rapidly from its mid-cycle value to about 10–15 ng ml^{-1} at 3–4 weeks (Shearer et al., 1972); the level then remains fairly constant for the remainder of gestation until a drop occurs shortly before the time of farrowing.

Although small amounts of progesterone may be derived from the placenta in late pregnancy (Godke, 1975), most is produced by the corpora lutea; the number of foetuses that survive in the uterus does not appear to affect the level of progesterone, the plasma concentration remaining within the normal range and corpora lutea functional even after all foetuses are dead (Torres and First, 1975). The minimum level of plasma progesterone for the maintenance of pregnancy is about 6 ng ml^{-1} (Ellicott and Dziuk, 1973): at lower concentrations the pregnancy is lost and higher levels do not apparently increase embryo survival rate. It would seem, as noted by Dziuk (1977), that the level of progesterone required for the maintenance of pregnancy is an all-or-none phenomenon with little quantitative effect from various levels.

24.2.1 Maintenance of pregnancy

The maintenance of pregnancy in the sow appears to be totally dependent on the presence of functional corpora lutea; removal of the ovaries, or any factor which results in luteal failure and cessation of progesterone production, will terminate pregnancy within 24–48 hours (Elliott and Dziuk, 1973; First and Staigmiller, 1973; Diehl and Day, 1974). The removal of the pituitary results in abortion in the pig (Kraeling and Davis, 1974), indicating that, in contrast to the corpus luteum of the oestrous

cycle, that of pregnancy is probably dependent on a continuous secretion of a pituitary luteotrophin. It would seem that the luteotrophic agent is almost certainly LH, because not only does treatment with anti-LH serum cause luteal regression and termination of pregnancy (Spies et al., 1967), but several LH-like preparations, including LH and hCG, are capable of maintaining the corpora lutea in the hysterecto-mized/hypophysectomized sow (Anderson and Melampy, 1967).

Although it is known that at least four corpora lutea are required to maintain pregnancy in the sow (Martin et al., 1977) and that there is a relationship between the plasma progesterone level and the number of corpora lutea, no clear correlation has yet been shown between progesterone concentration and the number of embryos in the litter (Wetteman et al., 1974; Meyer et al., 1975). However, there is the possibility that progesterone production by the corpora lutea may vary (Loy et al., 1958; Staigmiller, 1974) and on occasions be insufficient to provide for optimum embryo survival.

24.2.2 Daylight and season

One factor which may influence luteal function and progesterone production in pregnant pigs is daylight. Seasonal or daylight effects have been suggested by Russian workers (Klotchkov et al., 1971) who observed that the corpora lutea of sows exposed to additional light (up to 17 h per day) in winter months were heavier and appeared to be more active than those of sows which received no extra light; litter-size in early pregnancy and at term was also improved by providing additional light in winter. It has also been reported that litter size in sows kept in darkness were smaller than those provided with a natural daylight pattern (Steger et al., 1971). Seasonal effects on reproductive performance in pigs have been reported by several authors and certain of these could be associated with the duration and intensity of light (Hurtgen, 1976; Hurtgen and Leman, 1978; Stork, 1979; Tomes and Nielsen, 1979; Benjaminsen and Karlberg, 1981); the suggestion has been made that studies are necessary to determine whether patterns of secretion of LH, progesterone and other hormones do vary with the season (Wrathall, 1980). However, as mentioned earlier, in the wild pig, the evidence seems to be that reproductive activity is at its maximum in the winter months (Stork, 1979) when the length of day is at its lowest. There is certainly the possibility that there may be a relic of an annual photoperiodic rhythm in the domestic pig and that this may be a factor explaining certain of the seasonal variations in LH production which have been reported in prepubertal pigs (Foxcroft et al., 1979) although not as yet in pregnant sows.

Basal levels of plasma LH during pregnancy are reported to be about 1–2 ng ml^{-1} (Guthrie et al., 1972; Parvizi et al., 1976) which is almost twice the basal level found during the oestrous cycle (excluding the preovulatory LH surge): minor peaks of LH are evident at intervals of a few hours during pregnancy and are followed closely by increased plasma progesterone concentrations, which indicates a dependency of progesterone upon LH.

24.2.3 Embryonic hormones

The situation in early pregnancy is not alone a question of the hormones produced by the pregnant sow herself. Considerable evidence now exists to show that hormones are also secreted by the pig embryo; such early endocrine activities have been reported by workers in Britain (Perry et al., 1973, 1976; Heap et al., 1975; Heap and Perry, 1977; Gadsby et al., 1980) and elsewhere (Robertson and King, 1974; Robertson et al., 1978). Knowledge of such hormonal events in the pregnant sow is likely to be valuable in combating certain forms of embryonic mortality resulting from hormonal deficiencies/imbalances in early pregnancy as well as in arriving at new forms of early pregnancy diagnosis specifically based on the detection of a hormonal signal emanating from the pig embryo.

24.3 VAGINAL BIOPSY TECHNIQUE

The vagina of the pig is lined by an epithelium which undergoes regular cyclic changes related to the oestrous cycle and pregnancy. During dioestrus, the typical vaginal epithelium is three to five cells thick; just before the heat period, rapid cell proliferation occurs and at oestrus the epithelium continues to increase in thickness and the depth may vary from five to 20 cells. This wide variation is shown by the pronounced epithelial ridging which is typical at this time. During the period just after heat, a clear reduction continues until a depth of three to five cells, typical of dioestrus, is reached.

In the pregnant sow, examined 4–6 days after breeding, metoestrus sloughing of excess epithelial cells occurs as in the non-pregnant animal. Until the 17th or 18th day, the epithelium is reduced slowly and reaches a depth of three to four cells without mitosis; at the 20th to 22nd day, the vaginal epithelium of a pregnant sow has a depth of between two to four cells, occasionally 5, which is in marked contrast to the ridged epithelium of oestrus. Beyond the 22nd day of pregnancy, the sectioned epithelium has a depth of two to three cells with a regularity appearing in the rows of nuclei (Morton and Rankin, 1969).

The diagnostic accuracy of the method from 30–90 days of pregnancy has been reported by several authors as above 90% in the detection of pregnancy (O'Reilly, 1967; Done and Heard, 1968; Morton and Rankin, 1969; Mather et al., 1970; Walker, 1972; Diehl and Day, 1973; Williamson and Hennessy, 1975). The obvious disadvantage of the biopsy method lies in the fact that a diagnosis cannot be made immediately because of the need for laboratory histological examination. From a survey of the literature, Kawata and Fukui (1977) concluded that the biopsy technique was one of the most reliable and earliest methods for diagnosing pregnancy in pigs. Walker (1972), writing of experiences in the U.K., states that the method is capable of an overall accuracy of 95% either at about 21 days, assuming the person examining the slides is aware of the service date, or a little later without this knowledge; in England, the method has been available to breeders through commercial laboratories for some number of years. As with several other methods of pregnancy diagnosis, however, the method would not be accurate in detecting non-pregnant sows showing delayed return to oestrus, as shown in the report of Williamson and Hennessy (1975).

24.4 RECTAL PALPATION

The use of rectal examination to diagnose pregnancy in the sow has been described by several workers (Huchzermeyer and Plonait, 1960; Keel-Diffey, 1963; Bollwahn, 1972; Meredith, 1976; Cameron, 1977). Early descriptions of the technique were generally based on the thickness and type of pulse in the middle uterine artery. Cameron (1977) showed that further information leading to an earlier and more accurate diagnosis was possible by also making a careful examination of the size, tone and position of the cervix and uterus; in most non-pregnant sows, the cervix, uterus and bifurcation of the uterus could be easily palpated and the ovaries could also be felt in many instances.

In the U.K., a report by Meredith (1976) showed that the presence of a spontaneous fremitus pulse in the middle uterine artery felt by rectal examination could be taken as evidence of pregnancy from 35 days after breeding to full-term; by applying digital pressure to the uterine artery, where it crossed the external iliac, fremitus was produced at an earlier stage of pregnancy. Results of this work showed an overall accuracy of 98%. Based on a more extensive rectal examination, Cameron (1977) reported that when carried out at day-30 of gestation or at day-18 or -19 after mating in the sow, this was a valuable procedure which could be used as part of a regular herd health service to intensive pig units.

With sows in stalls or on tethers, it was found that a rectal examination took about a minute to carry out; with experience, it was found that pro-oestrus could be detected on the 18th or 19th day after an unsuccessful mating; this led to an accurate prediction that a non-pregnant sow was about to return to oestrus (Cameron, 1977). It should be mentioned that the vaginal biopsy technique has been used in detecting pigs about to return to service by taking a biopsy sample at 19 days after mating (Walker, 1972; Ryan, 1977); according to Cameron (1977), rectal examination is much simpler and can be easily applied as a routine measure where batch farrowing is carried out.

24.5 ULTRASONIC TECHNIQUES

Starting rather more than 10 years ago came the application of ultrasonic techniques to the diagnosis of pregnancy in pigs; first on the scene was the Doppler instrument, followed a few years later by A-mode sound equipment.

24.5.1 Doppler method

As already mentioned, the ultrasonic Doppler technique has been widely used in human medicine for some years past as one of the very accurate and safe means of providing information on pregnancy. Doppler ultrasound is employed to detect the motion of blood in the foetal heart or in the large umbilical blood vessels associated with the pig foetuses; ultrasound waves emanating from the instrument's transducer strike moving blood particles and are reflected back at a slightly altered frequency which can be converted into audio or visual signals (Fraser and Robertson, 1968; Fraser et al., 1971). In Scotland, Fraser and Robertson (1968) were among the first to use the ultrasonic Doppler method for pregnancy diagnosis in pigs, achieving an accuracy of about 75% from 6 to 12 weeks of gestation; other reports have come from a number of countries, including Denmark (Christiansen and Hansen, 1970), Japan (Kawata and Too, 1970; Fujui, 1972; Yamada and Misaizu, 1974) and the United States (Pierce et al., 1976).

A diagnostic procedure based on Doppler signals reflected from the uterine blood vessels of the sow through an intra-rectal probe has also been reported by some workers (Fraser, 1968; Pierce et al., 1976). Prior to the advent of ultrasonics, it was almost impossible to obtain information on foetal heart activity, especially in the early stages of pregnancy. Using the method, Frazer et al., (1971) and Kawata and Fukui (1977) have shown that there is a highly significant negative correlation between the foetal heart rate and the foetal age; according to this, when service dates are uncertain, the time of farrowing can be predicted with reasonable accuracy from foetal heart rate data. It would seem unlikely that this would be of interest to a busy pig producer, but on some occasion, it might be of value to keep this in mind.

24.5.2 Amplitude–depth analysis

A few years after Doppler sound was first employed, the amplitude–depth ultrasound procedure (also known as A-mode, A-scope, A-scan) proved to be a simpler and more reliable method. This method detects differences in the acoustical impedance between the contents of the pregnant uterus and the other abdominal viscera; allantoic and amniotic fluids play a major role in reflecting the echo pattern associated with early pregnancy in pigs. Work in other mammals has shown that allantoic and amniotic fluids are not only good transmitters of ultra sound but also provide excellent contrast in acoustical impedance to the adjacent foetal and maternal tissues (Taylor et al., 1964).

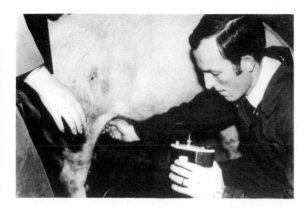

Fig. 24.1. Using A-mode ultrasonics in detecting pregnancy in the sow. Detecting pregnancy by the use of ultrasonics is particularly effective in the pig. Keeping sows that prove to be non-pregnant is costly to the producer in terms of feed, labour and housing. Many companies presently market ultrasound pregnancy testers. Even in the most efficient of herds, up to 10% of services may not actually get the sow pregnant, so routine pregnancy diagnosis must be considered an important part of pig management.

Allantoic fluid in the uterus of pregnant sows increases rapidly from day-23 of gestation until 60–65 days; amniotic fluid increases rather steadily from about day-30 until about day-80 and maximum growth of foetal membranes occurs between 30 and 65 days (Pomeroy, 1960). In the early work on this A-mode approach, Lindahl et al. (1975) used a solid-state amplitude–depth ultrasonic analyser in conjunction with a 2 MH$_z$ transducer placed on the lower flank of the standing sow; echoes were displayed on an oscilloscope. An easily recognized band of echoes was obtained from a depth of 15–20 cm in pregnant sows, in contrast to echoes from a depth of only about 5 cm in non-pregnant animals. Results for about 1000 sows examined showed the accuracy of the technique to be approaching 100% for diagnosing pregnancy in sows between 30 and 90 days of gestation.

The lower limit for high accuracy in diagnosing pregnancy (30 days or so) using this technique coincides with changes in the fluid content of the uterus and the beginning of 'rapid growth of foetal membranes rather than with rapid growth of the foetus. The upper limit for reliability of the procedure (about 90 days) coincides with a rapid decline in the foetal fluids associated with the pig foetuses.

According to Lindahl et al. (1975), sows can be tested with a minimum of restraint and the equipment is capable of being operated with ease and accuracy after a short-period of experience. Hansen and Christiansen (1976) employed an amplitude–depth analyser with a display system of light-emitting diodes instead of an oscilloscope; this reduced the cost and the instrument proved to be highly accurate. The general view among workers would be that the A-mode technique is the better one to employ in the pig from the point of view of simplicity and accuracy; comparisons of several commercially available amplitude-depth instruments have been conducted (te Brake and Arts, 1976; Arts and te Brake, 1978; Holtz et al., 1978). It should, however, be borne in mind that the upper limit of 90 days for attempting a diagnosis does not apply to the Doppler method and the A-mode technique does not provide evidence directly on the viability of foetuses.

24.6 PROGESTERONE ASSAY

Plasma progesterone levels have been reported on during early pregnancy by several workers; it would appear that the concentration of the steroid decreases rapidly from the mid-cycle level (25–35 ng ml^{-1} to about 10–15 ng ml^{-1} at 3–4 weeks (Parvizi et al., 1976); for the remainder of the gestation period, there is little further reduction in concentration. A method of early pregnancy diagnosis in the sow, based on the measurement of progesterone in the peripheral blood was described a decade ago by Robertson and Sarda (1971); results at the 22nd and 24th day after breeding showed an overall accuracy of 88%. In Japan, Kawata and Fukui (1977) mention the difficulty of applying the method on any scale because of the difficulties in collecting blood samples and the expense of the laboratory procedures involved in carrying out the assay. On the basis of their studies, Edqvist *et al.* (1972) suggested using the blood plasma test for progesterone at day–18 after mating. Elsewhere and subsequently, tests which showed plasma progesterone levels greater than 5 ng ml^{-1} at day-18 were found to be accurate in 97% of pregnant sows (Williamson *et al.*, 1980) but plasma levels below this value were much less accurate in detecting the non-pregnant animals (60% non-pregnancy accuracy) because of animals that subsequently returned to service.

24.7 OESTROGEN ASSAY

There is evidence that the concentration of conjugated oestrogen (oestrone sulphate) increases markedly from about day-16 to reach a sharp peak of 2 ng ml^{-1} serum by 25–30 days of pregnancy; it then falls to a very low level (<0.2 ng ml^{-1}) by about day-40 (Robertson and King, 1974; Robertson *et al.*, 1978; Hattersley *et al.*, 1980). In view of the fact that oestrone sulphate levels are negligible in non-pregnant sows, its has been suggested that measurement of this hormone at the appropriate time could be the basis of a sensitive and early pregnancy test. Studies by Saba and Hattersley (1981) have suggested that blood serum samples tested at 26–29 days after mating could be used to distinguish among sows in the following way: (1) pregnant if serum oestrone sulphate is greater than 0.5 ng ml^{-1}; (2) not pregnant with a level of 0.4 ng ml^{-1} or below; and (3) of uncertain status if levels are between 0.4–0.5 ng ml^{-1}. The same authors mention that large-scale field testing of this oestrogen assay were also underway from

their laboratory. Elsewhere, in Sweden, Edqvist *et al.* (1980) have reported some preliminary findings on the assay of oestrone sulphate in the blood plasma of gilts at 24–32 days after breeding which gave very accurate results; of 50 plasma samples tested, 42/42 pregnant and 7/8 non-pregnant pigs were correctly diagnosed.

After about day-60 of pregnancy, further increases in the level of conjugated oestrogens occur, to be followed, from about 80–90 days of gestation, by substantial rises in free oestrogens (oestrone and oestradiol) so that a maximum of 5 ng ml^{-1} plasma (total oestrogen) is reached just before term. These oestrogens are derived, largely if not entirely, from the foetal–placental unit (Fevre *et al.*, 1968; Ainsworth, 1972; Challis and Thorburn, 1975; Holness and Hunter, 1975).

24.8 OTHER PREGNANCY TESTING POSSIBILITIES

There has been a report by Martinat-Botte *et al.* (1980), dealing with the testing of blood samples, collected 13–15 days after mating for prostaglandin F$_{2\alpha}$; this test is based on the principle that in pregnant sows at this time PGF$_{2\alpha}$ levels are low whereas in non-pregnant pigs they are high. Samples taken on day-13 resulted in an accuracy of 94% for pregnancy and 63% for non-pregnancy. The problem with this, as well as poor prediction of non-pregnancy, is the effect that the blood sampling itself may have upon conception in the animal.

24.8.1 Immunological tests

As mentioned already, it would be very useful to have a technique which would permit diagnosis of non-pregnancy to be made in time to allow rebreeding at 3 weeks after service. It remains for investigators to demonstrate how best to detect the presence of the very early pig embryo; Australian studies on the detection of antigens specific to pregnancy in the pig in the early weeks after mating may result in the development of appropriate immunological tests (Cerini *et al.*, 1976).

24.8.2 Diagnosis by laparoscopy

For research purposes, laparoscopy has been found to be a useful tool (Wildt *et al.*, 1975); the method apparently allows observation of the reproductive tract with little or no adverse physical effects on either the cyclic or pregnant pig and provides a means of simultaneously diagnosing pregnancy, determining ovulation rate and observing the reproductive tract.

24.9 PREDICTING LITTER-SIZE

It has been suggested by Japanese workers that if litter-size were known before the time of farrowing it would be possible to perform earlier and more appropriate treatments aimed at decreasing the incidence of stillbirths. Fukui *et al.* (1978) attempted to estimate litter-size *in utero* using an ultrasonic Doppler technique (Heart-tone) but had very limited success (25% accuracy); the results were more accurate after 90 days of gestation than before that time. The technique took about 30 min to apply, with the sow in the sleeping position. Although it could be useful to know whether a particular sow has delivered all the piglets or not at some point during farrowing, the problems of making an accurate prediction would seem to be rather too considerable for this area of assessment to be of commercial interest.

24.10 FUTURE DEVELOPMENTS

In view of the fact that, with few exceptions (rectal palpation and vaginal biopsy in skilled hands; $PGF_{2\alpha}$ assay) none of the techniques described above enable a diagnosis to be made in time for a non-pregnant sow to be served again at its first return to oestrus, it would not seem that they can readily replace the traditional method of checking for non-return to oestrus, as already employed in the average herd. As pointed out by Wrathall (1975), in view of the expense and labour which may be involved in applying new procedures, there is the need to examine the conception rate in the herd, the accuracy of the technique proposed and the success rate achieved with the traditional methods that are already in operation in the herd.

24.11 REFERENCES

Ainsworth, L. (1972) The cleavage of steroid sulphates by sheep and pig fetal liver, fetal kidney and placental preparations *in vitro. Steroids* **19,** 741–750.

Anderson, L. L. and Melampy, R. M. (1967) Hypophysical and uterine influences on pig luteal function. In, *Reproduction in the Female Mammal.* Lamming and Amoroso, Ed., pp. 285–316 Butterworths, London.

Ash, R. W. and Heap, R. B. (1975) Oestrogen, progesterone and corticosteroid concentration in peripheral plasma of sows during pregnancy, parturition, lactation and after weaning. *J. Endocr.* **64,** 141–154.

Baldwin, D. M. and Stabenfeldt, G. H. (1975) Endocrine changes in the pig during late pregnancy, parturition and lactation. *Biol. Reprod.* **12,** 508–515.

Benjaminsen and Karlberg (1981) Post weaning oestrus and luteal function in primiparous and pluriparous sows. *Res. in Vet. Sci.* **30,** 318–322

Betteridge, K. J. and Raeside, J. (1962) Investigation of cervical mucus as an indicator of ovarian activity in pigs. *J. Reprod Fert.* **3,** 410–421.

Bollwahn, W. (1972) *Vet. Med. Rev.* **1,** 59.

Cameron, R. D. A. (1977) Pregnancy diagnosis in the sow by rectal examination *Aust. Vet. J.* **53,** 432–435.

Cerini, M., Findlay, J. K. and Lawson, R. A. S. (1976) Pregnancy-specific antigens in the sheep. *J. Reprod. Fert.* **46,** 65–69.

Challis, J. R. G. and Thorburn, G. D. (1975) Prenatal endocrine function. *Brit. Med. Bull.* **31,** 57–62.

Christiansen, I. J. and Hansen, L. H. (1970) Tests with an ultrasound apparatus for pregnancy diagnosis in sows. *Medlemsbl. danske Dyrlaegeforen,* **52,** 875–879.

Diehl, J. R. and Day, B. N. (1973) Utilization of frozen sections with the vaginal biopsy technique for early pregnancy diagnosis in swine. *J. Anim. Sci.* **37,** 114–117.

Diehl, J. R. and Day, B. N. (1974) Effect of prostaglandin $F_{2\alpha}$ on luteal function in swine. *J. Anim. Sci.* **39,** 392–396.

Done, J. T. and Heard, T. W. (1968) Early pregnancy diagnosis in the sow by vaginal biopsy. *Vet. Rec.* **82,** 64–66.

Dufour, J. J. and Fahmy, N. H. (1974) Follicular and luteal changes during early pregnancy in three breeds of swine. *Can. J. Anim. Sci.* **54,** 29–33.

Dziuk, P. J. (1977) Reproduction in pigs. In, *Reproduction in Domestic Animals.* (3rd ed.) Cole and Cupps, Eds., pp. 456–476. Academic Press, New York.

Edqvist, L., Einarsson, S. Ekmann, L., Gustafsson, B. and Lamm, A. (1972) Peripheres plasmaprogesteron bei trachtigen und gusten Sauen. *8th Int. Congr. Anim. Reprod. Artif. Insem* Munich.

Edqvist, L. E., Einarsson, B. and Settergren, I. (1974) Ovarian activity and peripheral plasma levels of oetrogens and progesterone in the lactatin sow. *Theriogen.* **1,** 43–49.

Edqvist, L. E., Einarsson, S. and Larsson, K. (1980) Early pregnancy diagnosis in pigs by assay of oestrone sulphate in peripheral blood plasma *Proc. Int. Pig Vet. Soc. Congr. Copenhagen* 27.

Ellicott, A. R. and Dziuk, P. J. (1973) Minimum daily dose of progesterone and plasma concentration for maintenance of pregnancy in ovariectomized gilts. *Biol. Reprod.* **9,** 300–304.

Fevre, J., Leglise, P. D. and Rombauts, P. (1968) Du role de l'hypophyse et des ovaries dons la biosynthese des-oestrogens au cours de la gestation chez la frure. *Ann. Biol. Anim. Biochim. Biophys* **8,** 225–233.

First, N. L. and Staigmiller, R. B. (1973) Effects of ovariectomy dexamethasone and progesterone on the maintenance of pregnancy in swine. *J. Anim. Sci.* **37,** 1191–1194.

Foxcroft, G. R., Stickney, K. and Edwards, S. (1979) The potential of using oestrogens for ovulatory control in the gilt and sow. *Proc. Ann. Conf. Soc. Study Fertil. Glasgow,* 18.

Fraser, A. F. and Robertson, J. G. (1968) Pregnancy diagnosis and detection of foetal life in sheep and pigs by an ultrasonic method. *Brit. Vet. J.* **124,** 239.

Fraser, A. F., Nagaratnam, V. and Callicott, R. B. (1971) The comprehensive use of doppler-ultra-sound in farm animal reproduction *Vet. Rec.* **88,** 202.

Fukui, Y. (1972) An experiment for the estimation of the litter size *in utero* in pigs by means of an ultrasonic doppler method. *Jap. J. Vet. Res.* **20,** 79.

Fukui, Y., Kawata, K. and Too, K. (1978) Studies on pregnancy diagnosis in domestic animals by an ultrasonic doppler method. II. An evaluation for predicting the litter size in utero in the pig. *Jap. J. Anim. Reprod.* **24,** 174–180.

Gadsby, J. E., Heap, R. B. and Burton, R. D. (1980) Oestrogen production by blastocyst and early embryonic tissue of various species. *J. Reprod. Fert.* **60,** 409–417.

Godke, R. A. (1975) Maternal and Fetal endocrine involvement in the prepartum pig. *Diss. Abst. Int. B,* **36B,** 986–987B.

Grunsell, C. S. and Robertson, A. (1953) A laboratory diagnosis of pregnancy in pigs. *Vet. Rec.* **65,** 366–367.

Guthrie, H. D., Henricks, D. M. and Handlin, D. L. (1972) Plasma estrogen, progesterone and L H prior to estrus and during early pregnancy in pigs. *Endocrin.* **91,** 675–679.

Hansen, L. H. and Christiansen, I. J. (1976) Early pregnancy diagnosis in sows by means of a newly developed ultrasonic A-scan device. *Zuchthygiene* **11**(1), 19–21.

Hattersley, J. P., Drane, H. M., Matthews, J. G., Wrathall, A. E. and Saba, A. N. (1980) Estimation of oestrone sulphate in the serum of pregnant sows. *J. Reprod. Fert.* **58,** 71–72.

Heap, R. B. and Perry, J. S. (1977) New developments in the biochemistry of early pregnancy in farm animals. *Vet. Sci. Commun.* 1, 131–140.

Heap, R. B., Perry, J. S., Gadsby, J. E. and Burton, R. D. (1975) Endocrine activities of the blastocyst and early embryonic tissue in the pig. *Biochem. Soc. Trans.* **3,** 1183–1188.

Holness, D. H. and Hunter, R. H. F. (1975) *Post-partum* oestrus in the sow in relation to the concentration of plasma oestrogens. *J. Reprod. Fert.* **45,** 15–20.

Holtz, W., Kaufmann, F. and Herrmann, H. H. (1978) Die Trachtiggeitsfeststellung mit dem Echolotverfahren beim Schwein. *Zuchthyg.* **13,** 183.

Horvath, G. (1961) Pregnancy diagnosis in sows by the cervical-mucus reaction and arbarixation. *Kiserl. Kozl Allattenyeszt.* **3,** 39–47.

Huchzermeyer, F. and Plonait, H. (1960) Trachtigkeits-diagnose und rectalunfersuchung beim. Schwein. *Tierartl. Umsch.* **15,** 399–401.

Hurtgen, J. P. (1976) Seasonal anestrus in a Minnesota swine breeding herd. *Proc. Int. Vet. Pig Congr.* D.22.

Hurtgen, J. P. and Leman, A. D. (1978) Seasonal breeding patterns in parous sows a slaughterhouse survey. *Proc. 5th Int. Pig. Vet Soc. Congr., Zagreb, MSO.*

Kawata, K. and Fukui, Y. (1977) Pregnancy diagnosis in the pig. A review. *Folia Vet. Latina* **7**(2), 91–110.

Kawata, K. and Too, K. (1970) Pregnancy diagnosis in the pig, cattle and birth by an ultrasonic doppler instrument. *Jap. J. Vet. Sci.* **32,** (Suppl.), 148.

Keel-Diffey, S. T. (1963) Pregnancy diagnosis in swine. *Vet. Rec.* **75,** 464.

Klotchkov, D. V., Klotchova, A. Ya., Kim, A. A. and Belyaev, D. K. (1971) The influence of photoperiodic conditions on fertility in gilts. *Proc. 10th Int. Congr. Anim. Prod. (Versailles),* Section II. p. 8.

Kraeling, R. R. and Davis, B. J. (1974) Termination of pregnancy by hypophysectomy in the pig. *J. Reprod. Fert.* **36,** 215–217.

Lindahl, I. L., Totsch, J. P., Martin, P. A. and Dziuk, P. J. (1975) Early diagnosis of pregnancy in sows by ultrasonic amplitude-depth analysis. *J. Anim. Sci.* **40,** 220–222.

Longenecker, D. E., Waite, A. B. and Day, B. N. (1978) Similarity in the number of corpora lutea during two stages of pregnancy in swine. *J. Anim. Sci.* **27,** 466–467.

Loy, R. G., McShan, W. H., Self, H. L. and Casida, L. E. (1958) Interrelationships of number, average weight and progesterone content of corpora lutea in swine. *J. Anim. Sci.* **17,** 405–409.

Martinat-Botte, F., Terqui, M., Thatcher, N. W. and Mauleon, P. (1980) Early pregnancy diagnosis in the sow. *Proc. Int. Pig Vet. Soc. Congr. (Copenhagen),* 29.

Martin, P. A., Bevier, G. W. and Dziuk, P. J. (1977) The effect of number of corpora lutea on the length of gestation in pigs. *Biol. Reprod.* **16,** 633–637.

Mather, E. C., Diehl, J. R. and Tumbleson, M. E. (1970) Pregnancy diagnosis in swine utilizing the vaginal biopsy technique. *J. Amer. Vet. Med. Ass.* **157,** 1522–1527.

Matsukawa, A. (1967) A diagnosis of pregnant sows by measuring the specific gravity of vaginal mucus. *J. Jap. Med. Ass.* **20** (Suppl.), 483–484.

Meridith, M. J. (1976) Pregnancy diagnosis in the sow by examination of the uterine arteries. *Proc. Int. Vet. Pig Congr.* D.5.

Meyer, J. N., Elsaesser, F. and Ellendorff, F. (1975) Trachtigkeits und fertility latstest beim Schweinmit Hilfer der Plasma-Progesteron-Bestimmung. *Dt. tierarztl. Wschr.* **82,** 473–475.

Morton, D. B. and Rankin, J. E. F. (1969) The histology of the vaginal epithelium of the sow in oestrus and its use in pregnancy diagnosis. *Vet. Rec.* **84,** 658–662.

Nishikawa, Y., Waide, Y. and Soejima, A. (1955) Studies on determination of the corpus luteum stage and the early diagnosis of pregnancy by the injection of oestrogen. *Bull. Nat. Inst. Agric. Sci. (Chiba) G.* **10,** 221–240.

O'Reilly, P. J. (1967) Studies on the vaginal epithelium of the sow and its application to pregnancy diagnosis. *Ir. Vet. J.* **21,** 234–238.

Parvizi, N., Elsaesser, F., Smidt, D. and Ellendorff, F. (1976) Plasma LH and progesterone in the adult female pig during the oestrous cycle, late pregnancy and lactation, and after ovariectomy and pentobarbitone treatment. *J. Endocr.* **69.** 193–203.

Perry, J. S., Heap, R. B. and Amoroso, E. C. (1973) Steroid hormone production by pig blastocysts. *Nature Lond.* **245,** 45–47.

Perry, J. S., Heap, R. B., Burton, R. D. and Gadsby, J. E. (1976) Endocrinology of the blastocyst and its role in the establishment of pregnancy. *J. Reprod. Fert. (Suppl.)* **25,** 85–104.

Pierce, J. E., Middleton, C. C. and Phillips, J. M. (1976) Early pregnancy diagnosis in swine using doppler ultrasound. *Proc. Int. Vet. Congr.* D3.

Pomeroy, R. W. (1960) Infertility and neonatal mortality in the sow. III. Neonatal mortality and foetal development. *J. Agric. Sci., Camb.* **54,** 31.

Rapic, S. (1961) Radiologic diagnosis of pregnancy. *Vet. Arh. Zagreb,* **31,** 171–175.

Robertson, H. A. and King, G. J. (1974) Plasma concentrations of progesterone oestrone, oestradiol-17$_B$ and of oestrone sulphate in the pig at implantation, during pregnancy and at parturition. *J. Reprod. Fert.* **40,** 133–141.

Robertson, H. A. and Sarda, I. R. (1971) A very early pregnancy test for mammals; its application to the cow, ewe, and sow. *J. Endocr.* **49,** 407–419.

Robertson, H. A., King, G. J. and Dych, G. W. (1978) The appearance of oestrone sulphate in the peripheral plasma of the pig early in pregnancy. *J. Reprod. Fert.* **52,** 337–338.

Saba, N. and Hattersley, J. P. (1981) Direct estimation of oestrone sulphate in the sow serum for a rapid pregnancy diagnosis test. *J. Reprod. Fert.* **62,** 87–92.

Sanada, T., Takeishi, M., Tamura, Y., Makimoto, K. and Tsunekane, M. (1975) Study for early pregnancy diagnosis in in the sow. II. Comparative study on Cuboni method and MAD-2-method. *Proc. 79th. Meet. Jap. Soc. Vet. Sci. Tokyo.*

Shearer, I. J., Purvis, K., Jenkin, G. and Hynes, N. B. (1972) Peripheral plasma progesterone and oestradiol-17$_B$ levels before and after puberty in gilts. *J. Reprod. Fert.* **30,** 347–360.

Spies, H. G., Slyter, A. L. and Quadri, S. K. (1967) Regression of corpora lutea in pregnant gilts administered antiovine LH rabbit-serum. *J. Anim. Sci.* **26,** 768–771.

Staigmiller, R. B. (1974) Control of luteal function during early pregnancy in the pig. *Diss. Abst. Int.* **34B,** 4842–4843.

Steger, H., Kirmse, K., Loeck, G., Huhn, V., Puschel, F. and Schremmer, H. (1971) Untersuchungen zur Hell-und Dunkelstallhaltung von Zuchtsauen und Ebin. *Arch. tierzucht.* **14,** 55–67.

Stork, M. G. (1979) Seasonal reproductive inefficiency in large pig breeding units in Britain. *Vet. Rec.* **104,** 49–52.

Taylor, E. S., Holmes, J. H., Thompson, H. E. and Gottesfield, K. R. (1964) Ultrasound diagnostic techniques in obstetrics and gynecology. *Am. J. Obstet. Gynecol.* **90,** 655.

Tomes, G. J. and Nielsen, H. E. (1979) Seasonal variations in the reproductive performance of sows under different climatic conditions. *Wld. Rev. Anim. Prod.* **15,** 9–19.

Torres, C. A. A. and First, N. L. (1975) Effect of surgical separation of uterus and ovaries on estrous cycle length in swine. *J. Anim. Sci.* **40,** 905–910.

Velle, W. (1960) Early pregnancy diagnosis in the sow. *Vet. R Vet.* **72,** 116–118.

Walker, D. (1972) Pregnancy diagnosis in pigs. *Vet. Rec.* **90,** 139–144.

Wetteman, R. P., Johnson, R. K. and Omtvedt, I. T. (1974) Plasma progesterone and number of C.L. in gilts. *J. Anim. Sci.* **38,** 227.

Wildt, D. E., Morcom, C. B. and Dukelow, W. R. (1975) Laparoscopic pregnancy diagnosis and uterine fluid recovery in swine. *J. Reprod. Fert.* **44,** 301–304.

Williamson, P. and Hennessy, D. (1975) As assessment of the vaginal biopsy technique of pregnancy diagnosis in sows. *Aust. Vet. J.* **51,** 91–93.

Williamson, P., Hennessy, D. P. and Cutler, R. (1980) The use of progesterone and oestrogen concentrations in the diagnosis of pregnancy and in the study of seasonal infertility in sows. *Aust. J. Agric. Res.* **31,** 233–238.

Wintzer, H. H. (1964) Zum trachtigkeitsnachweis beim Schwein und Schafmit hilfeder rontgenuntersuchung. *Dtsh. tierarztl Wschr.* **71,** 153–156.

Wrathall, A. E. (1975) *Reproductive Disorders in Pigs.* Commonwealth Agric. Bureau, Farnham Royal.

Wrathall, A. E. (1980) Mechanisms of porcine reproductive failure. *Vet. Ann.* **20,** 265–274.

Yamada, Y. and Misaizu, Y. (1974) Pregnancy diagnosis in swine by ultrasonic doppler effect. *J. Jap. Soc. Zootech. Sci.* **45** (Suppl.), 151.

CHAPTER 25

Control of Farrowing

25.1 INTRODUCTION

The pig industry in many countries is tending more and more towards an intensive total confinement operation. One of the most efficient methods of operating intensive units is by way of regular batch farrowings. This requires close control over all aspects of the reproductive cycle such as weaning, breeding and birth of the young so that farrowing batches can be maintained. However, even in well-managed units, farrowings to controlled breeding (oestrus control in cyclic gilts by hormonal agents; control in sows by weaning) can be spread out over some number of days and an effective form of inducing parturition might enable the pig producer to exercise control over this phase of his operations. Controlled parturition would enable all the piglets to be born during the normal working day or at other times, including the night, which might be considered most appropriate for ensuring the survival of as many piglets as possible; there is plenty of evidence to suggest that the majority of stillbirths in pigs could be prevented if a skilled stockman could be in attendance at the time of farrowing.

25.2 DURATION OF PREGNANCY

It would seem that variations in breed or age of sow or in environmental effects have little influence on the length of gestation in the pig; the normal range can be from 110 to 120 days with the average being around 114–116 days (Hughes and Varley 1980). There appears to be a natural tendency for sows to farrow during the night rather than during the daytime (Bichard et al., 1976). The length of gestation can be influenced to a minor extent by genetic factors; Joubert and Bonsma (1975) recorded a significant effect of the sire and others have found evidence of small but genuine differences in the duration of pregnancy between breeds (Garnett and Rahnefeld, 1979).

The number of foetuses carried by the sow can have an effect with small litters being carried somewhat longer than large litters (Omtvedt et al., 1965; Martin et al., 1977). There is lack of any effect of sex ratio on gestation length in the reports of those who have investigated this (Clegg, 1959; Omtvedt et al., 1965; Garnett and Rahnefeld, 1979). When it comes to farrowing itself, the normal period of delivery is from 2 to 6 h, with a piglet being born every 12–16 min, the young being delivered randomly from the two uterine horns and with the placentas being passed mainly after the last piglet is delivered (First, 1979; Fahmy and Friend, 1981).

25.3 ENDOCRINOLOGY OF LATE PREGNANCY

Progesterone produced by the corpora lutea established at time of mating maintains pregnancy until full-term, the steroid being essential in suppressing contractions of the uterine myometrium. The pituitary gonadotrophin responsible for the maintenance of the corpora lutea of pregnancy is still in dispute, and according to some it may be prolactin rather than LH (First, 1979).

The onset of farrowing in the pig is preceded by a sequence of hormone changes of both maternal and foetal origin. The events on the maternal side, which include the withdrawal of progesterone from the circulation, have been studied by several groups (Killian et al., 1973; Molokwu and Wagner, 1973; Robertson and King, 1974; Ash and Heap, 1975; Baldwin and Stabenfeldt, 1975; Martin et al., 1977; Ellendorff et al., 1979); changes on the foetal side, because of the technical difficulties involved have been less well documented (Dvorak, 1972; Fevre, 1975; Godke, 1975; Silver et al., 1979).

25.3.1 Oestrogen and progesterone levels

Dealing with maternal events, hormone changes occur in sequential fashion, starting with an increase in the level of oestrogens, particularly the unconjugated oestrogens, during the last 2–4 weeks of pregnancy. The increase in oestrogen concentration alone in the face of the progesterone levels found in pregnancy does not cause parturition (Bosc et al., 1974; Nellor et al., 1975; Coggins and First, 1977; Martin et al., 1977). The progesterone concentration decreases slowly over the last 2 weeks of gestation but then, in the final days before farrowing, drops more quickly to reach a level of <2–3 ng ml^{-1} plasma at time of parturition and <0.5 ng ml^{-1} afterwards. Any relationship between LH and progesterone level which operates earlier in pregnancy no longer holds true in the last 2 days of gestation (Ellendorff et al., 1979), indicating that this may be a period when luteotrophic support of the corporal lutea is reduced.

25.3.2 Corticosteroid levels

There is some evidence of a minor rise in the level of corticosteroids in the maternal plasma in the last 1 or 2 days of pregnancy (Baldwin and Stabenfeldt, 1975; Silver et al., 1979) but on the foetal side the increase is proportionately greater and starts at least a week or so before parturition (Dvorak, 1972; Fevre, 1975; Silver et al., 1979).

25.3.3 Relaxin

It is known that the polypeptide, relaxin, is produced by the corpora lutea of the pig from day-28 to 105 of pregnancy, is stored in the corpora lutea and mainly discharged around the time of parturition (Belt et al., 1971; Larkin et al., 1977). It is known that the plasma concentration of relaxin rises in the days of preceding parturition, with peak activity shown about 12–14 hours before the start of farrowing (Sherwood et al., 1975; Ellendorff et al., 1979); these events are known to coincide with changes in uterine motility from a quiescent to a labour type pattern (Taverne et al., 1976). Certainly, it is recognized that relaxin is of considerable importance by virtue of its effect on cervical dilation; the hormone is essential for ensuring that the birth canal is fully dilated, thus facilitating the rapid expulsion of all the foetuses during the farrowing process (First, 1979).

25.4 EVENTS AT PARTURITION

For parturition to occur, the mechanisms for the maintenance of pregnancy must cease to operate; in the case of the sow, electromyographic studies have shown that uterine motility changes rapidly from a quiescent to an active state about one-half day before the end of gestation (Zerobin and Sporri, 1972). The changes occurring in uterine motility also coincide with nest-building behaviour in the sow and with a marked decline in the maternal progesterone level (Taverne et al., 1979).

In fact, the overriding controlling factor in the onset of parturition in the pig appears to be the level of progesterone. If the concentration of the hormone declines below a certain value farrowing can and will occur; if the progesterone level is maintained, then parturition does not occur, despite the concentrations that other hormones may reach. Experimentally, it has been shown that ovariectomy at any stage of the gestation period removes most if not all of the progesterone in circulation, resulting in abortion or "parturition" in 24–48 h (Du Mesnil du Buisson and Dauzier, 1957); on the other hand, pregnancy can be maintained in spayed pigs by administering progesterone (Ellicott and Dziuk, 1973).

It is also now well accepted that just as the early developing pig embryos are responsible for extending the life of the corpora lutea, so too, at the end of pregnancy, it is primarily a foetal effect which brings luteal function and the associated progesterone production to an end. In the pig foetus, as in the sheep, the evidence suggests that the pituitary–adrenal axis has a critical role to play in the initiation of parturition. This has been demonstrated experimentally by the fact that foetal decapitation (Stryker and Dziuk, 1975) or hypophysectomy (Bosc et al., 1974) or corticosteroid treatment (North et al., 1973) induces premature parturition.

25.4.1 Foetal effects

The view of events which is currently favoured is that ACTH from the foetal pituitary stimulates production of glucocorticoids from the foetal adrenals; these corticoids then appear to initiate prostaglandin production, luteal regression and the subsequent events culminating in parturition. Maternal prostaglandin levels are known to remain low until farrowing begins but then a dramatic rise occurs; in the foetal blood, the prostaglandin level rises earlier and coincides with the decline in progesterone (Silver et al., 1979). Oxytocin concentration increases above basal levels only when plasma progesterone falls below about 10 ng ml^{-1}; the concentration undergoes a further marked increase during the expulsion phase (Ellendorff et al., 1979).

Wrathall (1980) draws attention to the importance of foetal maturation with regard to the timing of the events that normally take place at the end of gestation; this is shown in the fact that litters in which thyroid deficient foetuses are present tend to be farrowed late (Lucas et al., 1958; Wrathall et al., 1977). It is well recognized that thyroid hormones are known to be responsible for many maturation processes in the foetus (Nathanielsz, 1975), including those that take place in the brain and probably the pituitary–adrenal axis as well.

25.4.2 Foetal signals

One area in which some uncertainty exists is that of knowing whether there is a co-ordinated production of corticosteroids by all foetuses in the litter simultaneously or whether timing of parturition is triggered initially by just one or two of the more mature foetuses. There is evidence that the presence of one or two decapitated (Stryker and Dziuk, 1975), hypophysectomized (Bosc et al., 1974) or hypothyroid (Wrathall et al., 1977) foetuses causes little or no delay in parturition; when affected foetuses outnumber the intact ones, then pregnancy is prolonged. Stryker and Dziuk (1975) showed that in litters containing decapitated foetuses in the ratio of 4:1, pregnancy was prolonged; when the litter consisted of only one intact foetus and no decapitated foetuses, the length of the gestation period was normal.

The indications are that one normal foetus can initiate farrowing but four decapitated foetuses can prolong gestation, despite the one intact litter-mate; maintenance of pregnancy may therefore be the result of a positive signal and the initiation of parturition not simply the response to withdrawal of a signal. The same study (Stryker and Dziuk, 1975) showed that farrowing is usually not a local uterine–foetal phenomenon because decapitated foetuses in one uterine horn were born simultaneously with the intact litter-mates of the other horn.

25.4.3 Udder effects

Oedema of the udder, which presumably is a result of prolactin activity, begins about 24 h before delivery and milk ejection, an oxytocin induced response, begins within 12 h *pre-partum* (First, 1979).

25.5 PIGLET MORTALITY

A crucial area in which further research effort should be concentrated is on attempts to improve the viability of the new-born pig; low weight piglets and those that are weak for other reasons are the most demanding in terms of the conditions which must be provided and the skill and effort needed to ensure their survival.

Evidence in the literature has indicated that about 6% of all piglets are stillborn (Friend et al., 1962; Sovljanski et al., 1971; Leman et al., 1972; Randall, 1972); more than 80% of these stillbirths occur in the last third of the litter (Randall, 1972). Farrowings of long duration and increased time-intervals between piglets at birth are associated with a greater incidence of intrapartal stillbirths (Milosavljevic et al., 1972; Randall, 1972; Sprecher et al., 1974). In addition to stillbirths, a further 15% or more of piglets may fail to survive the early weeks of life, with most of these dying during the first few days of life (Kernkamp, 1965; Sharpe, 1966; Fahmy and Bernard, 1971; Edwards, 1972; Bereskin et al., 1973; Hartsock et al., 1977; Fahmy et al., 1981). Weakness at birth is responsible for many losses, since it contributes

Fig. 25.1. Factors influencing the survival of the newborn piglet. Improvement in piglet survival rate depends on sound management systems and attention to detail. It is essential for the newborn piglet to start sucking the mother at the earliest opportunity — many of the deaths that occur in the very young pig can arise because of a failure to suck in the early hours of life. Piglet birthweight can be slightly improved by feeding during pregnancy but only by way of marked increases in food intake which may not be cost-effective.

to starvation, chilling, overlying and general disease (Stanton and Carroll, 1974).

25.5.1 Relaxin and stillbirths

It has been observed by those who have recovered pig foetuses directly from the uterus by surgery that nearly all the young are alive *in utero* (Dziuk, 1979), which clearly shows that the life of the piglet is seldom endangered before the birth process begins. It is, for that reason, important to know as much as possible about parturition in the pig and the factors associated with it which may influence the extent of piglet losses. There is a certain amount of circumstantial evidence to suggest that some stillbirths may be caused by suboptimal release of relaxin (First, 1979); uterine contractions may not always result in the delivery of live piglets unless the birth canal, under relaxin, is capable of dilating fully and thereby facilitating the ready exit of the young.

25.5.2 Herdsman's role

The importance of a conscientious stockman in minimizing piglet mortality has been emphasized in several reports. Dziuk (1979) refers to a study involving more than 150 supervised farrowings in which the loss of all piglets from birth to weaning was less than 6% in contrast to more than 20% in the same herd before and after the period of supervision. Elsewhere, resuscitation of a substantial proportion of apparently dead piglets by an attendant has been shown to be possible (Milosavljevic *et al.*, 1972); in this, 30% of apparently stillborn piglets revived after the attendant cleared the upper respiratory tract of mucus and fluid and provided artificial respiration.

It has been suggested that in most pig units in the U.K. farrowing accommodation and the management system in operation tended to cater only for the top 85% or so of the liveborn piglets (English, 1981); management did not provide adequately for the remaining 15% of the smaller and less viable pigs. According to this author, it is the point at which the piglet starts to decline towards death that is the important time to detect; routine monitoring of events, both during and after farrowing to permit early correction of problems, is required.

25.5.3 Advantages of controlled farrowings

Because farrowings in the normal way do occur at all hours of the night and day and gestation periods can vary in length from one sow to the next by several days, precise scheduling of personnel for supervision can be costly and difficult and perhaps even impossible to arrange unless the time of parturition can be closely controlled. As well as controlled farrowings as the means of reducing piglets deaths around the time of birth, concentrated farrowings in the pig unit could have other potential advantages; piglets could readily be transferred from the larger to smaller litters, routine operations such as iron injections or clipping teeth could be carried out on larger numbers of piglets at the same time. There could also be other advantages, such as reducing the age range of pigs at weaning and in avoiding weekend and holiday farrowings, thereby minimizing labour requirements during these high cost periods.

25.5.4 Oestrone and piglet survival

There is some evidence that hormonal events during late pregnancy can be related to the subsequent viability of piglets. Work in Canada by Hacker *et al.* (1979) has shown a relationship between the level of urinary oestrone secreted in late pregnancy and the viability of piglets; the precise nature of the relationship is not clear, but oestrone measurement may perhaps give some warning about the viability of young which can trigger measures in the farrowing house to ensure appropriate management.

25.5.5 Interval between births

In natural farrowings, there is evidence that the time interval between the birth of piglets is related to the incidence of stillbirths; live births occur at an average interval of 12–15 minutes, whereas the incidence of stillbirths increases as the interval from the preceding birth reaches 20 min (Milosavljevic *et al.*, 1972; Randall, 1972; Sprecher *et al.*, 1974). As noted by Dziuk (1979), it is not clear whether the stillborn piglet is a result of a long interval or whether the foetus dies *in utero* and the prolonged interval arises from that; in view of evidence, already mentioned, that some apparently dead pigs can be revived, Dziuk

(1979) suggests that death is probably caused by the prolonged delivery rather than vice-versa.

25.5.6 Pre-natal treatments to reduce mortality

The effect of feeding a high energy diet (15% fat) to perinatal sows and gilts, starting on day-109 of gestation was reported by Cieslak et al. (1980); these workers found that the survival of piglets and their rate of growth in the first 3 weeks of life was significantly increased, this presumably being a result of the diet increasing the birthweight of the young.

25.6 INDUCTION BY GLUCOCORTICOID/ OXYTOCIN

Already mentioned is the fact that in cattle and sheep, parturition can be induced in the last week of the gestation period (earlier in cattle) by exogenous glucocorticoid. The sow, on the other hand, is not responsive to such steroid treatment until after the 100th day of pregnancy and only then to large doses given on successive days (Coggins and First, 1973; North et al., 1973; First and Staigmiller, 1974; Coggins and First, 1977; Huhn et al., 1978). A decrease in the maternal concentrations of progesterone preceding far-rowing induced by glucocorticoid treatment has been observed by Coggins (1975) and Coggins and First (1977); results reported by Nara and First (1981) indicate that the mode of action of a glucocorticoid in terminating luteal function in the pig prior to the start of farrowing is not direct but is mediated through stimulation of the biosynthesis or the release of prostaglandin $F_{2\alpha}$. For the practical pig producer, glucocorticoid treatment has no place as an induction agent because of the much more satisfactory alterna-tives which are available.

25.6.1 Oxytocin induction

There have been reports on the use of oxytocin to induce parturition in pigs under certain conditions (Muhrer et al., 1955; Costello, 1976; Nara and First, 1977); the range of time, when this hormone proves to be effective, appears to be restricted to those few hours just before the normal start of farrowing. The general rule with

oxytocin is that it proves effective only after the time that milk can be expressed from the udder. As noted later, oxytocin may have some use as a follow-on to prostaglandin $F_{2\alpha}$ treatment.

Other smooth muscle stimulants such as acetylcholine, pilocarpine, eserine and related compounds have been tried as inducers with much the same negative outcome as with oxytocin (Dziuk, 1979). As mentioned earlier, the process of parturition involves much more than just substances which are known to influence the contraction of uterine muscle.

25.7 PROSTAGLANDINS AND ANALOGUES

A single intramuscular injection of the natural prostaglandin $F_{2\alpha}$ (5–12.5 mg) has proved to be effective in the induction of parturition in a high proportion of sows treated within a few days of normal full-term (Diehl et al., 1974, 1977; Handlin et al., 1974; Henricks and Handlin, 1974; Killian and Day, 1974; Robertson et al., 1978; Wetteman et al., 1974, 1977; Ehnvall et al., 1976; Iwamoto et al., 1977; Mortimer, 1978; King et al., 1979). Potent analogues of $PGF_{2\alpha}$ (e.g. 175 μg Cloprostenol) have also been employed with considerable success (Ash and Heap, 1973; Bosc et al., 1975; Downey et al., 1976; Hammond and Carlyle, 1976; Cerne and Nikolic, 1977; Lynch and Langley, 1977; Walker, 1977; Cerne, 1978; Hammond, 1978; Hansen, 1979; Willemse et al., 1979; Hammond and Matty, 1980).

25.7.1 Timing of prostaglandin

In many of the early induction trials, the tendency was for prostaglandin to be adminis-tered between days 108 and 113 of gestation, but with experience it became evident that the overall efficacy of the treatment was reduced when prostaglandin was administered more than 2 or 3 days before the usual expected date of parturition. Under these circumstances, for pig breeders using PG in commercial practice, it is important to establish accurately, from previous records, the average gestation period for the herd in question over the previous 3–6 months; it is also necessary to have accurate service dates for

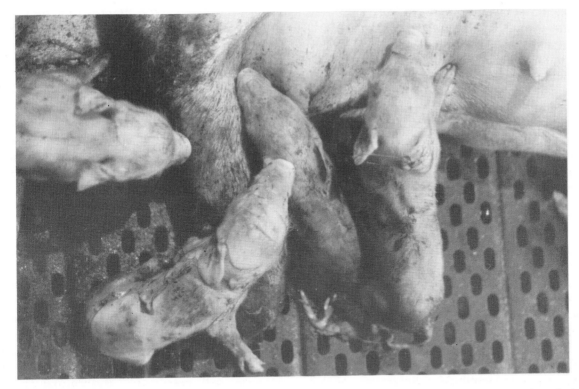

Fig. 25.2. Birth of piglets after the induction of farrowing with prostaglandin. Prostaglandins can be very effective for inducing parturition in the sow but it is necessary for the exact date of conception to be known. It is usually a matter of determining the average gestation length for sows in the herd and employing the prostaglandin 2 days ahead of that figure. The usual reasons for interest in controlled farrowings include the need to reduce week-end births, to assist in the supervision of farrowings and to provide for appropriate fostering of piglets and the matching up of uneven litters.

those sows that are to receive the agent, so that prostaglandin is only given to individual pigs at the appropriate time.

25.7.2 Action of prostaglandin

The administration of $PGF_{2\alpha}$ to pregnant gilts or sows results in an immediate, sharp decline in plasma progesterone levels and an associated regression of the corpora lutea (Diehl et al., 1974, 1977; Bosc et al., 1975; Bosc and Martinat-Botte, 1976; Fonda et al., 1977). It is evident that PG treatment also induces the release of relaxin; some reports show peak concentrations of this hormone occurring 45 min after the induction agent was given (Sherwood et al., 1977). All the evidence suggests that an essentially orderly and normal sequence of events is initiated when PG is given; when applied under appropriate conditions, the induction treatment is without deleterious effect on the health of the piglets, the

duration of farrowing does not appear to be influenced and milk production remains unaffected. However, the induction of farrowing by administering prostaglandin at day 108 may well yield piglets that are lighter in weight and less likely to survive than young produced by injection at day 111–112 (Bosc and Martinat-Botte, 1976). Clearly, any procedure which brings about the birth of the young several days earlier than normal is likely to be faced with piglets of smaller than average weights; the closer to the normal gestation period average that the young are born, then the better their chances of survival.

25.7.3 Time interval to farrowing

The time between treatment and farrowing can be influenced to a minor extent according to whether the natural prostaglandin agent or an analogue is employed. Using natural $PGF_{2\alpha}$, the interval to the onset of parturition has been reported by several workers as being about 29 h on average (Diehl et al., 1974; Killian and Day, 1974; Cropper et al., 1975; Wierzchos and Pejsak, 1976; King et al., 1979). Some reports have shown intervals between 24–27 h (Robertson et al., 1974; Coggins, 1975; Hansen and Jacobsen, 1976); other authors found the period to be much longer (Henricks and Handlin, 1974; Gustafsson et al., 1976; Diehl et al., 1977; Wetteman et al., 1977) and in some instances a proportion of the pigs which had been treated with the natural agent did not respond.

The synthetic analogues of $PGF_{2\alpha}$ that have been employed would appear to give a reasonably uniform response (means between 24–28 h) as far as the time between treatment and parturition is concerned (Ash and Heap, 1973; Bosc et al., 1975; Downey et al., 1976; Hammond and Carlyle, 1976; Holtz et al., 1979; Hammond and Matty, 1980; Jainudeen and Brandenburg, 1980). Cooper (1981), dealing with the Cloprostenol analogue, reported the peak time of farrowing as 26 h after injection, with 95% of the sows farrowing within 36 h; in fact, 86% of sows were found to give birth in the 18-h period between 18–36 h after treatment. The same author stresses the importance of studying herd records carefully so that the timing of induction (2-days ahead of herd average) can be appropriately selected.

25.7.4 Comparisons between PG and analogues

Comparisons between natural prostaglandin $F_{2\alpha}$ and the analogue Cloprostenol have been made (Boland et al., 1979), the results showing the agents to be similarly effective when given 2 days ahead of the herd average, in terms of the induction of farrowing. At Nottingham, however, the work of Brown and Cole (1980) showed that when treatment with the natural agent and an analogue was applied on days 110, 111 and 112 of gestation, all pigs receiving the analogue responded within 48 h, but with the natural prostaglandin, the percentage responding within 48 h increased from 29% on day-110 to 70% on day-111 to 100% on day-112; there was a clear and significant interaction between product and the day of treatment.

25.7.5 Transient side effects

The transient side-effects reported (Diehl et al., 1974; Kingston, 1978; Robertson et al., 1978; Russell, 1979) after treating sows with natural $PGF_{2\alpha}$ (restlessness, increased respiration rate, salivation, tendency to urinate and defecate, scratching and biting) have not been reported to the same extent after using analogues such as Cloprostenol; presumably, the natural agent increases smooth muscle activity to a greater extent, and although the side-effects do not adversely affect the outcome of the induction treatment, the differences described between agents should be kept in mind.

Induction of parturition with prostaglandin, natural or analogue, does not affect lactation, return to oestrus after farrowing or subsequent fertility (Walker, 1977; Robertson et al., 1978); there is, however, as discussed in a later section,

Table 25.1 Outcome of prostaglandin treatment in the induction of parturition in the sow (Boland et al., 1979)

	I	II	III
Treatment (dose)	Lutalyse (10 mg)	Planate (175 mcg)	Saline
No. of sows	27	26	28
Interval (h) to parturition	23.0±10.8	24.9±8.9	54.7±32.8
Litter size	12.3	11.1	11.1
No. dead at birth	0.6	1.0	2.5
Mean birth wt. (lb)	2.6	2.6	2.6
Alive at three weeks	9.7	8.4	8.8
Mean wt. at 3 weeks (lb)	10.6	10.9	10.4
Days empty	4.8	4.6	4.8

some indication that induced farrowings may decrease the frequency of the metritis, mastitis and agalactia (MMA) syndrome.

25.7.6 Prostaglandins in practice

On the basis of reports in the literature and their own experience, King et al. (1979) suggested that a single injection of $PGF_{2\alpha}$ given near 08.00 h. in the morning late in gestation should result in one-half to two-thirds of the treated pigs producing their litters during the following day; these same workers did note that during the normal day, the herdsman is engaged in his routine work and may not have the time to provide continual supervision.

In an effort to improve the quality and duration of the supervision programme on an 800-sow commercial farm, Hammond and Matty (1980) induced farrowings during the night, thereby enabling the stockman to be fully occupied attending the parturient animals and permitting daytime staff to resume supervision the following morning; effectively, this provided a period of close supervision of about 18 h for each batch of farrowing sows. During the year-long trial, there was a significant increase in the average number of piglets weaned (amounting to 353 extra piglets). Hammond and Matty (1980) concluded that the use of the controlled night farrowing system offered a good opportunity under some conditions to improve the supervision of farrowings and to ensure better piglet survival; an obvious limitation of the system is finding stockmen who are willing to work night shifts. As well as the natural $PGF_{2\alpha}$ agent being available commercially in some number of countries, several analogues are also marketed; in Ireland, ICI introduced their Cloprostenol analogue a few years ago (Planate) for use at the 175 μg dose level (in 2 ml volume) 2 days before the herd average; the initial development work involved practical evaluation in 22 major pig producing countries.

25.7.7 Improving response to PG

Several factors influence the response of the sow to prostaglandin and it would be desirable in certain instances to have a more precise control over the time interval between administration of the agent and the start of the farrowing process. Certainly, there can be a spread in the time of farrowings with the present technique which can mean that some sows may not deliver their young on the day chosen; such a delay could prevent the producer from emptying the entire farrowing unit on a closely scheduled basis. It is for such reasons that some have suggested that there may be merit in examining the use of oxytocin towards the end of the day of programmed farrowings as a means of taking care of sows that would otherwise not farrow until the next day (First, 1979; Schultz, 1980). In talking about factors affecting the time interval to farrowing it might be noted that this can be shorter for large rather than small litters and shorter when natural PG is given close to term rather than earlier (First, 1979).

25.8 SHORTENING FARROWING

The average duration of farrowing in sows and gilts is usually taken to be between 4–6 h (Friend et al., 1962; Jones, 1966; Randall, 1972; Fahmy and Friend, 1981) and there does not appear to be any evidence to suggest that prostaglandin treatment affects the process or its duration to any extent. In view of the fact that the incidence of stillbirths increases during the last third of the farrowing period, the possibility of employing agents to speed up delivery has obviously been considered by some. When uterine smooth muscle was stimulated by an appropriate parasympatho-mimetic drug, Leman and Sprecher (1976) did obtain an extra 0.5 piglets per litter born alive by such means; this type of intervention, with the associated time and attention required for the individual sow, does not seem likely to have any commercial appeal. Better to concentrate on saving the piglets when they are born.

25.8.1 Life-saving measures

Already mentioned is the fact that some proportion of piglets apparently born dead can be revived by life-saving measures. Survival of the newly born piglet has also been aided by administering glucose solution by injection shortly after birth (Macpherson and Jones, 1976).

Such measures can only be applied if close and immediate attention is available at the time of parturition and this can be arranged more conveniently with programmed farrowings.

25.8.2 Mating and farrowing

In talking about arranging for farrowings to occur on selected days of the week there would be an obvious advantage in controlling the day of mating in the gilt by hormonal means; with sows, there would be the appropriate grouping of weaning dates to permit matings to occur within predetermined time-limits.

25.9 THE MMA SYNDROME

The incidence of the metritis, mastitis and agalactia (MMA) syndrome has been reported to vary between 6 and 12% (Jones, 1971); two main features characterize this condition, the involvement of the uterus (metritis) and the mammary gland (agalactia, mastitis). As already mentioned, there is now evidence suggesting that the use of prostaglandin to induce parturition in sows can reduce the frequency of MMA in herds with a high incidence of this condition (Einarsson et al., 1975; Backstrom et al., 1976; Ehnvall et al., 1976, 1977; Liptrap, 1980). In the normal occurrence of the MMA syndrome, it is recognized that some herds suffer from the problem more than others and this is thought to be related to the general level of health and management in the herd; dealing with the problem is a matter of considering feeding, housing, health and hygiene and some number of treatments have been suggested.

25.9.1. Prostaglandin and MMA

There would seem to be evidence that prostaglandin treatment for induced farrowings could assist in minimizing the incidence of MMA by bringing about a clearcut fall in progesterone levels which may not otherwise occur as a result of the uterus failing to produce appropriate amounts of $PGF_{2\alpha}$ itself (Liptrap, 1980); this could make the prostaglandin induction treatment of particular value in herds that experience a high incidence of the MMA syndrome.

25.10 DELAYING PARTURITION

The synchronization of farrowings may be achieved by shortening the normal length of gestation, as with prostaglandins; it may also be achieved by prolonging gestation a few days longer than usual. The known involvement of both prostaglandin and progesterone in the initiation of parturition in pigs has resulted in the use of these agents to control the time of farrowing. The prostaglandins have already been referred to but investigations have also been made, and are still being made, using progesterone or progestagens.

25.10.1 Progesterone and progestagens

Several reports appeared in the sixties and seventies in which exogenous progesterone or progestagens were employed to maintain pregnancy by hormonal support (Curtis et al., 1969; Minar and Schilling, 1970; First and Staigmiller, 1974; Nellor et al., 1975; Coggins et al., 1977; Sherwood et al., 1978); however, almost without exception in these investigations, foetal mortality rate was increased, often substantially. It did appear, however, that piglets could remain alive and healthy in utero (shown by Caesarean delivery of live young) for as much as 11 days beyond the expected date of parturition (Nellor et al., 1975) and the difficulties would seem to arise in the delivery of the young; the indications were that an abnormal hormonal situation was probably operating at farrowing time.

When the source of progesterone was induced luteal tissue (after PMSG and hCG treatment) formed a few days prior to normal term, Coggins et al. (1977) found that the piglet mortality rate at birth was similar to that in untreated pigs, even in instances when pregnancy was prolonged to 120 days or more. The same workers (Coggins et al., 1977) thought that the induction of new "accessory" corpora lutea may have been a more physiological method of prolonging gestation length in pigs without the problem of high mortality than administering hormones (induced corpora lutea in pigs are assumed to have a non-regressable steroidogenically-active life-span of at least 12 days); other workers, however, have reported a high rate of mortality even when parturition was delayed by the induction of accessory corpora lutea (Martin et al., 1977).

In considering such results, account may be taken of evidence that low doses of progestagen, probably insufficient to inhibit the parturition process, can result in a dose-related increase in dystocia and stillbirths (Jochle et al., 1974); it has been suggested that under natural conditions, incomplete luteal regression at parturition, with elevated maternal progesterone levels, could occur and give rise to prolonged farrowing and other disorders (Wrathall, 1980). Thus, even with induced corpora lutea, if regression did not occur in such a way that the progesterone level was brought down sufficiently low, problems may not be altogether unexpected. On the basis of the evidence available at that time, Dziuk (1977) concluded that control of the time of parturition by extending gestation beyond day-115 or shortening it to less than 110 days was unlikely to be of any practical significance because the piglet survival rate would be adversely affected.

However, in Australia, it was shown that sows in which farrowing was prolonged by treatment for 3 days with high doses of progesterone (100 mg day^{-1}) showed no significant increase in piglet mortality (Gooneratne et al., 1979); there was also a decline in progesterone levels in the pigs entirely comparable to that observed in control animals. It is known that prolonging gestation in pigs using certain dose levels of progesterone can result in erratic peripartum surges of the steroid in the blood and a prepartum decrease in the concentration of oestrogen (Wilson et al., 1981). It has also been shown that sows with their gestation period prolonged by exogenous progesterone may show a normal increase in relaxin level prior to the expected full-term but fail to show the elevation in the hormone when exogenous progesterone was withdrawn (Sherwood et al., 1978). Thus erratic progesterone levels, lower than usual oestrogen levels and perhaps the absence of relaxin could be involved in the abnormal peripartum endocrine patterns that may be the result of the delaying treatment.

25.10.2 Regumate for delaying parturition

Studies on the use of Regumate, administered in oral doses of 20 mg from day-111 until day-118

or-120, have been reported from the U.K. (Varley, 1981); on withdrawal of the progestagen from the feed, sows farrow down about 30 h after the last application. The use of the treatment has allowed these workers to extend parturition to as long as day-120 of gestation; at that stage, however, there can be almost a 20% stillbirth rate and they have attempted to counter low oestrogen levels by administering oestradiol benzoate at 6 h after Regumate withdrawal. Whether it is possible to achieve a "normal" parturition remains to be demonstrated. As pointed out by Varley (1981), prostaglandin and progestagen may eventually

Fig. 25.3. Ways and means of delaying the onset of farrowing in the sow and consequences for piglet survival. There may be merit in having techniques available that can delay rather than advance the date of farrowing. Although a temporary postponement of parturition in the sow seems possible using the tocolytic agent Planipart (clenbuterol hydrochloride), if it is days rather than hours that are required, then current research in which progestagens are being used may be able to provide an answer.

be employed according to whether synchronized farrowing arrangements for the unit
demand longer or shorter gestation periods.
Certainly, it is an area of reproduction control in
pigs that warrants much further attention.

25.11 PREPARTUM STRESS

In the United States, Hansen and Curtis (1980)
have drawn attention to the fact that prepartal
activity of the sow may be influenced by the type
of farrowing accommodation provided; such
accommodation may be a factor in explaining
some of the farrowing and lactation problems
which are encountered in commercial units in
the U.S.A. In North America, prior to farrowing,
sows are often held in rectangular stalls with bare
floors in many present-day farrowing systems;
this is regarded as a sound arrangement in several
important respects, but it may not be held in such
high regard by the sow herself. The fact that the
farrowing stall is often devoid of material that
sows normally use to prepare a nest before
parturition, means that the pig often substitutes
vigorous activity for nest-building a few hours
before the onset of farrowing; such activity can
often leave the sow with lacerations, contusions
and abrasions and sometimes even result in
apparent exhaustion. Hansen and Curtis (1980)
make the points that the prepartal stress arising
from the relatively barren, restraining environment of the farrowing stall may be a factor
explaining prolonged farrowings and some
problems associated with lactation.

25.12 FUTURE DEVELOPMENTS

Controlling parturition is one area of reproduction control which is likely to be of good solid
interest to pig producers. It seems to be a matter
of refining the prostaglandin and progestagen
treatments that exist currently with the aim of
providing the farmer with the maximum
flexibility in the choice of techniques which he
may wish to employ in getting sows and gilts
farrowing at the most appropriate time.

25.13 REFERENCES

Ash, R. W. and Heap, R. B. (1973) The induction and
synchronization of parturition in sows treated with ICI
79939, an analogue of prostaglandin $F_{2\alpha}$. J. Agric. Sci., Camb.
81, 365–368.

Ash, R. W. and Heap, R. B. (1975) Oestrogen, progesterone
and corticosteroid concentrations in peripheral plasma of
sows during pregnancy, parturition, lactation and after
weaning. J. Endocr. **64,** 141–154.

Backstrom, L., Einarsson, S., Gustafsson, B. and Larsson, K.
(1976) Prostaglandin $F_{2\alpha}$ induced parturition for prevention
of agalactia syndrome in the sow. Proc. 4th Int. Pig Vet Soc.
Congr. Ames, Iowa.

Baldwin, D. M. and Stabenfeldt, G. H. (1975) Endocrine
changes in the pig during pregnancy, parturition and
lactation. Biol. Reprod. **12,** 508–515.

Belt, W. D., Anderson, L. L., Cavazos, L. F. and Melampy, R. M.
(1971) Cytoplasmic granules and relaxin levels in porcine
corpora lutea. Endocrin. **89,** 1–10.

Bereskin, B., Shelby, C. E. and Cox, D. F. (1973) Some factors
affecting pig survival. J. Anim. Sci. **36,** 821–827.

Bichard, M., Stork, M. G., Rickatson, S. and Pease, A. H. R.
(1976) The use of synchronized farrowing in large pig units.
Anim. Prod. **22,** 138–139 (Abs).

Boland, M. P., Craig, J. and Kelleher, D. L. (1979) Induction of
farrowing: Comparison of the effects of prostaglandin $F_{2\alpha}$
(Lutalyse) and an analogue (Cloprostenol). Ir. Vet. J. 33(3),
45–47.

Bosc, M. J. and Martinat-Botte (1976) Induction de la
parturition chez la truie av moyen de prostaglandines.
Econ. Med. Anim. **17,** 235–244.

Bosc, M. de Mesnil du Buisson, F. and Locatelli, A. (1974) Mise
en evidence d'uncantrole foetal de la parturition chez la
truie. Interactions aved la fonction luteale. C.R. Acad. Sci.
Paris **278D,** 1507–1510.

Bosc, M. J., Martinat-Botte, F. and Duchene, P. (1975)
Induction of parturition in the sow with a PGF_2 x analogue:
Breeding results. Ann. Zootech. 24(4), 651–670.

Brown, A. C. G. and Cole, D. J. A. (1980) Prostaglandins and
parturition in the sow. J. Anim. Sci. **51,** (Suppl. 1), 263 (Abs).

Cerne, F. (1978) Induction of farrowing with Cloprostenol on a
commercial pig breeding farm in Yugoslavia. Vet. Rec. **103,**
469–471.

Cerne, F. and Nikolic, P. (1977) Application of synthetic
prostaglandine — Cloprostenol (ICI 80996) in the induction
and synchronization of partus in sows. The first application
in Yugoslavia. Vet. Glas. 31(7), 499–505.

Cieslak, D. G., Leibbrandt, V. D. and Benevenga, N. J. (1980)
The effect of feeding 15% fat to perinatal sows on survival
and growth of piglets. J. Anim. Sci. 51 (Suppl. 1, 59
(Abs).

Clegg, M. T. (1959) Factors affecting gestation length and
parturition. (Eds. Cole and Cupps) Reprod. in Domestic
Animals, Acad. Press. N.Y.

Coggins, E. G. (1975) Mechanisms controlling parturition in
swine. Ph.D. Thesis, Univ. of Wisconsin.

Coggins, E. G. and First, N. L. (1973) Response of swine and
rabbits to dexamethasone at different stages of gestation. J.
Anim. Sci. **37,** 305.

Coggins, E. G. and First, N. L. (1977) Effect of dexamethasone,
methallibure and fetal decapitation on porcine gestation. J.
Anim. Sci. **44,** 1041–1049.

Coggins, E. G:, Van Horn, D. and First N. L. (1977). Influence of prostaglandin $F_{2\alpha}$, dexamethasone, progesterone and induced Ch on porcine parturition. *J. Anim. Sc.*, **46,** 754–762.

Cooper, M. (1981) Prostaglandins in veterinary practice. In *Practice* 3(1), 30–34.

Costello, W. (1976) Controlled breeding in pigs. *M. Agr. Sc. Thesis, N.U.I. Dublin.*

Cropper, N., Leman, A. D. and Diehl, J. R. (1975) Effects of $PGF_{2\alpha}$ and neostigmine on parturition in swine. *J. Anim. Sci.* **41,** 451 (Abs).

Curtis, S. E., Rogler, J. C. and Martin, T. G. (1969) Neonatal thermostability and body composition of piglets from experimentally prolonged gestations. *J. Anim. Sci.* **29,** 335.

Diehl, J. R., Godke, B. A., Killian, D. R. and Day, B. M. (1974) Induction of parturition in swine with prostaglandin $F_{2\alpha}$. *J. Anim. Sci.* **38,** 1229–1234.

Diehl, J. R., Baker, D. H. and Dziuk, P. J. (1977) Effect of $PGF_{2\alpha}$ on sow and litter performance during and following parturition. *J. Anim. Sci.* **44,** 89–94.

Downey, B. R., Conlon, P. D., Irvine, D. S. and Baker, R. D. (1976) Controlled farrowing program using a prostaglandin analogue AY 24,655. *Can. J. Anim. Sci.* **56,** 655–659.

Du Mesnil du Buisson, F. and Dauzier, L. (1957) Influence de l'ovariectomie chez la truie pendant la gestation. *C. R. Seances Soc. Biol. Filiales,* **151,** 311.

Dvorak, M. (1972) Adrenocortical function in foetal, neonatal and young pigs. *J. Endocrin.* **54,** 473–481.

Dziuk, P. J. (1977) Reproduction in pigs. Chpt in: *Reproduction in Domestic Animals* (Cole and Cupps) (3rd Ed.), 456–474.

Dziuk, P. (1979) Control and mechanics of parturition in the pig. *Anim. Reprod. Sci.* **2,** 335–342.

Edwards, B. L. (1972) Causes of death in new born pigs. *Vet. Bull* **42,** 249.

Ehnvall, R., Einarsson, S., Gustafsson, B. and Larsson, K. (1976) A field study of prostaglandin induced parturition in the sow. *Proc. Int. Vet. Pig Congr.* (1976), D.6.

Ehnvall, R., Einarsson, S., Larsson, K., Segarstad, C. H. and Esterberg, L. (1977) Prostaglandin induced parturition in swine — a field study on its accuracy after treatment with different amounts of $PGF_{2\alpha}$. *Nord. Vet. Med.* **29,** 376–380.

Einarsson, S., Gustafsson, B. and Larsson, K. (1975) Prostaglandin induced parturition in swine with some aspects on prevention of the MMA (Metritis, Mastitis, Agalactia) Syndrome. *Nord. Vet. Med.* **27,** 429–436.

Ellendorff, F., Forsling, M., Parvizi, N. Williams, H., Taverne, M. and Smidt, D. (1979) Plasma oxytocin and vasopressin concentrations in response to prostaglandin injection into the pig. *J. Reprod. Fert.* **56,** 573–577.

Ellicott, A. R. and Dziuk, P. J. (1973) Minimum daily dose of progesterone and plasma concentration for maintenance of pregnancy in ovariectomized gilts. *Biol. Reprod.* **9,** 300–304.

English, P. R. (1981) Management in late pregnancy and lactation. In, *Control of Pig Reproduction,* Butterworths, London. (In Press).

Fahmy, M. H. and Bernard, C. (1971) Causes of mortality in Yorkshire pigs from birth to 20 weeks of age. *Can. J. Anim. Sci.* **51,** 351.

Fahmy, M. H. and Friend, D. W. (1981) Factors influencing, and repeatability of the duration of farrowing in Yorkshire sows. *Can. J. Anim. Sci.* **61,** 17–22.

Fevre, J. (1975) Corticosteroides maternels et foetaux chez la trure en finde gestation. *C.R. Acad. Sci. Paris* **281D,** 2009–2012.

First, N. L. (1979) Mechanisms controlling parturition in farm animals. *Anim. Reprod (BARC, Symp. No. 3. H. Hawk, Ed.), Allenheld, Osmun. Montclair* 215–257.

First, N. L. and Staigmiller, R. B. (1974) Effects of ovariectomy dexamethasone and progesterone on the maintenance of pregnancy in swine. *J. Anim. Sci.* **37,** 1191–1194.

Fonda, E. S., Thrasher, D. M. and Godke, R. A. (1977) Induced farrowing in swine $PGF_{2\alpha}$ and prostaglandin analogue (ICI 80,996). *Proc. Am. Soc. Anim. Sci. Ann. Mt.* **158.**

Friend, D. W., Cunningham, H. M. and Nicholson, J. W. G. (1962) The duration of farrowing in relation to the reproductive performance of Yorkshire sows. *Can. J. Comp. Med. Vet. Sci.* **26,** 17–130.

Garnett, I. and Rahnefeld, G. W. (1979) Factors affecting gestation length in the pig. *Can. J. Anim. Sci.* **59,** 83–87.

Godke, R. A. (1975) Maternal and fetal endocrine involvement in the pre-partum pig. *Diss. Abs. Int.* **36B,** 986–987.

Gooneratne, Anoma., Hartmann, P. E., McCauley, I. and Martin, C. E. (1979) Control of parturition in the sow using progesterone and prostaglandin. *Aust. J. Biol. Sci.* **32,** 587–595.

Gustafsson, B., Einarsson, S., Larsson, K. and Edqvist, L. E. (1976) Sequential changes of estrogens and progesterone at PG induced parturition in the sow. *Am. J. Vet. Res.* **37,** 1017–1020.

Hacker, R. R., Hazeleger, W., Van Poppel, F. J. J., Osinga, A., Verstegen, M. W. A. and Van de Wiel, D. F. M. (1979) Urinary oestrone concentration in relation to piglet viability, growth and mortality. *Livest. Proc. Sci.* **6,** 313–318.

Hammond, D. (1978) Management factors related to induced farrowing. *Pig. Vet. Soc. Proc.* **4,** 71–75.

Hammond, D. and Carlyle, W. W. H. (1976) Controlled farrowing on commercial pig breeding units using Cloprostenol, a synthetic analogue of $PGF_{2\alpha}$. *Proc. 8th Int. Congr. Anim. Prod. A.I. (Krackow),* 103.

Hammond, D. and Matty, G. (1980) A farrowing management system using cloprostenol to control the time of parturition. *Vet. Rec.* **106,** 72–75.

Handlin, D. L., Henricks, D. H. and Eargle, J. G. (1974) Control of parturition in sows. *J. Anim. Sci.* **38,** 228.

Hansen, L. H. (1979) Reproductive efficiency and incidence of MMA after controlled farrowing using a prostaglandin analogue cloprostenol. *Nord. Vet. Med.* **31,** 122–128.

Hansen, K. E. and Curtis, S. E. (1980) Prepartal activity of sows in stall or pen. *J. Anim. Sci.* **51,** 456–460.

Hansen, L. H. and Jacobsen, M. I. (1976) The course of puerperium in a MMA herd after induction of parturition with prostaglandin. *Nord. Vet. Med.* **28,** 357–360.

Hartsock, T. G., Graves, H. P. and Baumgardt, B. R. (1977) Agonistic behaviour and nursing order in suckling piglets: relationships with survival, growth and body composition. *J. Anim. Sci.* **44,** 320.

Henricks, D. M. and Handlin, D. L. (1974) Induction of parturition in the sow with prostaglandin $F_{2\alpha}$. *Theriogen.* **1,** 7–14.

Holtz, W., Diallo, T., Spangenberg, B., Rockel, P., Bogner, H., Smidt, D. and Leidl, W. (1979) Induction of parturition in sows with a prostaglandin $_{2\alpha}$-analogue. *J. Anim. Sci.* **49,** 367–373.

Hughes, P. and Varley, M. (1980) *Reproduction in the Pig.* Butterworths, London.

Huhn, Von R., Konig, I. and Lutter, K. (1978) Results of orientation studies to extend pregnancy in swine. *NH Vet Med.* 33(3), 90–93.

Iwamoto, M., Asai, T., Ogawa, T., Kawakami, T., Nishida, Y.,

Akasaka, M., Yoshida, T. and Okita, M. (1977) Induced parturition in sows through administration of $PGF_{2\alpha}$. *Jap. J. Swine Res.* **14,** 3, 13–19.

Jainudeen, M. R. and Brandenburg, A. C. (1980) Induction of parturition in cross-bred sows with cloprostenol an analogue of prostaglandin $F_{2\alpha}$. *Anim. Reprod. Sci.* **3,** 161–166.

Jochle, W., Orozoo, L., Zerobin, K., Esparaza, H. and Hidalge, M. A. (1974) Effects of a progestin and parturition and the post-partum period in pigs. *Theriogen.* **2,** 11–20.

Jones, J. E. T. (1966) Observations on parturition in the sow. II. The pertinent and post-parturient phases. *Br. Vet. J.* **122,** 471–478.

Jones, J. E. T. (1971) Reflections on post-parturient diseases associated with lactational failure in sows. *Vet. Rec.* **89,** 72–77.

Kernkamp, H. C. H. (1965) Birth and death statistics on pigs of pre-weaning age. *J. Am. Vet. Med. Ass.* **146,** 337–340.

Killian, D. B. and Day, B. N. (1974) Controlled farrowing with prostaglandin $F_{2\alpha}$. *J. Anim. Sci.* **39,** 214 (Abs).

Killian, D. B., Farverick, H. A. and Day, B. N. (1973) Peripheral plasma progesterone and corticoid levels at parturition in the sow. *J. Anim. Sci.* **37,** 1371–1375.

King, G. J., Robertson, H. A. and Elliott, J. I. (1979) Induced parturition in swine herds. *Can. Vet. J.* **20,** 157–160.

Kingston, N. (1978) Induced farrowing in sows. *Vet. Rec.* **103,** 544.

Larkin, L. H., Fields, P. A. and Oliver, R. M. (1977) Production of antisera against electrophoretically separated relaxin and immunofluorescent localization of relaxin in the porcine corpora lutea. *Endocrin.* **101,** 679–685.

Leman, A. D. and Sprecher, D. J. (1976) Effect of parasympathomimetics on farrowing and stillbirth rate. *Proc. Int. Pig Vet. Soc. Ames, Iowa.* D.20.

Leman, A. D., Knudson, C., Rodeffer, H. E. and Mueller, A. G. (1972) Reproductive performance of swine on 76 Illinois farms. *J. Am. Vet Med. Ass.* **161,** 1248–1250.

Liptrap, R. M. (1980) Prostaglandin $F_{2\alpha}$ and progesterone in experimental hypogalactia in sows. *Res. Vet. Sci.* **29,** 240–247.

Lucas, J. J., Brunstad, G. E. and Fowler, S. H. (1958) The relationship of altered thyroid activity to various reproductive phenomena in gilts. *J. Endocr.* **17,** 54–62.

Lynch, P. B. and Langley, O. H. (1977) Induced parturition in sows using prostaglandin analogue (ICI 80,996). *Ir. J. Agric. Res.* **16,** 259–265.

MacPherson, R. M. and Jones, A. S. (1976) The effect of administration of glucose on survival of the neonatal pig. *Anim. Prod.* **22.**

Martin, P. A., Norton, H. W. and Dziuk, P. J. (1977) The effects of corpora lutea induced during pregnancy on the length of gestation in the pig. *Biol Reprod.* **17,** 712–717.

Milosavlijevic, S., Miljkovic, V., Soljanski, B., Radovid, B., Trbojevic, C. and Stankov, M. (1972) The revival of apparently stillborn piglets. *Acta. Vet. Beograd.* **22,** 71–76.

Minar, V. M. and Schilling, E. (1970) Die beinflussung des gerbuttster, oms beom schwein durch gestagene hormone. *Deutsch. Tierarztl, Wschr.* **77,** 428.

Molokwu, E. C. and Wagner, W. X. (1973) Endocrine physiology of the puerperal sow. *J. Anim. Sci.* **36,** 1158–1163.

Mortimer, D. T. (1978) Induced farrowing in sows. *Vet. Rec.* **103,** 291.

Muhrer, M. E., Shippen, O. F. and Lasley, J. F. (1955) The use of oxytocin for initiating parturition and reducing farrowing time in sows. *J. Anim. Sci.* **14,** 1250.

Nara, B. S. and First, N. L. (1977) Effect of indomethacin and prostaglandin $F_{2\alpha}$ on porcine parturition. *69th Ann. Mt. Amer. Soc. Anim. Sci.*, 191.

Nara, B. S. and First, N. L. (1981) Effect of indomethacin on dexamethasone-induced parturition in swine. *J. Anim. Sci.* **52,** 788–793.

Nathanielsz, P. W. (1975) Thyroid function in the foetus and newborn mammal. *Br. Med. Bull.* **31,** 51–56.

Nellor, J. E., Daniels, R. W., Hoefer, J. A., Wildt, D. E. and Dukelow, W. R. (1975) Influence of induced delayed parturition on fetal survival in pigs. *Theriogen.* **4**(1), 23–31.

North, S. A., Hauser, E. R. and First, N. L. (1973) Induction of parturition in swine and rabbits with the corticosteroid dexamethasone. *J. Anim. Sci.* **36,** 1170–1174.

Omtvedt, I. T., Stanislaw, C. M. and Whatley, Jr. J. A. (1965) Relationship of gestation length, age and weight at breeding and gestation gain to sow productivity at farrowing. *J. Anim. Sci.* **24,** 531–535.

Randall, G. C. B. (1972a) Observations on parturition in the sow. I. Factors associated with the delivery of the piglets and their subsequent behaviour. *Vet. Rec.* **90,** 178–182.

Randall, G. C. B. (1972b) LL. Factors influencing stillbirth and perinatal mortality. *Vet. Rec.* **90,** 183–186.

Robertson, H. A. and King, G. J. (1974) Plasma concentrations of progesterone and of oestrone, oestradiol-17β and oestrone sulphate in the pig at implantation, during pregnancy and at parturition. *J. Reprod. Fert.* **40,** 133–141.

Robertson, H. A., King, G. J. and Elliot, J. I. (1974) Induction of parturition in the pig. *J. Anim. Sci.* **39,** 994 (Abs).

Robertson, H. A., King, G. J. and Elliot, J. I. (1978) Control of the time of parturition in sows with prostaglandin $F_{2\alpha}$. *Can. J. Comp. Med.* **42,** 32–34.

Russell, C. A. (1979) The benefits of planned farrowing. *Livestock Int.* **34,** 6–7.

Schultz, R. H. (1980) Experiences and problems associated with usage of prostaglandins in countries other than the United States. *J. Am. Vet. Med. Assoc.* **176,** 1182–1186.

Sharpe, H. B. A. (1966) Pre-weaning mortality in a herd of large white pigs. *Br. Vet. J.* **122,** 99–111.

Sherwood, O. D., Chang, C. C., De Vier, G. W., Diehl, J. R. and Dziuk, P. J. (1975) Relaxin concentrations in pig plasma following the administration of prostaglandin $F_{2\alpha}$ during late pregnancy. *Endocr.* **98,** 875–879.

Sherwood, O. D., Martin, P. A., Chang, C. C. and Dziuk, P. J. (1977) Plasma relaxin levels during late pregnancy and at parturition in pigs with altered utero-ovarian connections. *Biol. Reprod.* **17,** 101–103.

Sherwood, O. D., Wilson, M. E., Edgerton, L. A. and Chang, C. C. (1978) Serum relaxin concentrations in pigs with parturition delayed by progesterone administration. *Endocr.* **102,** 471.

Silver, M., Barnes, R. J., Comline, R. S., Dowden, A. L., Clover, L. and Mitchell, M. D. (1979) Prostaglandins in the fetal pig and prepartum endocrine changes in mother and fetus. *Anim. Reprod. Sci.* **2,** 305–322.

Sovljanski, B., Milosavljevic, S., Miljkovic, V., Stankov, M., Trbojevic, C. and Radovic, B. (1972) Dependence of the occurrence of stillborn piglets upon the body position of the piglets at farrowing. *Acta. Vet. Beograd.* **21,** 241–245.

Sprecher, D. J., Leman, A. D., Dziuk, P. J., Cropper, M. and Dedecker, M. (1974) Causes and control of swine stillbirths. *J. Am. Vet. Med. Ass.* **165,** 689–701.

Stanton, H. C. and Carroll, J. K. (1974) Potential mechanisms responsible for prenatal and perinatal mortality or low viability of swine. *J. Anim. Sci.* **38,** 1037.

Stryker, J. L. and Dziuk, P. J. (1975) Effects of fetal decapitation on fetal development parturition and lactation in pigs. *J. Anim. Sci.* **40,** 282–287.

Taverne, M. A. M., Van der Weyden, G. C., Fontijne, P., Ellendorff, F., Naaktgeboren, C. and Smidt, D. (1977) Uterine position and presentation at mini-pig fetuses and their order and presentation at birth. *Am. J. Vet. Res.* **38,** 1761–1764.

Taverne, M., Willemse, A. H., Dieleman, S. J. and Bevers, M. (1979). Plasma prolactin, progesterone and oestradiol-17β concentrations around parturition in the pig. *Anim. Reprod. Sci.,* **I,** 257–263.

Varley, M. (1981) New ways to control farrowing. *Pig Farm. Aug.* 38–40.

Walker, N. (1977) The effects of induction of parturition in sows using an analogue of prostaglandin $F_{2\alpha}$. *J. Agric. Sci., Camb.,* **89,** 267–271.

Wettemann, R. P., Hallford, D. M. Kreider, D. L. and Turman, E. J. (1974) Parturition in swine after prostaglandin $F_{2\alpha}$. *J. Anim. Sci.* **39,** 228 (Abs).

Wettemann, R. P., Hallford, D. M., Kreider, D. L. and Turman, E. J. (1977) Influence of prostaglandin F_2 on endocrine changes at parturition in gilts. *J. Anim. Sci.* **44,** 106–111.

Wierzchos, E. and Pejsak, Z. (1976) Induction of parturition in sows with prostin F_2 in commercial swine farms. *Proc. 8th Int. Congr. Anim. Reprod. A.I. (Kracow),* **3,** 418–420.

Willemse, A. H., Taverne, M. A. I., Roope, L. J. J. A. and Adams, W. N. (1979) Induction of parturition in the sow with a prostaglandin analogue (ICI 80996). *Vet. Q.* **1**(3), 145–149.

Wilson, M. E., Edgerton, L. A., Cromwell, G. L. and Stanly, T. S. (1981) Progesterone and estrogen concentrations in gilts with delayed parturition 1,2. *J. Anim. Sci.* **52,** 323–329.

Wrathall, A. E. (1980) Ovarian disorders in the sow. *Vet. Bull.* **50,** 253–272.

Wrathall, A. E., Bailey, J., Wells, D. D. and Herbert, C. N. (1977) Studies on the barker (neonatal respiratory distress) syndrome in the pig. *Cornell Vet.* **67,** 543–598.

Zerobin, K. and Sporri, H. (1972). *Adv. Vet. Sci. Comp. Sci.,* **16,** 303.

CHAPTER 26

More Frequent Farrowings in Pigs

26.1 INTRODUCTION

Sow productivity is closely related to the number of weaned pigs produced per sow per year; this, in turn, is a function of the number of piglets born and reared per litter and the number of litters per sow per year. Management and husbandry techniques can influence the number of piglets born. The level of feeding can be increased between weaning and remating, particularly for first and second litter animals; older sows will also benefit in the same way if they have lost excessive weight during lactation. Results are better with cross-bred animals, which are known to produce larger litters and more viable piglets.

Beyond factors such as those, however, there is one major way in which sow productivity can be influenced; this is by reducing the age of weaning. Decreasing the length of the lactation period by early weaning could increase the number of litters per sow per year from 2.05, when piglets are weaned at 8 weeks to 3.0 when pigs are weaned at birth, assuming an interval of 7 days between weaning and conception. The effect of age of weaning on the possible number of pigs reared per sow annually has been dealt with by Newport (1977) with U.K. conditions in mind; his calculations showed that, compared with weaning at 21 or 56 days of age, weaning at

birth could increase sow productivity by about 40 and 70%, respectively.

Although in theory it may appear that the sow is capable of producing three litters per year, there are, in practice, several difficulties facing the pig producer who attempts pushing his pigs towards that level of performance. The sow, in contrast to the cow, is normally in a state of anoestrus during lactation and for that reason cannot normally be bred to the boar until some days after piglets are weaned. It follows, therefore, that methods of overcoming lactational anoestrus could be of some importance in evolving techniques for increasing the number of litters per sow per year.

26.2 ENDOCRINOLOGY OF LACTATIONAL ANOESTRUS

With the exception of the anovulatory heat period that occurs in a proportion of sows within 5 days of parturition (Burger, 1952; Baker et al., 1953; Self and Grummer, 1958; Heitman and Cole, 1956), oestrous activity is inhibited during lactation in the sow. It would seem that lactational anoestrus is maintained until weaning, provided that more than one sucking piglet is continuously present (Parvizi et al., 1976) and that lactation itself is not unusually prolonged.

The underlying endocrine mechanisms at work during lactation in the sow are only partly understood. It is clear that ovarian and pituitary activity are suppressed while the sow is nursing the piglets; follicular growth and corpora lutea are absent during the entire lactation (Crighton and Lamming, 1969), plasma progesterone levels are consistently low and plasma oestrogen concentrations are almost undetectable (Ash and Heap, 1975; Baldwin and Stabenfeldt, 1975; Parvizi et al., 1976). Although high levels of FSH have been reported, pituitary LH content (Crighton and Lamming, 1969) and plasma LH levels (Parvizi et al., 1976) are very low and an inability of the lactating sow to increase LH synthesis has been suggested (Crighton and Lamming, 1969). There is, however, the possibility that the anterior pituitary is unable to release LH during lactation because the stimulatory positive oestrogen feedback mechanism has been shown to be incapable of operating normally during early lactation (Elsaesser and Parvizi, 1980).

26.2.1 Prolactin levels

It seems likely that the release of prolactin, as a result of the suckling stimulus, plays an important role in the mechanism of the blockade of the stimulatory oestrogen feedback action. The antigonadal role of prolactin is well established in other species (Kann et al., 1977, and lactating sows have high prolactin levels compared with values in the post-weaning period (Bevers et al., 1978; Landeghem and Wiel, 1978). An impairment of LH release after the administration of oestrogen by hyperprolactinaemic ewes has been reported and it does not appear to be due to a reduced responsiveness of the pituitary to Gn–RH (Kann et al., 1976, 1977).

If prolactin also plays an important role in lactational anoestrus in pigs, the recovery of oestrogen-induced LH release during late lactation (Elsaesser and Parvizi, 1980) could be explained on the basis of the progressive decrease of plasma prolactin levels in the period between farrowing and weaning (Landeghem and Wiel, 1978). There is evidence in the rat that the suckling stimulus rather than high circulating

levels of prolactin is primarily responsible for suppressing LH release; during late lactation, as a result of increased solid food intake by piglets, it is possible that there may be a partial recovery of the stimulatory oestrogen feedback mechanism, as observed by Elsaesser and Parvizi (1980).

Prolactin levels in sows during pregnancy, parturition and the early weeks of lactation have also been reported on by Dusza and Krzymowska (1981) who found increases in prolactin just before farrowing and a very high level at the time of parturition (147 ng ml^{-1}); after farrowing, the level gradually decreased, reaching 43 ng ml^{-1} on the 5th day of lactation. These findings on prolactin levels were in agreement with other reports (Bevers et al., 1978; Landeghem and Wiel, 1978; Mulloy and Malvern, 1979).

26.2.2 Involution of the uterus

In any question of rebreeding the sow in the early weeks after parturition, one obvious consideration, quite apart from the question of ovarian activity, is that of uterine involution. Dealing with information in the literature, Hughes and Varley (1980) note that with conventional weaning systems, the pig's uterus rapidly loses length and weight in the first 2–3 weeks after farrowing and then remains in this state until after weaning, when weight and length increase in response to the action of the ovarian steroids; although complete involution does not occur until about 3 weeks into lactation, it seems that most of the important changes have taken place by day-7 of lactation and it appears that the uterus should be able to function normally again by 2–3 weeks after parturition (Palmer et al., 1965a, b; Svajgr et al., 1974). It should be noted, however, that the rate of uterine involution is probably influenced by whether or not the sow is suckled after farrowing; it seems possible that very short lactations slow down the rate of loss in weight of the post-partum uterus and if mating occurs very soon after parturition, then conditions in the reproductive tract may not be particularly favourable for fertilization and implantation (Hughes and Varley, 1980).

26.3 INITIATING OVARIAN ACTIVITY

Based on experimental evidence, the sow ovary appears to be responsive to stimulation by gonadotrophins administered exogenously during lactation, but does not appear to be actively secreting significant amount of steroids until after weaning (Stevenson and Britt, 1981); as already mentioned, ovulation during lactation appears to be inhibited due to reduced LH synthesis or secretion that can only be increased by weaning or perhaps a reduction in suckling intensity.

26.3.1 Management practices

Although the sow does not normally show heat periods during lactation, there are certain circumstances under which it seems possible to overcome the inhibitory effect on ovarian activity. Two management practices have occasionally been known to initiate oestrus in lactation; these involve either partial separation of the sow and litter or grouping of sows and their litters in the presence of the boar. Partial separation of sow and litter on a daily basis, imposed experimentally, has been successful in some instances (Crighton, 1961; Smith, 1961; Mitic *et al.*, 1966) but without effect in others (Crighton, 1968; Cole *et al.*, 1972).

A system of management involving the grouping of sows, together with their litters, in the presence of a boar and under an *ad lib.* feeding regime, has been found by some investigators to be highly effective in getting lactating sows in oestrus about 5 weeks after parturition (Rowlinson and Bryant, 1975, 1976; Rowlinson *et al.*, 1975); these workers exposed groups of three to eight sows and their litters to continuous physical boar exposure from day-24 *post-partum* to weaning at day-42. The interval from grouping to oestrus in this work was 11 days; in one trial, 100% of the lactating sows showed a heat period and of those bred 85% conceived.

In contrast to such results, other authors have recorded no appreciable incidence of oestrus (Petchey *et al.*, 1978; Petchey and Jolly, 1979; Petchey and English, 1980). In attempting to analyse the reasons for the apparent lack of success, Petchey *et al.* (1978) showed that grouping *per se* did not initiate lactational oestrus. Petchey and Jolly (1979) have put forward the view that the experience of the sow in the previous pregnancy may be important in understanding the phenomenon of lactational oestrus; failure in response to grouping may be related to low feed levels or a negative nitrogen balance during the previous pregnancy.

In a further report, Petchey and English (1980), although recording a low incidence of oestrus in their groups of lactating sows, did note that the interval between exposure to the boar and the onset of the heat period was much shorter than when the boar was absent from the group; they suggest that the boar probably has a crucial, although secondary, role to play in the successful stimulation of oestrus in lactation, possibly by influencing the sow's gonadotrophin status. From the farmer's viewpoint, clearly much more information is required before serious thought could be given to this particular management approach towards getting lactating sows to breed.

26.4 ARTIFICIAL INDUCTION OF OESTRUS

As already mentioned, it has been suggested that lactational anoestrus in pigs is the result of the suckling stimulus acting via the hypothalamus to inhibit the synthesis or release of LH and the release of FSH. Attempts that have been made over the years to induce oestrus and ovulation in the nursing sow have therefore centred on overcoming this gonadotrophin deficiency, either by trying to facilitate the release of the animal's endogenous hormones or by using exogenous gonadotrophins.

An ovulatory oestrus may be induced in lactating sows by the administration of gonadotrophic hormones; injection of appropriate dose levels of PMSG (1000–2000 i.u.), given after day-40 of lactation has been shown to be consistently effective in inducing oestrus 4 or 5 days later, typical responses being 96% (Cole and Hughes, 1946) and 86% (Heitman and Cole, 1956). When workers have attempted to administer the gonadotrophin at an earlier stage of lactation (e.g. day-20), the response has been both lower and much less consistent; in such instances, it may be as low as 20% (Cole and Hughes, 1946) or 17% (Allen et al., 1957). It is evident that the response to gonadotrophins may be influenced by genetic and management factors; Crighton (1970) employed a system of partial weaning in conjunction with PMSG at day-20 of lactation and found that this facilitated response (80 vs 38%) as compared with that found using gonadotrophin alone.

26.4.1 Inducing pregnancy in lactating sows

Attempts to induce conception in lactating sows have been reported in the U.S.A. by Kinney et al. (1977), Guthrie et al. (1978) and Hausler et al. (1980). There was a particularly successful outcome to the approach employed by Hausler et al. (1980), who used PMSG/hCG treatment (1500 i.u. PMSG with 1000 i.u. hCG 96 h later) followed by artificial insemination at a pre-determined time (24 and 36/42 h after the hCG dose). These workers succeeded in inducing ovulation and conception as early as 15 days post-farrowing without this influencing the normal growth rate of the piglets; the conception rates, number of corpora lutea and litter-sizes appeared to be comparable to those achieved in a natural breeding programme. The results of these same workers (Hausler et al., 1980) support the view that the ovaries of the lactating sow are responsive in some instances by day-10 and certainly by day-15 post-partum; however, conception failure in sows treated on day-10 may have been the result of inadequacies in the uterine environment. As noted earlier, uterine involution and repair of the endometrial epithelium is not complete until 3 weeks post-partum (Palmer et al., 1965a, b).

26.5 EARLY WEANING AND REBREEDING

Apart from inducing pregnancy in the lactating pig, a further approach to increasing sow productivity lies in either removing the piglets at or within a few hours of birth (zero-weaning) and rearing them artificially or using one or other forms of early weaning. In normal commercial practice, there exists a wide range of ages at which piglets are early-weaned from the sow; this would include the traditional 6–8 week weaning system down to very early weaning at 10 days of age. Over the course of the last 10 years in Ireland and the U.K., producers have tended on average to reduce the time the sow spends in lactation in pursuit of greater annual sow productivity; the fact is that earlier rebreeding of sows after farrowing is one of the few areas of pig reproduction where increases in output are still possible.

26.5.1 Problems in early weaning

Whether it has been attempted in an experimental situation or in commercial practice, early weaning, particularly below 21 days of age, has been accompanied by a decline in the size of the subsequent litter (Dyrendahl et al., 1958; Van der Heyde, 1972; Aumaitre, 1973; Pay, 1973; Miskovic and Stejanovic, 1974; Krug et al., 1974). Cole et al. (1975) examined the effect of lactations varyng in length from 4 to 42 days on subsequent litter-size and found a decrease from 12.7 piglets per litter when weaning at 21 days to 9.6 when the young were removed earlier than that time. Such reductions in litter-size would seem to be the result of a higher than usual incidence of embryo mortality in the first 3 weeks of pregnancy (Varley and Cole, 1976a, b).

Data provided by Van der Heyde (1972) in Belgium and Cole et al. (1975) in the U.K. indicate that weaning at 7 days of age or earlier is liable to reduce subsequent litter-size by two piglets on average; Newport (1977) calculated that this reduced the potential sow productivity after very early weaning to little more than that operating with weaning at 21 days. It should also be noted that experimental work has shown several adverse effects of very early weaning, other than reduced litter-size; these include an increase in the duration and variability of the interval from weaning to a subsequent fertile oestrus (Self and Grummer, 1958; Van der Heyde, 1972; Aumaitre, 1973; Cole et al., 1975), reduced conception rate (Moody and Speer, 1971; Pay, 1973) and an increase in the incidence of cystic ovarian degeneration (Baker et al., 1953; Self and Grummer, 1958; Peters et al., 1969).

In first parity sows, early weaning may pose a special problem because of the prolonged weaning to oestrus interval which may often occur and the disappointing average size of second litters. According to Love (1979), some Australian pig producers now deliberately delay mating of first parity sows until at least 12 days after weaning; it appears that increased litter-size more than compensates for the increased maintenance costs incurred and it is believed that the improved reproductive performance is due to a reduction in embryonic mortality rather than to any increase in the basic ovulation rate.

In summing up the present view on early weaning systems, it would appear that a lactation length of 3 weeks should provide maximum sow output with minimum reproductive malfunction. There is evidence to show that sow productivity, under commercial conditions, does

increase when piglets are weaned at 3–4 weeks rather than at 5–8 weeks (Ridgeon, 1976; Newport, 1977).

26.6 PARTIAL WEANING TECHNIQUES

As already mentioned, by about the third week of lactation in the pig, a fertile oestrus can be induced by separating the sow from the litter for periods of 12 h for 3 consecutive days and injecting a gonadotrophin such as PMSG to stimulate ovarian activity (Crighton, 1970). Elsewhere, Greek workers attempted something similar, using partial weaning (separation of sow and litter for 12 h daily) in the period 15–21 days *post-partum* and a dose of 1000 i.u. PMSG on day-21 (Alifakiotis *et al.*, 1979); results showed an oestrous response in 65% of the sows, which is

Fig. 26.1. Problems in the early weaning of pigs. After weaning the sow's first litter of piglets, postweaning oestrus may be delayed much more frequently compared with older sows. When it is a question of weaning earlier than 3 weeks after farrowing, then the modern lean, low appetite young pig may not be able to meet the demands on the reproductive system with the usual type of feeds that are available. There are those who would see the high-oil feed supplement as having a useful contribution to make in this area.

below the 80% figure recorded by Crighton (1970).

The effect of the stage of lactation on the outcome of this type of treatment is shown in work reported for German Landrace sows by Polanco et al. (1980); treatment involved the use of gonadotrophin (400 i.u. PMSG and 200 i.u. hCG) after removing young at 21 days for 24 h, but the oestrous response was low. When the same regimen was applied at the normal 6-weeks weaning date, it was much more effective.

26.7 ZERO-WEANING AND ITS PROBLEMS

The ultimate early-weaning system, zero-weaning, is that in which the piglets are removed from the sow at farrowing or within a few hours of birth and reared artificially. Polge (1972) drew attention to the lack of information on the reproductive consequences of this procedure. Although he noted that the post-partum uterus was probably capable of functioning reasonably well within 2 weeks of farrowing, as uterine regeneration should be well advanced by then, he also observed that such uterine repair may occur more slowly than usual in the zero- or very early-weaned sow. In Canada, Elliot et al. (1980), found that zero-weaning resulted in an increase in the interval from farrowing to conception, a concomitant increase in the farrowing interval, a greater incidence of cystic ovarian degeneration and a reduced conception rate as compared to controls weaned at 30 days post-partum; such results were similar to those previously recorded by other investigators, although no reduction in litter-size was observed in the Canadian work. Treatment by these same investigators (Elliot et al., 1980) of zero-weaned sows with PMSG and hCG (the gonadotrophins given at 48 h post-partum) in an effort to induce ovulation and thereby establish normal cyclical breeding activity offered no advantage over weaning at 3 weeks; the Canadians suggested that it might be better trying to suppress pituitary function for a period post-partum to mimic the effect in the lactating sow.

26.7.1 Suppressing early gonadotrophin activity

Dealing with the endocrinology of the early post-partum period in the sow, Polge (1972) drew attention to the fact that the development of cystic follicles and infertility can be a serious problem with systems of very early weaning and suggested that it might be useful to suppress pituitary gonadotrophin activity for a short period after farrowing. Walker and Eddie (1974) did, in fact, use the gonadotrophin inhibitor methallibure for 12 days post-partum to inhibit ovarian activity and gave 1000 i.u. PMSG on the day after this treatment ended; pigs that received the inhibitor had substantially larger litters than did controls (11.7 vs 8.5 piglets).

In further work, Walker and Eddie (1975) treated sows weaned 10 days after farrowings with methallibure, but this time for 5 days, PMSG being administered on the following day; synchronization and conception rate appeared to be acceptable but litter-size was below that in controls and the authors suggest that the more prolonged treatment with the inhibitor in their earlier work may have had a direct effect on litter-size. As mentioned previously, the pituitary inhibitor is no longer available to pig producers in most parts of the world.

26.7.2 General conclusions

From the information presently available, it is clear that zero-weaning has an adverse effect on the subsequent reproductive performance of the sows and there is no advantage, in terms of sow productivity, over a system of 3-week weaning. As seen by Elliott et al. (1980), the only feasible means of overcoming the reproductive problems created by zero-weaning is to combine such a system with the production of the once-bred gilt, marketing the gilt soon after weaning.

26.8 REFERENCES

Alifakiotis, T., Matsoukas, I., Gavriilidis, G. and Mantzaris, E. (1979) Hormonal induction of breeding in lactating sow. Geonida, 254/255. 234–240.
Allen, A. D., Lasley, J. F. and Uren, A. W. (1957) The effects of gonadotrophic hormone injections on induction of estrus in lactating sows. J. Anim. Sci. 16, 1097–1098.
Ash, R. W. and Heap, R. B. (1975) Oestrogen, progesterone

corticosteroid concentrations in peripheral plasma of sows during pregnancy, parturition, lactation and after weaning. *J. Endocr.* **64,** 141–154.

Aumaitre, A. (1973) Influence de mode de sevrage sur la productivite des truies. *Wld. Rev. Anim. Prod.* **9,** 56–63.

Baker, L. N. Woehling, H. L., Casida, L E. and Grummer, R. H. (1953) Occurrence of estrus in sows following parturition. *J. Anim. Sci.* **12,** 33–38.

Baldwin, D. M. and Stabenfeldt, G. H. (1975) Endocrine changes in the pig during late pregnancy, parturition and lactation. *Biol. Reprod.* **12,** 508–515.

Bevers, M. M., Willemse, A. H. and Kruip, TL. A. M. (1978) Plasma prolactin levels in the sow during lactation and the *post-weaning* period as measured by RIA. *Biol. Reprod.* **19,** 628–634.

Burger, J. F. (1952) Sex physiology of pigs. *Onderstepoort J. Vet. Res.* **25,** Suppl. No. 2, 1–218.

Cole, D. J. A., Brooks, P. H. and Kay, R. M. (1972) Lactational anoestrus in the sow. *Vet. Rec.* **90,** 681–683.

Cole, D. J. A., Barley, M. A. and Hughes, P. E. (1975) Studies in sow reproduction. 2. The effect of lactation length on the subsequent reproductive performance of the sow. *Anim. Prod.* **20,** 401–406.

Cole, H. H. and Hughes, E. H. (1946) Induction of estrus in lactating sows with equine gonadotrophin. *J. Anim. Sci.* **5,** 25–29.

Crighton, D. B. (1961) Pig nutrition with special reference to early weaning. *M.Sc. Thesis. Univ. of Edinburgh.*

Crighton, D. (1968) The induction of oestrus and ovulation during the lactational anoestrus of the sow. *Proc. 6th Int. Congr. Reprod. and A.I. (Paris)* 1415–1417.

Crighton, D. B. (1970) The induction of pregnancy during lactation in the sow; the effects of a treatment imposed at 21 days of lactation. *Anim. Prod.* **12,** 611–617.

Crighton, D. B. and Lamming, G. E. (1969) The lactational anoestrus of the sow: the status of the anterior pituitary-ovarian system during lactation and after weaning. *J. Endocr.* **43,** 507–519.

Dusza, L. and Krzymowska, H. (1981) Plasma prolactin levels in sows during pregnancy, parturition and early lactation. *J. Reprod. Fert.* **61,** 131–134.

Dyrendahl. S., Olsson, B. Borck, G. and Ehlers, T. (1958) Artificial raising of baby pigs. Part II. Additional experiments including the effect of early weaning on the fertility of sows. *Acta. Agric. Scand.* **8,** 3–19.

Elliot, J. I., King, G. J. and Robertson, H. A, (1980) Reproductive performance of the sow subsequent to weaning piglets at birth. *Can. J. Anim. Sci.* **60,** 65–71.

Elsaesser, F. and Parvizi, N. (1980) Partial recovery of the stimulatory oestrogen feedback action on LH release during late lactation in the pig. *J. Reprod. Fert.* **59,** 63–67.

Guthrie, H. D., Pursel, V. G. and Frobish, L. T. (1978) Attempts to induce conception in lactating sows. *J. Anim. Sci.* **47,** 1145–1151.

Hausler, C. L., Hodson, H. H. Jr., Kuo, D. C., Kinney, T. J., Rauwolf, V. A. and Strack, L. E. (1980) Induced ovulation and conception in lactating sows. *J. Anim. Sci.* **50,** 773–778.

Heitman, H., Jr., and Cole, H. H. (1956) Further studies in the induction of estrus in lactating sows with equine gonadotrophin. *J. Anim. Sci.* **15,** 970–977.

Hughes, P. and Varley, M. (1980) *Reproduction in the Pig.* Butterworth, London.

Kann, G. D., Martinet, J. and Schirar, A. (1976) Impairment of LH release following oestrogen administration to hyper-prolactinaemic ewes. *Nature, Lond.* **264,** 465.

Kann, G., Habert, R., Neusnier, C. and Ryniewicz, H. S. (1977) Prolactin release in response to nursing or milking stimulus in the ewe. It is mediated by thyrotrophin releasing hormone. *Ann. Biol. Anim. Biochim. Biophys.* **17,** 441–452.

Kinney, T. J., Hausler, C. L., Hodson, H. H. Jr. and Snyder, R. A. (1977) Induced follicular development, ovulation and conception in lactating sows. *Proc. 69th Ann. Meet. ASAS,* 447.

Krug, J. L., Harp, V. W., Cromwell, G. L. Dutt, R. H. and Kratzer, D. D. (1974) Effect of lactation length on reproductive performance of swine. *J. Anim. Sci.* **39,** 216 (Abs).

Landeghem, A. A. J., Van and Wiel, D. F. M. Van de (1978) RIA for porcine prolactin: plasma levels during lactation, suckling and weaning aid after TRH administration. *Acta Endocr.* **88,** 653–658.

Love, R. J. (1979) Reproductive performance of first parity sows. *Aust. Adv. Vet. Sci.* 42.

Miskovic, N. and Stojanovic, S. (1974) The effect of shortening on fertility of sows. *Acta. Vet.* **24,** 79–86.

Mitic, N., Bokorov, T. and Sreckovic, A. (1966) The effect of the management of sows during lactation on oestrus and reproduction. *Art poljopr Nauke* **19,** 3–14.

Moody, N. W. and Speer, J. C. (1971) Factors affecting sow farrowing interval. *J. Anim. Sci.* **32,** 510–514.

Mulloy, A. L. and Malvern, P. V. (1979) Relationships between concentrations of porcine progesterone in blood serum and milk of lactating sows. *J. Anim. Sci.* **48,** 876–881.

Newport, M. J. (1977) Early weaning of pigs: a major advance in pig production. *World Animal Review,* **24,** 34–39.

Palmer, W. M., Teague, H. S. and Venzke, W. G. (1965a) Macroscopic observations on the reproductive tract of the sow during lactation and early post weaning. *J. Anim. Sci.* **24,** 541–545.

Palmer, W. M., Teague, H. S. and Venzke, W. G. (1965b) Histological changes in the reproductive tract of the sow during lactation and early post weaning. *J. 'Anim. Sci.* **24,** 1117–1125.

Parvizi, N., Elsaesser, F., Smidt, D. and Ellendorff, F. (1976) Plasma LH and progesterone in the adult female pig during the oestrous cycle, late pregnancy and lactation, and after ovariectomy and pentobarbitone treatment. *J. Endocr.* **69,** 193–203.

Pay, M. G. (1973) The effect of short lactations on the productivity of sows. *Vet. Rec.* **92,** 255–259.

Petchey, A. N. and English, P. R. (1980) A note on the effects of boar presence on the performance of sows and their litters when penned as groups in late lactation. *Anim. Prod.* **31,** 107–109.

Petchey, A. M. and Jolly, G. M. (1979) Sow service in lactation: an analysis of data from one herd. *Anim. Prod.* **29,** 183–191.

Petchey, A. M. Dodsworth, T. L. and English, P. R. (1978) The performance of sows and litters penned individually of grouped in late lactation. *Anim. Prod.* **27,** 215–221.

Peters, J. B., Short, R. E., First, N. L. and Casida, L. E. (1969) Attempts to induce fertility in post partum sows. *J. Anim. Sci.* **29,** 20–29.

Polanco, von A., Hesse de Polanco, E., Kalm, E., Smidt, D. and Holtz, W. (1980) Estrus induction in sows during and after lactation. *Zuchthyg.* **15,** 40–46.

Polge, C. (1972) Reproductive physiology in the pig with special reference to early weaning. *Proc. Br. Soc. Anim. Prod.* **1,** 5–18.

Ridgeon, R. F. (1976) Pig management scheme results for 1976.

Cambridge Agric. Econ. Unit. Dept. Land Economy, Univ. Cambridge.

Rowlinson, P. and Bryant, M. J. (1975) Effect of the interval between farrowing and grouping on the incidence and timing of oestrus in sows during lactation. *Proc. Br. Soc. Anim. Prod.* **4,** 103–104.

Rowlinson, P. and Bryant, M. J. (1976) The effect of lactation management on the incidence and timing of oestrus in lactating sows. *Anim. Prod.* **22,** 139.

Rowlinson, P., Boughton, H. G. and Bryant, M. J. (1975) Mating of sows during lactation: observations from a commercial unit. *Anim. Prod.* **21,** 233–241.

Self, H. L. and Grummer, R. H. (1958) The rate and economy of pig gains and the reproductive behaviour in sows when litters are weaned at 10 days, 21 days or 56 days of age. *J. Anim. Sci.* **17,** 862–868.

Smith, D. M. (1961) The effect of daily separation of sows from their litters upon milk yield, creep intake, and energenic efficiency. *N.Z. Jl. Agric. Res.* **4,** 232–245.

Stevenson, J. S. and Britt. H. H. (1981) Interval to estrus in sows

and performance of pigs after alteration of litter size during late lactation. *J. Anim. Sci.* **53,** 177–181.

Svajgr, A. J., Hays, V. W., Cromwell, G. L. and Dutt, R. H. (1974) Effect of lactation duration and reproductive performance of sows. *J. Anim. Sci.* **38,** 100–105.

Van Der Heyde, H. (1972) A practical assessment of early weaning. *Proc. Brit. Soc. Anim. Prod.* **1,** 33–36.

Varley, M. A. and Cole, D. J. A. (1976a) The importance of pre-implantation losses in the embryonic mortality of the early weaned sow. *Anim. Prod.* **22,** 161–162 (Abs),

Varley, M. A. and Cole, D. J. A. (1976b) Studies in sow reproduction. The effect of lactation length of the sow on the subsequent embryonic development. *Anim. Prod.* **22,** 79–85.

Walker, N. and Eddie, S. M. (1974) The effect on sow productivity following a two-day lactation. *Anim. Prod.* **18,** 153–158.

Walker, N. and Eddie, S. M. (1975) A note on the effect of sow productivity of methallibure administration following a 10-day lactation. *Anim. Prod.* **20,** 303–305.

CHAPTER 27

Increasing Litter-Size in Pigs

27.1 INTRODUCTION

Litter-size in the pig, as in other farm animals, is a function of ovulation rate, fertilization rate and intra-uterine mortality; obviously, the number of eggs released at ovulation will set the upper limit of litter-size for any particular gestation. A comprehensive review of factors affecting ovulation rate and litter-size was provided by Wrathall (1971), who drew attention to the way in which the uterus imposes a limitation upon the number of foetuses surviving in the pig; it can limit by virtue of its length (its actual inability to hold more than a certain number of young) and it can limit by the evenness or otherwise of distribution and spacing of the embryos.

It would appear that when the ovulation rate is increased to well beyond the normal physiological level (by use of gonadotrophin treatment), the benefits of any small increase in the average litter-size will almost certainly be outweighed by the variability in the size of the litters and in the birth weights of the piglets born in these litters. Reviewing the various possibilities for increasing the number of young born alive per litter, Wrathall (1971), at that time, concluded that while ovulation rate should be kept as high as possible by natural means, attempts to produce increases artificially would probably not be of commercial interest.

27.2 BREED, FEED, AGE AND SIRE EFFECTS

Reproductive performance is measured primarily by the number of living pigs at birth in the sow; under normal systems of weaning (i.e. 3 weeks and above), a target of 11–12 piglets born alive per litter should be the aim for the sow and 9–10 piglets for the gilt (Hughes and Varley, 1980).

27.2.1 Breeding considerations
The heritability of litter-size in the pig is regarded as being very low and there is little to be gained by selecting for it; Legault (1970), on the basis of an extensive review of the literature at that time, estimated it to be no greater than 0.10. Pig cross-breeding studies, dating from the 1930s using inbred and other animals, have shown that heterosis for reproductive traits, including litter-size, ranges from 5 to 25%, depending on the breeds used in the cross (Bradford et al., 1953; Nelson and Robinson, 1976; Johnson et al., 1978). Consequently, it has become a widespread commercial practice in many countries to use crossbred or hybrid sows as the breeding females.

27.2.2 Feeding effects
Adequate nutrition of the gilt or sow is obviously important; the ovulation rate can be influenced by feeding before oestrus and evidence suggests that total feed or energy intake

Fig. 27.1. A good litter-size is essential for profitability in pig production. Litter-size is not strongly inherited but it can differ according to breed and according to whether the sow herd is purebred or crossbred. There may have been some tendency to select for lean, fast-growing pigs without paying so much attention to the litter size. Apart from the genetic considerations, various other factors can enter into the picture, not only feed but also the boar and the system of mating used.

is of greatest significance. Although a deficient nutritional regime may depress ovulation rate (Brooks and Cooper, 1972; Cooper et al., 1973) there is less certainty as to whether energy levels above those necessary for normal maintenance and production have merit other than to ensure a normal ovulation rate (Self et al., 1955; Staigmiller and First, 1973).

At one time, on the basis of work at Nottingham, it was thought that increased feed intake during oestrus might affect ovulation rate (Lodge and Hardy, 1968); there was a trend towards higher ovulation rates as post-mating feed intake was raised from 1.4 to 4.1 kg day, but the differences were not significant. The effect on litter-size of doubling the feed intake on the day of mating was subsequently investigated over a wide range of management conditions in a field trial (Brooks and Cole, 1972); it became clear that only in isolated instances did such short-term feeding produce an effect. However, there was a

suggestion that the level of feeding between weaning and remating might influence the size of the subsequent litter.

In other work at Nottingham, Brooks and Cole (1972) showed that feed intakes of 1.8, 2.7 and 3.6 kg day were associated with litters of 9.4, 10.1 and 11.5 piglets and farrowing rates of 58.3%, 75% and 100%, respectively. As observed subsequently by Cole (1975), it appears unlikely that such a response would be obtained consistently but that it could operate under certain conditions (e.g. in sows where there was a large weight loss in lactation or in first parity sows); the same author draws attention to the importance of nutrition on long-term reproductive performance, as well as on the immediate litter. According to Brooks (1976), in planning for a potential herd life of six litters, a sow should increase her liveweight by 12–15 kg between successive matings at least up to the fourth litter; such increases are the result of the anabolic effects of pregnancy in the pig.

27.2.3 Age effects

Age as a factor affecting litter-size is well enough accepted, but there is some difference in opinion as to the source of the variations that occur with age. The number of pigs farrowed, according to Anderson and Melampy (1972) increases between the first and fourth litters, but by the eighth litter the number of live births declines, while the number of stillborn young increases; when litter-size is related to age, a decline is noted after about 4.5 years. French et al. (1979) discussed the view that previous reproductive "experience" can increase litter-size in pigs; the suggestion has been advanced by some that such "experience" on the part of the uterus can better prepare it for carrying a large number of young to term. The authors showed that most data in the literature relating age and parity to litter-size show the two factors to be highly confounded; experimental evidence was presented indicating that litter-size continues to rise as the age of the sow increases (until at least 2 years of age) and that parity has little or no direct effect on litter-size.

27.2.4 Sire effect

As well as age, several authors have reported finding evidence of a significant sire effect on litter-size (Legault, 1970; Rahnefeld and Swierstra, 1970); in one report, the advantage of crossing sows with a boar of a different breed is given as 0.2 extra live piglets.

27.3 EMBRYONIC AND FOETAL MORTALITY

From the research viewpoint, the question of litter-size is one of examining factors that influence the basic ovulation rate; more important still, it involves an examination of factors affecting the incidence of embryonic mortality. The sow differs from other farm animals in that litter-size depends less upon the available number of eggs released from the ovaries and much more upon the number of foetuses that survive in the uterus. The evidence shows that the incidence of prenatal mortality is highest during early gestation (Pomeroy, 1960)

with estimates of losses running as high as 40% or so.

27.3.1 Early pig embryo

From studies conducted to determine the time at which embryonic mortality occurs in the pig, Varley and Cole (1976a, b) concluded that the bulk of the loss takes place at or around the time of attachment (i.e. embryos aged 2–3 weeks). The pig embryo at day-10 of pregnancy is a spherical blastocyst about 3–5 mm in diameter (Anderson, 1978); at 12 days, as a result of rapid elongation of the trophoblast, it has increased to several centimetres in length. As described by Wrathall (1980), by 2 weeks of age, each embryo can now occupy about 20–30 cm of uterus, each horn of which can be about 100–150 cm in length; provided the number of embryos is sufficient, the whole uterine lumen is occupied by trophoblast. Points of loose contact between trophoblast and endometrium are evident at day-14, but intimate attachment is not established until day-18 (Crombie, 1970). The physiological and endocrinological mechanisms which control uterine capacity in the first few weeks of pregnancy, whether in the very early-weaned or in the normal sow, remain obscure.

27.4 INCREASING EMBRYO SURVIVAL

The extent of prenatal mortality in the sow has prompted several investigations into the effect on embryo survival of treating the dam with steroid hormones during the early part of pregnancy. There would seem to be some evidence that there is competition among embryos for some essential ingredient produced by the uterus; if this is so, then clearly it might be possible to influence the supply of this ingredient by some means. Workers at North Carolina have reported evidence that uterine capacity may be influenced by the level of progesterone around day-13 of gestation (Rampacek et al., 1975); although the administration of progesterone alone, even in very high doses, does not appear to influence litter-size, there is some evidence that a combination of progesterone and oestrogen may be more effective.

27.4.1 Progesterone:oestrogen treatments

Administration of progesterone and oestrogen (oestrone or oestradiol) in a 2000:1 ratio apparently resulted in an increase in the number of live embryos in the uteri of gilts examined at mid-pregnancy (Reddy et al., 1958; Day et al., 1963). Results reported by Wildt et al. (1976) also indicated that treatment with a 2000:1 progesterone, oestrone combination during early pregnancy had a beneficial effect on embryo survival, although results were not wholly unequivocal. Morcom et al. (1976) employed the progesterone:oestrone combination on day-16 and -17 and reported a tendency for the treated pigs to have larger litters; it was suggested by these authors that treatment may have induced an increase in the uterine proteins usually synthesized in limited quantities during this critical phase of implantation, enabling a greater proportion of the embryos to survive.

East German workers, on the other hand, used progesterone alone or in combination with oestradiol in early pregnancy in 607 gilts and sows without observing any positive effect (Heidler et al., 1979); they concluded that there was no practical benefit to be gained from this approach. Elsewhere, McGovern et al. (1981) reported work with the progesterone–oestrone combination which was also without effect on litter-size; however, these authors did find that the steroid treatment had a transient effect on the development of the allantochorion without conferring any obvious benefit on the survival of the developing embryo.

27.4.2 Nutrition during pregnancy

During pregnancy, large variations in protein and energy intake have been shown to have profound effects on sow weight, but in the majority of cases have not resulted in significant differences in the number of pigs born. The one exception to this is the gilt, in which high dietary energy levels in early gestation can result in an increased incidence of embryonic mortality and a reduction in litter-size (Cole, 1975; Brooks, 1976). It is generally accepted that variations in feed intake towards the end of gestation are more likely to influence birthweights than litter-size.

27.5 GONADOTROPHINS AND LITTER-SIZE

As a means of increasing the number of eggs shed, the administration of gonadotrophins during the follicular phase of the pig's oestrous cycle can be quite effective. Obviously, this is something of particular interest and value to those concerned with embryo transfer in pigs, where it may be desirable to get as high an egg yield as possible from a particular donor pig.

Anderson and Melampy (1972), reviewing data from many different studies conducted by investigators, calculated that the injection of PMSG (doses of 500–1500 i.u.) induced the release of an average of 4.8 additional eggs, but that only one extra foetus survived at day-30 of gestation. A report by Deneke and Day (1973) dealt with studies in which PMSG was used in conjunction with the pituitary inhibitor methallibure (PMSG administered 24 h after withdrawal of the inhibitor); the gonadotrophin treatment resulted in about 13 additional ovulations and 2.5 more foetuses on average at 70 days of gestation than in the controls.

Although high doses of PMSG will greatly increase the number of eggs shed and will increase embryo number to some extent, the change in mean litter-size at term may be so small as to be of no practical interest. A different approach was attempted by Emerson and Hendricks (1977); the aim in their work was to give a minimal effective dose (600 i.u. PMSG) on the basis that this would cause the least disturbance to the animal's endocrine system. Although there was a significant increase in ovulation rate, this was not associated with a greater number of foetuses at day-25 of gestation.

Used as part of a synchronizing treatment, the superovulatory effect of PMSG may be useful enough, especially in bringing litter-size in the gilt up to a level which otherwise might not be achieved. However, apart from that consideration, until such time as the hormonal and physiological mechanisms involved in embryonic mortality are much better understood, the application of gonadotrophin treatment as a means of raising the ovulation rate would not seem likely to be of interest to the pig producer.

27.6 FRATERNITY SIZE AND LITTER SIZE

During the past decade, some intriguing evidence has been reported on the way in which the early *post-natal* environment of the gilt may influence the size of the litter which it produces in later life. Rearing gilts in small fraternities (six or so pigs in a group) causes a phenotypic increase of about one pig at first parity (Nelson and Robinson, 1976; Rutledge, 1980a, b). It is not easy to suggest a mechanism by which small neonatal fraternity size operates to produce a change in litter-size in the animal when it grows up and starts reproducing 8 months or so later, although it may involve events occurring in the ovary of the newborn animal.

There is evidence to show that the pig differs from many other mammals in its pattern of oogenesis (Fulka *et al.*, 1972), which apparently lasts until at least 35 days after birth. It has been estimated that only about 50% of the germ cell population survive the transformation of oogonia to oocytes in the early weeks of the piglet's life (Black and Erickson, 1968). It has been suggested (Rutledge, 1980a, b) that a small fraternity size might provide conditions within the ovary whereby a larger proportion of primordial follicles survive and that this might be a factor influencing the ovulation rate of the same animal subsequently. There is a need to investigate further the influence of fraternity size on fecundity at second parity and beyond and to examine the process of oogenesis in newborn piglets subjected to a series of fraternal sizes. From the biological viewpoint, it is of obvious interest in the question of how species can regulate their populations under nature.

27.7 REFERENCES

Anderson, L. L. (1978) Growth, protein content and distribution of early pig embryos. *Anat. Rec.* **190,** 154.

Anderson, L. L. and Melampy, R. M. (1972) Factors affecting ovulation rate in the pig. In, *Pig Production.* Cole Ed. pp. 329–368. Butterworths, London.

Black, J. L. and Erickson, B. H. (1968) Oogenesis and ovarian development in the prenatal pig. *Anat. Rec.* **161,** 45.

Bradford, G. E., Chapman, A. B. and Grummer, R. H. (1953) Performance of hogs of different breeds and from straight bred and crossbred dams on Wisconsin farms. *J. Anim. Sci.* **12,** 582.

Brooks, P. H. (1976) Nutritional problems and sow reproduction. *Pig Vet. Soc. 1977*; Proc. of Meet & Joint Refresher Course on Pig Production, Aberdeen, Oct. 1976. 17–27.

Brooks, P. H. and Cole, D. J. A. (1972) Studies in sow reproduction. 1. The effect of nutrition between weaning and remating on the reproductive performance of primiparous sow. *Anim. Prod.* **15,** 259–264.

Brooks, P. H. and Cooper, K. H. (1972) Short-term nutrition and litter size. In, *Pig Production* Cole, D. J. A., Ed, pp. 385–398, Butterworths, London.

Cole, D. J. A. (1975) Towards greater sow productivity. *Span* **18**(3), 111–113.

Cooper, K. H., Brooks, P. H., Cole, D.J.A. and Haynes, N. B. (1973) The effect of feed level during the oestrous cycle on ovulation, embryo survival and anterior pituitary LH potency in the gilt. *J. Reprod. Fert.* **32,** 71.

Crombie, P. R. (1970) Ultra-structure of the foetal-maternal attachment in the pig. *J. Physiol. Lond.* **210,** 101–102.

Day, B. N., Romack, F. E. and Lasley, J. F. (1963) Influence of progesterone-estrogen implants on early embryonic mortality in swine. *J. Anim. Sci.* **22,** 637–639.

Deneke, W. A. and Day, B. N. (1973) Effect of superovulation on litter-size of swine at 70 days of gestation. *J. Anim. Sci.* **36,** 1137–1138.

Emerson, D. D. and Henricks, D. M. (1977) The effects of low levels of PMSG and flush feeding upon embryonic survival in gilts. *Theriogen.* **8**(5), 281–291.

French, L. R., Rutledge, J. J. and First, N. L. (1979) Effect of age and parity on litter size in pigs. *J. Reprod. Fert.* **57,** 59–60.

Fulka, J., Kopecny, V. and Trebichavsky, J. (1972) Studies on oogenesis in the early post-natal pig ovary. *Biol. Reprod.* **6,** 46.

Heidler, W., Nowak, P., Knuppel, K., Tschirner, R. and Huhn, U. (1979) Experimental application of steroids to sows in early gravidity to increase litter size. *Arch. Exp. Vet. Med. Leipzig* **33,** 639–644.

Hughes, P. and Varley, M. (1980) *Reproduction in the Pig.* Butterworths, London.

Johnson, R. K., Omtvedt, I. T. and Walters, L. E. (1978) Comparison of productivity and performance for two-breed and three-breed crosses in swine. *J. Anim. Sci.* **46,** 69.

Legault, C. (1970) *Ann. Genet. Sel. Anim.* **2,** 209.

Lodge, G. A. and Hardy, B. (1968) The influence of nutrition during oestrus on ovulation rate in the sow. *J. Reprod. Fert.* **15,** 329–332.

Morcom, C. B., Wildt, D. E. and Dukelow, W. R. (1976) Progesterone:Estrone injections during gestation in swine for increasing litter size. *Proc. Int. Vet. Pig Congr. (1976),* D.25.

McGovern, P. T., Morcom, C. B., de Sa, S. R. and Dukelow, W. R. (1981) Chotionic surface area in conceptuses from sows treated with progesterone and oestrogen during early pregnancy. *J. Reprod. Fert.* **61,** 439–442.

Nelson, R. E. and Robinson, O. W. (1976) Effects of post-natal maternal environment on reproduction of gilts. *J. Anim. Sci.* **43,** 71–77.

Pomeroy, R. W. (1960) Infertility and neonatal mortality in the sow. III. Neonatal mortality and foetal development. *J. Agric. Sci., Camb.* **54,** 31–56.

Rahnefeld, G. W. and Swierstra, E. (1970) Influence of the sire on litter size in swine. *Can. J. Anim. Sci.* **50,** 671.

Rampacek, G. R., Robinson, O. W. and Ulberg, L. C. (1975) Uterine capacity and Progestin levels in superinducted gilts. *J. Anim. Sci.* **41,** 564–567.

Reddy, V. B., Mayer, D. T. and Lasley, J. F. (1958) Hormonal modification of the intra-uterine environment in swine and its effect on embryonic viability. *Res. Bull Mo. Agric. Exp. Sta.,* No. 667.

Rutledge, J. J. (1980a) Fraternity size and swine reproduction. I. effect on fecundity of gilts. *J. Anim. Sci.* **51,** 868–870.

Rutledge, J. J. (1980b) Fraternity size and swine reproduction. II. Genetical consequences. *J. Anim. Sci.* **51,** 871–874.

Self, H. L., Grummer, R. H. and Casida, L. E. (1955) The effects of various sequence of full and limited feeding on the reproductive phenomena in Chester White and Poland China gilts. *J. Anim. Sci.* **14,** 573–592.

Staigmiller, R. B. and First, N. L. (1973) The effect of a single feed flush on ovulation rate in gilts. *J. Reprod. Fert.* **35,** 573.

Varley, M. A. and Cole, D. J. A. (1976a) Studies in sow reproduction. *Anim. Prod.* **22,** 71–77.

Varley, M. A. and Cole, D. J. A. (1976b) Studies in sow reproduction. *Anim. Prod.* **22,** 79–85.

Wildt, D. E., Culvert, A. A., Morcom, C. G. and Dukelow, W. R. (1976) Effect of administration of progesterone and oestrogen on litter size in pigs. *J. Reprod. Fert.* **48,** 209–211.

Wrathall, A. E. (1971) *Ovulation Rate and its Influence on Prenatal Survival and Litter Size in Pigs.* Commonwealth Agric. Bureau, Farnham Royal. (Commonwealth Bureau of Anim. Health Review Series No. 9).

Wrathall, A. E. (1980) Ovarian disorders in the sow. *Vet. Bull.* **50,** 253–272.

CHAPTER 28

Embryo Transfer in Pigs

28.1 INTRODUCTION

Effective techniques for embryo transfer in pigs are well-established and are widely used in research (Dziuk and Day, 1977); as yet, however, the transfer procedure has only been employed to a very limited extent in commercial practice. According to Polge (1980) at Cambridge, the most important practical application of the embryo transfer technique in pigs is probably in relation to disease control by permitting greater flexibility for the introduction of new genetic material into "closed" herds. At present this is done by way of artificial insemination or by introducing new pigs which have been delivered by hysterectomy. As shown by Curnock *et al.* (1976), embryo transfer can be used very effectively as an alternative to hysterectomy in getting disease-free piglets into a specific pathogen free (SPF) herd. The donor sow does not suffer loss as with hysterectomy and the risks of introducing disease should be less with embryo transfer. Indeed, studies in which deliberate attempts have been made to infect pig embryos with a virus disease (pseudorabies virus) suggest that they may be protected by the zona pellucida from infection (Bolin *et al.*, 1979); this type of work is obviously valuable in examining the potential of the transfer procedure in pigs.

A further situation in which Polge (1980) saw the technique being useful was that in which there had been a serious breakdown in the health status of the "closed" herd and embryo transfer was used as a means of "salvaging" valuable genetic material by transferring embryos into a "clean" herd elsewhere. Such opportunities for application of the method as those just described certainly should be borne in mind by the commercial pig producer.

28.1.1 Breeding improvement and other advantages

The usual reason for interest in embryo transfer in the farm animals is in order to obtain as many young as possible from the genetically out-standing female; this applies in pigs, as it does in cattle and sheep. It may, for instance be possible for the valuable but aged sow to serve as a donor of several batches of embryos when she has gone beyond the point of carrying a litter to term and rearing them herself. Certainly in the U.S.A., several of the pig breed associations have agreed to register purebred litters produced by embryo transfer, always provided that certification of transfer is available from the veterinarian performing the operation.

The export–import side of embryo transfer in pigs would obviously become much more feasible if pig embryos could be frozen in the same way as those of cattle and sheep. Until that does become possible, they can still be shipped around the world in the fresh state; instances of such shipments reported in the literature include the transport of embryos between the U.S.A. and Spain (James and Reeser, 1979) and between Canada and the U.K. (Wrathall *et al.*, 1970). A further example would be the studies reported by James *et al.* (1980) in which embryos recovered surgically from Chester White and Hampshire sows and gilts in the U.S.A. were shipped to England and there transferred to Large White gilts; in all, 227 embryos were transferred to 12 recipients, resulting in the birth of seven litters and a total of 58 piglets.

28.2 SUPEROVULATION TECHNIQUES

Although the sow normally releases several eggs at oestrus, there is still the need to induce an increased ovulation rate for embryo transfer purposes. Increased ovulation rates have been obtained in the post-pubertal gilt and sow by administering a single dose of PMSG at the beginning of the follicular phase of the oestrous cycle (optimum stage appears to be days 15 and 16); the number of ovulations has been found to follow a typical dose-response relationship when PMSG/hCG are employed. Hunter (1964) calculated a regression coefficient of 1.89 ± 0.5 corpora lutea/100 iu PMSG. The treatment with gonadotrophins usually reduces the length of the oestrous cycle by about one day and increases the duration of oestrus itself; normal fertilization rates can be expected in the superovulated animals bred by the usual procedures (Hunter, 1964; Phillipo, 1968; Guthrie *et al.*, 1974).

The administration of PMSG (doses of the order of 1500 i.u.) is also effective in the induction of superovulation when given 24 h after the last day of methallibure treatment (Dziuk, 1969; Christenson *et al.*, 1973); it is possible to inject hCG 96 h after PMSG to achieve more precise timing of ovulation (Polge and Day, 1967). Unfortunately, as noted previously, methallibure was withdrawn from market some years ago because of its teratogenic effect when fed to sows in early pregnancy.

There are few reports dealing with preparations other than PMSG in superovulation attempts; Day *et al.* (1959) employed pure FSH (Armour preparation) and reported increasing the ovulation rate when the gonadotrophin was given in the follicular phase but not in the luteal phase of the oestrous cycle in gilts.

28.2.1 Prepubertal gilts

For research purposes and for developing embryo transfer technology in pigs, prepubertal gilts can be regarded as an inexpensive source of embryos (Baker and Coggins, 1968; Baker *et al.*, 1974; Baker, 1979). The induction of superovulation is not complicated by the presence of an oestrous cycle, which enables gonadotrophin treatments to be applied at any time. Providing prepubertal gilts are reasonably well-grown (>80 kg), treatment with 1000 i.u. PMSG, followed 72 h later with 500 i.u. hCG, and then insemination at 24 h beyond that, has given satisfactory results; about 90% of eggs can be recovered and of these some 60% are fertilized (Baker, 1979). With an ovulation rate of 25, this means 22 eggs per pig recovered and 13 of these fertilized. Work elsewhere (Day, 1979) with pigs has produced evidence of a marked seasonal variation in response to PMSG; ovulatory response proved to be twice as high in spring (March/April) as in other months.

28.3 OOCYTE CULTURE AND *IN VITRO* FERTILIZATION

The observation of Pincus and Enzmann (1935) that isolated rabbit oocytes will mature spontaneously *in vitro* has been extended to some number of other mammalian species, including the pig (Edwards, 1965). A number of reports in the literature have dealt with the possibility of recovering pig eggs directly from ovarian follicles, maturing them *in vitro* and subsequently bringing about fertilization of the matured cell. As in cattle and sheep, the first meiotic division of the pig oocyte begins in prenatal life but is only normally completed in the final hours before ovulation in the postpubertal animal (Mauleon and Mariana, 1977). The oocyte spends most of its life with its nucleus in a particular stage of prophase of the first meiotic division; this is the diplotene stage, which is characterized morphologically by the presence of a large spherical nucleus (the germinal vesicle).

Oocyte maturation includes dissolution of the nuclear envelope of the germinal vesicle, condensation of the chromatin into discrete bivalents and segregation of homologues between the oocyte and first polar body during the first meiotic division. In the normal way, pig oocytes remain at the germinal vesicle stage until their follicles have grown to a large preovulatory size. The maternal influence is inhibitory, as shown by the fact that pig oocytes undergo spontaneous maturation if removed from vesicular follicles and cultured in an appropriate medium (McGaughy and Polge, 1971; Motlik, 1972; Tsafriri and Channing, 1975; Motlik and Fulka, 1976; McGaughey and Van Blerkom, 1977); after 40–50 h of culture, 50–70% of oocytes reach the second meiotic metaphase, which is the stage at which the egg is normally released at ovulation.

28.3.1 Development competency of oocytes

Although a variable proportion of oocytes are capable of fertilization after maturing in vitro (Motlik and Fulka, 1974; Iritani et al., 1978), there is a high incidence of abnormalities in such eggs; there is a strong suggestion that nuclear and cytoplasmic maturity of the pig oocyte cannot be achieved after liberating the oocyte from the follicle and culturing it in vitro (McGaughey and Polge, 1971; Motlik and Fulka, 1974). However, the fact that in rabbits a small but significant proportion of oocytes do appear to undergo normal maturation in vitro and to acquire competency for fertilization and apparently normal embryogenesis has suggested that pools of oocytes harvested for maturation studies are heterogenous relative to their developmental competencies (McGaughey, 1977; Van Blerkom and McGaughey, 1978).

Working on the in vitro maturation of pig oocytes, McGaughey et al. (1979) suggest that only those recovered from large, preovulatory follicles may be developmentally competent to undergo completely normal maturation and

fertilization; the acid test, however, lies in obtaining viable young derived from such oocytes. The same problems have already been referred to in relation to cattle and sheep oocytes.

28.3.2 Attempts to fertilize oocytes

Attempts to effect fertilization of pig oocytes have been made in vivo and in vitro. In early studies at Cambridge, pig oocytes matured in vitro were subsequently transferred to the oviducts of inseminated gilts; although sperm penetration occurred in some instances, there was a high incidence of chromosomal abnormalities suggesting that the block to polyspermy was defective in the oocytes (Polge and Dziuk, 1965). In other work, some apparently normal embryos were obtained after similar fertilization attempts with oocytes collected from gilts as early as 24–28 h after injection of hCG, which was estimated to be about 12–16 h ahead of the expected time of ovulation (Leman and Dziuk, 1971). Other work on fertilization attempts with in vitro matured oocytes in the pig oviduct was reported by Motlik and Fulka (1974).

Although an early claim for in vitro fertilization of pig oocytes was that of Harms and Smidt (1970), the evidence was not convincing. Studies reported by Cambridge workers (Baker and Polge, 1976; Polge, 1977), involving more than 500 oocytes failed to achieve in vitro fertilization; it was concluded that the problem lay in an inability to achieve capacitation of the boar sperm used in the experiments. Work by Iritani et al. (1978) suggested that it was possible to capacitate boar sperm in the isolated genital tract of the anoestrous sow; these same workers reported evidence of in vitro fertilization in about 28% of oocytes (showing morphologically normal male and female pronuclei).

It remains for further work to develop methods whereby normal nuclear and cytoplasmic maturation of pig oocytes can occur. It is well recognized that in the preovulatory follicle there is an accumulation of newly synthesized proteins in the germinal vesicle of the oocyte during the period of meiotic maturation as well as changes in the pattern of protein synthesis (Motlik et al., 1980); these events are believed to be essential for normal fertilization and embryonic developments.

28.4 CLONING POSSIBILITIES IN PIGS

As already mentioned, there is good evidence from a number of species, including the pig, that single blastomeres from an early cleavage egg are capable of further cleavage and development, even to full-term. Moore et al. (1969) reported that 35% of single blastomeres surviving after the destruction of three and five cells in four-cell and six-cell pig eggs were capable of further development provided transfer to recipients was made with the isolated blastomere protected within the zona pellucida; the continued cleavage of the egg was taken to suggest that more than one and possibly all, of the pig blastomeres possess the potential for full development. The variable rates of cleavage observed in the pig eggs was ascribed to leucocytic invasion through the aperture made by the micromanipulation technique employed with subsequent "digestion" of the blastomere rather than to the damage per se.

In fact, Dziuk et al. (1964) had much earlier reported that the survival rate of the pig eggs penetrated by a micromanipulation technique, but otherwise undamaged, was comparable to that of untreated eggs. Data have been presented by Menino and Wright (1979) suggesting that successful culture of isolated blastomeres from four- and eight-cell pig eggs up to the blastocyst stage in vitro and outside the zona pellucida has been achieved; by 96 h of culture, most of the cell stages were degenerate. It appears that survival and development of isolated blastomeres in recipient animals is dependent on their enclosure in a relatively intact zona pellucida; naked blastomeres have been rapidly destroyed in attempts to produce identical in pigs (Moore et al., 1969). As noted previously, the studies of Willadsen et al. (1981) have shown that it is now possible to produce pig identicals using micromanipulation techniques.

28.5 SURGICAL EGG RECOVERY

Methods employed for the collection of pig eggs are much the same today as they were almost 20 years ago (Hancock and Hovell, 1962; Dziuk et al., 1964; Vincent et al., 1964; Polge, 1966; James and Reeser, 1979). Embryo recovery is generally carried out by way of mid-ventral laparotomy under general anaesthesia induced by sodium thiopental or other effective agents, and usually maintained by a closed circuit system (Dziuk et al., 1964). The reproductive tract is exteriorized with manipulation of the oviducts and uterine horns kept to a minimum; aseptic precautions are taken at all stages of the recovery process.

Oviducal eggs can be collected after flushing the tube from the uterotubal junction (UTJ) through the cannulated infundibular end of the oviduct with 20–30 ml of warm flushing fluid (Day, 1979). The flushing medium has to be injected into the oviduct and not the uterine horn, since, in the pig, the structure of UTJ does not permit back-flushing into the oviduct from the uterus. Pig eggs may be expected to be in the Fallopian tubes 2 to 3 days after oestrus; the four-to six-cell stage of development is the time at which the pig egg is believed normally to enter the uterus (Oxenreider and Day, 1965).

28.5.1 Eggs for transfer

Four-cell eggs are frequently required for transfer and these can be recovered 4 days after the onset of heat in most pigs (Day, 1979). At this time, however, the eggs may be located in either the oviduct or the tip of the uterine horn. The usual method employed to recover such eggs involves flushing fluid through the oviduct from the ovarian end into the uterine horn and trapping it in a segment of the uterus; a cannula can then be inserted through the uterine wall to recover the fluid and eggs (Hancock and Hovell, 1962; Dziuk et al., 1964; Smidt et al., 1965). Modifications of this procedure are described by Day (1979), including one in which a silicone rubber tube is inserted into the oviduct 5–10 mm above the UTJ and 1.5–2.0 cm of this tube is threaded into the uterine horn; flushing fluid is then injected into the uterus and collected back through the cannula. The fertility of pigs after applying this technique has not been determined but there is some evidence suggesting that it may not have a serious effect on subsequent fertility (Davis, 1977).

Using techniques such as those described, within 6 days of ovulation, it would appear that recovery rates of the order of 80–90% or more can be achieved (Polge, 1977; Day, 1979); the length and nature of the sow's cervix and uterine horns would seem to rule out any possibility of using non-surgical recovery procedures (Polge, 1977). Repeated collections (5 times in 90 days) have been reported by some workers with promising results (James and Reeser, 1979).

28.6 EVALUATION OF EMBRYOS

The normal development of the pig egg and embryo has been closely studied (Hunter, 1974). Cleavage from the single cell to the four-cell stage occurs in the oviduct during the first 36 h after fertilization. As noted earlier, pig eggs enter the uterus at the four- to six-cell stage; recovery of two-cell eggs from the uterine horn usually represents an abnormality. On the basis of observations on several thousand pig eggs at Cambridge, Polge (1977) records that development is arrested at the four-cell stage for up to 48 h and four-cell eggs are not uncommon when recovery is made as late as 70–80 h after ovulation; it is during this diapause that new proteins are synthesized in the egg. When cleavage resumes, division occurs about every 12 h, but by no means all four-cell eggs start continued development together; for this reason, it is not unusual to recover four-cell eggs in the presence of those consisting of eight to sixteen-cells. It is known that those eggs that are later than usual in resuming development do show normal progress subsequently.

Considerable variation in size among the embryos can be evident after hatching of blastocysts from the zona pellucida, which takes place betweeen the 6th and 7th day after ovulation, but such differences as occur do not appear to influence the survival of the embryos subsequently (Polge, 1977).

28.6.1 Fragmentation phenomenon

One feature of pig eggs which is rarely encountered with cattle and sheep is that of fragmentation. This fragmentation occurs in unfertilized eggs, infrequently during the first 40 h after ovulation when the eggs are in the oviduct, but very commonly after this time when the eggs have entered the uterus (Dziuk, 1960). Fragmentation can take the form of a very even cleavage to two cells, but is more usually an uneven fragmentation of the cytoplasm. According to Polge (1977), in normally developing fertilized pig eggs, the blastomeres become fused together at the eight-cell stage and from then on it is impossible to count accurately the number of cells present within an embryo except by a process of fixing and staining.

28.7 SHORT AND LONGER-TERM STORAGE OF EMBRYOS

In most of the studies involving embryo transfer in the pig, it has been a matter of transferring the eggs into the appropriate recipients with a minimum of time spent in storage. Polge (1977) describes work at Cambridge on the short-term storage of pig eggs; storage temperature appears to be critical (no survival at storage below $+15°C$) but it is possible for four-cell eggs to be kept at $20°C$ for 24 h in appropriate media and to survive reasonably well after transfer. Culture media in the Cambridge work included Brinster's medium, Medium 199, Ham's F-10 and Dulbecco's PBS enriched with pyruvate and lactate.

28.7.1 Cell-stages cultured

The proportion of two-cell pig eggs which continue development in vitro has not been high, regardless of culture system (Pope and Day, 1977; Wright, 1977). Early development of the egg is characterized by a diapause at the four-cell stage, which may last as long as 48 h in some pigs; one and two-cell eggs cultured in vitro develop to four-cells, but they frequently block at this stage and protein synthesis does not occur as it does in the in vivo situation. Kane (1978) has suggested that the eggs of spontaneous ovulators such as the pig, as compared with induced ovulators, may normally require some hormonal trigger for the early stages of development; he observes that one-cell eggs of induced ovulators such as rabbit, ferret and cat can apparently be cultured to the blastocyst stage without running into "blocks" at any point.

Pig eggs at later stages of development (beyond the four-cell stage) have been successfully cultured to the blastocyst stage. (Schneider et al., 1975; Polge, 1977; Pope and Day, 1977; Wright, 1977). However, what happens when such cultured eggs are transferred to recipient pigs will vary according to the length of the culture period. Davis and Day (1978) cultured pig eggs in a modified Krebs Ringer bicarbonate medium (modified KRB) containing combinations of glucose, lactate, pyruvate and bovine serum albumin; culture for longer than 24 h markedly decreased egg survival rate after transfer. Markedly reduced viability of cultured eggs has also been recorded by Polge (1977, 1981) who found that culturing in vitro for 48 h resulted in embryonic survival rates of only 20–30%.

28.7.2 Pigs and rabbits

In contrast to what occurs after in vitro systems, the culture of early pig eggs in the rabbit or sheep oviduct does permit normal embryonic development (Polge, 1981) when these are later transferred to recipient gilts. As previously mentioned for cattle and sheep, it is known that pig eggs will continue developing when transferred to the ligated oviducts of oestrous and pseudopregnant rabbits (Polge et al., 1972); a high embryo survival rate (90%) was achieved when eggs kept for 2 days in the rabbit were retransferred to recipients.

28.7.3 Frozen storage of pig embryos

Although attempts to cool early-stage pig eggs below 15°C have met with failure (Polge et al., 1974), it has now been found that some embryos may be able to survive freezing and thawing when they are frozen in liquid nitrogen at the expanded blastocyst stage; although no pregnancy was reported, thawed blastocysts did apparently continue to develop in culture (Anon., 1979).

28.8 SYNCHRONIZING DONORS AND RECIPIENTS

Exact synchrony of the oestrous cycle stage between donor and recipient pigs is desirable but work by Webel et al. (1970) indicated that transfers in which the donor was 1 or 2 days earlier or 1 day later than the recipient were as successful as synchronous transfer; in that work, the donors and recipients were aligned by methallibure and gonadotrophin treatment. A later assessment of synchrony requirements by Polge (1981) showed that there was no reduction in pregnancy rate when donors were one day earlier than recipients but transfers to recipients more advanced than donors did result in a decrease. As compared to the situation in cattle and sheep, there are few figures available on the precise effects of synchronization on embryo survival in the pig.

28.9 TRANSFER METHODS

The first report of the birth of litters of normal size after embryo transfer in pigs was that of Hancock and Howell (1962); in fact, successful transfer between pigs was recorded prior to that but the number of young born had been abnormally low (Kvasnickii, 1951; Poneroy, 1960).

28.9.1 Cell-stage at transfer

Although acceptable embryo-survival rates have been achieved by the collection of and transfer of fertilized single-cell and two-cell eggs to the oviducts of synchronized recipients (Pope et al., 1972), the use of one-cell eggs presents difficulties in deciding whether they are fertilized or not; eggs at the one- or two-cell stage are transferred to the oviducts of recipients using a pipette with a fire-polished tip. Eggs are aspirated into the pipette in a small amount of transfer medium (M199, Dulbecco's PBS) and deposited in the lower ampulla via the fimbriae (Pope et al., 1972).

Eggs at the four-cell or later stages of development are transferred to the tip of the uterine horn by means of a pipette, the uterine wall having first been fully punctured with the blunt end of a suture needle; care is taken to ensure that eggs are deposited in the lumen of the uterus. Another method of transferring eggs to the uterus is by flushing them into the uterus by way of the oviduct (Polge, 1977); this avoids puncturing the uterine wall and the possibility of inducing bleeding, which could have an adverse effect on embryo survival.

Usually transfer has been carried out with eggs at the four to eight-cell stage of development (Day, 1979); normal cleavage is more apparent in the four-cell egg than at later stages, and after the eight-cell stage, it is often difficult to distinguish individual blastomeres and an incorrect evaluation of normal cleavage or degeneration is more likely than at the four- to eight-cell stage.

Transfers need only be carried out on one side of the uterus; subsequent migration of eggs ensures that they space themselves out in a reasonably uniform manner between the two uterine horns (Polge and Dziuk, 1970). The aim is to transfer about 16 embryos per recipient and survival rates of 60–65% have been achieved (Polge, 1980); these results compare favourably with normal survival rates in pigs. The fact that eggs of the early cleavage stages (even two-cell stages) can be transferred successfully to the uterus of the pig is sharply in contrast to what can be done in cattle and sheep.

On the other hand, sheep and cattle embryos can be transferred as late as the 12th day of the oestrous cycle, whereas in pigs the pregnancy rate has fallen off sharply when transfers have been attempted after the 6th day (Hunter et al., 1967; Webel et al., 1970). At Cambridge, however, a transfer technique has been developed which permits a high survival rate (60%) of hatched blastocysts transferred on day-9 of the cycle, a stage at which no success had previously been achieved (Anon., 1979). The pig embryos are transferred to recipients by way of a fine pipette introduced through a small incision in the base of the oviducts and slid down into the uterine horn through the UTJ. It is claimed that this procedure reduces the likelihood of causing endometrial trauma and haemorrhage which could otherwise prove very damaging to embryos at this stage of development. It was considered, in this report (Anon., 1979), that this successful transfer of late-stage blastocysts would extend the scope of

Cambridge work on the freezing of pig embryos. If it should be a question of freezing week-old embryos, as is now routinely done in cattle and sheep, then it is essential that these can be successfully transferred. A recent report by Polge (1981) mentions more about results after use of the new transfer method; it appears that transfer of 3-7-day-old embryos gave a 75% pregnancy rate but that transfers on days 8 and 9 of the cycle were less successful.

A further difference to be kept in mind when talking about pig transfer work is that pregnancy may not be maintained unless the recipient pig receives at least four eggs (Polge et al., 1966); presumably, this is a matter of inadequate luteotrophic effect unless a certain minimum number of embryos is present in the uterus.

28.9.2 Non-surgical transfer

Although Polge and Day (1968) have shown that it is possible to achieve a pregnancy after non-surgical embryo transfer in pigs (1/32 attempts), this is regarded as being a particularly difficult approach due to the anatomy of the sow's cervix, which makes it exceedingly difficult to introduce a catheter into the uterus.

28.10 REFERENCES

Anon. (1979) *Agric. Res. Council Ann. Rep.* 1978.

Baker, R. D. (1979) Embryo recovery from prepuberal gilts. *Theriogen.* **11**(1), 91.

Baker, R. D. and Coggins, E. G. (1968) Control of ovulation rate and fertilization in prepuberal gilts. *J. Anim. Sci.* **27,** 1607–1610.

Baker, R. D. and Polge, C. (1976) Fertilization in swine and cattle. *Can. J. Anim. Sci.* **56**(2), 105–119.

Baker, R. D., Shaw, C. A. and Downey, B. R. (1974) Effect of PMSG, HCG or GnRH on ovulation in gilts. *J. Anim. Sci.* **39,** 197 (Abs.).

Bolin, S. R., Runnels, L. J., Sawyer, C. A., Atcheson, K. H. and Gustafsson, D. P. (1979) Exposure of fertilized porcine ova to pseudorabies virus. *Theriogen.* **11**(1), 92 (Abs.).

Christenson, R. K., Pope, G. E., Zimmerman, V. A. and Day, B. N. (1973) Synchronization of estrus and ovulation in superovulated gilts *J. Anim. Sci.* **36,** 914–918.

Curnock, R. M., Day, B. N. and Dziuk, P. J. (1976) Embryo transfer in pigs: A method for introducing genetic material into primary specific-pathogen-free herds. *Am. J. Vet. Res.* **37**(1), 97.

Davis, D. L. (1977) Cleavage and blastocyst formation by pig eggs *in vitro.* Ph.D. Thesis, Univ. of Missouri, Columbia.

Davis, D. L. and Day, B. N. (1978) Cleavage and blastocyst formation by pig eggs *in vitro. J. Anim. Sci* **46,** 1043–1053.

Day, B. N. (1979) Embryo transfer in swine. *Theriogen.* **11**(1), 27–31.

Day, B. N., Anderson, L. L. and Melampy, R. M. (1959) Synchronization of oestrus and ovulation in swine. *J. Anim. Sci.* **18**, 909.

Dziuk, P. J. (1960) Frequency of spontaneous fragmentation of of ova in unbred gilts. *Proc. Soc. Exp. Biol., N.Y.* **103**, 91–92.

Dziuk, P. J. (1969) Egg transfer in cattle, sheep and pigs. In, *The Mammalian Oviduct* (Hafez and Blandau, ED.) Univ. Chicago Press, London.

Dziuk, P. J. and Day, B. N. (1977) Research applications of embryo transfer in pigs. *Embryo Transfer in Farm Animals* (Betteridge, Ed.) 10–13. Monograph 16, Canada Dept. Agric., Ottawa.

Dziuk, P. J., Polge, G. and Rowson, L. E. (1964) Intra-uterine migration and mixing of embryos in swine following egg transfer. *J. Anim. Sci.* **23**, 37–42.

Edwards, R. G. (1965) Maturation *in vitro* of mouse, sheep, cow, Rhesus monkey and human ovarian oocytes. *Nature, Lond.* **208**, 349–351.

Guthrie, H. D., Henricks, D. M. and Handlin, D. L. (1974) Plasma hormone levels and fertility in pigs induced to superovulate with PMSG. *J. Reprod. Fert.* **41**, 361–370.

Hancock, J. L. and Hovell, G. J. R. (1962) Egg transfer in the sow. *J. Reprod. Fert.* **4**, 195–201.

Harms, V. E. and Smidt, D. (1970) *In vitro* fertilization of follicular and tubal eggs of swine. *Ber. Murnch Tierarztl Wochenschr* **83**, 269–275.

Hunter, R. H. F. (1964) Superovulation and fertility in the pig. *Anim. Prod.* **6**, 189–194.

Hunter, R. H. F. (1974) Chronological and cytological details of fertilization and early embryonic development in the domestic pig. *Sus scrofa. Anat. Rec.* **178**, 169–186.

Hunter, R. H. F., Polge, C. and Rowson, L. E. A. (1966) The recovery, transfer and survival of blastocysts in pigs. *J. Reprod. Fert.* **14**, 501–502.

Iritani, A., Niwa, K. and Imai, H. (1978) Sperm penetration *in vitro* of pig follicular oocytes matured in culture. *J. Reprod. Fert.* **54**, 379–383.

James, J. E. and Reeser, P. D. (1979) Embryo recovery in swine. *Theriogen.* **11**(1), 47–50.

James, J. E., Reeser, P. D., Davis, D. L., Straiton, E. C., Talbot, A. C. and Polge, C. (1980) Culture and long-distance shipment of swine embryos, *Theriogen.* **14**, 463–469.

Kane, M. T. (1978) Culture of mammalian ova. In, *Control of Reproduction in the Cow Galway*, pp. 383–397. C.E.C., Luxembourg.

Kvasnickii, A. V. (1951) Interbreed transplantation of ova. *Sov. Zootekh.* **1**, 36.

Leman, A. D. and Dziuk, P. J. (1971) Fertilization and development of pig follicular oocytes. *J. Reprod. Fert.* **26**, 387–389.

McGaughey, R. W. (1977) The maturation of porcine oocytes in minimal, defined culture media with varied macromolecular supplements and varied osmolarity. *Exp. Cell Res.* **109**, 25–30.

McGaughey, R. W. and Polge, C. (1971) Cytogenetic analysis of pig oocytes matured in vitro. *J. Exp. Zool.* **176**, 383–391.

McGaughey, R. W. and Van Blerkom, J. (1977) Patterns of polypeptides synthesis of porcine oocytes during maturation *in vitro. Devel. Biol.* **56**, 241–254.

McGaughey, R. W., Montgomery, D. H. and Richter, J. D. (1979) Germinal vesicle configurations and patterns of polypeptide synthesis of porcine oocytes from antral

follicles of different size, as related to their compentency for spontaneous maturation. *J. Exp. Zool.* **269**, 239–254.

Mauleon, P. and Mariana, J. C. (1977) Oogenesis and folliculogenesis. In, *Reproduction in Domestic Animals* Cole and Cupps, Ed. 3rd Ed., pp. 175–202. Academic Press.

Menino, A. R., Jr. and Wright, R. W., Jr. (1979) Culture of blastomeres isolated from four and eight cell porcine embryos. *Theriogen.* **11**(1), 103 (Abs.).

Moore, N. W., Polge, C. and Rowson, L. E. A. (1969) The survival of single blastomeres of pig eggs transferred to recipient gilts. *Aust. J. Biol. Sci.* **22**, 979–982.

Motlik, J. (1972) Cultivation of pig oocytes *in vitro. Folia Biol. Praha*, **18**, 345–349.

Motlik, J. and Fulka, J. (1974) Fertilization of pig follicular oocytes cultivated *in vitro. J. Reprod. Fert.* **36**, 235–237.

Motlik, J. and Fulka, J. (1976) Breakdown of the germinal vesicle in pig oocytes *in vivo* and *in vitro. J. Exp. Zool.* **198**, 155–162.

Motlik, J., Kopecny, V., Pibko, U. and Fulka, J. (1980) Distribution of proteins labelled during meiotic maturation in rabbit and pig eggs at fertilization. *J. Reprod. Fert.* **58**, 415–419.

Oxenreider, S. L. and Day, B. N. (1965) Transport and cleavage of ova in swine. *J. Anim. Sci.* **24**, 413–417.

Phillipo, M. (1968) Superovulation in the pig. *Adv. Reprod. Physiol.* **3**, 147–166.

Pincus, G. and Enzmann, E. V. (1935) The comparative behaviour of mammalian eggs *in vivo* and *in vitro*. I. The activation of ovarian eggs. *J. Exp. Med.* **62**, 665–675.

Polge, C. (1966) Egg transplantation in the pig. *Wld. Rev. Anim. Prod.* **4**(4), 79–84.

Polge, C. (1977) *In vitro* fertilization and use of follicular oocytes. In, *Embryo transfer in Farm Animals*. Monograph No. 16, Agric., Canada, p. 43.

Polge, C. (1980) Embryo transplantation: a place in the future of pig production? *Pig Farming* **28**(12), 75–79.

Polge, C. (1981) Embryo transplantation and preservation. In, *Control of Pig Production*. Butterworth, London.

Polge, C. and Day, B. N. (1967) Induced ovulation in pituitary-suppressed gilts. *J. Anim. Sci.* **26**, 1495.

Polge, G. and Day, B. N. (1968) Pregnancy following non surgical egg transfer in pigs. *Vet. Rec.* **82**, 712.

Polge, C. and Dziuk, P. J. (1965) Recovery of immature eggs penetrated by spermatozoa following induced ovulation in the pig. *J. Reprod. Fert.* **9**, 357–358.

Polge, C. and Dziuk, P. J. (1970) Time of cessation of intrauterine migration of pig embryo. *J. Anim. Sci.* **31**, 565–567.

Polge, C., Rowson, L. E. A. and Chang, M. C. (1966) The effect of reducing the number of embryos during early stages of gestation on the maintenance of pregnancy in the pig. *J. Reprod. Fert.* **12**, 395–397.

Polge, C., Adams, C. E. and Baker, R. D. (1972) Development and survival of pig embryos in the rabbit oviduct. *Proc. 7th Int. Congr. Anim. Prod. A.I. (Munich)*, 513–517.

Pomeroy, R. W. (1960) Infertility and neonatal mortality in the sow. I. to IV. *J. Agric. Sci. Camb.* **54**, 31–56.

Pope, G. E. and Day, B. N. (1977) Transfer of preimplantation pig embryos following *in vitro* culture for 24 to 48 hours. *J. Anim. Sci.* **44**, 1036–1040.

Pope, G. E., Christenson, R. K., Zimmerman-Pope, V. A. and Day, B. N. (1972) Effect of number of embryos on embryonic survival in recipient gilts. *J. Anim. Sci.* **35**, 805–808.

Schneider, H. J. Jr., Drug, J. L. and Olds, D. (1975) Observations on recovery and culture of sow ova. *J. Anim. Sci.* **40,** 187 (Abs.).

Smidt, D., Steinbach, J. and Scheven, B. (1965) Modified methods for the *in vivo* recovery of fertilized ova in swine. *J. Reprod. Fert.,* **10,** 153–156.

Tsafriri, A. and Channing, C. P. (1975) Influence of follicular maturation and culture conditions on the meiosis of pig oocytes *in vitro. J. Reprod. Fert.* **43,** 149–152.

Van Blerkom, H. and McGaughey, R. W. (1978) Molecular differentiation of the rabbit ovum. *Develop. Biol.* **63,** 151–164.

Vincent, C. K., Robinson, O. W. and Ulberg, L. C. (1964) A technique for reciprocal embryo transfer in swine. *J. Anim. Sci.* **23,** 1084–1088.

Webel, S. K., Peters, J. B. and Anderson, L. L. (1970) Synchronous and asynchronous transfer of embryos in the pig. *J. Anim. Sci.* **30,** 565–568.

Willadsen, S. M., Lehn-Jensen, H., Fehilly, C. B. and Newcomb, R. (1981) The production of monozygotic twins of preselected parentage by micromanipulation of non-surgically collected cow embryos. *Therogen.* **15,** 23–29.

Wrathall, A. E., Done, J. T., Stuart, P., Mitchell, D., Betteridge, K. J. and Randall, G. C. B. (1970) Successful Intercontinental pig conceptus transfer. *Vet. Rec.* **87,** 226–268.

Wright, R. W., Jr. (1977) Successful culture *in vitro* of swine embryos to the blastocyst stage. *J. Anim. Sci.* **44,** 854–858.

CHAPTER 29

Breeding Pigs at Younger Ages

29.1 INTRODUCTION

Many of the piglets produced each year are farrowed by gilts and it follows from this that the age at which these females reach puberty is of considerable practical interest. It has been estimated that in the U.K. between 15 and 25% of litters produced in pig units are from gilts; because gilts have smaller litters and longer weaning to re-mating intervals than sows, the percentage of gilts in a herd can have a marked effect on overall productivity. The efficiency of reproduction in the pig unit can be further reduced if gilts are present in the herd for prolonged periods prior to mating.

In the past decade, there has been a great deal of research interest in ways and means of reducing the age at first farrowing as a method of producing more pigs per breeding animal each year; as a part of this, a technique for advancing and synchronizing the onset of puberty in gilts could be of practical interest.

As noted by Cole (1975), the general rule in practice in the U.K. has been to mate the gilt for the first time at a liveweight between 120 and 135 kg (175–300 lb) and after at least the third heat period. In approaching the question of the commercial merit of earlier breeding, it is obviously desirable to have full information on factors likely to influence the attainment of puberty in the gilt.

29.2 ENDOCRINOLOGY OF PUBERTY IN GILTS

Although it can be demonstrated that the ovaries of the gilt are capable of responding to exogenous gonadotrophins well in advance of the time when the animal reaches natural puberty, it is also true that pigs differ in some respects from cattle and sheep in what can be done in getting eggs from the very young prepubertal animal. Investigators have generally failed to bring about follicular development or ovulation in piglets in the first 2 months or more of life after treatment with gonadotrophins (Casida, 1935; Kather and Smidt, 1975; Oxender et al., 1979); this would agree with the observation that vesicular (tertiary) follicles do not appear in the ovaries until the piglet is more than 60 days old (Mauleon, 1961; Oxender et al., 1979).

Gilts usually reach puberty between 6 and 8 months of age; although considerable variation may exist in the time of heat onset according to genetic and environmental factors, the dominant changes that initiate puberty are believed to occur in the hypothalamus. It is clear that these changes are mediated by way of interactions between the animals's internal and external environment, the extra-hypothalamic brain centres, the hypothalamic–pituitary axis and the ovaries.

Available evidence in the gilt suggests that the onset of puberty is neither limited by the functioning of the stimulatory oestrogen feedback mechanisms nor by the secretory activity of the pituitary or the ovary; each of these mechanisms can be activated in the prepubertal gilt by treatment with appropriate hormones. It would appear that in the pig, as in the other farm mammals, puberty is brought about by a reduction in the activity of intrinsic neural inhibitory mechanisms and/or a decrease in the negative feedback action of ovarian steroids resulting in stimulation of pulsatile Gn-RH release and consequently augmentation of episodic LH-secretion which in turn stimulates ovarian function.

29.3 BREED AND ENVIRONMENTAL FACTORS

In wild pig communities, young gilts would normally reach puberty in the late autumn, at about 8 months of age; it is generally accepted that in such communities, the attainment of puberty is more closely related to the age than to liveweight which may help to explain why, under normal commercial feeding regimes, the effect of diet on puberty may not be of such great importance.

29.3.1 Breed effects

The literature reports similar mean values of around 200–210 days for the age of pigs at natural puberty in different breeds of pigs (reviews by Duncan and Lodge, 1960; Anderson and Melampy, 1972). Several papers from authors in Canada and the U.S.A, show the normal range of ages at puberty as being from about day-140 to day-250 with around 200 days being the average value (Dyck, 1971; Cunningham et al., 1974; Callaghan and King, 1977).

According to Dziuk (1977), the plane of nutrition used in rearing the gilt may influence to a minor extent the age at which first oestrus

occurs but much of the variability of age at puberty appears to be related to the genetic background of the gilt and to other aspects of the environment in which she is kept.

29.3.2 Puberty in total confinement systems

Delayed puberty can be a problem to pig producers who use total confinement systems of management and it has been suggested in several reports that this may be the result of the environment imposing a physiological stress on the gilts (Christian and Davis, 1964; Christian et al., 1966; Jensen et al., 1970; Blackwood, 1972); there is some evidence that group-penned gilts reach puberty a little earlier than tethered pigs (England and Spurr, 1969; Jensen et al., 1970), although with tethered pigs delayed puberty was more of a problem in spring-born animals. Ford and Teague (1978) investigated the effects of crowding gilts kept in a total confinement system to the point that growth rate and feed efficiency was depressed but did not find that the age of puberty was affected.

29.3.3 Seasonal and other effects

Whether season affects puberty in pigs reared outdoors is not altogether clear. Gossett and Sorensen (1959) and Sorensen et al. (1961) found no difference in the age of puberty between spring and autumn-born animals; in contrast, there was a report by Mavrogenis and Robinson (1970) who found that autumn-born pigs reached puberty earlier than spring-born ones. Wiggins et al. (1950) and Scanlon and Drishnamurthy (1974) have also presented evidence indicating that the proportion of gilts reaching puberty increases during periods of increasing daylength. Zimmerman et al. (1960) found evidence of a breed difference between spring-born Chester White gilts, which reached puberty earlier than autumn-born animals, and Poland China pigs which showed the reverse.

There would appear to be a lack of experimental evidence on the effects of light intensity or exposure on puberty, although Dufour and Bernard (1968) in Canada did report that continuous darkness did hasten the onset of first oestrus in gilts. Other factors which may influence age of puberty include changing gilts to another environment (Du Mesnil du Buisson and Signoret, 1962) and by transporting them for a few hours (Bourn et al., 1974); this latter "transport effect" may be of practical use, particularly when replacement gilts are being brought in to the pig unit from a different herd.

29.4 THE BOAR EFFECT

It has been shown by several authors that the age at which gilts reach puberty can be influenced by the age at which they have first contact with boars (Brooks and Cole, 1969, 1970, 1973; Zimmerman et al., 1969; Shearer and Adam, 1973; Robison, 1974; Alliston et al., 1974; Bourn et al., 1974; Hughes and Cole, 1975, 1976; Mavrogenis and Robinson, 1976; Thompson and Savage, 1978; Kirkwood and Hughes, 1979, 1980; Walker, 1979; Paterson and Lindsay, 1980; Kirkwood et al., 1981). The essential steps in this, under Irish and U.K. pig conditions, include keeping the gilt out of sight, sound and smell of the boar until she reaches about 160 days of age and 160 lb liveweight; she then gets a change in environment and is exposed to a sexually active boar, an experience which can have the effect of bringing her and companion females in oestrus within 1 week. This exposure to the boar can take the form of 30 min each day or it may be continuous; although young boars can induce a response, they may not be as effective as an older, mature boar. The boar effect can reduce the age at first service (at the second oestrus) by several weeks; it also means a smaller pig producing the first litter and lower feed costs for the replacement gilt.

29.4.1 Rearing of gilts

Brooks and Cole (1969) in their early work, did suggest that introducing the boar to gilts which are too young might delay puberty due to habituation to the presence of the male. In studies which have examined this question, the gilts were either reared with castrate male contemporaries or in total isolation from male pigs (Brooks and Cole, 1970; Aherne et al., 1976) or were reared with intact male pigs (Walker, 1979; Paterson and Lindsay, 1980). The fact that it

is now common commercial practice not to castrate male bacon pigs means that gilts can be exposed to the smell, sight and sound of males throughout growth to puberty. Certainly, it would appear that gilts will respond to the introduction of mature boars just the same when intact males have been reared with them as when castrate males have been with them (Walker, 1979; Paterson and Lindsay, 1980). For the pig producer, it is useful to know that the practice of not castrating male pigs reared for slaughter is compatible with using boars to advance puberty in gilts. It has been found that with gilts younger than 160 days or less than 60 kg liveweight, response to boar contact is poor, presumably due to physiological immaturity of the processes controlling puberty (Paterson and Lindsay, 1980).

29.4.2 Source of stimulus

Results reported by Kirkwood et al. (1981) at Leeds indicated a significant role for olfaction in the precocious induction of puberty in gilts kept in close proximity to a boar; the study showed that the "boar effect" could be completely eliminated by rendering prepubertal gilts anosmic. The way in which the boar achieves its

Fig. 29.1. The "boar effect" requires a male that is suitably mature if it is to work. Factors influencing the attainment of puberty and the consequences of earlier breeding on subsequent reproductive performance in gilts have been quite well investigated during the past decade. In noting the "boar effect" on the young gilt, it has been shown that although a young boar may be fully capable of mating, his full pheromone capacity may lag behind. For that reason, gilts penned alongside their male contemporaries may fail to come in heat whereas an older boar can induce a response. Apart from the boar, transportation, group size, season, exposure to various hormone treatments can affect puberty in gilts.

effect appears to differ from that recorded in mice, where the source of primer pheromone is known to be in the male's urine. In the boar, however, studies utilizing either isolated urinary pheromones (known to have signaller pheromone properties) or boar urine, have not been successful in advancing puberty. It now appears that the primer pheromones in the boar are present in the saliva produced by the submaxillary salivary glands (Kirkwood et al., 1981).

How these primer pheromones act has not been elucidated in the pig but work with mice suggests that the primary response to the introduction of the male is a change in the basal secretion of LH; this change, in turn, initiates follicle growth and an extended period of elevated plasma oestradiol precedes the pre-ovulatory LH surge and ovulation.

29.4.3 Long-term effects

The subsequent reproductive performance of gilts which have had puberty advanced by the boar effect has been the subject of some studies (Brooks et al., 1970; Brooks and Smith, 1980) which have shown that although earlier mating may result in a reduction in the size of the first litter, it is likely to result in improved productivity when other factors are taken into account; over five litters, the earlier mated gilts produced just as many piglets and showed a 6% better food conversion efficiency. Brooks and Smith (1980) note, however, that producers contemplating earlier breeding of gilts should not cull on the basis of first litter performance as they might otherwise be accustomed to do with normal aged animals.

29.4.4 Other considerations

Aside from the important implications which earlier breeding may have on the efficiency of the gilt's total breeding life, accelerated puberty is clearly relevant to the feasibility of the once-bred gilt system, where the idea is to take a litter from the pig before dispatching her to the heavy hog market (Brooks and Cole, 1973). However, there is the difficulty that it may require several weeks beyond the time of weaning for acceptable mammary involution to occur in such animals. As noted earlier, there are those who maintain that

the only way to overcome the reproductive problems created by very early- or zero-weaning systems is to combine such a weaning procedure with the use of the once-bred gilt, marketing the gilt soon after weaning (Elliot et al., 1980).

Before leaving the question of natural puberty in pigs, it should be mentioned that some proportion of gilts may not show their first oestrus until as late as 9 months and for that reason can be considered as abnormal; Einarsson and Linde (1974) estimate that about 12% of gilts in Swedish breeding herds fall into this category.

29.5 INDUCTION USING GONADOTROPHINS

After the age of about 3 months, it is possible to induce follicle development, oestrus and ovulation in the prepubertal gilt with gonadotrophins such as PMSG, as shown first more than 45 years ago (Casida, 1935); if the animals are bred, fertilization and early embryonic development does occur (Dziuk and Baker, 1962; Baker and Coggins, 1968). However, whether the gilt remains pregnant or not may largely be a question of its physiological age at the time of treatment. In this regard, the pig is unlike the prepubertal sheep, in which it is possible to establish pregnancy and see it maintained in the young ewe without any great difficulty.

29.5.1 Hormonal regimens

Treatment with gonadotrophins has taken the form of PMSG followed by hCG or a combined PMSG/hCG treatment. Dziuk and Gehlbach (1966) reported that 90% of gilts (90–130 days old; 45–55 kg liveweight) can be induced to ovulate by treatment with PMSG followed by hCG; however, the proportion of gilts showing oestrus at the time of insemination or remaining pregnant after mating was low; other workers reported much the same (Shaw et al., 1971; Ellicott et al., 1973; Segal and Baker, 1973). It has been suggested that the problem in the gilts may be due to the uterus being insufficiently developed to allow normal implantation and to prevent luteolysis (McMenamin and King, 1974) but treatments applied in an effort to promote uterine development did not result in any apparent improvement. There is also the view that the corpora lutea of the prepubertal gilt may not be maintained by pituitary luteotrophins unless the animal is close to normal puberty (Segal and Baker, 1973).

29.5.2 PMSG/hCG combination

For reasons such as those described, the use of gonadotrophins in prepubertal gilts must be approached with due caution. On the one hand, there have been reports of acceptable results with a PMSG/hCG combination. Schilling and Cerne (1972) used such a treatment (400 i.u. PMSG and 200 hCG) in gilts 150–165 days old; gilts were bred by AI on the 4th and 5th days after giving the combination and 66% of all pigs were pregnant at slaughter 30 days after breeding. On the other hand, low pregnancy rates, of the order of 10–33%, have been reported by Rampacek *et al.* (1976) in similarly aged gilts (155–175 days) that received this form of treatment.

The PMSG/hCG combination has been employed with varying success by Canadian workers (Baker and Rajamahendran, 1973; Baker and Downey, 1975) and reported on by several East German and Eastern European authors; the general finding has been that pregnancy rate and litter-size to the gonadotrophin treatment improves the closer the gilt approaches the natural age of puberty (Schlegel *et al.*, 1978, 1979; Miskovic and Stancic, 1978).

29.5.3 Maintenance of cyclic activity

Recent studies have looked not only at the question of oestrous response immediately following gonadotrophin treatment but at the maintenance of regular cyclical activity as may occur in the absence of mating. Studies reported by Paterson and Lindsay (1981) using PMSG/hCG showed that when prepubertal gilts were housed in contact with mature boars, there was a much greater tendency for cyclical activity to be maintained than when the gilts were kept isolated from the males (85% cyclic vs 45%). The same authors found that the ovulation rate varied widely at the first (induced) heat but at the second was much more consistent and normal; the results were taken to indicate that PMSG/hCG (PG600; Intervet Ltd.) may be of commercial

value in inducing early puberty if cycles can be maintained and the gilts mated at the second occurring heats. Other studies reported by these authors (Paterson and Lindsay, 1980) showed that cyclic activity may not always be maintained, even when gilts had been housed in contact with the boar; however, it was thought that this may have been a result of stress arising from blood sampling.

Fig. 29.2. Although oestrus may be induced with relative ease in prepubertal gilts, the maintenance of pregnancy may not always follow. Although it is possible to induce puberty in young ewes and even in young cattle and get them pregnant, in pigs it has been found that pregnancy may not always be maintained in the gilt after hormonal induction treatment. Obviously, in dealing with the gilt, it is not only a matter of inducing oestrus and ovulation but one of ensuring that the corpora lutea keep going into pregnancy in the same way as in the older sow.

29.6 OESTROGEN TREATMENT

As well as the gonadotrophin approach, some studies have been reported on the use of steroid hormones as a means of activating the hypothalamic–pituitary axis. In Canada, the steroid hormone, 5α–androstane–3β–17β–diol was employed, on the basis that it has been detected in the blood of immature rats around the time of puberty (Eckstein *et al.*, 1970; Eckstein and David, 1974). It has been suggested (Callaghan and King, 1977) that this steroid could be involved in the mechanism of the onset of puberty in the gilt; however, injections were given to gilts varying in age from 109 to 180 days without success.

In the U.K., work with oestrogens was partly based on information derived from mice, in which it had been reported that exogenous oestrogen could induce puberty in 60–70% of immature females (Bronson, 1975); it was also known that when puberty was induced in gilts by gonadotrophins or boar contact one of the first changes occurring in plasma hormones was an elevation in the oestradiol concentrations. At Nottingham, treatment of gilts consisted of six doses of oestradiol benzoate (0.2 mg/dose) given over 3 days; the treatment was effective (60% responding within 5 days) in gilts 140 days old but not in those aged 120 days (Hughes and Cole, 1976, 1978) and the pigs were put to the boar at the second oestrus after treatment.

29.6.1 Seasonal variations

Although the Nottingham work with oestrogen did result in oestrus and ovulation, studies reported by Paterson and Day did not, despite the use of older gilts and a wide range of oestradiol benzoate treatments. A report summarizing further studies at Nottingham mentions seasonal variability in the response of the gilt, with reduced ovulatory response to the oestrogen in the mid-summer period; studies suggest that there may be a nocturnal increase in the amount of gonadotrophin released by the gilt's pituitary and that this may be a factor involved in seasonal variations in response to the exogenous steroid.

From the pig producer's viewpoint, there is a possibility that exogenous oestrogen treatment may eventually provide a method of inducing puberty in gilts on a commercial basis, if the effects of factors such as season can be accurately assessed and treatment regimens modified accordingly.

29.7 FUTURE DEVELOPMENTS

Clearly, in the years ahead the possibility will exist for exerting much closer control over the mechanisms involved in puberty in pigs. It is, as some observers have pointed out, somewhat surprising that such variability exists in the age at which natural puberty occurs after the many years of selection and domestication of this species.

29.8 REFERENCES

Aherne, F. X., Christopherson, R. J., Thompson, J. R. and Hardin, R. T. (1976) Factors affecting the onset of puberty, post-weaning estrus and blood hormone levels of Lacombe gilts. Can. J. Anim. Sci. **56,** 681–692.

Alliston, C. W., Haglof, S. A., Wilson, S. P., Aberle, E. D. and Judge, M. D, (1974) Presence of boars and sexual maturity in gilts. J. Anim. Sci. **39,** 967 (Abs).

Anderson, L. L. and Melampy, R. M. (1972) Factors affecting ovulation rate in the pig. In, Pig Production Cole, D. J. A. Ed., pp. 329–366. Butterworths, London.

Baker, R. D. and Coggins, E. C. (1968) Control of ovulation rate and fertilization in prepuberal gilts. J. Anim. Sci. **27,** 1607–1610.

Baker, R. D. and Downey, B. R. (1975) Induction of estrus, ovulation and fertility in prepuberal gilts. Ann. Biol. Anim. Biochim. Biophys. **15**(2), 375–382.

Baker, R. D. and Rajmahendran, R. (1973) Induction of oestrus, ovulation and fertilization in prepuberal gilts by a single injection of PMSG, hCG and PMSG:hCG combination. Can. J. Anim. Sci. **53,** 593–694.

Blackwood, R. D. (1972) Effect of confinement on development of the reproductive system and age at puberty in gilts. M. Sc. Thesis. Texas Techn. Univ.

Bourn, P., Carlson, R., Lantze, B. and Zimmerman, D. R. (1974) Age at puberty as influenced by age at boar exposure and transport. J. Anim. Sci. **39,** 937 (Abs).

Brooks, P. H. and Cole, D. J. A. (1969) The effect of boar presence on the age at puberty of gilts. Rpt. Sch. Agric., Univ. Nottingham. 74–77.

Brooks, P. H. and Cole, D. J. A. (1970) The effect of boar presence on the age at puberty of gilts. J. Reprod. Fert. **23,** 435–440.

Brooks, P. H. and Cole, D. J. A. (1973) Meat production from sows which have farrowed. 1. Reproductive performance and food conversion efficiency. Anim. Prod. **17,** 305–315.

Brooks, P. H. and Smith, D. A. (1980) The effect of mating age on the reproductive performance, food utilization and liveweight change of the female pig. Livest. Prod. Sci. **7,** 67–78.

Brooks, P. H., Pattison, M. A. and Cole, D. J. A. (1970) Reproduction in the young gilt. Rpt. Sch. Agric. Univ. Nottingham. 65–67.

Bronson, F. H. (1975) Male-induced precocial puberty in female mice: confirmation of the role of estrogen. Endocrin. **96,** 511–514.

Callaghan, B. and King, G. J. (1977) Effect of 5α-androstane-3ß, 17ß-diol on inducing early puberty in gilts. Can. J. Anim. Sci. **57,** 599–600.

Casida, L. E. (1935) Prepuberal development of the pig ovary and its relation to stimulation with gonadotrophic hormone. Anat. Rec. **61,** 389–396.

Christian, J. J. and Davis, D. E. (1964) Endocrines, behaviour and population. Science **146,** 1550.

Christian, J. J., Lloyd, J. A. and Davis, D. E, (1966) The role of endocrines in the self-regulation of mammalian populations. Rec. Prog. Hormone Res. **21,** 501–578.

Cole, D. J. A. (1975) Towards greater sow productivity. *Span* **18**(3), 111–142.

Cunningham, P. J., Naber, C. B., Zimmerman, D. R. and Peo, E. R. (1974) Influence of nutritional regime on age at puberty in gilts. *J. Anim. Sci.* **39**, 64–67.

Dufour, J. and Bernard, C. (1968). Effect of light on the development of market pigs and breeding gilts. *Can. J. Animal Sci.* **48**, 425–430.

Du Mesnil du Buisson, F. and Signoret, J. P. (1962) Influence de facteurs externes sur le declechement de la puberte chez la truie. *Ann. Zootech.* **11**, 53–59.

Duncan, D. L. and Lodge, G. A. (1960) Diet in relation to reproduction and viability of the young. *Ill. Pigs Tech. Comm. Comm. Bur. Anim. Nutr.* No. 21, 106pp.

Dyck, G. W. (1971) Puberty, post-weaning estrous and estrous cycle length in Yorkshire and Lacombe swine. *Can. J. Anim. Sci.* **51**, 135–140.

Dziuk, P. J. (1977) Reproduction in pigs. In, *Reproduction in Domestic Animals* Cole and Cupps, Ed., 3rd Ed., pp. 456–474. Academic Press, N.Y.

Dziuk, P. J. and Baker, R. D. (1962) Induction and control of ovulation in swine. *J. Anim. Sci.,* **21**, 697–699.

Dziuk, P. J. and Gehlbach, G. D. (1966) Induction of ovulation and fertilization in the immature gilt. *J. Anim. Sci.* **25**, 410–413.

Eckstein, B., Mechoulam, R. and Burstein, S. H. (1970) Identification of 5α–androstane–3α, 17β–diol as a principle metabolite of pregnenolone in rate ovary at onset of puberty. *Nature, Lond.* **228**, 886.

Eckstein, B. and David, R. (1974) On the mechanism of the onset of puberty identification and pattern of 5α–androstone–3β, 17β–diol and its 3α epimer in peripheral blood of immature female rats. *Endocrin.* **94**, 224–229.

Ellicott, A. R., Dziuk, P. J. and Polge, C. (1973) Maintenance of pregnancy in prepuberal gilts. *J. Anim. Sci.* **37**, 971.

Elliot, J. I., King, G. J. and Robertson, H. A. (1980) Reproductive performance of the sow subsequent to weaning piglets at birth. *Can. J. Anim. Sci.* **60**, 65–71.

England, D. C. and Spurr, D. T. (1969) Litter size of swine confined during gestation. *J. Anim. Sci.* **28**, 220–223.

Ford, J. J. and Teague, H. S. (1978) Effect of floor space restriction on age at puberty in gilts and on performance of barrows and gilts. *J. Anim. Sci.* **47**, 828–832.

Gossett, J. W. and Sorensen, A. N., Jr. (1959) The effects of two levels of energy and seasons on reproductive phenomena of gilts. *J. Anim. Sci.* **18**, 40–47.

Hughes, P. E. and Cole, D. J. A. (1975) The influence of age and weight at puberty on ovulation rate and embryo survival in the gilt. *Amin. Prod.* **21**, 183–189.

Hughes, P. E. and Cole, D. J. A. (1976) The effect of exogenous oestrogen on the attainment of puberty in the gilt. *Anim. Prod.* **22**, 140 (Abs).

Hughes, P. E. and Cole, D. J. A. (1978) Reproduction in the gilt. 3. The effect of exogenous oestrogen on the attainment of puberty and subsequent reproductive performance. *Anim. Prod.* **27**, 11–20.

Jensen, A. H., Yen, J. T., Gehring, M. M., Baker, D. H., Becker, D. E. and Harmon, B. G., (1970). Effects of space restriction and management on pre and post-puberal response of female swine. *J. Anim. Sci.* **31**, 745–750.

Kather, L. and Smidt, D. (1975) Vergleichende untersuchungen zur ovariellen reaktron infantiler, weiblicher schweine der Deutchen Landrasse und des Gottlinger minatur schweines auf gonadotorpe stimulierung. *Zuchthygiene.* **10**, 10–15.

Kirkwood, R. N. and Hughes, P. E. (1979) The influence of age at first boar contact on puberty attainment in the gilt. *Anim. Prod.* **29**, 231–238.

Kirkwood, R. N. and Hughes, P. E. (1980) A note on the efficacy of continuous vs. limited boar exposure on puberty attainment in the gilt. *Anim. Prod.* **31**, 205–207.

Kirkwood, R. N., Forbes, J. M. and Hughes, P. E. (1981) Influence of boar contact on attainment of puberty in gilts after removal of the olfactory bulbs. *J. Reprod. Fert.* **61**, 193–196.

McMenamin, H. and King, G. J. (1974) Uterine development in prepubertal gilts after single or multiple stimulation by gonadotrophins. *J. Reprod. Fert.* **39**, 109–110.

Mauleon, P. (1961) Derovlement de l'ovogenese compatre chez differenis mammiferes domestiques. *Proc. 4th Int. Cong. Anim. Reprod. A.I. (The Hague),* **2**, 348–354.

Mavrogenis, A. P. and Robison, O. W. (1976) Factors affecting puberty in swine. *J. Anim. Sci.* **42**, 1251–1255.

Miskovic, M. and Stancic, B. (1978) Oestrus, ovulation and fertility in prepubertal gilts treated with exogenous gonadotrophins. *Vetrinaria* **27**, 69–76.

Oxender, W. D., Colenbrander, B., Van de Wiel, D. F. M. and Wensing, C. J. G. (1979) Ovarian development in fetal and prepubertal pigs. *Biol. Reprod.* **21**, 715–721.

Paterson, A. M. and Lindsay, D. R. (1980) Induction of puberty gilts. 1. The effects of rearing conditions on reproductive performance and response to mature boars after early puberty. *Anim. Prod.* **31**, 291–297.

Paterson, A. M. and Lindsay, D. R. (1981) Induction of puberty in gilts. 2. The effect of boars on maintenance of cyclic activity in gilts induced to ovulate with pregnant mare's serum gonadotrophin and human chorionic gonadotrophin. *Anim. Prod.* **32**, 51–54.

Rampacek, G. B., Keaeling, R. D. and Ball, G. D. (1976) Luteal function in the hysterectomized prepuberal gilt. *J. Anim. Sci.* **43**, 792–794.

Robison, O. W. (1974) Effects of boar presence and group size on age at puberty in gilts. *J. Anim. Sci.* **39**, 224.

Scanlon, P. F. and Krishnamurthy, S. (1974) Puberty attainment in slaughterweight gilts in relation to month examined. *J. Anim. Sci.* **39**, 160.

Schilling, E. and Cerne, F. (1972) Induction and synchronization of oestrus in pre-puberal gilts and anoestrous sows by a PMS/HCG-compound. *Vet. Rec.* **91**, 471–474.

Schlegel, von W., Wahner, M. and Stenzl, S. (1978) Studies into further course of cycle in gilts, following biotechnical action to induce puberty. *Vet. Med.* **33**(3), 85–87.

Schlegel, von W., Wahner, M. and Heinze, A. (1979) Studies into possible reduction of PMSG/HCG dose for cycle induction in the context of biotechnically induced puberty of gilts to use second oestrus. *Mh. Vet. Med.* **34**, 187–188.

Segal, D. H. and Baker, R. D. (1973) Maintenance of corpora lutea in prepuberal gilts. *J. Anim. Sci.* **37**, 62–767.

Shaw, G. A., McDonald, B. E. and Baker, R. D. (1971) Fetal mortality in the prepuberal gilt. *Can. J. Anim. Sci.* **51**, 233.

Shearer, I. J. and Adam, J. L. (1973) Nutritional and physiological developments in reproduction of pigs. *Proc. N.Z. Soc. Anim. Prod.* **33**, 62–86.

Sorensen, A. M. Jr., Thomas, W. W. and Gossett, J. W. (1961) A further study of the influence of level of energy intake and season on reproductive performance of gilts. *J. Anim. Sci.* **20**, 347–349.

Thompson, L. H. and Savage, J. S. (1978) Age at puberty and ovulation rate in gilts in confinement as influenced by exposure to a boar. *J. Anim. Sci.* **47**, 1141–1144.

Walker, N. (1979) The occurrence of puberty in gilts reared in presence or absence of growing boars. *Agric. Rec.* **27,** 1–4.

Wiggins, E. L., Casida, L. E. and Grummer, R. H. (1950) The effect of season of birth on sexual development in gilts. *J. Anim. Sci.* **9,** 277–280.

Zimmerman, D. R., Spies, H. G., Self, H. L. and Casida, L. E. (1960) Ovulation rate in swine as affected by increased energy intake just prior to ovulation. *J. Anim. Sci.* **19,** 295–301.

Zimmerman, D. R., Carlson, R. and Nippert, L. (1969) Age at puberty in gilts as affected by daily heat checks with a boar. *J. Anim. Sci.* **29,** 203 (Abs).

PART IV

The Control and Manipulation of Reproduction in Horses

CHAPTER 30

Introduction to Controlled Breeding in Horses

30.1 INTRODUCTION

As observed elsewhere (Allen, 1978), until about 50 years ago, the horse was in many respects the most important of man's domestic animals, being used in all types of farming, in transport, in war and as a source of meat when necessary. The many advances which have occurred in the developed countries in farm mechanization, especially from the time of the second World War, have rendered the horse obsolete in most of its previous activities; today, for those living in many countries of the Western world, the horse has become an animal mainly for use in sport and recreation.

Consequently, the horse, which from the time of its domestication several thousand years ago until the advent of the steam and internal combustion engine had been the major source of power, is now experienceing a rebirth of importance for recreational purposes in many of those industrial countries from which it had practically disappeared as a source of draft power on farms and in the cities.

As living standards improve, as the working week grows shorter and as retired people live longer, the amount of time for leisure increases; as a result, certainly, in countries such as the U.S.A., the demands for horses for recreational purposes increases (Phillips, 1962, 1969). However, with the decline in the need for horses in farming and other areas, there may have been

Fig. 30.1. Horses for leisure rather than work. As in many countries, the horse and pony has disappeared off the farm in Ireland except for their use in sport and leisure activities. Although it is well recognized that Ireland can produce some of the finest horses in the world, low fertility in both Thoroughbred and non-Thoroughbred mares is a problem in this country as it is in other well-known horse producing countries. Some surveys have shown only about 55 out of every 100 mares producing a live foal — hardly a level of performance which can be accepted in this day of high technology.

some decrease in straight commercial pressure to maximize breeding efficiency in the species (Allen, 1978). On the other hand, although research into methods of controlling and manipulating reproduction in the horse has not kept pace with similar work in cattle, sheep and pigs, it must be recognized that substantial improvements in an understanding of reproduction in horses has occurred, particularly during the most recent decade, when new investigational procedures (RIA methods and such) have become available.

30.1.1 Increasing knowledge in the seventies

It has been recognized for some time that the mare is unique in certain of its reproductive characteristics, but precise data relating to reproductive steroid and polypeptide hormones, have not been available until recently. The two international symposia devoted to horse reproduction, the first held at Cambridge in the U.K. in 1974, the second at Davis, California, in 1978, have contributed substantially to an understanding of reproduction in the species; these meetings, the next due to be held in Sydney in 1982, have served to provide a forum for biologists, animal scientists and veterinarians to exchange information and to produce guidelines for future research. Quite apart from the value of information in dealing with current problems in horse reproduction there is an increasing realization that knowledge derived from studies in equines can advance a general understanding of the various physiological and endocrinological mechanisms which control the reproductive processes in mammals. A further valuable addition to the literature on mare reproduction is the book written by Ginther (1979).

The considerable increase in knowledge in horse reproduction over the past 10 years may be regarded as all the more remarkable in that research with this species tends to be extremely costly; part of the explanation, according to Dawson (1977) is probably that many people simply like horses, although the hope of an economic return for the research undertaken is no doubt important in many developing countries where horses remain valuable as draft animals.

30.2 AREAS OF CONTROLLED BREEDING

There are several areas in which the reproductive management of the mare may be facilitated by the application of controlled breeding techniques. In dealing with the breeding efficiency of what may often be extremely valuable animals, there is an obvious need for advantage to be taken of such new technology as may be available.

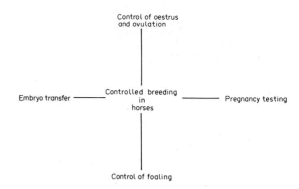

Fig. 30.2. Areas of controlled breeding in horses.

30.3 FACTORS AFFECTING FERTILITY IN MARES

Unlike the literature dealing with cattle, sheep and pigs, there is a lack of information about the age at which puberty occurs in the filly (Ginther, 1979); in general, it would appear to be at about 1½ years (Nishikawa, 1959; Rossdale and Ricketts, 1980; Wesson and Ginther, 1980, 1981). As already mentioned in the case of the other farm animals, nutrition is accepted as a factor influencing puberty; it is known that restricted feeding can delay the occurrence of the first oestrus.

Attention has been drawn by several authors to the fact that a major problem in horse breeding arises because the natural reproductive season does not always coincide with the breeding season imposed on horses by many breed and registry associations who have established January 1st (in the Northern Hemisphere) as a universal date of birth for all foals born in a calendar year (Stabenfeldt and Hughes, 1977;

Allen, 1978). In order that horses may compete at the race track or in the horse-show arena as yearlings or as 2- and 3-year olds, the mating season must commence in February or March. This is because of the 11-month gestation period of the mare and the fact that the animal needs to gain sufficient maturity to enable it to compete during the summer months as a yearling or older.

However, February and March is a time of year when normal ovarian activity in the mare may not yet be established. The mare, like many other mammals and birds in temperate climates, is a seasonal breeder; the horse is an example of a long-day breeder, showing a distinct breeding season during the spring and summer months and, under natural conditions in northern latitudes, passing through a period of genuine physiological anoestrus between November and March. In Ireland, an examination of 1886 mares (including Thoroughbreds, Half-Breds, Draft horses and ponies) showed only about 10% of mares to be ovulating in the months January to March (Jennings, 1977). On the other hand, the mating season for Thoroughbred and other racing breed mares, has, for more than a century, been arbitrarily fixed by the breed associations as running from 15 February to 1 July in the northern hemisphere and from 15 September to 31 December in the southern hemisphere. This means that an appreciable portion of the arbitrary "covering" season lies outside the natural breeding season of the mare and that many Thoroughbred mares have only 2 months or less (which is no more than one or two normal oestrous cycles) in which to be mated and to conceive.

Although the majority of mares are seasonally polyoestrous, there are also those that appear to be genuinely polyoestrous and capable of producing a foal in any month of the year. With modern stud management procedures, which include comfortable stabling, an excellent level of feeding and high quality care and attention, it might be expected that a genuinely polyoestrous condition would occur in Thoroughbreds more than in some of the other categories of horses and ponies.

The fact that the natural and the imposed breeding seasons are markedly out-of-phase is regarded as being by far the greatest limiting factor to increasing the fertility in Thoroughbreds and other breeds upon which arbitrary seasons are imposed (Allen, 1978). The situation makes it all the more important that effective methods are developed for artificially controlling all phases of the oestrous cycle of the mare with a view to increasing the frequency of oestrous cycles and breeding opportunities during the stud season. Horse owners and trainers are probably more concerned with the training and racing aspects of Thoroughbred horse management than with optimum breeding practices.

30.4 FERTILITY LEVELS IN HORSES

The mare is generally considered as having the lowest reproductive efficiency of all the farm livestock; whereas conception rates to first service of the order 85–95%, 80–90% and 55–65% are regarded as the norm in pigs, sheep and cattle, the equivalent figure for the horse appears to be 40–50% (Ginther, 1979). In Ireland, where there is a breeding population of 8000 Thoroughbred mares and about 400 stallions, poor fertility as a major problem in both Thoroughbred and non-Thoroughbred mares has been shown by Cunningham et al. (1980); among the Thoroughbreds, they record a 40% foaling rate to a single service, which corresponds to the figure recorded by Sullivan et al. (1975) in similar mares in the U.S.A. In a report by Badi et al. (1981), dealing with 2466 coverings recorded for 1528 mares in Ireland, for every 100 services, 39.8% of Thoroughbreds subsequently foaled to that service.

30.4.1 Genetics and fertility

One recent Irish study (Mahon and Cunningham, 1980) examined the historical structure of the Thoroughbred population and the relationship between inbreeding and fertility; in an analysis of data relating to about 10 000 mares, little evidence of either inbreeding or any effect of inbreeding on fertility was found and the authors concluded that the cause of the low fertility should be sought elsewhere. Others have drawn attention to the fact that little selection for reproductive performance has been practised in either the mare or the stallion (Stabenfeldt and Hughes, 1977); the predominant value of the horse has usually been determined by its competitive excellence rather than its reproductive ability.

30.4.2 Conceptions to all services

In farm livestock other than horses, the percentage of breeding females which remain barren in any year should be no more than 10%, and is generally much less than that in breeding ewes and sows. In the U.K., Laing (1979) recorded that only 55% of Thoroughbreds which went to stud in a particular year (1976) produced live foals; sampling problems led the author to believe that a figure of 75% for conceptions to all services was probably nearer the true mark. That would be along the lines of figures reported by Sullivan et al. (1975) in the U.S.A.; they recorded a cumulative pregnancy rate after five services of 85% for the Quarterhorse and 77% for Thoroughbred mares.

It can be expected that Irish, British and American data on Thoroughbred fertility relates to stud farms with good management and that breeding efficiency among horses on less well-managed farms could well be poorer than some of those quoted. As observed by Mahon and Cunningham (1980), Thoroughbred horses are the most expensive, and probably the best cared for, of all the domestic animals, and their poor reproductive rate is unlikely to be due to such factors as poor feeding or management. On the other hand, among those horses which are largely left to nature (e.g. ponies at free range) fertility is usually found to be high under good climatic conditions (Laing, 1979).

30.5 BREEDING AT THE FOAL HEAT

It has been stressed by several authors that the fertility associated with the *post-partum* (or foaling) heat in the mare is of considerable practical importance (Ginther, 1979); failure of the mare to become pregnant at this time has often meant a considerable delay because the foal heat may have been followed by a greatly prolonged inter-oestrus interval. Many reports agree in showing that pregnancy rates are lower for mares bred during the foal heat than for those mated during a subsequent oestrus; figures quoted from the literature by Ginther (1979) show the pregnancy rate for the *post-partum* oestrus to be about 17% lower on average than for subsequent heats. In Ireland, where breeding at the foal heat is commonly practised, work reported by Badi et al. (1981) showed that such matings were much less successful than those carried out at the next normal heat (29% conceptions as against 49%). However, as noted by Ginther (1979) the various reports which are available on conception rates at the foal heat come from data accumulated in the field rather than from controlled experiments, in which the conditions of service are kept the same. It is known that the conception rate at the foal heat can be influenced by the time at which it occurs; a study by Lieux (1973) showed that the pregnancy rate for mares bred before 16 days *post-partum* was 11% lower than for mares bred between 25 and 35 days.

30.5.1 Parturition to foal heat interval

An average figure of 8.6 days is given by Nishikawa (1959) as the time interval between foaling and the occurrence of the *post-partum* oestrus; in Ireland, a figure of 9.8 days has been reported (Cunningham et al., 1980; Badi et al., 1981).

30.6 MATING PRACTICES IN STUDS

Although mating practices vary considerably from stud to stud, according to breed and conventions observed, it has been observed that the most striking feature of equine mating procedures, compared to those employed in the other farm species, is the high degree of managerial preparation and assistance involved. For mating, it may be a matter of providing various forms of mare restraint, protective gear and hygienic preparations (washing the perineal area); during the act of mating, the attendant may manoeuvre the mare's tail and the stallion's penis to guide it through the vulva.

30.7 TWINS IN THE MARE

As observed by Asdell (1964) dealing with multiple ovulations, multiple pregnancies and multiple births in horses, the mare is obviously unable, as a rule, to carry twins through to term; the figure quoted for twin births was of the order 0.5–1.0% in the literature he reviewed at that time. Horse twins are almost always dizygotic and their high rate of loss during gestation has been attributed to placental insufficiency; it has been reported that the combined surface area of the placenta of twins is only slightly larger than that of a single foetus (Jeffcott and Whitwell, 1973). Such apparent placental insufficiency may be related to the particular structure of the uterus, as discussed by Ginther (1979).

30.8 SEASONAL NATURE OF BREEDING ACTIVITY

Domestication of the horse has not markedly changed the seasonal pattern of ovarian activity in the mare, as already mentioned. It has been estimated that about 75–80% of mares have a period of seasonal anoestrus in the autumn and winter during which ovarian activity is suspended (Marshall, 1922; Osborne, 1966; Ginther, 1974; Hughes et al., 1975); in contrast, 90% or so of mares can be expected to have regular oestrous cycles and ovulate during "long-day" seasons.

It has been observed (Allen, 1978) that increasing daylength, increasing ambient temperature and (under natural conditions) increasing food supply are the three most important factors stimulating the start of cyclical ovarian activity in the anoestrous mare. The main part of the breeding season (ovulatory activity at its greatest) occurs from April to June in the northern hemisphere (Andrews and McKenzie, 1941; Hutton and Measham, 1968) whereas in the southern hemisphere it is from November to January (Osborne, 1966). Of the various environmental factors involved, daylength is probably the most important; the early work of Burkhardt (1947) at Cambridge and the later studies reported by Nishikawa (1959) in Japan

have shown this to be true for the stallion as well as the mare. Burkhardt (1947), during the December to February period, kept mares under conditions of gradually increasing artificial light (to simulate the natural increase in daylength in the February to April period) and significantly hastened the onset of oestrous activity.

Elsewhere, artificial light control applied to horse and pony mares in the middle of the anovulatory season has hastened the onset of the breeding season by as much as 2 months (Loy, 1968; Kooistra and Ginther, 1975; Oxender et al., 1977; Freedman et al., 1979). The current situation is one in which large numbers of Thoroughbred and other horses are routinely maintained under artificial lighting during the late winter and early spring months in North America, Europe and Australasia (Allen, 1978). This is part of the breeders' efforts to try and breed their mares as early as possible in the stud season to achieve an age, weight and strength advantage over foals born later in the year.

In contrast to the story with light, the importance of temperature and nutrition are less well-defined as factors affecting the mare's breeding season. Thoroughbreds and other European breeds do not exhibit consistent cyclical activity in the very hot and arid regions of the world and they apparently show a pronounced breeding season even under the constant daylength conditions which prevail in the equatorial countries of Africa and Asia; in such countries, breeding activity is closely related to the onset of the rainy season, although according to Allen (1978), the real stimulatory factor is probably the sudden flush of grass that occurs at this time. The same author (Allen, 1978) observes that in yarded mares suddenly turned out to fresh spring grass, response may be quite dramatic; some 80% have been noted to come in oestrus and ovulate within as short an interval as 14 days.

Although most studies on the breeding season have been with race horses, it is well accepted that wild and semi-wild breeds have a definite breeding season when the days are increasing to the maximum length so that their foals are born in the spring of the following year (Hammond, 1960). With domestication, the duration of the breeding season has increased and some proportion will even breed throughout the year. At Cambridge, about half of the Welsh and Shetland ponies investigated were found to breed throughout the year, while the others refused to breed from October to March (Hammond, 1960); the same author also recorded that in the U.K. the more primitive breeds of northern origin such as the Shetland pony have a more restricted breeding season than the more improved breeds such as the Clydesdale.

30.9 STALLION ACTIVITY AND FERTILITY

The level of fertility shown by the mare will be influenced to a marked extent by routine stud management procedures (Rossdale and Ricketts, 1980) which include the handling and teasing of mares, feeding practices and breeding routines; good fertility will also mean using stallions with good service behaviour and which produce semen of good quality.

Although sexual activity may be influenced to a minor extent by the season of the year, stallions will usually breed at any time thoughout the 12 months (Stabenfeldt and Hughes, 1977). The ejaculate of the stallion varies from 50 to 200 ml, with an average figure of 125 ml being quoted by Asdell (1964). Sperm production is influenced by several factors, including season, size of testes, frequency of ejaculation and age of the animal. In one report (Pickett and Voss, 1972), total sperm numbers in the autumn and winter were approximately one-half the number found in the spring and early summer. In another American report, Cornwell et al. (1972) found, on the basis of evaluations made at 2-week intervals throughout the year, that the semen of poorest quality, in terms of density and motility was produced during November and December. On the question of male sex drive, Berndtson et al. (1974) found that the concentration of testosterone in peripheral blood plasma of the stallion was highest (>3 ng ml^{-1}) in spring and fell steadily to less than one-half this value by the month of October in autumn. At an earlier date, Asdell (1964) quoted evidence showing that the oestrogen titre in stallion urine was highest in spring and summer and lowest in the winter.

30.10 PLACE OF ARTIFICIAL INSEMINATION

It is frequently quoted that the earliest reference to any form of artificial insemination was probably that in Arabic scriptures of the 13th century referring to its use in horses; it is certainly a fact that the first systematic exploitation of this breeding method took place with horses in the work of the Russian physiologist Ivanoff at a government stud farm at the beginning of the present century. In the Soviet Union and various Eastern European countries, horse AI has been employed in breed improvement schemes on some scale; Swire (1962) noted that in Russia alone, 450 000 horses were bred by the technique in 1953. For all that, and even though horse AI is not technically difficult, it still has very limited use in most countries around the world.

Apart from Soviet Russia, artificial insemination in the mare, using raw, diluted or frozen semen has been employed in many breeds of horses and in numerous countries including China, Germany, Poland, Holland the Scandinavian countries and Japan; in North America and Australasia, AI with raw and diluted fresh semen has been used most often in Standardbreds, Quarterhorses and some Arabians (Stabenfeldt and Hughes, 1977). According to Allen et al. (1976) the technique is now used routinely and has replaced natural service entirely on many large studs in North America and Australasia. However, it should also be said that there is a long way to go with the horse industry before the full benefits of the AI technique can be reaped; according to Bartlett (1973) only 6 of 75 equine registry associations in the U.S.A. at that time permitted the registration of foals born from the use of frozen semen and the major breed associations were not among these. It should be mentioned that in the U.S.A. the first foal was born after frozen AI in 1968 and some 600 had been born by the end of 1974 (Ginther, 1979).

Most U.S.A. registries do accept foals produced by AI if the insemination is carried out at the time and place of semen collection; this rule precludes the transportation of semen and calls for the immediate use of the semen in a raw or diluted state. The conception rates and foaling percentages after AI have been shown to be equal to or better than those achieved by natural service (Bowen, 1969; Pickett and Voss, 1972; Pickett *et al.*, 1974; Pace and Sullivan, 1974) primarily through disease control and service at the most appropriate time for maximal conception rate (Hughes and Loy, 1970). It is held that in a well managed horse breeding programme, including the use of AI, the pregnancy rate in mares should be as high as that observed in cattle (Sullivan *et al.*, 1975).

30.10.1 Collecting semen

The technique of collecting stallion semen with an artificial vagina has been described by many authors from different countries since the pioneering work of Walton (1936), Berliner (1940) and others who used AV's which were relatively cumbersome and difficult to use. Improvements in the design of the horse AV have been made over the years which have simplified the collection procedure and have made the evaluation of the semen more accurate (Nishikawa, 1959; Pickett, 1968). In Australia, Dowsett and Pattie (1980) have reported a satisfactory technique for collecting semen from untrained stallions at stud, using minimal restraint techniques.

30.10.2 Insemination procedures

When carrying out AI with raw semen, only the sperm-rich fraction is used; the undiluted semen is normally inseminated within an hour of collection and a volume as low as 0.6 ml has been shown to result in conception rates as high as those obtained with much larger volumes (50–60% at a single heat; 85–92% over three heats). The total number of live sperm inseminated must be at least 100 million to ensure success (Demick *et al.*, 1976).

A typical stud management routine as now practised on Standardbred and Quarterhorse studs in the U.S.A. and Australasia is one in which semen is collected routinely from the stallion on alternate days throughout the breeding period;

oestrous mares are bred every second day throughout the heat period.

30.10.3 Diluents

A variety of diluents have been employed for short-term stallion semen storage at 4°C (Pickett, 1968; Bowen, 1969; Hughes and Loy, 1970; Pickett and Back, 1973; Pickett *et al.*, 1974; Demick *et al.*, 1976). Semen extended with cream–gelatin diluent can apparently retain its fertilizing capacity for up to 3 days; milk product diluents appear to be superior to sugar–egg yolk diluents (Allen *et al.*, 1976). In the U.S.A., Voss *et al.* (1979) reported on the successful use of inseminates containing 100 million motile sperm extended in 5 ml of a skim-milk diluent; mares were inseminated each day during oestrus or at the time of expected oestrus.

30.10.4 Horse AI advantages

The use of fresh or frozen horse semen could be the means of avoiding the need to transport mares over long distances to visit the stallion of choice. West German experience of horse AI (Merkt, 1976) showed that the most satisfactory results were obtained when the mare was inseminated under stud farm conditions where oestrus could be detected by a teaser and there was a daily veterinary check. Artificial insemination could obviously be the means of substantially increasing the number of mares covered by a stallion in the stud season; Allen *et al.* (1976) noted that many Quarterhorse stallions in the U.S.A. at that time were covering 130–180 mares per season.

30.11 USE OF FROZEN SEMEN

A number of reports dealing with the freezing of stallion semen have appeared since the mid-sixties. Workers in Japan and West Germany (Merkt and Krause, 1966; Nagase *et al.*, 1966; Krause and Grove, 1967; Oshida *et al.*, 1967; Bader and Mahler, 1968; Nishikawa, 1975) developed practical methods for freezing stallion semen based on the pellet storage system designed originally for bull semen by Nagase and Niwa (1964). Subsequent efforts by von Horsten

(1972) showed that there was no loss of sperm motility when the volume of pellets was increased from 0.1 to 0.5 or 1.0 ml using various concentrations of glycerol and an elongated form of pellets. Martin et al. (1979) conducted studies in which semen was diluted (EDTA-diluent) before pre-freezing centrifugation and then frozen in large volume plastic straws (5–6 ml capacity); a fertility rate of 63% to single inseminations was reported. In the U.S.A., workers have also developed freezing techniques using pellets and glass ampoules as the storage system (Pace and Sullivan, 1975).

30.11.1 Conception with frozen semen

According to Allen et al. (1976), the work in horse AI up to that time suggested that the fertilizing lifespan of stallion sperm in the mare's reproductive tract is markedly reduced after freezing, from 3 to 4 days to less than 12 h. However, good pregnancy rates can be achieved if ovulation occurs soon after the time of insemination, as reported by Japanese (Nishi-kawa, 1975) and German (Merkt et al., 1975) workers; the fact that the mare's heat period can be so variable tends to reduce the commercial potential of frozen AI but makes it all the more important to develop effective methods for precisely controlling the time of ovulation in the mare. As it is, satisfactory conception rates are only possible if mares are inseminated frequently during oestrus or subjected to rectal examinations to ensure the most appropriate timing of a single insemination. In Germany, Merkt (1976) checked follicle development by daily rectal examination and carried out AI at the appropriate time (using a double insemination with a 12 h interval between doses).

Workers in North America take the view that frozen semen gives much less acceptable conception rates than fresh semen and that further improvements in freezing–thawing techniques are necessary (Klug et al., 1975; Pace and Sullivan, 1975). Among the problems in freezing stallion semen is the fact that glycerol depresses the fertility of the sperm; it is also clear that the semen of some stallions freezes poorly (Tischner, 1979).

30.12 REFERENCES

Allen, W. R. (1978) Control of oestrus and ovulation in the mare. In, *Control of Ovulation* Crighton, Foxcroft, Haynes and Lamming, Eds. pp. 453–468. Butterworths, London.

Allen, W. R., Bowen, J. M., Frank, C. J., Jeffcoate, L. B. and Rossdale, P. D. (1976) The current position of AI in horse breeding. *Equine Vet. J.* **8**(2), 72–74.

Andrews, F. N. and McKenzie, F. F. (1941) Estrus, ovulation, and related phenomena in the mare. *Univ. Mo. Agric. Exp. Sta. Res. Bull.* **329**, 1–117.

Asdell, S. A. (1964) *Patterns of Mammalian Reproduction (2nd edn)*, Cornstock, Cornell, NY.

Bader, H. and Mahler, R. (1968) Tiefgefrier und Besamung-suersuche mit hengstsperma unter Anwendung des pellet ver fahrens. *Zuchthygiene* **3**, 6–13.

Badi, A. M., O'Byrne, T. M. and Cunningham, E. P. (1981) An analysis of reproductive performance in thoroughbred mares. *Ir. Vet. J.* **35**(1), 1–12.

Bartlett, D. E. (1973) Use of artificial insemination for horses. In, *Stud Manager's Handbook*, Vol. 9, Agriservices Foundation, Clovis, CA.

Berliner, V. R. (1940) An improved artificial vagina for the collection of stallion and jack semen. *J. Am. Vet. Med. Ass.* **96**, 667–670.

Berndtson, W. E., Pickett, B. W. and Nett, T. M. (1974) Reproductive physiology of the stallion. *J. Reprod. Fert.* **39**, 115–118.

Bowen, J. M. (1969) Artificial insemination in the horse. *Equine vet. J.* **1**, 98–110.

Burkhardt, J. (1947) Anoestrus in the mare and its treatment with estrogen. *Vet. Rec.* **59**, 341–342.

Coop, I. E. and Clark, V. R. (1955) The influence of method of rearing as hoggets on the lifetime productivity of sheep. *N.Z. Jl. Sci. Technol.* **37**, 214–228.

Cornwell, J. C., Guthrie, L. D., Spillman, T. E., McGraine, S. E., Haner, E. P. and Vincent, C. K. (1972) Seasonal variation in stallion semen. *12th Ann. Livestock Producers Day*, L.50.

Cunningham, E. P., Alwan, S., Badi, A. M. and O'Byrne, T. M. (1980) High levels of infertility in horses. *Farm Fd Res.* **11**(2), 41–43.

Dawson, F. L. M. (1977) Recent advances in equine reproduction. *Equine Vet. J.* **9**(1), 4–11.

Demick, D. S., Voss, J. L. and Pickett, B. W. (1976) Effect of cooling, storage, glycerolization and spermatozoal numbers on equine fertility. *J. Anim. Sci.* **43**, 633–637.

Dowsett, K. F. and Pattie, W. A. (1980) Collection of semen from stallions at stud. *Aust. Vet. J.* **56**, 373–378.

Freedman, L. J., Farcia, M. C. and Ginther, O. J. (1979) Influence of photoperiod and ovaries on seasonal reproductive activity in mares. *Biol. Reprod.* **20**, 567–574.

Ginther, O. J. (1974) Occurrence of anestrus, estrus, diestrus and ovulation over a 12-month period in mares. *Am. J. Vet. Res.* **35**, 1173–1179.

Ginther, O. J. (1979) *Reproductive Biology of the Mare.* McNaughton & Gunn, Ann. Arbor.

Hammond, J. (1960) *Farm Animals*, Arnold, London.

Horsten, von D. (1972) Tiefgefrier versuche on Hengstsperma. Einfluss von glyzerinkonzentration, pelletgrosse und auftaumedium auf die spermienubertebens rate. *Vet. Med. Diss, Hannover, Tier. Hochschule.*

Hughes, J. P. and Loy, R. G. (1970) Artificial insemination in the equine. A comparison of natural breeding and artificial insemination of mares using semen from six stallions. *Cornell Vet.* **60**, 463–475.

Hughes, J. P., Stabenfeldt, G. H. and Evans, J. W. (1975) The estrous cycle of the mare. *J. Reprod. Fert.* (Suppl.) **23**, 161.

Hutton, C. A. and Meacham, T. N. (1968) Reproductive efficiency on fourteen horse farms. *J. Anim. Sci.* **27**, 434–438.

Jagusch, K. T., Smith, J. F. and Kelly, R. W. (1977) Effect of feeding lucerne during mating on the fertility of ewes. *Proc. Nat. Sci. N.Z.* **2**, 161.

Jeffcott, L. B. and Whitwell, K. E. (1973) Twinning as a cause of foetal and neonatal loss in the thoroughbred mare. *J. Comp. Path.* **83**, 91–166.

Jennings, J. J. (1977) *AFT Annual Report, Animal Production.*

Johnson, K. R., Ross, R. H. and Fourt, B. L. (1958) Effect of progesterone administration on reproductive efficiency. *J. Anim. Sci.* **17**, 386–390.

Klug, E., Treu, H., Hillman, H. and Heinze, H. (1975) Results of insemination of mares with fresh and frozen semen. *J. Reprod. Fert.* (Suppl. 23) 107–110.

Kooistra, L. H. and Ginther, O. J. (1975) Effect of photoperiod on reproductive activity and hair in mares. *Am. J. Vet Res.* **36**, 1413–1419.

Krause, D. and Grove, D. (1967) Deep-freezing of Jackass and Stallion semen in concentrated pellet form. *J. Reprod. Fert.* **14**, 139–141.

Laing, J. A. (1979) Normal fertility and the incidence of infertility. In, *Fertility and Infertility in Domestic Animals* Laing, J. A. Ed. pp. 1–4. 3rd Ed. Bailliere, Tindall, London.

Lieux, P. (1973) Computerized results of a breeding practice. Proc. 19th Ann. Conv. Amer. Assoc. Equine Practice, Atlanta.

Loy, R. G. (1968) Effects of artificial lighting regimes on reproductive patterns in mares. Proc. Ann. Conv. Amer. Assoc. Equine Practice.

Mahon, G. A. T. and Cunningham, E. P. (1980) Inbreeding and infertility in Thoroughbred mares. *Farm Food Res.* **11**(3), 72–73.

Marshall, F. H. A. (1922) *The Physiology of Reproduction*, 2nd Ed., Longmans, Green, London.

Martin, J. C., Klug, E. and Gunzel, A. R. (1979) Centrifugation of stallion semen and its storage in large volume straws. *J. Reprod. Fert. (Suppl.)* **27**, 47–51.

Merkt, H. (1976) Equine artificial insemination. *Vet. Rec.* **99**, 69–71.

Merkt, H. and Krause, D. (1966) Tiefgefrierungmit equidensperma unter anwendungdes spg. pelletuerfahrens. *Dt. tierarztl. Wschr.* **73**, 267–268.

Merkt, H., Klug, E., Krause, D. and Bader, H. (1975) Results of long term storage of stallion semen frozen by the pellet method. *J. Reprod. Fert.* (Suppl.) **23**, 105.

Nagase, H. and Niwa, T. (1964) Deep freezing bull semen in concentrated pellet form. *Proc. 5th Int. Congr. Anim. Reprod. A.I. (Trento)*, 410–415.

Nagase, H., Suejima, S., Niwa, T., Oshida, H., Sagara, Y., Ishizaki, N. and Hoshi, S. (1966) Studies in the freezing storage of stallion semen. I. Fertility results of stallion semen frozen in concentrated pellet form *Jap. J. Anim. Reprod.* **12**, 48–52.

Nishikawa, Y. (1959) *Studies on Reproduction in Horses; Singularity and Artificial Organ Control in Reproductive Phenomena.* Japan Racing Association, Tokyo.

Nishikawa, Y. (1975) Studies on the preservation of raw and frozen horse semen. *J. Reprod. Fert.* (Suppl.) **23**, 99–104.

Osborne, V. E. (1966) An analysis of the pattern of ovulation as it occurs in the annual reproductive cycle of the mare in Australia. *Aust. Vet. J.* **42**, 149–154.

Oshida, H., Ruchi, S., Takahishi, H., Tomizika, T. and Nagase, H. (1967) Studies on the freezing of stallion semen. III. Pellet frozen semen preserved in liquid nitrogen. *Jap. J. Anim. Reprod.* **13**, 136–140.

Oxender, W. D., Noden, P. A. and Hafs, H. D. (1977) Estrus, ovulation and serum progesterone, estradiol and LH concentrations in mares after an increased photoperiod during winter. *Am. J. Vet. Res.* **38**, 203.

Pace, M. M. and Sullivan, J. J. (1975) Effect of timing of insemination, numbers, of spermatozoa and extender components on the pregnancy rate in mares inseminated with frozen stallion semen. *J. Reprod. Fert.* (Suppl.) **23**, 63–66.

Phillips, R. W. (1962) The era of the horse. *The Cattleman* **49**, 42–44.

Phillips, R. W. (1969) Factors favouring animal production. Proc. 2nd Wld. Conf. Anim. Prod. 15–23.

Pickett, B. W. (1968) Collection and evaluation of stallion semen. Proc. 2nd Techn. Conf. on AI. and Reproduction. Nat. Assoc. Anim. Breeders. 80–86.

Pickett, B. W. and Voss, J. L. (1972) Reproductive management of stallions. Proc. 18th Ann. Conv. Amer. Assoc. Equine Practice, 501.

Pickett, B. W. and Voss, J. L. (1975) The effect of semen extenders and sperm number on mare fertility. *J. Reprod. Fert.* (Suppl.) **23**, 95–98.

Pickett, B., Back, D. G., Burqash, L. D. and Voss, J. L. (1974) The effect of extenders, spermatozoal numbers and rectal palpation on equine fertility. Fifth N.A.A.B. Tech. Conf. A.I. Reprod., 47–58.

Rossdale, P. D. and Ricketts, S. W. (1980) *Equine Stud Farm Medicine.* 2nd Ed. Bailliere Tindall, London.

Sharp, D. C. and Ginther, O. J. (1975) Stimulation of follicular activity and estrous behaviour in anestrous mares with light and temperature. *J. Anim. Sci.* **41**, 1368–1372.

Stabenfeldt, G. H. and Hughes, J. P. (1977) Reproduction in horses. In, *Reproduction in Domestic Animals* Cole, H. and Cupps, P. Eds. pp. 401–431. 3rd Ed. Academic Press, London.

Sullivan, J. J., Turner, P. C., Self, L. C., Gutteridge, H. B. and Bartlett, D. E. (1975) Survey of reproductive efficiency in the quarter-horse and thoroughbred. *J. Reprod. Fert.* (Suppl.) **23**, 315–318.

Swire, P. W. (1962) A.I. in the horse. In, *The Semen of Animals and Artificial Insemination.* J. P. Maule, Ed. pp. 281–297. Commonwealth Agricultural Bureau, Slough.

Tischner, M. (1979) Evaluation of deep-frozen semen in stallions. *J. Reprod. Fert. Suppl.* **27**, 53–59.

Voss, J. L., Wallace, R. A., Squires, E. L., Pickett, B. W. and Schideler, R. K. (1979) Effects of synchronization and frequency of insemination on fertility. *J. Reprod. Fert.* (Suppl.) **27**, 257–261.

Walton, A. (1936) Notes on artificial insemination of sheep, cattle and horses. Holborn Surgical Instrument, London.

Wesson, J. A. and Ginther, O. J. (1980) Plasma gonadotrophin concentrations in intact female and intact and castrated male prepubertal ponies. *Biol. Reprod.* **22**, 541–549.

Wesson, J. A. and Ginther, O. J. (1981) Influence of season and age on reproductive activity in pony mares on the basis of a slaughterhouse survey. *J. Anim. Sci.* **52**, 119–129.

CHAPTER 31

The Mare's Oestrous Cycle and Seasonal Breeding Activity

31.1 INTRODUCTION

The concentrations of ovarian steroids and pituitary gonadotrophins in the circulation during the different reproductive states of the mare have not as yet been well documented; however, there has been a considerable increase in knowledge with the application of RIA procedures during the past decade.

31.2 DURATION AND INTENSITY OF OESTRUS

Between heat periods, the mare is not at all receptive to the advances of the stallion and may show this with aggressive behaviour should the male attempt to mount (e.g. by moving away, kicking and such behaviour). The onset of oestrus is regarded as being more gradual in the mare than in other domesticated animals; the actual period of standing oestrus is usually characterized by the mare spreading the hind-legs, lifting the tail to one side, expelling fluids, lowering the pelvis, shrinking the labia and repeatedly exposing the pink tissue of the vulva. Mounting of companion females seldom occurs with the horse during oestrus. Patterns of sexual behaviour in the mare have been described by several authors (Marshall, 1922; Andrews and McKenzie,

1941; Berliner, 1959; Nishikawa, 1959; Waring *et al.*, 1975).

A comprehensive review of the behavioural symptoms of oestrus is in the work of Ginther (1979); according to this author, it is commonly stated that the intensity of behavioural symptoms of oestrus in the mare increases progressively during the period, reaching maximum intensity as ovulation approaches. Although this conclusion was reached on the basis of evidence from at least two groups of workers (Andrews and McKenzie, 1941; Nishikawa, 1959), work reported by Ginther (1979) showed that there was no clear support for this view; in his work, it was found that in a short oestrus of 3–4 days, intensity did increase until ovulation occurred, but if the heat period was longer, the increase in intensity in early oestrus was followed by a prolonged plateau.

31.2.1 Duration of heat

The oestrous period is very variable in length and this is a major contributing factor to the variability observed in the mare's oestrous cycle; the typical average duration quoted is 5–6 days. The duration of oestrus itself, but not the interval between heats, is said to be influenced by season, the heat period being longest at the start of the breeding season in the early spring, shortest (3–4 days) in mid-summer and tending to lengthen again in the autumn prior to the onset of the winter anoestrus (Andrews and McKenzie, 1941).

31.2.2 Detecting without the stallion

For those situations in which a stallion or teaser is not available, studies have been reported in which appropriate stimuli (acoustic, tactile and olfactory) have been successfully applied (Veekman, 1980); these stimuli included a playback of acoustic expressions of a courting stallion and using the brush previously employed on a stallion.

31.3 THE OESTROUS CYCLE

As noted earlier, the most distinguishing feature of the mare's oestrous cycle is the relatively long portion occupied by the heat period itself; whereas in cattle, sheep and pigs, oestrus is short enough to be measured in hours, in the mare it is usually a matter of several days. According to the literature, the average length of the oestrous cycle is 21–22 days, the heat period itself being on average, 5–6 days long. There can be marked differences in cycle length among individual mares and differences between oestrous cycles in the same animal; heat period of 3–10 days in duration must be regarded as being within normal limits (Allen, 1978); ovulation is said to occur fairly consistently between 24 and 36 h before the end of heat.

31.3.1 Ovulation fossa

The mare differs from the other farm species in ovulating follicles from just the one specific area of the ovary (Witherspoon and Talbot, 1970; Witherspoon, 1975), i.e. the ovulation fossa; the mature pre-ovulatory follicle is particularly large in the mare and usually reaches a size of 35–55 mm prior to ovulation (Stabenfeldt and Hughes, 1977). The speed with which the process of luteinization and corpus luteum development occurs in the mare is reflected in the rapid increase in the concentration of plasma progesterone.

31.3.2 Endocrinology of oestrous cycle

During the 1970s, the endocrinology of the oestrous cycle and pregnancy in the mare was examined by investigators in some detail. It became apparent from these studies (Pattison et al., 1972; Whitmore et al., 1973; Noden et al., Evans and Irvine, 1975; Geschwind et al., 1975; Nett et al., 1975) that there is a major difference between the mare and the other farm mammals in the pattern of LH release during the oestrous cycle. Instead of the normal pulsatile type of LH peak of brief duration which occurs in cattle and sheep in response to the pre-oestrus oestrogen build up, baseline plasma LH concentrations of 10–15 ng ml^{-1} in the mare rise steadily throughout heat period to reach a peak of 50– ng ml^{-1} 1 or 2 days after ovulation (Whitmore et al., 1973; Geschwind et al., 1975); levels then fall steadily, usually reaching base line levels by 4–6 days after the end of oestrus.

31.3.3 Luteal phase ovulations

The fact that high concentrations of LH are still present in the blood of most mares for at least 4 days after ovulation may help in explaining the origins of the "silent" ovulations reported to occur during dioestrus in mares (Hughes et al., 1972) and the high incidence of multiple ovulations which has been reported in horses (Stabenfeldt et al., 1972); the interval from the initial ovulation to the luteal phase ovulation may be as short as 2 days and as long as 12 days (Evans and Irvine, 1975; Geschwind et al., 1975). Although the fertility level at such luteal phase ovulations is unknown, it has been suggested that this phenomenon may account for the small but embarrassing number of Thoroughbred and other valuable mares which conceive twins despite the fact that only a single mature follicle was detectable in the ovaries at time of mating.

31.3.4 FSH concentrations

The pattern of FSH secretion in the mare appears to be as unusual and unique as that of LH; Evans and Irvine (1975) reported a bimodal pattern for FSH during the oestrous cycle, with high concentrations of the gonadotrophin (around four times basal level) during late oestrus/early luteal phase coinciding with the main LH peak of the cycle, the other between days 10 and 13 of dioestrus without any associated LH activity. The same authors (Evans and Irvine, 1975) concluded that the mid-cycle release of FSH exerts the priming stimulus for ovarian follicular development and that LH rather than FSH, or perhaps the combined action of the gonado-trophins, acts during oestrus to induce full maturation of the follicle.

This view is in agreement with earlier data showing that administration of an anti-serum prepared against horse pituitary extract, if administered between days 7 and 10 of dioestrus suppresses follicular development and oestrus (Pineda and Ginther, 1972; Pineda et al., 1973). As well as the 10-day episodic releases of FSH observed during the oestrous cycle, there is also evidence that these continue on into early pregnancy in the mare. At an earlier time, South African workers (Van Rensburg and Van Niekerk, 1968) had reported waves of follicular growth and ovarian oestrogen production occurring around days 12, 22 and 32 after ovulation; Evans and Irvine (1975) showed FSH peaks around days 10, 20 and 30 of gestation.

Bimodal FSH secretion has not been found by all investigators; Turner et al. (1979) found that such bimodality was less common late in the mare's breeding season and Miller et al. (1980) found very little evidence for its occurrence, again in the late breeding season.

31.3.5 Progesterone concentrations

As mentioned already, the process of luteiniza-tion and formation of the corpus luteum proceeds rapidly in the mare after rupture of the follicle and this is shown in the early increase in the concentration of plasma progesterone; appreciable luteal activity (4 ng ml^{-1}) is evident as early as 24–48 h after ovulation and peak functional activity can be evident by about day-6 (6–15 ng ml^{-1}). There is general agreement among reports that the life-span of the mare's corpus luteum is about 14 days; a sharp decline in progesterone concentration is evident between days 14 and 16, the level reaching a value of less than 1 ng ml^{-1} by the first day of oestrus (Smith et al., 1970; Stabenfeldt et al., 1972; Palmer and

Jousset, 1975; Plotka et al., 1975). The patterns of progesterone secretion have been shown to diverge between pregnant and nonpregnant mares about 15 days after ovulation (Allen and Hadley, 1974; Squires et al., 1974; Sato et al.; 1977a, b).

31.3.6 Oestrogen levels

The concentration of oestrogen in peripheral plasma rises progressively from 6 to 10 days before ovulation and reaches maximum levels (20–60 pg ml^{-1} total unconjugated oestrogens) 24–28 h before the event; it would seem that there is considerable variation between indi-vidual mares in both the height and the position of the oestrogen peak relative to the time of ovulation (Palmer and Jousset, 1975).

31.4 PROSTAGLANDINS AND LUTEOLYSIS

The rapid decline in progesterone production towards the end of the oestrous cycle in the mare is closely paralleled by a sharp increase in the concentration of a metabolite of prostaglandin $F_{2\alpha}$, the evidence suggesting that $PGF_{2\alpha}$ is probably a major component of the uterine luteolytic hormone in the mare (Stabenfeldt et al., 1978); it has also been shown by Ginther and First (1971) that hysterectomy in the mare greatly prolongs the life-span of the functional corpus luteum. In contrast to the situation in the farm ruminants (cattle, sheep), luteolysis in the mare is not dependent on retention of the uterine horn situated ipsilateral to the ovary containing the active corpus luteum, suggesting that the natural luteolysin may reach the mare's ovary by way of the peripheral circulation, rather than via a local utero-ovarian pathway (Ginther and First, 1971; Del Campo and Ginther, 1973).

31.5 PROLONGED LUTEAL FUNCTION

Spontaneous prolongation of luteal function has been commonly observed in mares that are apparently free of uterine anomalies and infections (Stabenfeldt et al., 1974; Hughes et al., 1975; Palmer and Jousset, 1975; Ricketts, 1978);

according to Allen (1978), complete luteolysis fails to occur at the end of the cycle and a small amount of active luteal tissue remains lodged deep within the ovary. The average duration of this persistence of the luteal phase is given as two months by Stabenfeldt and Hughes (1977); in the work of Allen (1978), a period varying from 4 weeks to 4 months is quoted. Follicular development and oestrogen production can continue during this persistent luteal phase and although oestrus does not occur, there have been instances of mares ovulating (Hughes et al., 1975).

Affected mares can often show plasma progesterone concentrations of 3–5 ng ml^{-1} (Allen and Rossdale, 1973); luteal function is finally terminated abruptly and cyclical ovarian activity resumed. The problem is thought to arise because of inadequate release of uterine luteolysin at the end of the normal luteal phase of the cycle; the cause of the inadequacy is not known, although it has been suggested that it may be due to a failure of endometrial cells in the uterus to synthesise or secrete sufficient luteolysin at the appropriate time. In the past, prolonged luteal function has been one of the important problems in horse reproduction; this is no longer the case with the availability of prostaglandin F$_{2\alpha}$, as will be noted later. A failure of a mare to return to oestrus if not bred, would be a prime reason for suspecting the presence of a persistent corpus luteum; a check on progesterone blood levels should serve to confirm the diagnosis.

31.6 ENDOCRINOLOGY OF THE POST-PARTUM PERIOD

Ovarian activity is not inhibited during the post-partum period in the mare; as noted earlier, a foal heat (first oestrus shortly after parturition) occurs in a high proportion of mares and usually begins between the 6th and 13th days after foaling (Palmer, 1978). After this foal heat, the lactating mare should show regular oestrous cycles but some proportion may not continue to cycle because of a problem of a persistent corpus luteum (Allen and Cooper, 1975).

An understanding of the endocrine events which result in the foal heat is important; failure of the mare to start ovulatory cycles within a week or two is commonly associated with infertility in the mare (Irvine and Evans, 1978; Burns et al., 1979). Studies in New Zealand (Irvine and Evans, 1978) have shown FSH surges occurring 24 and 14 days prior to the post-partum ovulation (12 and 2 days before foaling in their study), which is similar to the 10-day episodic release pattern they had found earlier in the cyclic mare (Evans & Irvine, 1975); the surprising fact is that such FSH activity occurred in the face of the elevated, oestradiol concentrations that operate in the mare prior to foaling.

31.6.1 Lactational and suckling effects

Although post-partum anoestrus is clearly recognized as a problem in beef suckler cattle and occasionally in other cattle as well, little is known of endocrine factors associated with anoestrus in the mare after foaling; a certain percentage of foaling mares do fail to exhibit oestrus while nursing, whereas other mares may have a normal foal heat and subsequently enter a period of anoestrus. According to a report by Ginther et al. (1972), mares whose foals were removed at birth showed evidence of greater ovarian activity during the first 6 days after parturition than did mares which were suckled; certainly, there may be a very high frequency of the suckling stimulus (>40 suckling periods daily) in lactating mares (Palmer, 1978).

Although it is not practicable to remove the foal completely at birth, it may be possible to lessen the suckling stimulus; some evidence, reported by Henneke and Kreider (1979) has shown that mares on a restricted suckling regimen (which did not impair foal growth) exhibited oestrus and ovulated earlier than mares nursing foals in the usual way.

31.7 REFERENCES

Allen, W. R. (1978) Control of oestrus and ovulation in the mare. In, Control of Ovulation. Crighton, Haynes, Foxcroft and Lamming, Eds. pp. 453–470. Butterworths, London.

Allen, W. R. and Cooper, M. J. (1975) The use of synthetic analogues of prostaglandins for inducing luteolysis in mares. *Ann. Biol. Anim. Bioch. Biophys.* **15**, 461–469.

Allen, W. E. and Hadley, J. C. (1974) Blood progesterone concentrations in pregnant and non-pregnant mares. *Equine Vet. J.* **6**, 87–93.

Allen, W. R. and Rossdale, P. D. (1973) A preliminary study upon the use of prostaglandins for inducing oestrus in non cycling thoroughbred mares. *Equine Vet. J.* **5**, 137–140.

Andrews, F. N. and McKenzie, F. F. (1941) Estrus, ovulation and related phenomena in the mare. *Mo. Agr. Exp. Sta. Res. Bull.* 329.

Berliner, V. R. (1959) The estrous cycle of the mare. *(Cole and Cupps, eds.), Reproduction in Domestic Animals,* Acad. Press, New York.

Burns, S. J., Irvine, C. H. G. and Amoss, M. S. (1979) Fertility of prostaglandin-induced oestrus compared to normal post-partum oestrus. *J. Reprod. Fert. (Suppl.)* **27**, 245–250.

Campo, C. H. del and Ginther, O. J. (1973) Vascular anatomy of the uterus and ovaries and the unilateral luteolytic effect of the uterus: horses, sheep and swine. *Am. J. Vet. Res.* **34**, 305.

Evans, M. J. and Irvine, C. H. G. (1975) The serum concentrations of FSH, LH and progesterone during the oestrous cycle and early pregnancy in the mare. *J. Reprod. Fert. (Suppl.)* **23**, 193–200.

Geschwind, I. I., Dewey, R., Hughes, J. P., Evans, J. W. and Stabenfeldt, G. H. (1975) Plasma LH levels in the mare during the oestrous cycle. *J. Reprod. Fert. (Suppl.)* **23**, 207–212.

Ginther, O. J. (1979) *Reproductive Biology of the Mare.* McNaughton & Gunn, Ann Arbor.

Ginther, O. J. and First, N. L. (1971) Maintenance of the corpus luteum in hysterectomized mares. *Am. J. Vet. Res.* **32**, 1687–1691.

Ginther, O. J., Whitmore, H. L. and Squires, E. L. (1972) Characteristics of estrus, diestrus, and ovulation in mares and effects of season and nursing. *Am. J. Vet. Res.* **33**, 1935–1939.

Henneke, D. R. and Kreider, J. L. (1979) Effects of restrictive suckling on *post partum* reproductive performance in mares. *Am. J. Vet. Res.* **40**, 1281–1284.

Hughes, J. P., Stabenfeldt, G. H. and Evans, J. W. (1972) Clinical and endocrine aspects of the estrous cycle of the mare. *Proc. 18th Ann. Conv. Amer. Equine Pract.*, 119–148.

Hughes, J. P., Stabenfeldt, G. H. and Evans, J. W. (1975) The oestrous cycle of the mare. *J. Reprod. Fert.* (Suppl.) **23**, 161–166.

Irvine, C. H. G. and Evans, M. J. (1978) FSH and LH concentrations preceding *post-partum* ovulation in the mare. *N.Z. Vet. J.* **26**, 310–311.

Marshall, F. H. A. (1922) *Physiology of Reproduction* 2nd Ed., Longmans Green, London.

Miller, K. F., Berg, S. L., Sharp, D. C. and Ginther, O. J. (1980) Concentrations of circulating gonadotrophins during various reproductive states in mares. *Biol. Reprod.* **22**, 744–750.

Nett, T. M., Holtan, D. W. and Estergreen, V. L. (1975) Levels of LH, prolactin and oestrogens in the serum of *post-partum* mares. *J. Reprod. Fert. (Suppl.)* **23**, 201–206.

Nishikawa, Y. (1959) *Studies on Reproduction in Horses.* Jap. Racing Assoc., Tokyo.

Noden, P. A., Oxender, W. D. and Hafs, H. D. (1974) Estrus, ovulation, progesterone and LH after prostaglandin F$_{2\alpha}$ in mares. *Proc. Soc. Exp. Biol. Med.* **145**, 145–150.

Palmer, E. (1978) Control of the oestrous cycle of the mare. *J. Reprod. Fert.* **54**, 495–505.

Palmer, E. and Jousset, B. (1975) Urinary oestrogen and plasma progesterone levels in non-pregnant mares. *J. Reprod. Fert. (Suppl.)* **23**, 213–221.

Pattison, M. L., Chen, C. L. and King, S. L. (1972) Determination of LH and E$_2$-17$_\beta$ surge with reference to the time of ovulation in mares. *Biol. Reprod.* **7**, 136 (Abs).

Pineda, M. H. and Ginther, O. J. (1972) Inhibition of estrous and ovulation in mares treated with an antiserum against an equine pituitary fraction. *Amer. J. Vet. Res.* **33**, 1775–1780.

Pineda, M. H., Garcia, M. C. and Ginther, O. J. (1973) Effect of antiserum against an equine pituitary fraction on corpus luteum and follicles in mares during diestrus. *Am. J. Vet. Res.* **34**, 181–183.

Plotka, E. D., Foley, C. W., Witherspoon, D. M., Schmoller, G. C. and Goetsch, D. D. (1975) Periovulatory changes in peripheral plasma progesterone and estrogen concentrations in the mare. *Am. J. Vet. Res.* **36**, 1359–1362.

Ricketts, S. W. (1978) Histological and histopathological studies of the endometrium of the mare. Fellowship Thesis, Royal College of Vet. Surgeons.

Sato, K., Miyake, N., Yoshikawa, T. and Kambegawa, A. (1977a) Studies on serum oestrogen and progesterone levels during the oestrous cycle and the early pregnancy in mares. *Equine Vet. J.* **9**, 57–60.

Sato, K., Miyake, M., Tsunoda, N., Yoshikawa, T. and Kambegawa, A. (1977b) Concentration of serum progesterone and cortisol during estrous cycle and early pregnancy in mares. *Jap. J. Zootech. Sci.* **48**(12), 721–723.

Smith, D., Bassett, J. M. and Williams, T. (1970) Progesterone concentrations in the peripheral plasma of the mare during the oestrous cycle. *J. Endocr.* **47**, 523–524.

Squires, E. L., Wentworth, B. C. and Ginther, O. J. (1974) Progesterone concentration in blood of mares during the estrous cycle, pregnancy and after hysterectomy. *J. Anim. Sci.* **39**, 759–767.

Stabenfeldt, G. H. and Hughes, J. P. (1977) Reproduction in horses. In, *Reproduction in Domestic Animals.* (3rd Ed.), Cole and Cupps, Eds., pp. 401–431, Academic Press, London.

Stabenfeldt, G. H., Hughes, J. P. and Evans, J. W. (1972) Ovarian activity during the estrous cycle of the mare. *Endocrin.* **90**, 1379–1384.

Stabenfeldt, G. H., Hughes, J. P. and Evans, J. W. (1974) Spontaneous prolongation of luteal activity in the mare. *Equine Vet. J.* **6**, 158.

Stabenfeldt, G. H., Edqvist, L. E., Kindahl, H., Gustafsson, B. and Bane, A. (1978). Practical implications of recent physiologic findings for reproductive efficiency in cows, mares, sows and ewes. *J. Am. Vet. Med. Ass.* **172**, 667–675.

Turner, D. D., Garcia, M. C. and Ginther, O. J. (1979) Follicular and gonadotropic changes throughout the year in pony mares. *Am. J. Vet. Res.* **40**, 1694–1700.

Van Rensburg, S. J. and Van Niekerk, C. H. (1968) Ovarian function, follicular oestradiol-17$_\beta$ and luteal progesterone and 20$_\alpha$-hydroxy-preg-4-en-3-one in cycling and pregnant equines. *Onderstepoort. J. Vet. Res.* **35**, 301.

Veeckman, J. (1980) The detection of oestrus in mares by behavioural appraisal. *Proc. 9th Int. Congr. Anim. Reprod. A.I. (Madrid)*, **2**, 601–605.

Waring, G. H., Wierzbowski, S. and Hafez, E. S. D. (1975) The behaviour of horses. In, *The Behaviour of Domestic Animals,* pp. 330–369, Bailliere, Tindall, London.

Whitmore, H. L., Wentworth, B. C. and Ginther, O. J. (1973) Circulating concentrations of LH during estrous cycles of mares determined by RIA. *Am. J. Vet. Res.* **34,** 631–636.

Witherspoon, D. M. (1975) The site of ovulation in the mare. *J. Reprod. Fert. (Suppl.)* **23,** 329–330.

Witherspoon, D. M. and Talbot, R. B. (1970) Ovulation site in the mare. *J. Am. Vet. Med. Ass.* **157,** 1452–1458.

CHAPTER 32

Artificial Control of Oestrus and Ovulation

32.1 INTRODUCTION

Treatments in the mare may be concerned with bringing the animal in oestrus earlier than otherwise would be the case in the spring months of the year, with controlling oestrus and ovulation in the cyclic mare to facilitate breeding — whether by natural or artificial insemination, and with overcoming problems associated with abnormal ovarian conditions (persistent corpus luteum).

32.2 LIGHT MANIPULATION

Daylength is regarded as being by far the most important environmental factor controlling reproductive seasonality in the mare (Ginther, 1979); the lines of evidence pointing to this include the fact that (1) daylength is the most predictive of the environmental factors and is likely to be the one to which mares are keyed; (2) an increase in daylength parallels the increase in the percentage of mares ovulating; and (3) reproductive seasonality can be manipulated in

mares by varying the duration of light while keeping other factors constant.

32.2.1 Use of light control

As mentioned already, practical use has been made of the fact that it is the increase in daylength which is held to be the main natural factor bringing the mare's period of anoestrus to an end in the early spring. Burkhardt (1947) and several groups subsequently (Loy, 1968; Oxender et al., 1977) employed a 16 h photoperiod after a progressive increase; others have used an abrupt rather than a gradual increase in light up to the 16 h (Kooistra and Ginther, 1975). Although comparative trials have not been reported, it appears that both approaches achieve the same results. Treatments are started at different times in the autumn between mid-October and mid-December and ovarian activity can be expected to commence in February, one to three months earlier than in controls (Palmer, 1978); the minimum light intensity or the length of day required to produce the optimum response have not been determined.

Much remains unknown about the effect of

photoperiodism in the mare. Experimental work reviewed by Ginther (1979) has indicated that the pineal gland may be involved; studies reported by Sharp and Seamans (1980) suggested that there may be an evening photosensitive phase in the mare which may be important in regulating her seasonal activity (i.e. time of day of exposure to light may be more critical than duration of light exposure). There also seems to be some evidence that exposure of the mare to a long, fixed daily photoperiod throughout the year causes both an earlier onset and a delayed termination of the breeding season (Ginther, 1979).

Those studying endocrine events report evidence indicating that LH levels are low, as in the late luteal phase in the cyclic mare, during the winter (Garcia and Ginther, 1976; Oxender et al., 1977); the concentration of LH was only found to increase a few days prior to the first ovulation of the season (Oxender et al., 1977) although follicular activity may be evident for many weeks before that time in mares kept under a suitable light regimen (Sharp and Ginther, 1975).

As noted by Allen (1978), the maintenance of stabled mares on a high plane of nutrition and under artificial light is expensive and only partially effective; according to this author, there is a need to be able to induce a fertile oestrus cheaply and at will in maiden and barren mares during February and March of the year.

32.3 HORMONES TO OVERCOME ANOESTRUS

There is much evidence to show that the ovaries of the mare are very resistant to exogenous gonadotrophic stimulation; Day (1940) was among the first to report a total lack of ovarian response by winter anoestrous mares given a single or multiple injections of large amounts of gonadotrophins such as PMSG and hCG; a similar lack of response was observed by other authors in pony mares given one to four injections on alternate days with equine, bovine or porcine FSH or PMSG (Stockell-Hartree et al., 1968). In the U.S.A., however, gonadotrophin treatment in the form of 14 daily injections of a crude horse pituitary extract successfully induced normal oestrus in a majority of anoestrous

pony mares (Douglas et al., 1974; Lapin and Ginther, 1977).

According to Irvine and Evans (1979) the lack of success in the earlier work with gonadotrophic preparations could probably be explained on the basis of what is now known about the role of FSH and LH in follicular maturation and ovulation; to be adequately primed, a follicle must be exposed to FSH for about 2 weeks, after which increased LH levels can cause final maturation, ovulation and establishment of the corpus luteum. Brief courses of treatment with FSH preparations are probably insufficient to prime follicles and LH-like hormones (both PMSG and hCG in the mare) are likely to be ineffective in the absence of any preovulatory follicles.

Allen (1978) took the American results as encouraging in that they showed that the ovaries of the genuinely anoestrous mare are capable of responding quickly and without any long-term priming stimuli (such as increased daylength); the cost and difficulty of obtaining sufficient pituitary extract and the need for 14 daily injections makes the treatment impracticable in commercial horse-breeding. A further difficulty would be the incidence of multiple ovulations (Palmer, 1978).

32.3.1 Gn-RH possibilities

An alternative approach to gonadotrophins may lie in the use of Gn-RH, now that New Zealand workers have administered Gn-RH and progesterone to anoestrous mares according to a regimen designed to simulate the FSH, LH and progesterone concentrations of the normal oestrous cycle (Evans and Irvine, 1976, 1977, 1979); although ineffective in deep winter anoestrous mares, their treatment regimen (three courses of Gn-RH given 10 days apart with daily injections of progesterone for 10 days in the mid-part) was successful in mares treated in shallow anoestrus. The New Zealand studies also produced some evidence that progesterone itself may play a role in follicular maturation in the mare; this may be a factor in explaining why Allen and Alexeev (1980), using similar doses of the same Gn-RH analogue as the New Zealand workers, failed to get any response in mares at the start of the breeding season.

32.3.2 Oestrogen treatment

In Japan, Nishikawa (1959) reported that daily injections of diethyl stilboestrol (5–10 mg) for 10–20 days during the luteal phase of the cycle and towards the end of the breeding season, would inhibit follicular development for 2–4 months after the final injection. After this oestrogen-induced anoestrus, ovarian activity apparently resumed in mid-winter with heat periods occurring at regular intervals throughout the rest of the non-breeding season; oestrous, accompanied by ovulation, and normal pregnancy after breeding was found by the Japanese worker.

32.4 LIGHT AND PROGESTAGENS

Treatments with progesterone or progestagens may be employed towards the end of the mare oestrus or in conjunction with increasing daylength regimens to induce oestrus in the horse. According to Allen et al. (1980), it is probably the absence of a functional corpus luteum in the ovaries of the anoestrous mare, the regression of which would normally bring about the release of sufficient LH to bring about follicular maturation and ovulation, which prolongs the non-breeding period or gives rise to abnormal ovarian activity. Progesterone (and progestagen) is known to exert a powerful negative feedback action on the release of LH (Stabenfeldt et al., 1975; Garcia et al., 1979). A sharp increase in the rate of secretion of pituitary LH, similar to that which occurs at the time of oestrus in the cyclic mare (Miller et al., 1980), is regarded as an essential pre-requisite of the first ovulation of the new breeding season (Freedman et al., 1979).

The results of Allen et al. (1980), who employed the synthetic progestagen, allyl trenbolone (Regumate, Roussel Uclaf, France) over a period of 10–15 days (30 mg dose daily by mouth) showed that this was a practical means of hastening the onset of the breeding season in mares; the results with Regumate supported earlier findings reported by van Niekerk et al. (1973) who had used daily injections of 100–125-mg progesterone over a period of about a week.

Treatment with Regumate is relatively simple and may have considerable potential as a management tool, but it is only effective with mares that are in the transitional phase between anoestrus and the breeding season; several reports make it clear that the agent cannot be employed in mares that are in deep anoestrus (Palmer, 1979; Squires et al., 1979; Heeseman et al., 1980; Scheffrahn et al., 1980).

32.4.1 Light aids response

Palmer (1979) achieved a high rate of success after attempts to induce and synchronize oestrus and ovulation in pony mares in February and March by feeding (10 mg daily) Regumate for 10 days at the end of a 2-month period of increased artificial lighting. Similarly, Squires et al. (1979) reported that mares fed Regumate for 12 days in March responded much better than when the same treatment was applied 2 months earlier in January. The evidence is that extra daylength shifts the mare from deep anoestrus into the transitional phase when she will be able to respond to the Regumate.

At Illinois, Scheffrahn et al. (1980) reported on studies in pony mares in which they employed Norgestamet (SC-21009) ear implants for 10 days in combination with prostaglandin $F_{2\alpha}$ (given on day-7 of treatment); they found the treatment used in conjunction with increasing natural daylength, effective in synchronizing oestrus in pony mares in spring.

32.5 PROGESTAGENS IN CYCLIC MARES

Progesterone or progestagens have been employed in various ways and using different means of administration to control oestrus and ovulation in the mare exhibiting regular oestrous cycles within the breeding season.

32.5.1 Inhibition of oestrus

From the practical point of view, there may be the need to delay the occurrence of oestrus in the cyclic mare that is being used in racing or show jumping. As in the other farm animals, endogenous progesterone from the corpus luteum inhibits oestrus and ovulation in the mare during the period of luteal activity; as a treatment based on this, daily injections of 50 mg progesterone for pony mares (Holtan et al., 1977) and 100 mg or more for large mares (Loy and Swan, 1966) have been employed to suppress oestrus for the duration of treatment. Daily injections of the natural steroid on a liveweight basis (0.3 mg progesterone/kg bodyweight) have been employed by some (Van Niekerk et al., 1973).

In France, however, Palmer (1976) found that a progesterone dose which inhibited oestrus would not necessarily suppress ovulation; although 100 mg progesterone daily prevented heat in large ponies, 27% of them ovulated during the treatment. Several pieces of evidence suggest that a dose of 200–300 mg progesterone daily may be necessary to achieve the concentrations normally circulating in mares during the luteal phase of the cycle (Evans et al., 1975; Ganjam et al., 1975); such treatment should be followed, 3–7 days after terminating progesterone injections, by a normal fertile oestrus.

32.5.2 Synchronizing oestrus

Synthetic orally active progestagens which have been used to control oestrus in cattle and sheep (e.g. MAP) have proved to be much less effective in mares (Loy and Swan, 1966; Bowen, 1968; Hoppe et al., 1974). In the U.S.A., Webel (1975) reported that the progestagen Regumate would effectively block oestrus and ovulation in cyclic mares when given orally at doses of 0.176–0.44 mg/kg bodyweight. As already mentioned, both Palmer (1979) and Squires et al. (1979) have used Regumate in combination with increasing light to induce an earlier start to breeding in horses. Squires et al. (1979) also found Regumate to be effective in preventing irregular sexual activity (split oestrus/anovulatory oestrus) which commonly occurs in the early part of the mare's breeding season (Ginther, 1974). It might be mentioned that the non-steriodal pituitary inhibitor, methallibure, has been used in synchronizing oestrus but had undesirable side-effects, including the refusal of feed (First, 1973).

32.5.3 Administering progestagens

As noted by Palmer (1979), for practical oestrus control purposes, progesterone or progestagens are limited in their appeal until effective means are available for long-term administration to avoid the present need for daily treatment; the same author administered Regumate in intra-vaginal sponges (500–1000 mg doses) over a 20-day period. The Regumate sponges were dusted with antibiotic and inserted during the luteal phase of the cycle; a dose of prostaglandin $F_{2\alpha}$ was given 24 h later to induce regression of the cyclical corpus luteum. No loss of sponges was experienced in this French work and a satisfactory fertility rate (71% in 24 mares) was achieved after mating every 48 h during the controlled heat. The intravaginal mode of progestagen administration could be useful where horse breeders wish to keep their mares out on pasture without the need for individual daily feeding.

The use of progestagens should be limited to cyclic mares, once the breeding season has started, in view of evidence showing that most mares suffering from persistent luteal activity remain in the same condition after progestagen treatment (Palmer, 1979).

32.6 PROSTAGLANDINS IN OESTRUS CONTROL

In cyclic farm mammals, the hormonal event associated with the onset of oestrus and follicular maturation is the termination of progesterone production by the corpus luteum. The natural luteolytic factor in the mare, of uterine origin, is believed to be prostaglandin $F_{2\alpha}$ (Ginther and First, 1971); this belief is supported by the presence of a surge of prostaglandin in uterine venous blood (Douglas and Ginther, 1976) and of a metabolite of $PGF_{2\alpha}$ in peripheral plasma (Kindahl et al., 1976) and by the presence of $PGF_{2\alpha}$ receptors in the mare's corpus luteum (Kimball and Wyngarde, 1977).

During the early seventies, several groups of workers showed that $PGF_{2\alpha}$ and its analogues are highly luteolytic in the mare at considerably lower dose levels than those required to induce complete regression of the corpus luteum in cattle; Allen and Rowson, 1973; Noden et al., 1973; Allen et al., 1974; Douglas and Ginther, 1975; Miller et al., 1976); data in most reports indicated that doses of 10 mg $PGF_{2\alpha}$ were luteolytic in the mare. It has been suggested (Palmer, 1978) that the absence of a local effect from the uterine horn to the adjacent ovary in the mare explains why systemic administration of the agent does not call for a higher dose than that needed for intrauterine administration. As in cattle, it appears that the corpus luteum in horses is refractory to the action of luteolytic agents until it is about 5 days old (Allen and Rowson, 1973).

32.6.1 PG analogues

Workers at Cambridge (Allen and Rowson, 1973; Allen et al., 1974) studied the luteolytic activity, in pony and Thoroughbred mares, of two synthetic prostaglandin analogues structurally related to $PGF_{2\alpha}$ (ICI-79939 and ICI-81008); doses of 80 μg ICI-79939 and 125 μg ICI-81008 in the Thoroughbred, given between the 4th and 13th days of dioestrus, consistently induced complete luteolysis. The analogue eventually marked by ICI Ltd. for use in the mare (Equimate; ICI-81008; fluoprostenol) is usually employed at the 250 μg dose level (Berwyn-Jones and Irvine, 1974; Allen and Cooper, 1975; Douglas and Ginther, 1975; Palmer and Joussett, 1975). Other analogues are also available (Witherspoon et al., 1975).

32.6.2 General considerations

Whether it is the natural $PGF_{2\alpha}$ agent itself or one of the analogues, the ability of prostaglandins to control oestrus in the cyclic mare cheaply and effectively has provided the horse-breeder with a valuable reproductive management tool. In most countries in which prostaglandins are marketed, regulatory clearance probably occurred earlier for the horse product than for the cow agent because the milk and tissue residue considerations that arise in the food-producing animals would not apply in horses (Schultz, 1980). On the question of side-effects, it is known that luteolytic doses of $PGF_{2\alpha}$ can result in sweating, diarrhoea and suchlike arising from the action of the agent on smooth muscle activity; although symptoms pass off rapidly enough, it has been mentioned as a factor in favour of the analogues that they do not produce such side-effects to the same extent (Cooper, 1981). In almost all reproductively active mares treated at an appropriate stage of the oestrous cycle with prostaglandin, oestrus can be expected to occur 2–5 days later; at the induced heat, hormonal events and fertility are regarded as normal (Allen and Cooper, 1975; Oxender et al., 1975; Nelson, 1976).

32.6.3 Timing of oestrus after PG

It would appear that it is not possible to exercise precise control of oestrus and the occurrence of ovulation in the mare by modifying the luteal phase; attention has been drawn to the fact that there can be considerable variation in the interval to ovulation (Loy et al., 1979). According to Bowen et al. (1978), most mares should come in oestrus about 72 h after the administration of prostaglandin; the same author notes that even in those mares where oestrus is not shown after the treatment, pregnancies may be established by inseminating at 2-day intervals on several occasions.

32.6.5 PG and hCG

In France, for the synchronization of oestrus and ovulation in groups of cyclic mares selected at random, Palmer and Jousset (1975) adopted a routine based on the double prostaglandin regimen developed originally for cattle. On this treatment schedule, mares were given a luteolytic dose of 250 μg. Equimate on day-0, followed on day-6 or 7 by an injection of hCG (1500 i.u.) designed to induce ovulation in those mares which had responded to the PG: on day-14, when most mares could be expected to be between the 4th and 15th days of dioestrus, they were again given Equimate, followed on day -20 or 21 by a second dose of hCG in conjunction with a single mating or insemination. Allen et al. (1976) reported ovulation occurring during a 24 h period in 10/13 pony mares subjected to this same double PG, double hCG regimen.

32.6.5 Prostaglandin–progestagen comparisons

Holton *et al.* (1977) did a comparison of progesterone and prostaglandin treatments, using 18 daily doses of progesterone, two prostaglandin doses given 18 days apart or a single $PGF_{2\alpha}$ dose on day-7 of a 10-day daily progesterone treatment schedule; all three treatments were followed in 5 or 6 days by a single ovulating dose of 2000 i.u. hCG. It was concluded that all three regimens provided a good degree of synchronization of oestrus in pony mares. Allen (1978) suggests that oestrus synchronization, both with prostagens and prostaglandins (with hCG used to control ovulation), would allow batch mating of large groups of mares and that even in Thoroughbreds and other breeds where AI is not permitted by the breed registration authorities, the techniques could prove useful for the planned natural mating of individual mares on specified dates. The same author notes that the use of the hormonal techniques would obviate the need for frequent teasing of mares for oestrus detection and rectal examinations to determine follicular development and ovulation.

is now regarded as the treatment of choice for all forms of prolonged dioestrus, in view of the fact that the persistent corpus luteum remains sensitive to luteolytic doses of this agent (Allen *et al.*, 1974; Berwyn-Jones and Irvine, 1974; Allen and Cooper, 1975; Kenney *et al.*, 1975; Nelson, 1976; Shepherd, 1976). The reason for the failure of the uterus to synthesize or release adequate luteolysin is not clear, but the condition of persistent corpus luteum can occur in maiden mares and horses with normal genital tracts; the condition can persist for 30–90 days (average about 2 months) with a return to cyclic ovarian activity presumably when the uterus regains the capacity to synthesise and release $PGF_{2\alpha}$.

Treatment with exogenous prostaglandin brings about a rapid return to oestrus, with a subsequent fertile ovulation in more than 80% of mares treated. As noted by Allen (1978), in view of the very short "breeding season" of Thoroughbred and Standardbred mares, the availability of this cheap, simple and effective prostaglandin treatment provides a most welcome solution to this long-standing problem.

32.7 PROSTAGLANDIN AND PERSISTENT CORPUS LUTEUM

Naturally-occurring prolongation of luteal activity in the non-pregnant mare is one of the most important causes of infertility in the horse (Stabenfeldt *et al.*, 1974, 1980). The cause of the problem is believed to be the failure of the uterus to release adequate amounts of prostaglandin at about 14 days after ovulation (Connor *et al.*, 1976); some release of prostaglandin may occur with the effect of dampening luteal activity without actually bringing it to an end.

For many years, treatment for prolongation of the luteal phase in the mare consisted of irrigation of the uterus with a large volume of normal or slightly hypertonic saline (Allen, 1978); in about 50% of mares, such treatment succeeded in bringing the mare into oestrus 2–3 days later and it was assumed that irrigation induced release to luteolysin from the uterine endometrium.

Uterine infection can be a sequel to the irrigation treatment, however, and prostaglandin

32.8 CONTROL OF OVULATION

As already mentioned, the LH concentrations during natural and artificially controlled oestrus in the horse do not show the peak found in the other farm species; there is, in effect, no pronounced hormonal signal preceding ovulation. Nonetheless, the preovulatory follicle in the mare appears to be perfectly capable of responding to a short surge of ovulating gonadotrophin — a dose of 1500–3000 i.u. hCG can induce ovulation about 24–48 h later (Loy and Hughes, 1966; Sullivan *et al.*, 1973) when mares are treated on the second day of oestrus.

In fact, hCG has been employed routinely for ovulation control from the time of Day (1940) who was the first to show that a single injection of as little as 1000 i.u. of this gonadotrophin would result in ovulation 34–36 h later, provided a well-defined follicle was evident in the ovaries when administering the agent. Irvine and Evans (1979) have mentioned the need for some caution in using hCG on the basis of evidence indicating antibody production to this agent in some studies (Sullivan et al., 1973; Cole et al., 1975; Voss et al., 1975; Roser et al., 1979); the same authors (Irvine and Evans, 1979) suggest restricting the use of hCG to those mares in which a specific lack of LH seems evident.

32.8.1 Gn-RH

When Gn-RH first became available in the 1970s it was thought that this hormone, being identical to that produced by the mare and for that reason non-antigenic, would provide a more natural approach to inducing an LH surge. However, although there have been reports showing success in inducing ovulation (Irvine et al., 1975; Kreider et al., 1975) other workers who have used Gn-RH have not always achieved control (Ginther and Wentworth, 1974; Garcia and Ginther, 1975; Noden and Oxender, 1976; Wallace et al., 1977); there is evidence that response is influenced by stage of oestrus (Foster et al., 1979) and by oestradiol level at time of administration (Vivrette and Irvine, 1979). At present, it would seem that data are insufficient for a conclusive view on the usefulness of the agent in oestrus control (Palmer, 1978; Irvine and Evans, 1979). The point has also been made (Allen, 1978) that Gn-RH is known to induce the release of both FSH and LH in the mare and its use may increase the risk of twin ovulations.

32.8.2 Progestagen-oestrogen combination

In a recent report by Loy et al. (1981) there is some evidence that a particular progesterone-oestrogen combination may result in ovulations in cyclic mares occurring in a very restricted interval; the hormonal regimen involved daily doses of 150 mg progesterone and 10 mg oestradiol for 10 days, with a luteolytic dose of prostaglandin given at the end of this treatment. The authors suggest that the combined progesterone–oestrogen technique may decrease the variability in follicular development found at the end of treatment when progesterone alone is employed.

32.9 INDUCING OESTRUS AFTER THE FOAL HEAT

As mentioned earlier, most mares can be expected to come into foal heat rather more than a week after parturition; breeding at the foal heat can result in a lower pregnancy rate than that seen at later periods. Nonetheless, the mare may often be bred at the foal heat to prevent the possibility of the mare experiencing lactational anoestrus and to avoid the animal being bred too late in the breeding season. According to Roberts (1971), even after a normal foaling, the uterine endometrium may not have returned to its normal state by 10 days post-partum, although recovery usually is complete between days 13 and 25; there are however, those who maintain that tissue repair is complete by the time of the foal heat (Loy et al., 1975).

An injection of prostaglandin $F_{2\alpha}$ given about a week after the end of the foal heat, has been shown to induce oestrus about five days later (Kreider et al., 1975); by 3 weeks or so after parturition, or so the reasoning goes, when this controlled heat occurs, the uterine epithelium has had a longer period in which to recover and the conception rate should be correspondingly higher. According to Schultz (1980), this is a practice which is successful and is gaining popularity in the United States. It might be noted, however, that not all investigators are agreed that the prostaglandin controlled heat is likely to give a higher conception rate; Burns et al. (1979) found no difference in conception rate after foal heat and the delayed induced heat. In view of the fact that there may often be pressure on stud managers to breed mares at the foal heat, the additional delay involved with the prostaglandin treatment would clearly have to confer some useful advantage; further studies would seem worthwhile in this area.

32.10 SYNCHRONIZING THE MARE'S REPEAT HEAT

In carrying out oestrus synchronization in sheep and cattle, rams or bulls are generally used to pick up the females that fail to become pregnant and subsequently return in oestrus. In the horse industry, however, there could be merit in developing a complete reproductive management system for controlling heat in mares on several occasions without the need to detect oestrus (Palmer, 1979).

For synchronizing the return to oestrus in mated non-conceiving mares, French workers have given Regumate from days 7 to 21 after mating; the rebreeding of non-pregnant mares was decided after progesterone assay of day-21 blood plasma and matings carried out on days 27 and 28, with hCG injection on day-28. After three such controlled mating periods, the cumulative fertility was 88% in non-lactating mares and 58% in lactating mares (Palmer, 1979).

32.11 FUTURE DEVELOPMENTS

Clearly, there is every need for simple and effective oestrus and ovulation control methods in horses. At present, much less information is available on the effectiveness of techniques in the horse than with the other farm animals, but research efforts, particularly in the U.K., France, the U.S.A. and Australasia are rapidly changing that situation.

32.12 REFERENCES

Allen, W. R. (1978) Control of oestrus and ovulation in the mare. In, *Control of Ovulation* Crighton, Foxcroft, Haynes and Lamming, Eds., pp. 453–468. Butterworths, London.

Allen, W. E. and Alexeev, M. (1980) Failure of an analogue of gonadotrophin releasing hormone (HOE-766) to stimulate follicular growth in anoestrous pony mares. *Equine Vet. J.* **12**(1), 27–28.

Allen, W. R. and Cooper, M. J. (1975) The use of synthetic analogues of prostaglandins for inducing luteolysis in mares. *Ann. Biol. Anim. Biochim. Biophys.* **15**, 461–469.

Allen, W. R. and Rowson, K. E. A. (1973) Control of the mare's oestrous cycle by prostaglandins. *J. Reprod. Fert.* **33**, 539–543.

Allen, W. R., Stewart, F., Cooper, N. J., Crowhurst, R. C., Simpson, D. J., McEnry, R. J., Greenwood, R. E. S., Rossdale, P. D. and Ricketts, S. W. (1974) Further studies on the use of synthetic prostaglandin analogues for inducing luteolysis in mares. *Equine Vet. J.* **6**, 31–35.

Allen, W. R., Stewart, F., Trounson, A. O., Tischner, M. and Bielanski, W. (1976) Viability of horse embryos after storage and long distance transport in the rabbit. *J. Reprod. Fert.* **47**, 387–390.

Allen, W. R., Urwin, V., Simpson, D. J., Greenwood, R. E. S., Crowhurst, R. C., Ellis, D. R., Ricketts, S. W., Hunt, M. D. N. and Wingfield Digby, N. J. (1980) Preliminary studies on the use of an oral progestogen to induce oestrus and ovulation in seasonally anoestrous thoroughbred mares *Equine Vet. J.* **12**, 141–145.

Berwyn-Jones, M. D. and Irvine, C. H. G. (1974) Induction of luteolysis and oestrous in mares with a synthetic prostaglandin analogue (ICI 81008). *N.Z. Vet. J.* **22**, 107–110.

Bowen, J. M. (1968) An induced cystic ovarian condition in the mare. *Proc. 6th Int. Congr. Anim. Reprod. A.I. (Paris),* 1559.

Bowen, J. M., Niang, P. S., Menard, L., Irvine, D. S. and Moffat, J. B. (1978) Pregnancy without estrus in the mare. *J. Equine Med. Surg.* **2**(5), 227–232.

Burkhardt, J. (1947) Transition from anoestrus in the mare and the effects of artificial lighting. *J. Agric. Sci. Camb.* **37**, 64.

Burns, S. J., Irvine, C. H. G. and Amoss, M. S. (1979) Fertility of prostaglandin-induced oestrus compared to normal *post-partum* oestrus. *J. Reprod. Fert. (Suppl.)* **27**, 245–250.

Cole, H. H., Dewey, R., Geschwind, I. I. and Chapman, M. (1975) Separation of progonadotropic and antigonadotropic activities in ovine and equine hCG antisera. *Biol. Reprod.* **12**, 516–521.

Cooper, M. J. (1981) Prostaglandins in veterinary practice. *In Practice* **3**(1), 30–34.

Day, F. T. (1940) Clinical and experimental observations on reproduction in the mare. *J. Agric. Sci., Camb.* **30**, 244.

Douglas, R. H. and Ginther, O. J. (1975) Effects of prostaglandin $F_{2\alpha}$ on estrous cycle or corpus luteum in mares and and gilts. *J. Anim. Sci.* **40**, 518–522.

Douglas, R. H. and Ginther, O. J. (1976) Concentration of prostaglandins F. in uterine venous plasma of anesthetized mares during the estrous cycle and early pregnancy. *Prostaglandins* **11**, 251.

Douglas, R. H., Nuti, L. and Ginther, O. J. (1974) Induction of ovulation and multiple ovulation in seasonally-anovulatory mares with equine pituitary fractions. *Theriogen.* 133.

Evans, M. J. and Irvine, C. H. G. (1976) Measurement of equine follicle stimulating hormone and luteinizing hormone: response of anestrous mares to gonadotropin releasing hormone. *Biol. Reprod.* **15**, 277–284.

Evans, M. J. and Irvine, C. H. G. (1977) Induction of follicular development, maturation and ovulation by gonadotropin releasing hormone administration to acyclic mares. *Biol. Reprod.* **16**, 452–462.

Evans, M. J. and Irvine, C. H. G. (1979) Induction of follicular development and ovulation in seasonally acyclic mares using gonadotrophin-releasing hormones and progesterone. *J. Reprod. Fert. (Suppl.)* **27**, 113–121.

Evans, J. W., Faria, D. A., Hughes, J. P., Stabenfeldt, G. H. and Cupps, P. T. (1975) Relationship between luteal and metabolic clearance and production rates of progesterone in the mare. *J. Reprod. Fert. (Suppl.)* **23**, 177–182.

First, N. L. (1973) Synchronization of estrus and ovulation in mare with methallibure. *J. Anim. Sci.* **36**, 1143–1148.

Foster, J. P., Evans, M. J. and Irvine, C. H. G. (1979) Differential release of LH and FSH in cyclic mares in response to synthetic Gn-RH. *J. Reprod. Fert.* **56**, 567–572.

Freedman, L. J., Farcia, M. C. and Ginther, O. J. (1979) Influence of photoperiod and ovaries on seasonal reproductive activity in mares. *Biol. Reprod.* **20**, 567–574.

Ganjam, V. K., Kenney, R. M. and Flickinger, G. (1975) Effect of exogenous progesterone on its endogenous levels; biological half life of progesterone and lack of progesterone binding in mares. *J. Reprod. Fert. (Suppl.)* **23**, 183–188.

Garcia, M. C. and Ginther, O. J. (1975) Plasma LH concentration in mares treated with Gn-RH and estradiol. *Am. J. Vet. Res.* **36**, 1581–1584.

Garcia, M. C. and Ginther, O. J. (1976) Effects of ovariectomy and season on plasma LH in mares. *Endocrin.* **98**, 958.

Garcia, M. C., Freedman, L. J. and Ginther, O. J. (1979) Interaction of seasonal and ovarian factors in the regulation of LH and FSH secretion in the mare. *J. Reprod. Fert. (Suppl.)* **27**, 103–111.

Ginther, O. J. (1974) Occurrence of anestrus, estrus, diestrus and ovulation over a 12-month period in mares. *Am. J. Vet. Res.* **35**, 1173.

Ginther, O. J. (1979) *Reproductive Biology of the Mare.* McNaughton and Gunn, Ann Arbor.

Ginther, O. J. and First, N. L. (1971) Maintenance of the corpus luteum in hysterectomized mares. *Am. J. Vet. Res.* **32**, 1687–1691.

Ginther, O. J. and Wentworth, B. C. (1974) Effect of a synthetic gonadotrophin-releasing hormone on plasma concentrations of LH in ponies. *Am. J. Vet. Res.* **35**, 79–81.

Heesemann, C. P., Squires, E. L., Webel, S. K., Shideler, R. K. and Pickett, B. W. (1980) The effect of ovarian activity and allyl trenbolone on the estrous cycle and fertility of mares. *J. Anim. Sci.* **51** (Suppl. 1), 284 (Abs.).

Holton, D. W., Douglas, R. H. and Ginther, O. J. (1977) Estrus, ovulation and conception following synchronization with progesterone, prostaglandin $F_{2\alpha}$ and human chorionic gonadotrophin in pony mares. *J. Anim. Sci.* **44**(3), 431–437.

Hoppe, R., Nienkowski, J. and Lipezynski, A. (1974) The treatment of non-cycling mares by oral application of chlormadinone acetate (CAP). *Theriogen.* **2**, 1.

Irvine, C. H. G. and Evans, M. J. (1979) Recent advances in reproductive endocrinology of the mare. *N.Z. Vet. J.* **27**, 176–180.

Irvine, D. S., Downey, B. R., Parker, W. G. and Sullivan, J. J. (1975) Duration of oestrus and time of ovulation in mares treated with synthetic GN-RH. *J. Reprod. Fert. (Suppl.)* **23**, 279–283.

Kenney, R. M., Ganjam, V. K., Cooper, W. L. and Lauderdale J. W. (1975) The use of prostaglandin F_2-Tham salt in mares in clinical anoestrus. *J. Reprod. Fert. (Suppl.)* **23**, 247.

Kimball, F. A. and Wyngarde, L. J. (1977) Prostaglandin $F_{2\alpha}$ specific binding in equine corpora lutea. *Prostaglandins* **13**, 553–564.

Kindahl, H., Edqvist, L. E., Bane, A. and Granstrom, E. (1976) Blood levels of progesterone and 15 keto-13-14 dihydr. $PGF_{2\alpha}$ during the normal oestrous cycle and early pregnancy. *Acta Endocrin.* **18**, 134–149.

Kooistra, L. H. and Ginther, O. J. (1975) Effect of photoperiod on reproductive activity and hair in mares. *Am. J. Vet. Res.* **36**, 1413.

Kreider, J., Cornwell, J., Bercouitz, A. and Godke, R. (1975) Induction of oestrus in mares after foal heat with $PGF_{2\alpha}$ *J. Anim. Sci.* **41**, 363–364.

Lapin, D. R. and Ginther, O. J. (1977) Induction of ovulation and multiple ovulations in seasonally-anovulatory mares with an equine pituitary extract. *J. Anim. Sci.* **44**, 834.

Loy, R. G. (1968) Effects of artificial lighting regimes on reproductive patterns in mares. Proc. Ann. Conv. Assoc. Equine Pract., 159–169.

Loy, R. G. and Swan, S. M. (1966) Effects of exogenous progestogens on reproductive phenomena in mares. *J. Anim. Sci.* **25**, 821.

Loy, R. G., Hughes, J. P., Richards, W.P.C. and Swan, S. M. (1975) Effects of progesterone on reproductive function in mares after parturition *J. Reprod. Fert. (Suppl.)* **23**, 291–295.

Loy, R. G., Buell, J. R. Stevenson, W. and Hamm, D. (1979) Sources of variation in response intervals after prostaglandin treatment in mares with functional corpus lutea. *J. Reprod. Fert. (Suppl.)* **27**, 229–235.

Loy, R. G., Pemstein, R., O'Canna, D. and Douglas, R. H. (1981) Control of ovulation in cycling mares with ovarian steroids and prostaglandin. *Theriogenology*, **15**, 191–200.

Miller, P. A., Lauderdale, J. W. and Geng, S. (1976) Effects of various doses of prostin $F_{2\alpha}$ on estrous cycles, rectal temperature, sweating, heart rate and respiration rate in mares. *J. Anim. Sci.* **42**, 901–911.

Miller, K. F., Berg, S. L., Sharp, D. C. and Ginther, O. J. (1980) Concentrations of circulating gonadotrophins during various reproductive states in mares. *Biol. Reprod.* **22**, 744.

Nelson, A. M. R. (1976) The therapeutic activity, post-treatment fertility and safety of prostaglandin $F_{2\alpha}$-tham sale in clinically anoestrous mares: A review. *Equine Vet. J.* **8**(2), 75–77.

Van Niekerk, C. H., Coubrough, R. I. and Dows, H. W. H. (1973) Progesterone treatment of mares with abnormal oestrous cycles early in the breeding season. *J. S. Afr. Vet. Ass.* **44**, 37–45.

Nishikawa, Y. (1959) *Studies on Reproduction in the Horse.* Jap. Racing Association, Tokyo.

Noden, P. A. and Oxender, W. D. (1976) LH and ovulation after Gn-RH in mares *J. Anim. Sci.* **42**, 1360.

Noden, P. A., Hafs, H. D. and Oxender, W. D. (1973) Progesterone, estrus and ovulation after prostaglandin $F_{2\alpha}$. *Fedn. Proc. Fedn. Am. Socs. Exp. Biol.* **32**, 229.

Oxender, W. D., Noden, P. A. and Hafs, H. D. (1975) Oestrus, ovulation and plasma hormones after prostaglandin $F_{2\alpha}$ in mares. *J. Reprod. Fert. (Suppl.)* **23**, 251–255.

Oxender, W. D., Noden, P. A. and Hafs, H. D. (1977) Estrus, ovulation and serum progesterone, estradiol and LH concentrations in mares after an increased photoperiod during winter. *Am. J. Vet. Res.* **38**, 203–207.

Palmer, E. (1976) Different techniques for synchronization of ovulation in the mare. Proc. 8th Int. Congr. Anim. Reprod. A.I. (Krakow), 495–498.

Palmer, E. (1978) Control of the oestrous cycle of the mare. *J. Reprod. Fert.* **54**, 495–505.

Palmer, E. (1979) Reproductive management of mares without detection of oestrus. *J. Reprod. Fert. (Suppl.)* **27**, 263–270.

Palmer, E. and Jousset, B. (1975) Synchronization of oestrus in mares with a prostaglandin analogue and hCG. *J. Reprod. Fert. (Suppl.)* **23**, 269–274.

Roberts, S. J. (1971) Examination for pregnancy. In, *Veterinary Obstetrics and Genital Diseases* 2nd Edn., pp. 24–29. Roberts, New York.

Roser, J. F., Kiefor, B. L., Evans, J. W., Neelu, D. P. and Pacheco, C. (1979) The development of antibodies to repeated injections of HCG into the cycling mare. *J. Reprod. Fert. (Suppl.)* **27**, 173–179.

Scheffrahn, N. S., Wiseman, B. S., Vincent, D. L., Harrison, P. C. and Kesler, D. J. (1980) Ovulation control in pony mares during early spring using progestins, $PGF_{2\alpha}$ hCG and GnRH. *J. Anim. Sci.* **51** (Suppl.), 325 (Abs.).

Sharp, D. C. and Ginther, O. J. (1975) Stimulation of follicular activity and estrous behaviour in anestrous mares with light and temperature. *J. Anim. Sci.* **41**(5), 1368–1372.

Sharp, D. C. and Seamans, K. W. (1980) Effect of time of day on photostimulation of the breeding season in mares. *J. Anim. Sci.* **51** (Suppl. 1), 329 (Abs.).

Shepherd, G. E., Findlay, J. K., Cooper, M. J. and Allen, W. R. (1976) The use of a synthetic prostaglandin analogue to induce oestrus in mares. *Aust. Vet. J.* **52**, 345–348.

Squires, E. L., Stevens, W. B., McGlothin, D. E. and Pickett, V. W. (1979) Effect of an oral Progestin on the oestrus cycle and fertility of mares. *J. Anim. Sci.* **49**, 729–735.

Stabenfeldt, G. H., Hughes, J. P., Evans, J. W. and Neely, D. P., (1974) Spontaneous prolongation of leteal activity in the mare. *Equine Vet. J.* **6**, 158–163.

Stabenfeldt, G. H., Hughes J. P., Evans, J. W. and Geschwind, I. I. (1975) Unique aspects of the reproductive cycle of the mare. *J. Reprod. Fert. (Suppl.)* **23**, 155–160.

Stabenfeldt, G. H., Neeley, D. P., Hughes, J. P. and Kindahl, H. (1980) Modification of uterine $PGF_{2\alpha}$ in domestic animals through pathologic or pharmacology processes. *Proc. 9th Int. Congr. Anim. Reprod. A.I. (Madrid)*, **2**, 27–34.

Stockell-Hartree, A., Mills, J. P., Welch, R. A. S. and

Thomas, M. (1968) Fractionation of protein hormones from horse pituitary glands. *J. Reprod. Fert.* **17**, 291–303.

Sullivan, J. J., Parker, W. G. and Larson, L. L. (1973) Duration of estrus and ovulation time in non-lactating mares given hCG during three successive estrous periods. *J. Am. Vet. Ass.* **162**, 895–898.

Vivrette, S. L. and Irvine, C. H. G. (1979) Interaction of oestradiol and Gn-RH on LH release in the mare. *J. Reprod. Fert. (Suppl.)* **27**, 151–155.

Voss, J. L., Sullivan, J. J. Pickett, B. W., Parker, W. G., Burwash, L. D. and Larson, L. L. (1975) The effect of hCG on duration of oestrus, ovulation time and fertility in mares. *J. Reprod. Fert. (Suppl.)* **23**, 297–301.

Wallace, R. A., Squires, E. L., Boss, J. L. and Pockett, B. W. (1977) Effectiveness of Gn-RH or Gn-RH analogue, in inducing ovulation and shortening estrus in mares. Proc. 69th Ann. Meet. Amer. Soc. Anim. Sci. Abs., 535.

Webel, S. K. (1975) Oestrus control in horses with a progestin. *J. Anim. Sci.* **41**, 385 (Abs.).

Witherspoon, D. M., Lamond, D. R., Thompson, F. N. and Stevenson, W. (1975) Efficacy of a prostaglandin analogue in reproduction in the cycling mare. *Theriogen.* **3**(1), 21–30.

CHAPTER 33

Pregnancy Testing in Horses

33.1 INTRODUCTION

Efforts are constantly being made to improve reproductive management practices in horses. In this regard, there is plenty of scope for methods which can be employed for the very early detection of pregnancy in the mare; a technique which could be used to detect non-pregnancy early enough for the mare to be rebred at the first possible heat period would be particularly valuable. In horses, perhaps more than in any of the farm animals, it is important to know as soon as possible whether a valuable female has conceived.

33.2 ENDOCRINOLOGY OF EARLY PREGNANCY

Studies in the mare have revealed interesting information on the nature of the embryo's signal to the dam which ensures that pregnancy is maintained (Irvine and Evans, 1979). If a horse embryo is present at day-15, but is then removed non-surgically, the next ovulation is delayed for several weeks; if it is removed on day-14 or earlier, however, the duration of the normal oestrous cycle is not likely to be affected in this way (Hershman and Douglas, 1979). As already

mentioned in dealing with other farm animals, it is believed that steroids secreted by the early embryo, especially oestradiol, inhibit the release of luteolysin from the endometrium that would otherwise result in regression of the corpus luteum. There is evidence that the horse embryo is able to produce increasing amounts of oestradiol by day-16 (Flood et al., 1979; Zavy et al., 1979); this synthesis of oestrogen and the secretion of progesterone by the corpus luteum are held to be important factors in the production of histotrophe and pregnancy-specific uterine proteins. The availability of an adequate amount of histotrophe may be particularly important in the mare since the embryo lies free within the uterine lumen until about day-38 of gestation, at which time initial attachment is made by way of the endometrial cups (Allen and Moor, 1972).

33.2.1 Progesterone levels

According to a review of events by Dawson (1977) dealing with the first half of gestation, progesterone concentrations in plasma reach a peak of 8–15 ng ml^{-1} between days 6 and 14 after ovulation and then decline steadily to around 4–6 ng ml^{-1} at days 30–35; there is a marked secondary rise which occurs with the development of the first of the accessory corpora lutea, with concentrations of 8–25 ng ml^{-1} being maintained until around day-150 when the corpora lutea start to regress. During most of the second half of the pregnancy period (days 150–300), plasma levels of progestagen remain low < 4 ng ml[-1]) but they increase steadily during the last 30–50 days of gestation to reach concentrations of 20–40 ng ml[-1] at term (Barnes et al., 1975).

Placental production of progesterone is thought to start in a gradual way during the first trimester of pregnancy; from day-70 onwards, however, it appears that sufficient progesterone is being secreted to maintain pregnancy in the ovariectomized mare (Holtan et al., 1979).

33.2.2 Placental oestrogen

Starting from day-70 onwards, the placenta produces increasingly large amounts of oestrogens, including the unique ring B unsaturated steroids, equilin and equilenin, the precursors of which are believed to be steroids formed in the foetal gonads (Raeside et al., 1979) which between the fourth and tenth months, have reached a size similar to those of the adult. Oestrogen production reaches a peak between days 280 and 320 and then the level of the steroid declines rapidly to the end of pregnancy; the mare appears to be unusual among the farm animals in showing a fall in oestrogen and a rise in progestagen in the terminal stages of pregnancy (Barnes et al., 1975).

33.3 RECTAL EXAMINATION

Probably the most commonly used method of diagnosing pregnancy in the mare is rectal palpation, which can be done at an early stage of gestation and gives an immediate answer. Several reports that have emerged over the last 40 years show that a satisfactory diagnosis can be made between 20 and 30 days after service by a person with sufficient experience of the technique (Day, 1940; Lensch, 1961; Bain, 1967; Sindelic, 1972; Knobloch, 1977). It is also accepted that an experienced veterinarian can estimate the stage of pregnancy within a week or so by this method (Day, 1940); this may prove useful in selecting

ponies for bleeding to recover PMSG, which rises to a well defined peak between days 55 and 75 (Allen and Stewart, 1978).

The relative size of the conceptus according to stage of gestation is well described in the report of Day (1940); important criteria employed by other workers at successive stages of pregnancy are also detailed by Van Niekerk (1965), Bain (1967) and Boyd (1979). According to Day (1957), it is possible to detect twin pregnancies by palpation at about 60 days after conception; beyond that time, the individual foetal sacs merge in such a way as to make accurate diagnosis of the twins no longer possible.

33.3.1 Timing of rectals

In South Africa, Van Niekerk (1965) found evidence of a high incidence of embryonic mortality between days 25 and 31 of gestation in nutritionally deprived mares; he suggested that rectal palpation might best be avoided between days 25 and 35 of gestation, the period during which the change from choriovitelline to chorioallantoic placentation is occurring. On the other hand, practitioners with considerable experience of rectal palpation do regularly conduct a majority of their examinations by day-35 (Mackay, 1979) and regard the method as both accurate and satisfactory.

33.4 VAGINAL EXAMINATION

After conception in the mare, the exposed mucous membrane of the vulva and vagina becomes pale and dry; from about 25 days after conception, the vaginal mucus becomes progressively more opaque and sticky. Insertion of an unlubricated speculum into the vagina is difficult because of the nature of this mucus. The mare's cervix also becomes small and dry and the cervical mucus becomes adhesive and pasty. According to Nishikawa (1959), during and after the third month of pregnancy the reliability of diagnosis increases as a result of an intensification of the various symptoms detectable by vaginal examination.

33.5 DETECTION OF PMSG

Although palpation of the mare's uterus *per rectum* can be highly accurate in pregnancy diagnosis, the technique does require considerable practice and diagnostic skill to detect the early stages of pregnancy. One way in which a positive diagnosis is possible is by establishing the presence of PMSG in the mare's blood; the test does mean, however, that the mare has to reach at least 40 days after conception. As mentioned earlier, PMSG is a glycoprotein secreted by structures known as the endometrial cups (Clegg *et al.*, 1954), local endometrial outgrowths which develop from an invasion of specialized trophoblast cells of the chorionic girdle into the maternal endometrium at about day-36 of gestation (Allen and Moor, 1972; Hamilton *et al.*, 1973); the hormone, which possess both FSH-like and LH-like properties, is present in the blood between days 40 and 130 of pregnancy (Cole and Hart, 1930). Pregnancy can be established either by determining the presence of PMSG by its biological activity or by its immunological properties.

33.5.1 PMSG in the non-pregnant mare

It should be noted that if the conceptus is lost from the mare's uterus after day-40 of gestation (i.e. removed surgically, or lost as a result of embryonic death, resorption or abortion), the endometrial cups continue to function normally for a prolonged period and secrete gonadotrophin as if the mare were still pregnant (Allen, 1969a,b, 1970; Mitchell and Betteridge, 1972; Allen and Rossdale, 1973; Mitchell and Allen, 1975); obviously, in such situations, a false positive value for PMSG is given. It would appear that the continuing high concentrations of gonadotrophin in the blood actively suppress rather than stimulate, ovarian activity and the mare passes into a prolonged period of sexual inactivity which is much the same as when she is in deep winter anoestrus. It is only when the endometrial cups cease functioning (day-130 or later) and the PMSG has disappeared from the mare's blood that a return to normal oestrus and ovulation can be expected.

33.5.2 PMSG concentrations

The amount of PMSG produced by the mare will depend on the total amount of endometrial cup tissue in the uterus; mares carrying twin foetuses, for example, will have two sets of endometrial cups and show double the normal level of the gonadotrophin in the blood (Rowlands, 1949). There is also evidence showing that factors such as season (Richter, 1963), maternal size (Day and Rowlands, 1947) and parity (Day and Rowlands, 1947; Richter, 1963) can influence the PMSG concentration.

The one factor having the most marked effect on the PMSG concentration is foetal genotype. Mares bred to a donkey and carrying a mule conceptus show greatly decreased PMSG levels and the gonadotrophin has usually disappeared from the blood as early as day-80 or so of pregnancy (Bielanski *et al.*, 1956; Clegg *et al.*, 1962; Allen, 1969b); donkeys bred to a horse stallion and carrying a hinny conceptus, on the other hand, show greatly enhanced PMSG concentrations which may be six to eight times higher than those in a donkey carrying a normal donkey conceptus (Clegg *et al.*, 1962; Allen, 1969a,b, 1975). Gonadotrophin concentrations in the donkey carrying the normal donkey conceptus are only of the order of 12% of those found in mares carrying the normal horse conceptus (Allen, 1975). It might also be noted that the hybrid mule and hinny conceptuses apparently both produce a form of gonadotrophin which has an FSH:LH ratio associated with the normal horse and donkey conceptuses (Stewart *et al.*, 1977).

33.5.3 Testing for PMSG

In carrying out tests for PMSG, urine is not suitable because of the very low gonadotrophin concentrations present; the PMSG molecule is apparently too large to pass from the blood through the kidney filtration apparatus into the urine. Until the sixties, detection of PMSG in blood was usually by way of a bioassay using female mice or rats (Cowie, 1948). The first account of a correspondingly accurate immunological test was that of Wide and Wide (1963); their procedure greatly reduced the requirement for laboratory animals and cut the time required to produce a result from 2½ days to 2 h.

As observed by Dawson (1977), a commercial kit for performing the immunological test on blood serum was marketed by the Denver Manufacturing Company of Connecticut, U.S.A. in the late sixties and several groups of workers confirmed the accuracy and economy of this immunological test (Jeffcott et al., 1969; Luttman and Von Lepel, 1971; McCaughey et al., 1973). A fully quantitative immunological assay for PMSG was developed by Allen (1969); the same worker went on to use the procedure to demonstrate the existence of marked variations in PMSG levels between individual mares. More recently, a simple, sensitive and rapid test for PMSG, based on the agglutination of latex particles coated with anti-PMSG immunoglobulins has been described in a report by Coster et al. (1980) in Belgium.

33.5.4 PMSG and secondary corpora lutea

As already mentioned, Evans and Irvine (1975) showed that FSH is released by the mare's pituitary at intervals of 10 days during early pregnancy. Plasma LH concentrations, on the other hand, do not apparently vary from basal values during this time (Allen and Schams, 1972). The increasing blood levels of PMSG after day-40 produce an LH-like effect, causing the FSH-primed follicles in the mare's ovaries to undergo final maturation, luteinization (usually without ovulation) with establishment of the secondary corpora lutea which supplement progesterone production from the primary corpus luteum.

Although PMSG hormone possesses rather more FSH-like than LH-like properties when employed in most animals, it seems that in the pregnant mare its actions are LH-like only (Stewart et al., 1976). It has only been in the last 15 years or so that it became evident that the primary corpus luteum of pregnancy (formed at ovulation) does not regress around the 40th day of gestation, as often reported, but is active for at least the first 3 months of pregnancy, and regresses in company with the secondary corpora lutea during the fifth and sixth months of gestation (Squires et al., 1974; Squires and Ginther, 1975; Ginther, 1979).

33.6 USE OF PROGESTERONE ASSAY

The concentration of plasma progesterone in the cyclic mare has been reported by several groups of workers (Stabenfeldt et al., 1972; Sharp and Black, 1973; Palmer and Jousett, 1975) and a limited amount of information is available on the diagnostic value of plasma and milk progesterone assays in the pregnant mare. Palmer et al. (1974) were among the first to investigate the possibility of early pregnancy diagnosis by determining the concentration of progesterone. In a breeding herd of Anglo-Arabs and French saddle horses, all bred mares whose blood serum contained less than 1.5 ng mL^{-1} progesterone on the 18th day after the end of oestrus were found to be non-pregnant; use of the assay in conjunction with the detection of heat enabled the French workers to diagnose pregnancy with an accuracy of 96%.

In studies reported by Hunt et al. (1978) pregnancy was diagnosed with 100% accuracy in a small number of mares on the basis of the concentration of plasma progesterone 16–17 days after bred mares were observed to go out of oestrus; in instances where plasma was not available, it was found possible for the diagnosis to be made successfully on the basis of a milk sample. As well as Hunt et al. (1978), the use of the milk progesterone test for determining pregnancy in the mare was also demonstrated around that time by Bailes and Holdsworth (1978) and Gunther et al. (1978); the latter workers (Gunther et al. 1978), saw progesterone assays not only as an aid to early pregnancy diagnosis but also as a means of detecting oestrous cycle irregularities. In a later report, Gunther et al. (1980) found evidence of significant differences in progesterone concentrations in milk and blood plasma between non-pregnant and pregnant mares from 17 to 22 days after oestrus; day-18–19 after a previous heat was seen to be the optimum time for taking milk and plasma samples for diagnosis. In the U.K., Booth (1980) used the same discriminatory limits as for cows in carrying out progesterone assay in milk from a small number of mares.

Although, with an experienced veterinarian, routine diagnosis of pregnancy in horses by palpation *per rectum* is rapid and accurate, such examinations among a large number of mares, or in the case of animals difficult to restrain, may present problems; in such circumstances, there may be a place for techniques such as the progesterone assay as part of a useful back-up service.

33.7 ULTRASONICS

Use of the ultrasonic Doppler method for diagnosing pregnancy in the mare was reported by Fraser *et al.* (1973) and by Mitchell (1973) using a rectal probe; a positive diagnosis was possible from day-56 onwards with detection of the foetal heart beat and the method had the merit of providing definite evidence that the foetus is alive. For this reason, attention has been drawn (Dawson, 1977) to the fact that the method may be much more accurate than assay methods based on the detection of PMSG, since, as already mentioned, concentrations of this particular hormone may remain high for many weeks after the death of the embryo or foetus.

33.7.1 Echography and early diagnosis

The advent of modern ultrasonic techniques now permits the visualization of the internal structure of organs such as the ovaries and uterus (Hackeloer, 1977). In human medicine, ultrasonic echography provides a valuable new method of monitoring the growth of Graafian follicles in the ovaries (Levy, 1978; Renaud *et al.*, 1980; Smith *et al.*, 1980) with negligible risk and discomfort to the patient; the technique employs B-mode grayscale ultrasound with a 3.5 MHz frequency transducer to provide an echogram.

Ultrasonic echography is now possible in the mare with the development of a real time echoscope with a small mobile probe that permits examinations to be made *per rectum*. In France, Palmer and Driancourt (1980) have reported encouraging results in the use of the technique; visualization of the conceptus was possible from day-14 of pregnancy and a very accurate (> 92%) early pregnancy diagnosis was found to be possible. The spherical aspect of the very early conceptus appears to be a peculiarity of

the horse and the human and it is this characteristic which makes such an early positive diagnosis possible (day-14 post-ovulation in the horse and day-20 in the human). The location of the conceptus in the mare was found to be very constant (in one horn near the body junction) which made it possible to detect the embryo within a minute or so after insertion of the rectal probe.

Palmer and Driancourt (1980), in comparing echography with progesterone assay, note that diagnosis can be made earlier (day-14 vs day-18) and there is no error arising from a persistent corpus luteum; the ultrasonic echography technique can be rapidly learned and has various points in its favour when compared with other methods. According to the French workers, it may prove possible to visualize twin pregnancies in the early stages of pregnancy as is already possible in humans (Levy, 1978).

33.8 FOETAL ELECTROCARDIOGRAPHY

The technical feasibility of recording the equine foetal electrocardiogram from electrodes on the maternal body surface has been shown by several groups of workers (Larks *et al.*, 1960; Holmes and Darke, 1968; Colles *et al.*, 1978); foetal electrocardiography has been suggested as a method of differentiating single from twin pregnancies, confirming the presence of a live foetus and identifying foetal distress during a difficult or prolonged parturition (Parkes and Colles, 1977). Limitations of the technique have recently been dealt with in a paper by Buss *et al.* (1980).

33.9 OTHER TESTS

Without attempting to draw up an exhaustive list of pregnancy testing methods, there are one or two other techniques that might be mentioned.

33.9.1 Cuboni test

Cuboni-type pregnancy tests, for the detection of oestrogen in the urine of mares after 90 days of pregnancy, may still be useful on occasions when the collection of blood or performance of a rectal examination proves to be inconvenient; according to Boyd (1979), when a representative urine sample is taken after the fifth month, a simple Cuboni test should be highly accurate ($> 95\%$) although some reports have recorded an accuracy as low as 80%.

33.9.2 Oestrogen in blood plasma

The biological significance of the great amounts of oestrogen produced in the pregnant mare remains largely unknown; oestrone is the principal oestrogen found during mid-pregnancy (Cox, 1976; Raeside et al., 1979). As mentioned already, unlike the situation in the other farm animals, oestrogen levels decline in the mare towards the end of pregnancy (Nett et al., 1973). Chemical and RIA procedures can be employed from day-85 onwards to establish pregnancy on the basis of the concentration of oestrone sulphate (Terqui and Palmer, 1979).

33.10 REFERENCES

Allen, W. R. (1969a) The immunological measurement of pregnant mare serum gonadotrophin. J. Endocrin. **43**, 593.

Allen, W. R. (1969b) Factors influencing pregnant mare serum gonadotrophin production. Nature, Lond. **223**, 64.

Allen, W. R. (1970) Endocrinology of early pregnancy in the mare. Equine Vet. J. **2**, 64.

Allen, W. R. (1975) The influence of foetal genotype upon endometrial cup development and PMSG and progestagen production in equids. J. Reprod. Fert. (Suppl). **23**, 405–413.

Allen, W. R. and Moor, R. M. (1972) The origin of the endometrial cups. 1. Production of PMSG by fetal trophoblast cells. J. Reprod. Fert. **29**, 313–316.

Allen, W. R. and Rossdale, P. D. (1973) A preliminary study upon the use of prostaglandins for inducing oestrus in non-cycling thoroughbred mares. Equine Vet. J. **5**, 137–140.

Allen, W. R. and Stewart, F. (1978) The biology of pregnant mare serum gonadotrophin (PMSG). In, Control of Reproduction in the Cow Sreenan, J. M. Ed., pp. 50–72. Galway, C.E.C.

Bailes, G. and Holdsworth, R. J. (1978). Brit. Vet. J. **134**, 214.

Bain, A. M. (1967) The ovaries of the mare during early pregnancy. Vet. Rec. **80**, 229–231.

Barnes, R. J., Nathanielsz, P. W., Rossdale, P. D., Comline, R. S. and Silver, M. (1975) Plasma progestagens and oestrogens in fetus and mother in late pregnancy. J. Reprod. Fert. (Suppl.), **23**, 617–623.

Bielanski, W., Ewy, Z. and Pigoniowa, H. (1956) Differences in the level of gonadotrophin in the serum of pregnant mares. Proc. 3rd. Int. Congr. Anim. Reprod. A.I. (Cambridge), 110–111.

Booth, J. M. (1980) Milk progesterone pregnancy testing in cattle and other species. Proc. 9th Int. Congr. Anim. Reprod. A.I. (Madrid), **2**, 109–117.

Boyd, H. (1979) Pregnancy diagnosis. In, Fertility and Infertility in Domestic Animals. 3rd Ed. Laing, J. A. Ed., pp. 36–58., Bailliere, Tindall, London.

Buss, D. B., Asbury, A. C. and Chevalier, L. (1980) Limitations in equine fetal electrocardiography. J. Am. Vet. Med. ss. **177**, 174–176.

Clegg, M. T., Boda, J. M. and Cole, H. H. (1954) The endometrial cups and allantochorionic pouches in the mare with emphasis on the source of equine gonadotrophin. Endocrin. **54**, 448.

Clegg, M. T., Cole, H. H., Howard, C. B. and Pigon, H. (1962) The influence of foetal genotype on equine gonadotrophin secretion. J. Endoc. **25**, 245.

Cole, H. H. and Hart, G. H. (1930) The potency of blood serum of mares in progressive stages of pregnancy in effecting the sexual maturity of the immature rat. Am. J. Physiol. **93**, 57.

Colles, C. M., Parkes, R. D. and May, C. J. (1978) Foetal electrocardiography in the mare. Equine Vet. J. **10**, 32–37.

De Coster, R., Cambiaso, C. L. and Masson, P. L. (1980) Immunological diagnosis of pregnancy in the mare by agglutination of latex particles. Theriogen, **13**, 433–436.

Cowie, A. T. (1948) Pregnancy Tests – a Review. Commonwealth Agric. Bureau.

Cox, J. E. (1975) Oestrone and equilin in the plasma of the pregnant mare. J. Reprod. Fert. (Suppl.), **23**, 463–468.

Dawson, F. L. M. (1977) Recent advances in equine reproduction. Equine Vet. J. **9**, (1), 4–11.

Day, F. T. (1940) Clinical and experimental observations on reproduction in the mare. J. Agric. Sci. Camb. **30**, 244–261.

Day, F. T. (1957) The veterinary clinician's approach to breeding problems in mares. Vet. Rec. **69**, 1258–1267.

Day, F. T. and Rowlands, I. W. (1947) Serum gonadotrophin in Welsh and Shetland ponies. J. Endocr. **5**, 1.

Evans, M. J. and Irvine, C. H. G. (1975) The serum concentrations of FSH, LH and progesterone in the oestrous cycle and early pregnancy in the mare. J. Reprod. Fert. (Suppl.), **23**, 193–200.

Flood, P. F., Betteridge, K. J. and Irvine, D. S. (1979) Oestrogens and androgens in blastocoelic fluid and culture of cells from equine conceptuses of 10 to 22 days gestation. J. Reprod. Fert. (Suppl.), **27**, 413–420.

Fraser, A. F., Keith, N. W. J. and Hastie, H. (1973) Summarized observations on ultrasonic detection of pregnancy and foetal life in the mare. Vet. Rec. **92**, 20.

Ginther, O. J. (1979) Reproductive Biology of the Mare. McNaughton and Gunn, Ann Arbor.

Hackeloer, B. J. (1977) The ultrasonic demonstration of follicular development during the normal menstrual cycle and after hormone stimulation. Proc. Int. Symp. Recent Advances in Ultrasound Diagnosis, Dubrovnik, 122–128

Hamilton, D. W., Allen, W. R. and Moor, R. M. (1973) The origin of equine endometrial cups. III. Light and electron microscopic study of fully developed equine endometrial cups. Anat. Rec. **177**, 503.

Hershman, L. and Douglas, R. H. (1979) The critical period for the maternal recognition of pregnancy in pony mares. J. Reprod. Fert. (Suppl.) **27**, 395–401.

Holmes, J. R. and Darke, P. G. G. (1968) Fetal electrocardiography in the mare. Vet. Rec. **82**, 651–655.

Holtan, D. W., Squires, E. L., Lapin, D. R. and Ginther, O. J.

(1979) Effect of ovariectomy on pregnancy in mares. *J. Reprod. Fert. (Suppl.)*, **27**, 457–463.

Hunt, B., Lein, D. H. and Foote, R. H. (1978) Monitoring of plasma and milk progesterone for evaluation of *post-partum* estrous cycle and early pregnancy in mares. *J. Am. Vet. Med. Ass.* **172**(11), 1298–1302.

Irvine, C. H. G. and Evans, M. J. (1979) Recent advances in reproductive endocrinology of the mare. *N.Z. Vet. J.* **27**, 176–180.

Jeffcott, L. B., Atherton, J. G. and Mingay, J. (1969) Equine pregnancy diagnosis. A comparison of two methods for the detection of gonadotrophin in serum. *Vet. Rec.* **81**, 80–81.

Knobloch, C. P. (1977) Pregnancy diagnosis in mares. *Equine Prof. Top.* **1**, 3–6.

Larks, S. D., Holm, L. W. and Parker, H. R. (1960) A new technique for the demonstration of the foetal electro-cardiogram in the large domestic animal (cattle, sheep, horse). *Carnell Vet.* **50**, 459–468.

Lensch, J. (1961) Pregnancy diagnosis in the mare at 18–30. *Zootec. Vet.* **15**, 186.

Levy, S. (1978) Ultrasonic assessment of the high rate of human multiple pregnancy in the first trimester. *J. Clin. Ultrasound* **4**, 3–5.

Luttmann, U. and Von Lepel, J. (1971) Pregnancy diagnosis in the mare with immunological test. *Dt. tierarztl. Wschr.* **78**, 270.

McCaughey, W. J., Hanna, J. and O'Brien, J. S. (1973) Comparison of 3 laboratory tests for pregnancy diagnosis in the mare. *Equine Vet. J.* **5**, 91–95.

Mackay, R. C. J. (1979) Pregnancy tests for mares — challenge. *N.Z. Vet. J.* **27**, 32.

Mitchell, D. (1973) Detection in foetal circulation in the mare and cow by doppler ultrasound. *Vet. Rec.* **93**, 365–368.

Mitchell, D. and Allen, W. R. (1975) Observations on reproductive performance in the yearling mare. *J. Reprod. Fert. (Suppl.)*, **23**, 531–536.

Mitchell, D. and Betteridge, K. J. (1972) Persistence of endometrial cups and serum gonadotrophin following abortion in the mare. *Proc. 7th Int. Congr. Anim. Reprod. A.I. (Munich)*, **1**, 567–570.

Nett, T. N., Holtan, D. W. and Estergreen, V. L. (1973) Plasma estrogens in pregnant and post-partum mares. *J. Anim. Sci.* **37**, 962–970.

Van Niekerk, C. (1967) Patterns of the oestrous cycle in mares. *J. S. Afr. Vet. Med. Ass.* **38**, 295.

Nishikawa, Y. (1959) *Studies on Reproduction in Horses.* Jap. Racing Assoc. Tokyo.

Palmer, E. and Driancourt, M. A. (1980). Use of ultrasonic echography in equine gynecology. *Theriogen*, **13**, 203–216.

Palmer, E. and Joussett, B. (1975) Urinary oestrogen and plasma progesterone levels in non-pregnant mares. *J. Reprod. Fert. (Suppl.)*, **23**, 213–221.

Palmer, E., Thimonier, J. and Lemon, M. (1974) Early pregnancy diagnosis in the mare by estimation of the level of progesterone in the peripheral blood. *Livestock Prod. Sci.* **1**, 197.

Parkes, R. D. and Colles, C. M. (1977) Fetal electrocardio-graphy in the mare as a practical aid to diagnosing singleton and twin pregnancy. *Vet. Rec.* **100**, 25–26.

Raeside, J. I., Liptrap, R. M., McDonnell, W. N. and Milne, E. J. (1979) Precursor role for dehydroepiandrosterone in feto placental unit for oestrogen formation in the mare. *J. Reprod. Fert. (Suppl.)*, **27**, 493–497.

Renaud, R. L., Macler, J., Dervain, I., Ehret, M. C., Aron, C., Plas-Roser, S., Spira, A. and Pollack, H. (1980) Echographic study of follicular maturation and ovulation during the normal menstrual cycle. *Fert. Sterility*, **33**, 272–276.

Richter, W. (1963) Interruption of pregnancy in mares. *Zuchthyg*, **7**, 81.

Rowlands, I. W. (1949) Serum gonadotrophin and ovarian activity in the pregnant mare. *J. Endocr.* **6**, 184.

Sharp, D. C. and Black, D. L. (1973) Changes in peripheral plasma progesterone throughout the oestrous cycle of the pony mare. *J. Reprod. Fert.* **33**, 533–538.

Sindelic, V. (1972) Experience in clinical diagnosis of early pregnancy in mares. *Veterinaria.* **21**, 114.

Smith, D. H., Picker, R. H., Sinosich, M. and Saunders, D. M. (1980) Assessment of ovulation by ultrasound and estradiol levels during spontaneous and induced cycles. *Fert. Sterility*, **33**, 387–390.

Squires, E. L. and Ginther, O. J. (1975) Collection technique and progesterone concentration of ovarian and uterine venous blood in mares. *J. Anim. Sci.* **40**, 275–281.

Squires, E. L., Douglas, R. H., Steffenhagen, W. P. and Ginther, O. J. (1974) Ovarian changes during the oestrous cycle and pregnancy in mares. *J. Anim. Sci.* **38**, 330–338.

Stabenfeldt, G. H., Hughes, J. P. and Evans, J. W. (1972) Ovarian activity during the estrous cycle of the mare. *Endocrin.* **90**, 1379–1384.

Stewart, F., Allen, W. R. and Moor, R. M. (1976) PMSG: Ratio of FSH and LH activities measured by radioreceptor assay. *J. Endoc.* **71**, 371–382.

Stewart, F., Allen, W. R. and Moor, R. M. (1977) Influence on foetal genotype on the FSH: LH ratio of pregnant mare serum gonadotrophin. *J. Endocr.* **73**, 419.

Terqui, M. and Palmer, E. (1979) Oestrogen pattern during early pregnancy in the mate. *J. Reprod. Fert. (Suppl.)*, **27**, 441–446.

Wide, M. and Wide, L. (1963) Diagnosis of pregnancy in mares by an immunological method. *Nature, Lond.* **198**, 1017–1018.

Zavy, M. T., Mayer, R., Vernon, M. W., Bazer, F. W. and Sharp, D. C. (1979) An investigation of the uterine luminal environment of non-pregnant and pregnant pony mares. *J. Reprod. Fert. (Suppl.)*, **27**, 403–411.

CHAPTER 34

Control of Foaling

34.1 INTRODUCTION

The hormonal mechanisms involved in parturition in the mare are not as well understood as those in cattle, sheep and pigs; studies have yet to be reported implicating the pituitary–adrenal axis of the foal in the initiation of parturition. If the foal does initiate its own birth, the mare still has the ability to modulate this foetal influence; it is well accepted that mares give birth when secluded and undisturbed and predominantly during the hours of darkness (First, 1979).

34.2 DURATION OF PREGNANCY

Accurate prediction of the duration of pregnancy in the mare can be a valuable management aid and to do this it is necessary to have knowledge of the various factors that may influence the length of gestation. In looking at the literature, it is evident that there are large variations in the gestation period of horses and that these variations are usually greater than in the other farm species; it has been suggested (Bos and Van der Mey, 1980) that the length of pregnancy in the horse may be influenced by environmental factors other than those affecting the other farm mammals, the most obvious factor being the photoperiod. The average length of gestation has been given as 335–343 days although the observed variations from these mean values may often be marked (Hammond et al., 1971; Evans, 1977; Bos and Van der Mey, 1980; Rossdale and Ricketts, 1980); in Ireland, Badi et al., (1981) report an average value of 340.7 days for Thoroughbreds.

34.2.1 Foetal genotype effects

It is well recognized that the foetal genotype can affect the duration of pregnancy in the horse (Rollins and Howell, 1951); if the mare is bred to a donkey, duration of gestation is likely to be 2 weeks longer on average than when a horse stallion is used (Hammond et al., 1971). The average gestation length of Thoroughbred mares giving birth to colts has been reported to be significantly longer (2.5 days) than for mares giving birth to fillies in the report of Hintz et al. (1979); in agreement with several earlier reports in the literature (Ropiha et al., 1969; Akkayan and Demirtel, 1974).

34.2.2 Seasonal effects

An effect of season of breeding on gestation length is well documented in the literature; Howell and Rollins (1951) found the average duration of pregnancy in Arabian mares to vary from 342 days for those bred in spring to 329 days for those bred in autumn. In fact, in this work, the season of breeding accounted for 44% of the variation observed in the gestation length.

Hammond et al. (1971) noted a marked seasonal variation in gestation length among Welsh pony mares and drew attention to similar variations being recorded by other authors. Hintz et al. (1979) recorded a range of 305–365 days in gestation length among Thoroughbreds in North America (average 340.5 days); there also was, in agreement with several other·reports (Henrikse, 1972; Bos and Van der Mey, 1980), evidence that gestation length decreased in mares bred late in the breeding season as compared with those bred early.

Among other factors which have been shown to influence gestation length in horses are nutrition (Tutt, 1944) and the carrying of twins (Jeffcott and Whitwell, 1973). It has been mentioned (Ginther, 1979) that one source of difficulty in dealing with published gestation length data may arise because some authors use day of breeding whereas others use day of expected ovulation.

34.3 INDUCTION BY CORTICOSTEROIDS

Foaling has been successfully induced in large saddle type mares by a treatment regime consisting of 100 mg of the glucocorticoid dexamethasone given daily for 4 days from day-321 of the gestation period (Alm et al., 1974, 1975); parturition appeared to be normal and started about a week after treatment with the foals being born alive and healthy. A less successful outcome of induction treatment had been reported around that time in pony mares; single or low dose levels of dexamethasone apparently failed to induce foaling in several studies (Campbell, 1971; Drost, 1972; Burns, 1973). Even with larger doses of 100 mg dexamethasone given over a 4 day period in late pregnancy to three pony mares, an unsuccessful outcome was reported by Rossdale and Jeffcott (1975); retention of foetal membranes occurred in all mares and two foals were stillborn.

Results reported by First and Alm (1977), on the other hand, showed that glucocorticoid (three to four daily doses of 100 mg dexamethasone from day-321) was fully effective in all five pony mares treated; foals were alive in all cases and there was

no retention of foetal membranes. These same authors (First and Alm, 1977) concluded that the dose and duration of corticosteroid treatment was critical if foaling was to be induced successfully. Other studies with glucocorticoids in mares around this time include those of Van Niekerk and Morgenthall (1976) who apparently employed with success a combination of flumethasone and prostaglandin $F_{2\alpha}$.

34.3.1 Mode of action

The mode of action of synthetic glucocorticoids in bringing about the initiation of parturition in the mare is as yet uncertain (First, 1979; Pashen and Allen, 1979). It still remains to be seen whether the mechanisms controlling foaling are similar to those involved in the birth of the lamb, with foetal stimuli dominating the timing of parturition (Currie, 1977), or are closer to those in the human where a built-in genetically controlled maturational signal apparently arises elsewhere in the conceptus (Liggins et al., 1977). Whether there is a prenatal surge in glucocorticoids in the foetal foal remains uncertain; there is some evidence suggesting an increase in foetal adrenal gland activity near term, but there is no marked rise in glucocorticoid concentration such as that seen in the foetal lamb just before birth (Nathanielsz et al., 1975). The action of a dose of glucocorticoid administered to the mare is apparently not by way of the ovaries; premature parturitions have been induced in ovariectomized ponies some 6 days after dexamethasone treatment in the work of First and Alm (1977).

34.4 PROGESTERONE AS AN INDUCTION AGENT

The fact that parturition can be induced in the mare by exogenous progesterone (Alm et al., 1975), and that response occurs in much the same time-scale as when a synthetic glucocorticoid (such as dexamethasone) is used, is something which is quite different from what happens in the other farm animals. As noted by First (1979), in the human, it is known that the adrenal glands of the foetus can readily convert placental progesterone to corticosteroids and this may be the explanation of the response observed in the horse.

34.5 INDUCTION BY PROSTAGLANDINS

It is known that in normal foaling, there is a rapid rise in the plasma concentrations of prostaglandin $F_{2\alpha}$ at time of parturition, coinciding with the period of delivery (First, 1979). Even so, authors such as Cooper (1979) and others before him (Alm et al., 1975) have recorded that natural $PGF_{2\alpha}$ on its own will not produce a response in many mares in late pregnancy, although the agent has been shown (Van Niekerk and Morgenthal, 1976) to be effective in the induction of foaling when administered in combination with a synthetic glucocorticoid.

In contrast to such experience with the natural agent, those using the synthetic prostaglandin analogue Equimate have found it to be a potent and rapid means of inducing parturition in the mare (Rossdale et al., 1976; Jeffcott and Rossdale, 1977). Mares can be expected to show clinical signs of first-stage labour (uneasiness, mold sweating, increased skin temperature, some abdominal discomfort) within 30 min of receiving a dose of Equimate and delivery of the foetus should start within about 4 hours of the first (or only) injection of the analogue (Rossdale et al., 1979); foetal membranes should be expelled within 2 h of the foal being delivered.

It is still not clear why the synthetic analogue should be much more efficient as an induction agent that the natural compound; Furr (1979) has suggested that, after absorption from the site of injection, Equimate is converted to a potent metabolite which causes a series of rapid endocrine changes that initiate parturition. It is apparent that the mechanism of action of prostaglandin is not by way of the ovaries (First, 1979); parturition has been induced in the ovariectomized mare by the agent and it seems probable that prostaglandin acts by inducing uterine contractions. Rossdale et al. (1979) have drawn attention to evidence in man where prostaglandin analogues have been found to be far more potent in stimulating uterine activity than are the natural compounds.

34.6 OXYTOCIN AS AN INDUCTION AGENT

Maternal plasma oxytocin levels have been shown to increase markedly during second-stage labour in the mare (Allen et al., 1973) and administering oxytocin to the mare at term can rapidly lead to strong uterine contractions and birth of the foal (Purvis, 1972, 1977; Hillman, 1975; Rossdale and Jeffcott, 1975; Hillman and Ganjam, 1979). As noted by Pashen and Allen (1979), the synergistic actions of oxytocin and prostaglandin in promoting uterine contractions are already well established in many mammalian species; oxytocin is also known to be involved in the increase in uterine contractions which results from the stretching of the cervix and vagina during the birth process. According to these same authors (Pashen and Allen, 1979) a relationship between oxytocin and $PGF_{2\alpha}$ does appear to exist in the mare and the administration of small i.v. doses of oxytocin (1–5 i.u.) near term causes an immediate rise of prostaglandin concentrations in maternal plasma to values comparable to those occurring during spontaneous foaling; there appears to be no merit and possibly some danger in using very high doses (60–120 i.u.). Stabenfeldt and Hughes (1977) recorded that delivery of the foal occurred with them after an average interval of 35 min from the time of injecting 40 i.u. oxytocin.

It should be emphasized that the use of oxytocin to induce foaling should only be undertaken when proper criteria have been employed to evaluate the mare for signs of impending parturition; such criteria should include a minimum of 330 days of gestation, relaxed sacrosciatic ligaments, softened cervix and a full udder with distended teats (Purvis, 1972; Hillman and Ganjam, 1979).

34.6.1 Oestrogen and oxytocin

Although oestrogen treatment alone will not cause premature parturition in the mare, when combined with oxytocin, the steroid has been used to bring about dilation of the cervix and to facilitate the birth process (Hillman, 1975).

34.7 TWINS AND TERMINATING PREGNANCY

Jeffcott and Whitwell (1973) and Platt (1973) are among authors recording the fact that twin pregnancy is the single most common cause of abortion in the mare; in the data they present, most of the twin pregnancies ended in both foals dead at birth. According to Jeffcott and Whitwell (1973), the incidence of twins in maiden Thoroughbred mares pregnant for the first time may even be as high as 20%. When twins are recognized by rectal examination or other means early in gestation, it may be convenient to terminate the pregnancy and attempt to get the mare bred again during the same breeding season (Dawson, 1977).

Among the methods now available for terminating pregnancy in the mare, whether for reason of unwanted twins or otherwise, is the use of prostaglandins, either the natural $PGF_{2\alpha}$ agent (Douglas et al., 1974; Douglas and Ginther, 1975) or one of its analogues (Allen and Rossdale, 1973); as already mentioned, prostaglandin can be employed as a highly effective abortifacient in cattle and pigs. Douglas et al. (1974) reported that all of 13 pony mares treated in early pregnancy aborted when given multiple doses of 2.5 mg $PGF_{2\alpha}$ at 12 h intervals; elsewhere, a single injection of 12.5 mg $PGF_{2\alpha}$ on day-32 of gestation was also found to be effective in terminating pregnancy in each of four mares (Kooistra and Ginther, 1976).

As later stages of pregnancy, single doses of prostaglandin may not prove adequate to induce abortion; a single dose of 2.5 mg administered during the period from days 100 to 150 of gestation, resulted in abortion in only one of five mares in one report (Douglas et al., 1974). Subsequently, studies reported by Squires et al. (1980) showed that a single dose of 250 μg of the analogue Equimate given on day-35 of gestation terminated pregnancy in 7/8 mares whereas the same treatment given in the period day-70 to day-77 proved to be ineffective; multiple doses of the analogue, however, starting on day-70 of gestation resulted in all pregnancies being terminated.

The same investigators (Squires et al., 1980) observed that the cervix of the pregnant mare began to soften and relax 1 or 2 days after the first administration of Equimate and this was followed by rupture of the foetal membranes and expulsion of the foetus within 2 or 3 days; no mare showed adverse side-effects and the animals expelled the foetal membranes within 12 h of abortion. Most mares in this study, exhibited oestrus (accompanied by ovulation) within a day of abortion when Equimate was given at day-35; in mares treated at day-70, oestrus and ovulation was delayed for some 40–50 days, and rebreeding within the same breeding season would have been much more difficult.

An earlier paper by Cooper (1979) records the use of daily doses of 10 mg $PGF_{2\alpha}$ in early gestation to terminate pregnancy in twin-bearing mares; the treatment was usually effective after three or four doses. The same author (Cooper, 1979) found natural $PGF_{2\alpha}$ to be ineffective as an abortifacient at the 6.5–7 months stage of gestation; ten daily doses of 10 mg $PGF_{2\alpha}$ was without effect and the mares duly delivered live foals at full term.

34.8 FUTURE DEVELOPMENTS

Pregnancy can be effectively terminated and parturition induced by the use of prostaglandin analogues; natural $PGF_{2\alpha}$, for reasons which are not clearly understood, is less effective than the analogues. The use of oxytocin is only relevant as an induction agent when signs of impending parturition are clearly obvious. The amount of data on which present views are based is still extremely limited. Quite apart from possible practical considerations, the study of parturition in the mare and the endocrine events associated with it are of considerable biological interest. As is evident in many other areas of reproduction, the species differences that obtain between the several farm mammals in the mechanisms controlling parturition may be quite marked. Future work will aim at defining such differences more precisely.

34.9 REFERENCES

Akkayon, C. and Demirtel, E. (1974) Factors affecting the duration of pregnancy in mares at the Karacebey Stud. *Ankara Univ. Vet. Fak-Dergisi* **20**, 575–587.

Alm, C. C., Sullivan, J. J. and First, N. L. (1974) Induction of premature parturition by parenteral administration of dexamethasone in the mare. *J. Am. Vet. Med. Ass.* **165**, 721–722.

Alm, C. C., Sullivan, J. J. and First, N. L. (1975) The effect of a corticosteroid (dexamethasone) progesterone, estrogen and prostaglandin F$_{2\alpha}$ on gestation length in normal and ovariectomized mares. *J. Reprod. Fert. (Suppl.)* **23**, 637–640.

Allen, W. R. and Rossdale, P. D. (1973) A preliminary study upon the use of prostaglandin for inducing oestrus in non-cycling thoroughbred mares. *Equine Vet. J.* **5**, 137–140.

Allen, W. R., Chard, T. and Forsling, M. L. (1973) Levels of oxytocin and vasopressin in the mare during parturition. *J. Endocr.* **57**, 175–176.

Badi, A. M., O'Byrne, T. N. and Cunningham, E. P. (1981) An analysis of reproductive performance in thoroughbred mares. *Ir. Vet. J.* **35**(1), 1–12.

Bos, H. and Van der Mey, G. J. W. (1980) Length of gestation periods or horses and ponies belonging to different breeds. *Livestock Prod. Sci.* **7**, 181–187.

Burns, S. J. (1973) Clinical safety of dexamethasone in mares during pregnancy. *Equine Vet. J.* **5**, 91–94.

Campbell, D. L. (1971) Corticosteroids in first trimester pregnant mares. *Southwest Vet.* **24**, 103.

Cooper, W. L. (1979) Clinical aspects of prostaglandins in equine reproduction. *Proc. 2nd Equine Pharm. Symposium*, 225–231.

Currie, W. B. (1977) Endocrinology of pregnancy and parturition in sheep and goats. In, *Management of Reproduction in Sheep and Goats*. Symp. Univ. Wisconsin, 72–78.

Dawson, F. L. M. (1977) Recent advances in equine reproduction. *Equine Vet. J.* **9**(1), 4–11.

Douglas, R. H. and Ginther, O. J. (1975) Effects of prostaglandin F$_{2\alpha}$ on estrous cycle or corpus luteum in mares and gilts. *J. Anim. Sci.* **40**, 518–552.

Douglas, R. H., Aquired, E. L. and Ginther, O. J. (1974) Induction of abortion in mares with prostaglandin F$_{2\alpha}$. *J. Anim. Sci.* **39**, 404–407.

Drost, M. (1972) Failure to induce parturition in pony mares with dexamethasone. *J. Am. Vet. Med. Ass.* **100**, 321–322.

Evans, J. W. (1977) Anatomy and physiology of reproduction in the mare. In, *The Horse*, Freeman, San Francisco.

First, N. L. (1979) Mechanisms controlling parturition in farm animals. In, *Animal Reproduction*. BARC Symp. No. 3, H. Hawks, Ed. pp. 215–257. Allenheld Osmun, Montclair.

First, N. L. and Alm, C. (1977) Dexamethasone induced parturition in pony mares. *J. Anim. Sci.* **44**, 1072–1075.

Ginther, O. J. (1979). *Reproductive Biology of the Mare. Basic and Applied aspects*. McNaughton & Gunn, Ann Arbor.

Hammond, J. Jr., Mason, I. L. and Robinson, T. J. (1971) Horses. In, *Hammond Farm Animals*, 4th Ed. pp. 31–47. Edward Arnold, London.

Hendrikse, J. (1972) Length of gestation in Dutch Horse Breeds. *Tijdschr. Diergeneesk*, **97**, 477–479.

Hillman, R. B. (1975) Induction of parturition in mares. *J. Reprod. Fert. (Suppl.)* **23**, 641–644.

Hillman, R. B. and Ganjam, V. K. (1979) Hormonal changes in the mare and foal associated with oxytocin induction of parturition. *J. Reprod. Fert. (Suppl.)* **27**, 541–546.

Hintz, H. F., Hintz, R. L., Lein, D. H. and Van Vleck, L. D. (1979) Length of gestation in thoroughbred mares. *J. Equine Med. Surgery* **3**(**b**), 289–292.

Howell, C. E. and Rollins, W. C. (1951) Environmental sources of variation in the gestation length of the horse. *J. Anim. Sci.* **10**, 789–793.

Jeffcott, L. B. and Rossdale, P. D. (1977) A critical review of current methods for induction of parturition in the mare. *Equine Vet. J.* **9**, 208–215.

Jeffcott, L. B. and Whitwell, K. (1973) Twinning as a cause of foetal and neonatal loss in the thoroughbred mare. *J. Comp. Path.* **83**, 91–106.

Kooistra, L. H. and Ginther, O. J. (1976) Termination of pseudo pregnancy by administration of prostaglandin F$_{2\alpha}$ and termination of early pregnancy by administration of prostaglandin F$_{2\alpha}$ or colchicine or by removal of embryo in mares. *Am. J. Vet. Res.* **37**, 35–39.

Liggins, G. C. R., Fairclough, R. J., Grieves, S. A., Forster, C. S. and Knox, B. S. (1977) Parturition in the sheep. In, *The Fetus and Birth*, pp. 15–30. Ciba. Found. Symp. 47, Elsevier, Excerpta Med. Holland.

Nathanielsz, P. W., Rossdale, P. D., Silver, M. and Comline, R. S. (1975) Studies on fetal, neonatal and maternal cortisol metabolism in the mare. *J. Reprod. Fert. (Suppl.)* **23**, 625–630.

Pashen, R. L. and Allen, R. (1979) The role of the fetal gonads and placenta in steroid production, maintenance of pregnancy and parturition. *J. Reprod. Fert. (Suppl.)* **27**, 499–509.

Platt, H. (1973) Actiological aspects of perinatal mortality in the thoroughbred. *J. Comp. Path.* **83**, 199.

Purvis, A. D. (1972) Electric induction of labour and parturition in the mare. Proc. 18th Ann. Conv. Amer. Assoc. Equine Pract, San Francisco, 113–116.

Purvis, A. D. (1977) The induction of labour in mares as a routine breeding farm procedure. Proc. 23rd Ann. Conv. Amer. Assoc. Equine Pract. (Vancouver), 145–160.

Rollins, W. C. and Howell, C. E. (1951) Genetic sources of variation in the gestation length of the horse. *J. Anim. Sci.* **10**, 797–801.

Ropiha, R. T., Matthews, R. G. and Butterfield, R. M. (1969) The duration of pregnancy in thoroughbred mares. *Vet. Rec.* **84**, 552–555.

Rossdale, P. D. and Jeffcott, L. B. (1975) Problems encountered during induced foaling in pony mares. *Vet. Rec.* **97**, 371–372.

Rossdale, P. D. and Ricketts, S. W. (1980) *Equine Stud Farm Medicine*. 2nd Ed. Balliere Tindall, London.

Rossdale, P. D., Jeffcott, L. B. and Allen, W. R. (1976) Foaling induced by a synthetic prostaglandin analogue (Fluoprostenol). *Vet. Rec.* **99**, 26–28.

Rossdale, P. D., Pashen, R. L. and Jeffcott, L. B. (1979) The use of synthetic prostaglandin analogue (Fluoprostenol) to induce foaling. *J. Reprod. Fert. (Suppl.)* **27**, 521–529.

Squires, E. L., Hillman, R. B., Pickett, B. W. and Nett, T. M. (1980) Induction of abortion in mares with Equimate: effect on secretion of progesterone, PMSG and reproductive performance. *J. Anim. Sci.* **50**, 490.

Tutt, J. B. (1944) Parturition in the thoroughbred mare. *Br. Vet. J.* **100**, 69–73.

Van Niekerk, C. H. and Morgenthal, J. C. (1976) Plasma progesterone and oestrogen concentrations during induction of parturition with flumethasone and prostaglandin. *Proc. 8th Int. Congr. Anim. Reprod. A.I. (Krackow)* **3**, 386–389.

CHAPTER 35

Embryo Transfer in Horses

35.1 INTRODUCTION

Authors reviewing embryo transfer in horses (e.g. Allen, 1977; Douglas, 1979) have drawn attention to the obvious scarcity of reports dealing with superovulation, recovery and transfer of embryos in this species. Clearly, the economic incentive for research in this area differs from that in species such as cattle, so that funds from within a country to support embryo transfer studies may often be difficult to obtain. There is also the fact, as observed by Douglas (1979) that the horse industry tends to be traditionally more conservative in viewing any new approach to breeding that has implications for the future propagation of purebred animals.

Allen (1977) has drawn attention to the continuing refusal of major breed registration authorities to accept for registration foals that have been born after artificial insemination or embryo transfer; the same author also notes the very high values of individual horses and the losses which may occur through wastage during pregnancy in Thoroughbreds and other breeds which makes embryo transfer useful both for breeding and research purposes. Towards facilitating a greater understanding of certain aspects of horse reproduction, the Thoroughbred Breeders' Association equine fertility unit at Cambridge has already employed embryo transfer to achieve two important developments (Anon, 1980). The first, involving embryo

transfers between the pony and donkey, is part of a long-term study into the possible causes of the high rate of early foetal death which may be experienced in the Thoroughbred mare; the second, which is the production of genetically identical twin foals, provides a completely new approach towards the elucidation of a variety of questions that may arise in horses.

35.1.1 Practical advantages

In considering the possible commercial benefits of embryo transfer to the horse industry at the present time, Douglas (1979) notes two areas; (1) in obtaining foals from mares that are subfertile or infertile as a result of extensive uterine pathology; (2) as a means of getting offspring from older valuable mares without exposing them to pregnancy and possible risks (e.g. uterine arterial haemorrhage) associated with that condition.

35.2 SUPEROVULATING THE MARE

It should be noted that techniques for superovulation that are satisfactory in cattle, sheep and pigs are of no avail in the mare. Already mentioned is the fact that pony mares injected with exogenous gonadotrophins (PMSG, hCG, pituitary FSH preparations) in various doses and treatment regimens failed to respond during the anovulatory season (Day, 1940). During the 1970s, however, reports did begin to appear in the U.S.A. showing that ovulation and multiple ovulation could be induced during the anovulatory season with a crude horse pituitary extract (Douglas et al., 1974) and that multiple ovulations (up to four ovulations) could be induced in the cyclic mare (Lapin and Ginther, 1977). In the studies, in which it was a question of maintaining the treatment over a sufficiently long period, crude horse pituitary extract was given on a daily basis for 14 days during anoestrus and for 6 days during the normal oestrous cycle (starting on day-11 or day-12 after ovulation).

Studies with a commercially available equine pituitary extract (Pitropin) reported by Douglas (1979) were successful in the induction of multiple ovulations (2.3 average); hCG was given to facilitate ovulation of mature follicles on day-20 after seven daily injections of Pitropin. No problem with presumed anaphylactic reaction to the preparation, such as that recorded in the study of Lapin and Ginther (1977) was observed by Douglas (1979), the latter author concluding that the absence of reaction was due to the fact that no pyogenic substance was present in the commercial preparation.

35.3 SURGICAL AND NON-SURGICAL RECOVERY TECHNIQUES

The surgical recovery of embryos from the mare's tract is carried out using procedures based on those previously developed in sheep and cattle. In the normal way, fertilized horse eggs enter the uterus some 5 or 6 days after ovulation (Hamilton and Day, 1945; Oguri and Tsutsumi, 1972; Betteridge et al., 1979). In attempting egg recovery, the donor mare is anaesthetized and maintained in dorsal recumbency with the head downwards on a slightly inclined operating table (Allen and Rowson, 1975); the ovary in which ovulation has occurred and the uterine horn on the same side are exteriorized through a ventral mid-line incision which is made between the umbilicus and the mammary gland. A short length of bent glass or polythene tubing with smoothed ends is inserted in the tip of the uterine horn through a small incision and securely ligated

in place; 30–50 ml of medium is flushed through the oviduct and into the ligated horn by way of a blunted 18-gauge needle held in the ovarian end of the Fallopian tube. Recovery rates of 77% have been achieved between days 1–6 after ovulation using this procedure (Allen and Rowson, 1975).

One problem in recovery mentioned by Allen (1977) is the difficulty of exteriorizing the ovary and oviduct in some 2-year old and maiden mares; this is apparently due to the "shortness" and immaturity of the ligaments in these horses. Allen et al. (1977) record good recovery rates in small 2-year old pony mares between days 7 and 10 after ovulation, after injecting 60 ml medium into the tip of the uterine horn and collecting the flushings by way of a cannula inserted at the base of the same horn.

35.3.1 Recovery of tubal eggs

The mare has an effective one-way valve arrangement in the form of a papilla at the uterotubal junction as in pigs; for this reason it is not possible to "milk" flushings back up the Fallopian tube from the uterus as can be done in sheep and cattle. A method of recovering tubal eggs with considerable efficiency was reported by Betteridge and Mitchell (1975); They inserted a fine nylon catheter through the uterotubal junction by way of a surgical incision in the tip of the uterine horn and flushed the oviduct with 15 ml medium, the fluid being collected by a cannula inserted in the ovarian end of the tube.

35.3.2 Non-surgical recovery

Several reports dealing with the non-surgical recovery of eggs in the mare have appeared in the literature, including those from studies in Japan (Oguri and Tsutsumi, 1972, 1974), the U.K. (Allen and Rowson, 1975), Poland (Tischner and Bielanski, 1980) and North America (Hershman and Douglas, 1975; Douglas, 1979; Vogelsang et al., 1979; Castleberry et al., 1980; Imel et al., 1980; Griffin et al., 1981). In their most successful recovery efforts, Japanese workers employed an instrument designed to occlude the cervix and flushed the whole uterus with 1500 ml of fluid; they reported a 90% recovery rate in 20 mares after flushing at 6–7 days after ovulation.

Tischner and Bielanski (1980) used a modification of the technique described by Allen and Rowson (1975); a plastic catheter with an inflatable cuff was passed through the cervix and the uterine horn ipsilateral to the corpus luteum flushed with 150 ml of medium; from a total of 70 flushings carried out on days 7–9 after ovulation, 27 embryos were recovered. The donor mares in this work appeared to conceive in the normal way at the oestrus following these recovery attempts. American efforts, as described by Douglas (1979) have usually employed a French Foley or similar catheter with a 30 ml inflatable cuff which is inserted into the uterine body and the catheter secured by inflating the cuff with 15–50 ml sterile water. With the catheter suitably secure, both uterine horns are filled simultaneously with flushing medium (400 ml in ponies; 1000 ml in horses) by gravity flow and the medium is then collected again by gravity flow; if eggs are not found after the first flush, it is repeated with the operator using palpation of the uterus *per rectum* to facilitate recovery of the fluid. Recovery rates in excess of 80% have been reported (Imel *et al.*, 1980) and flushings can be attempted on several occasions at intervals of 18 days without this causing difficulties; prostaglandin $F_{2\alpha}$ can be administered on the day of flushing to shorten the interval between treatments. In the report of Griffin *et al.* (1981), a non-surgical recovery rate of 59% was reported after 37 attempts in 16 mares dealt with during their normal cycle; one mare yielded three embryos within a 35-day period.

35.3.3 Unfertilized eggs in the mare

In the mare, it is difficult to be as certain as with the other farm mammals about the efficiency of recovery attempts because of the marked tendency for unfertilized eggs to be retained in the Fallopian tubes of the mare rather than passing into the uterus (Van Niekerk and Gerneke, 1966; Onuma *et al.*, 1972; David, 1975; Webel *et al.*, 1977); it would appear that the fertilized horse egg can influence its own transport to the uterus, in view of the fact that it can overtake old, unfertilized eggs en route (Betteridge and Mitchell, 1975; Onuma and Ohnami, 1975). The suggestion has been made (Flood *et al.*, 1979) that the early cleaving horse egg may produce humoral substances which act

by overcoming a general statis at the isthmo-ampullary junction in the Fallopian tube where retention most often occurs. In Canada, Betteridge *et al.* (1979) have reported evidence suggesting that the horse egg must develop beyond the two- to four-cell stage in the oviduct before its humoral signal is sufficient to enable normal transport into the uterus to proceed.

35.3.4 Recovery of flushing fluid

Although the efficiency of non-surgical recovery operations in the mare is complicated by tubal retention of unfertilized eggs, it is possible to check the recovery rate of the flushing medium. In work reported by Douglas (1979), involving 40 uterine flushings, at least 92% of the volume of medium infused was recovered; the same author found a lower egg recovery rate in mares after inducing superovulation with gonadrotrophin (35%) as compared to single ovulating controls (67%).

35.4 EVALUATING THE HORSE EMBRYO

There has been some controversy as to the state of nuclear maturation reached by the horse egg at the time of ovulation. Hamilton and Day (1945) claimed that dictyate oocytes are normally ovulated and that maturation is completed in the Fallopian tube; on the other hand, Van Niekerk and Gerneke (1966) were of the view that metaphase II occurs shortly before ovulation in the horse as it does in the other farm species. In more recent times, Webel *et al.* (1977) has suggested that both sets of observations are probably correct; they found oocytes at metaphase II, as well as less mature oocytes, when they examined eggs ovulated 42–52 h after ovulating hormone (hCG) administration. Those who have attempted to culture the horse oocyte released from the vesicular follicle *in vitro* report that the egg does require a relatively long period (40 h or so) for nuclear maturation to occur.

In the evaluation of the horse egg and embryo, several reports are available for consulting about the morphology of the developing organism (Oguri and Tsutsumi, 1972; Allen, 1977); it should be kept in mind that horse eggs recovered from the oviducts may contain old unfertilized eggs as well as the most recently ovulated one (Betteridge and Mitchell, 1975).

35.5 STORAGE OF EMBRYOS

Japanese researchers have employed physiological saline containing 2% gelatine for flushing the mare's tract and have stored the embryos in this or in a mixture of mare serum: Ringer's Solution (1:1 v/v) up to the time for transfer (Oguri and Tsutsumi, 1972, 1974). In work elsewhere, Medium 199 has been employed commonly for short-term storage and later Dulbecco's PBS, modified as in the report of Whittingham (1971).

In dealing with a longer storage period outside the mare tract, Allen et al., (1976) have described the development and durability of horse embryos after long-distance transport in the rabbit oviduct. In July, 1975, the Fallopian tubes of Welsh ponies in Cambridge were flushed and the embryos placed in the ligated oviducts of rabbits which were then transported by car to Cracow in Poland; the embryos were in the rabbit for 48 h before being transferred to four recipients, two of which delivered healthy foals in due course (Allen et al., 1977). Some preliminary observations on the freezing of the horse embryo have been reported by Griffin et al. (1981), but until such time as more information is available on that possibility, the ligated rabbit oviduct would appear to be a suitable method of relatively short-term storage.

35.6 SYNCHRONIZING DONOR AND RECIPIENT

As already mentioned, one effective means of oestrus control in the mare is by way of

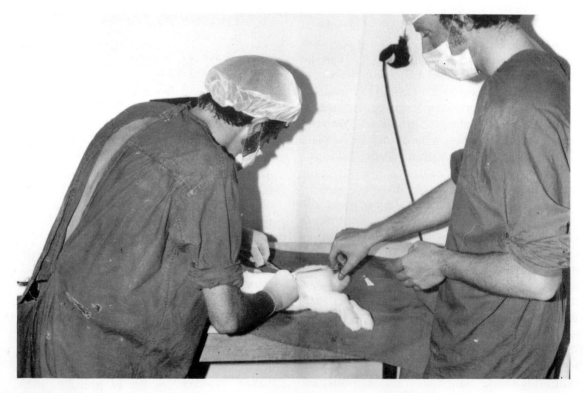

Fig. 35.1. The rabbit has been used to keep the embryos of all the farm animals, including the horse, alive for a period of several days. The rabbit oviduct has been used extensively to store the eggs of the farm animals in studies at Lyons Farm. A few years ago, horse eggs were transported from Cambridge to Poland in the rabbit to be born there 11 months later.

prostaglandin $F_{2\alpha}$. Allen et al. (1976) employed prostaglandin in combination with hCG with marked success in aligning ovulation in English donor mares with the same event in Polish recipient animals in their demonstration of long-distance transport of horse embryos. The Cambridge authors employed the hormonal regimen described by Palmer and Jousset (1975) in which the PG analogue Equimate is given on day-0, hCG on day-6 (to hasten ovulation in those in oestrus at the time, Equimate on day-14 (when mares should be between days 4 and 15 of dioestrus) and finally hCG on day-20 or 21 when donor mares were bred.

Although there is no precise information available on synchronization requirements for donor and recipient horses, it is accepted that these are likely to be similar to those in the other farm mammals (± 2 days being the limit of variation between donor and recipient).

35.7 SURGICAL AND NON-SURGICAL TRANSFER TECHNIQUES

Surgical transfer of embryos in the mare is carried out in much the same way as transfer in cattle (Allen and Rowson, 1975); eggs which have been recovered within two days of ovulation (two to eight-cell eggs) are inserted into the oviduct at the ovarian end, using a small volume of medium (0.2–0.5 ml) in a Pasteur pipette and morula/early blastocysts deposited in the uterus near the tip of the horn. When making the transfer to the uterus, the Pasteur pipette is passed through a small hole made in the uterine wall by the blunt end of a large round-bodied suture needle. As noted by various workers in cattle transfer work, the success of surgical transfer in the mare may be related to the age of the egg; Allen and Rowson (1975) record that only 1/8 eggs transferred between days 1 and 3 after ovulation continued development in Welsh pony mares as compared with 6/8 developing after transfer between days 4 and 6.

Although the survival of the horse embryo in relation to the site of transfer has not been reported on, it is known that a very high rate of transuterine migration occurs spontaneously in the mare (Day, 1940); the site of transfer relative to the corpus luteum may not be as important as in a species such as the cow. In terms of pregnancy rates which can be achieved by way of surgical intervention, it appears to be much the same as that found in cattle; a recent report by Imel et al. (1981) records a figure of 54% after surgical transfers.

35.7.1 Non-surgical transfer

The use of non-surgical transfer techniques was first reported by Oguri and Tsutsumi (1972); eleven embryos (5–7 days old) were transferred to the mare's uterus via the cervix but none of the recipients became pregnant. Later studies by the same workers (Oguri and Tsutsumi, 1980), in which 79 embryos were transferred into the uterus by various non-surgical methods, showed a pregnancy rate of 42%.

Elswhere, Allen and Rowson (1975) reported success in 5/7 (71%) animals after transfers in which 6–8-day embryos were simply deposited in the body of the mare's uterus with no special attempt to locate them in the uterine horn ipsilateral to the corpus luteum. In subsequent work, Allen et al. (1977) performed a similar non-surgical transfer via the cervix to the uterus of a single mare that duly gave birth to a live foal. In a review at the time, Allen (1977) noted that the results on the outcome of non-surgical transfers were equal to or better than those achieved by surgery.

The possible effect of medium for holding eggs on the outcome of non-surgical attempts is noted by Douglas (1980); using two different media (Medium 199 and Dulbecco's PBS) he recorded 0/12 pregnancies with M199 and 6/10 pregnancies with PBS after transfer. The author concluded that pregnancy rates after non-surgical transfer in the mare may be improved by modifying the transfer medium. Variable success was reported by Castleberry et al. (1980), with 3/5 pregnancies after surgical transfer and only 2/16 pregnancies after non-surgical attempts. It should be noted that in all these horse studies, the numbers involved are too few to draw any firm conclusions and the results quoted should be taken as nothing more than a general indication of what may be possible with the species.

35.8 REFERENCES

Allen, W. R. (1977) Techniques and results in horses. In, *Embryo Transfer in Farm Animals.* Betteridge, K. J., Ed. Canada Agriculture Monograph, 16, pp. 47–49.

Allen, W. R. and Rowson, L. E. A. (1975) Surgical and non-surgical egg transfer in horses. *J. Reprod. Fert. (Suppl.)* **23,** 525–530.

Allen, W. R., Stewart, F., Trounson, A. O., Tischner, M. and Bielanski, W. (1976) Viability of horse embryos after storage and long distance transport in the rabbit. *J. Reprod. Fert.* **47,** 387–390.

Allen, W. R., Bielanski, W., Cholewinski, G., Tischner, M. and Zwolinski, J. (1977) Blood groups in horses born after double transplantation of embryos. *Bull. Acad. Pol. Sci. Ser. Sci. Biol.* **25**(11), 757–759.

Anon (1980) Developments in equine research. *Vet. Rec.* **107,** 49–50.

Betteridge, K. J. and Mitchell, D. (1975) A surgical technique applied to the study of tubal eggs in the mare. *J. Reprod. Fert. (Suppl.)* **23,** 519–524.

Betteridge, K. J., Eaglesome, M. D. and Flood, P. F. (1979) Embryo transport through the mare's oviduct depends upon cleavage and is independent of the ipsilateral corpus luteum. *J. Reprod. Fert. (Suppl.)* **27,** 387–394.

Castleberry, R. S., Schneider, H. J., Jr. and Griffin, J. L. (1980) Recovery and transfer of equine embryos. *Theriogen.* **13,** 90.

David, J. S. E. (1975) A survey of eggs in the oviducts of mares. *J. Reprod. Fert. (Suppl.)* **23,** 513–517.

Day, F. T. (1940) Clinical and experimental observations on reproduction in the mare. *J. Agric. Sci., Camb.* **30,** 244–261.

Douglas, R. H. (1979) Review of induction of superovulation and embryo transfer in the equine. *Theriogen.* **11,**(1), 33–46.

Douglas, R. H. (1980) Pregnancy rates following non-surgical embryo transfer in the equine. *J. Anim. Sci.* **51** (Suppl. 1), 272 (Abs).

Douglas, R. H., Nuti, L., Ginther, O. J. (1974) Induction of ovulation and multiple ovulation in seasonally-anovulatory mares with equine pituitary fractions. *Theriogen.* **2**(6), 133–142.

Flood, P. J., Jong, A. and Betteridge, K. J. (1979) The location of eggs retained in the oviducts of mares. *J. Reprod. Fert.* **57,** 291–294.

Griffin, J. L., Castleberry, R. S. and Schneider, H. S., Jr. (1981) Influence of day of collection on recovery rate in mature cycling mares. *Theriogen.* **15,** 106 (Abs).

Hamilton, W. J. and Day, F. T. (1945) Cleavage stages of the ova of the horse with notes on ovulation. *J. Anat.* **79,** 127–130.

Hersham, L. and Douglas, R. H. (1979) The critical period for the maternal recognition of pregnancy in pony mares. *J. Reprod. Fert. (Suppl)* **27,** 395–401.

Imel, K. J., Squires, E. L. and Elsden, R. P. (1980) Embryo recovery and effect of repeated uterine flushing of mares. *Theriogen.* **13,** 97.

Lapin, D. R. and Ginther, O. J. (1977) Induction of ovulation and multiple ovulations in seasonally anovulatory and ovulatory mares with an equine pituitary extract. *J. Anim. Sci.* **44,** 834–842.

Oguri, N. and Tsutsumi, Y. (1972) Non-surgical recovery of equine eggs and an attempt at non-surgical egg transfer in horses. *J. Reprod. Fert.* **31,** 187–195.

Oguri, N. and Tsutsumi, Y. (1974) Non-surgical egg transfer in mares. *J. Reprod. Fert.* **41,** 313–320.

Oguri, N. and Tsutsumi, Y. (1980) Non-surgical transfer of equine embryos. *Arch. Andrology* **5,** 108–110 (Abs).

Onuma, H. and Ohnami, Y. (1975) Retention of tubal eggs in mares. *J. Reprod. Fert. (Suppl.)* **23,** 507–511.

Onuma, H., Nakamura, K., Nakanishi, H. and Fujishiro, T. (1972) Persistence of tubal ova in the mare. *Jap. J. Vet. Sci.* **34,** Suppl. 166.

Palmer, E. and Jousset, B. (1975) Synchronization of oestrus in mares with a prostaglandin analogue and hCG. *J. Reprod. Fert. (Suppl.)* **23,** 269–274.

Tischner, M. and Bielanski, A. (1980) Non-surgical embryo collection in the mare and subsequent fertility of donor animals. *J. Reprod. Fert.* **58,** 351–361.

Van Niekerk, C. H. and Gerneke, W. H. (1966) Persistence and parthogenetic cleavage of tubal ova in the mare. *Onderstepoort. J. Vet. Rec.* **31,** 195–232.

Vogelsang, S. G., Sorensen, A. M., Jr., Potter, G. D., Burns, S. J. and Draemer, D. C. (1979) Fertility of donor mares following non-surgical collection of embryos. *J. Reprod. Fert. (Suppl.)* **27,** 383–386.

Webel, S. K., Franklin, B., Harland, B. and Dziuk, P. J. (1977) Fertility, ovulation and maturation of eggs in mares injected with hCG. *J. Reprod. Fert.* **51,** 337–341.

Whittingham, D. G. (1971) Survival of mouse embryos after freezing and thawing. *Nature Lond.* **233,** 125–126.

Books and Journals Dealing
with Control and Manipulation
of Reproduction

Books

Adams, C. E. Ed. (1982) *Mammalian Egg Transfer.* CRC Press, Boca Raton, Florida.

Amann, R. P. and Seidel, G. E. Jr. Eds. (1982) *Prospects for sexing mammalian semen.* Colorado Assoc. Univ. Press, Boulder, Colorado.

Arthur, G. H. (1975) *Veterinary Reproduction and Obstetrics.* 4th Edn, Bailliere Tindall, London.

Asdell, S. A. (1964) *Patterns of Mammalian Reproduction.* 2nd Edn, Cornell University Press, Ithaca.

Austin, C. R. (1961) *The Mammalian Egg — a Study of a Specialized Cell.* Blackwell Scientific Publication, Oxford.

Austin, C. R. (1965) *Fertilization.* Prentice-Hall, Eaglewood Cliffs.

Austin, C. R. and Short, R. V., Eds. (1972) *Reproduction in Mammals.* 5 Vols. Cambridge University Press, London.

Betteridge, K. J. (1977) *Embryo Transfer in Farm Animals. A Review of Techniques and Applications.* Monograph 16, Canada Department of Agriculture, 92 pp.

Brackett, B. G., Seidel, G. E. Jr. and Seidel, S. M. Eds. (1982) *New Technologies in Animal Breeding.* Academic Press, New York, London.

Cole, D. J. A., Ed. (1972) *Pig Production.* Butterworths, London.

Cole, D. J. A. and Foxcroft, G. R. Eds. (1982) *Control of Pig Reproduction.* Butterworths, London.

Cole, H. H. and Cupps, P. T., Eds. (1977) *Reproduction in Domestic Animals.* 3rd Edn. Academic Press, New York.

Crighton, D. B., Foxcroft, G. R., Haynes, N. B. and Lamming, G. E., Eds. (1978) *Control of Ovulation.* Butterworths, London.

Daniel, J. C. Jr. Ed. (1978) *Methods in Mammalian Reproduction.* Academic Press, New York.

Ellendorf, F., Taverne, M. and Smidt, D. Eds. (1979) *Physiology and Control of Parturition in Domestic Animals.* Special Issue, *Animal Reproduction Science.*

Elliott, K. and Whelan, J. Eds. (1977) *Freezing of Mammalian Embryos.* Ciba Foundation Symposium No. 52, Excerpta Medica, Amsterdam.

Ginther, O. J. (1979) *Reproductive Biology of the Mare, Basic and Applied Aspects.* McNaughton and Gunn, Ann Arbor.

Hafez, E. S. E. Ed. (1975) *The Behaviour of Domestic Animals.* Bailliere Tindall, London.

Hafez, E. S. E. Ed. (1980) *Reproduction in Farm Animals.* 4th Edn. Lea and Febiger, Philadelphia.

Hafez, E. S. E. and Blandau, R. J. Eds. (1968) *The Mammalian Oviduct.* The University of Chicago Press, Chicago.

Hafez, E. S. E. and Semm, K. Eds. (1982) *In vitro Fertilization and Embryo Transfer.* Alan R. Liss, Inc, New York.

Hammond, J. (1927) *Reproduction of the Cow.* Cambridge University Press, Cambridge.

Hammond, J. Jr., Mason, I. L. and Robinson, T. J. (1971) *Hammond's Farm Animals.* 4th Edn. Edward Arnold, London.

Hawk, H. Ed. (1979) *Animal Reproduction.* BARC. Symposium No. 3, Allanheld, Osmun, Montclair.

Hughes, P. E. and Varley, M. A. (1980) *Reproduction in the Pig.* Butterworths, London.

Hunter, R. H. F. (1980) *Physiology and Technology of Reproduction in Female Domestic Animals.* Academic Press, London.

Jochle, W. and Lamond, D. R. (1980) *Control of Reproductive Functions in Domestic Animals.* Gustav Fischer Verlag., Jena.

Laing, J. A. Ed. (1979) *Fertility and Infertility in Domestic Animals.* 3rd Edn. Bailliere Tindall, London.

Lamming, G. E. and Amoroso, E. C. Eds. (1966) *Reproduction in the Female Mammal.* Butterworths, London.

McDonald, L. E. (1980) *Veterinary Endocrinology and Reproduction.* 3rd Edition, Lea and Febiger, Philadelphia.

Mann, T. (1964) *Biochemistry of Semen and of the Male Reproductive Tract.* Methuen, London.

Maule, J. P. Ed. (1962) *The Semen of Animals and Artificial Insemination.* Technical Communication No. 15, Commonwealth Agricultural Bureau. Slough.

Morrow, D. A. Ed. (1980) *Current Therapy in Theriogenology.* W. B. Saunder, Phil. U.S.A.

Nalbandov, A. (1976) *Reproductive Physiology of Mammals and Birds.* 3rd Edn. Freeman, San Francisco.

Nishikawa, Y. (1959) *Studies on Reproduction in Horses. Singularity and Artificial Control of Reproductive Phenomena.* Japan Racing Association, Tokyo.

Perry, E. J. Ed. (1968) *The Artificial Insemination of Farm Animals.* 4th Edn. Rutgers University Press, New Brunswick.

Robinson, T. J. Ed. (1967) *The Control of the Ovarian Cycle in the Sheep.* Sydney University Press, Sydney.

Rossdale, P. D. and Ricketts, S. W. (1980) *Equine Stud Farm Medicine.* 2nd Edn. Bailliere Tindall, London.

Rowlands, I. W. and Allen, W. R. Eds. (1979) *Equine Reproduction II.* Proceedings Second International Symposium. Supplement No. 27. *Journal of Reproduction and Fertility.*

Rowlands, I. W., Allen, W. R. and Rossdale, P. D. Eds. (1975) *Equine Reproduction* Proceedings First International Symposium. Supplement No. 23., *Journal of Reproduction and Fertility.*

Rowson, L. E. A. Ed. (1976) *Egg Transfer in Cattle* (Cambridge). Proceedings of an EEC Agricultural Research Seminar.

Salisbury, G. W., Van Denmark, N. K. and Lodge, J. R. (1978) *Physiology of Reproduction and Artificial Insemination of Cattle.* 2nd Edn. Freeman, San Francisco.

Scaramuzzi, R. J., Lincoln, D. W. and Weir, B. J. (1981) *Reproductive Endocrinology of Domestic Ruminants.* Supplement No. 30, *Journal of Reproduction and Fertility.*

Sreenan, J. M. Ed. (1978) *Control of Reproduction in the Cow.* (Galway). Proceedings of an EEC Agricultural Research Seminar 667 pp.

Tomes, G. L., Robertson, D. E. and Lightfoot, R. J. Eds. (1979) *Sheep Breeding.* 2nd Edn. Butterworths, London.

Wodzicka-Tomaszewska, M., Edey, T. N. and Lynch, J. J. Eds. (1980) *Behaviour in Relation to Reproduction, Management and Welfare of Farm Animals.* University of New England, Armidale.

Zemjanis, R. (1970) *Diagnostic and Therapeutic Techniques in Animal Reproduction.* Williams and Silkins, Baltimore.

Journals

Acta Agricultura Scandinavica. Hovslagargatan 2iii, Stockholm C, Sweden.

Acta Endocrinologica. Periodica, Skelmosevej 10, Copenhagen, Valby, Denmark.

American Journal of Veterinary Research. American Veterinary Medical Association, 600 S. Michigan Avenue, Chicago, Illinois, U.S.A.

Animal Behaviour. Bailliere Tindall & Co., London, WC2, England.

Animal Breeding Abstracts. Commonwealth Bureau of Animal Breeding and Genetics, Edinburgh, Scotland.

Animal Production. Longmans, Harlow, Essex, England.

Animal Reproduction Science. Elsevier Scientific Publishing Company, Amsterdam, Netherlands.

Australian Journal of Agricultural Research. CSIRO, East Melbourne, Victoria, Australia.

Australian Veterinary Journal. Australian Veterinary Association, 272 Brunswick Road, Brunswick, Victoria, Australia.

Bibliography of Reproduction. Reproduction Research Information Service Ltd., Newmarket Road, Cambridge, England.

Biology of Reproduction. Society for Study of Reproduction, 309 West Clark Street, Champaign, Illinois, U.S.A.

British Veterinary Journal. Bailliere Tindall, 33 Red Lion Square, London, WC1R 4SG, England.

Canadian Journal Animal Science. Canadian Society of Animal Science, Slater Street, Ottawa.

Cornell Veterinarian. Cornell Veterinarian Inc., Cornell University, Ithaca, New York 14853, U.S.A.

Endocrinology. Charles C. Thomas, Springfield, Illinois, U.S.A.

Fertility and Sterility. Paul P. Hoeber, Inc. New York, U.S.A.

Gamete Research. Alan R. Liss, Inc., 150 Fifth Avenue, New York, N.Y. 10011 U.S.A.

International Journal of Fertility. Ben Franklin Press, Pittsfield, Massachusetts, U.S.A.

Irish Veterinary Journal. Irish Veterinary Association, 53 Landsdowne Road, Dublin, Ireland.

Japanese Journal of Animal Reproduction. Japanese Society of Animal Reproduction. Azahu University, Japan.

Journal of Agricultural Science, Cambridge. Cambridge University Press, Cambridge, England.

Journal of the American Veterinary Medical Association. AVMA, 930 N. Meacham Road, Schaumburg, Illinois, U.S.A.

Journal of Animal Science. American Society of Animal Science, 209 West Clark Street, Champaign, Illinois, U.S.A.

Journal of Dairy Science. American Dairy Science Association, 309 West Clark Street, Champaign, Illinois, U.S.A.

Journal of Reproduction and Fertility. 22 Newmarket Road, Cambridge, England.

Livestock Production Science. Elsevier Scientific Publishing Company, Amsterdam, Netherlands.

New Zealand Veterinary Journal. New Zealand Veterinary Association, Wellington, New Zealand.

Prostaglandins. Geron-X inc., Los Altos, C 94022, U.S.A.

Reproduction, Nutrition, Development. Institut National de la Recherche Agronomique, Paris, France.

Research in Veterinary Science. British Veterinary Association, 7 Mansfield Street, London, England.

South African Journal of Animal Science. South African Society of Animal Production, Pretoria, South Africa.

Theriogenology. Geron-X inc., Los Altos, CA 94022, U.S.A.

Veterinary Record. British Veterinary Association, 7 Mansfield Street, London, England.

World Animal Review, FAO, Via delle Terme di Caracalla, Rome, Italy.

World Review of Animal Production. International Publishing Enterprises, Via di Tor Vergata, 85187 Rome, Italy.

Index